MW00837883

Groundwater and Wells
Third Edition

Groundwater and Wells

Third Edition

Edited by

Robert J. Sterrett, PhD, RG

A Weatherford Company
New Brighton, MN
2007

Library of Congress Cataloging-In-Publication Data

Groundwater and wells / edited by Robert J. Sterrett. -- 3rd ed.
   p. cm.
   Includes bibliographical references and index.
   ISBN-13: 978-0-9787793-0-6 (hardcover : alk. paper)
   ISBN-10: 0-9787793-0-4 (hardcover : alk. paper)
   1. Wells. 2. Groundwater. I. Sterrett, Robert J.
   TD405.S74 2007
   628.1'14--dc22

                            2007036773

Third Edition Disclaimer

The information and recommendations contained in this book have been compiled from sources believed to be reliable and that represent the best opinion on the subject as of 2007. No warranty, guarantee, or representation, express or implied, is made by Johnson Screens, a Weatherford Company, however, as to the correctness or sufficiency of this information or to the results to be obtained from the use thereof. It cannot be assumed that all necessary warnings, safety suggestions, and precautionary measures are contained in this book, or that any additional information or measures might not be required or desirable because of particular conditions or circumstances, or because of any applicable U.S. federal, state, or local law, or any applicable foreign law or any insurance requirements or codes. The warnings, safety suggestions, and precautionary measures contained herein do not supplement or modify any U.S. federal, state, or local law, or any applicable foreign law, or any insurance requirements or codes.

Printed in the United States of America

This volume is printed on acid-free paper by
Litho Tech, Bloomington, MN

Table of Contents

CHAPTER 1
Introduction and Acknowledgments

Robert J. Sterrett, PhD, RG
Engineering Management Support, Inc.

At the start of the twenty-first century, the demand for clean potable water is increasing at a greater rate due in part to a growing population. Additionally, societies are being forced to evaluate impacts on current and future water supplies as a result of energy and mineral development and climate changes. These evaluations include a determination of the quantity and quality of the groundwater resource.

Johnson Screens, a Weatherford company, for more than 100 years has been at the forefront in providing the water-well industry with well screens, well supplies, and—most importantly—application expertise for the evaluation, protection, and extractions of groundwater resources.

In 1936, a patent was issued to Edward E. Johnson, Inc. for a wire-wrapped screen (Figure 1.1). Since then, Johnson Screens has expanded to supply a wide variety of screens, drilling fluids, and well-treatment products that are used worldwide. In 1929, Johnson Screens began publishing the *Drillers Journal*. The journal became the "official" trade journal for water-well professionals. This was the beginning of a long tradition of Johnson Screens being a leader in providing educational and reference materials to the groundwater community. A copy of each issue of the *Drillers Journal* can be found in Appendix 1 on this book's companion DVD.

In 1947, *Ground Water, Its Development, Uses and Conservation,* was published by Edward E. Johnson, Inc. In 1966, Johnson Screens published the first edition of *Ground Water and Wells*—one of the first comprehensive references on the state of the practice for the evaluation and installation of groundwater production wells. The first edition was translated into Spanish, and its release found worldwide use—because it truly was a handbook that could be taken into the field.

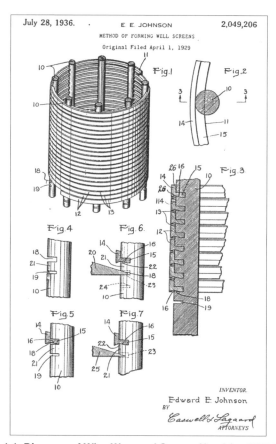

Figure 1.1. Diagram of Wire-Wrapped Screen Used for 1936 Patent.

Twenty years later, in response to the need for updated information, Fletcher Driscoll (PhD)—with the assistance of groundwater professionals from both within and outside of Johnson Screens—authored the 1986 second edition of *Groundwater and Wells*. The second edition soon was considered the comprehensive reference manual for the evaluation of groundwater resources and the design of water wells. More than 150,000 copies of the second edition have been sold worldwide.

Since the publication of the 1986 edition, the use of computers and digital technology has exploded within the groundwater industry, and our basic understanding of the groundwater environment has expanded greatly. Seeing this increase in the use of technology, Johnson Screens—as part of its 100th anniversary celebration—decided to revise and update the second edition to reflect the significant changes in the groundwater industry.

Discussions with a wide variety of groundwater professionals soon made apparent the need for a handbook on the subject of water-well technology. The industry needed a book that users could take into the field but which still would provide the necessary background and reference materials. This new third edition is designed to fulfill both requirements.

The approach of this third edition of *Groundwater and Wells* is pragmatic rather than theoretical. The material is presented so the interested reader—regardless of background—can gain a good understanding of the physics, chemistry, and hydraulics of groundwater and the various technologies used to develop this resource. In each subject area presented, a significant effort is directed toward explaining the practical elements; theoretical aspects are discussed wherever they serve to directly strengthen practical knowledge.

This edition focuses on the borehole and well, and the book contains no discussions on the hydrologic cycle, the hydrogeology of North America, surface geophysics, contracting, or water rights. Importantly, instead of a single author revising the entire text, recognized experts and practitioners from various areas of the groundwater industry contributed and reviewed chapters, based upon their areas of expertise.

Groundwater and Wells, third edition, borrows from the second edition in those areas that have not changed significantly. The many updates to this classic reference, however, include addition of information about a hydrogeologic classification system for logging water-well boreholes, borehole geophysics, well design, treatment for mineral and biological plugging of wells, and artificial storage and recharge. Advances such as horizontal drilling and wells along with direct-push technologies for exploration also are addressed.

This book is written for several groups of water-well professionals—water-well contractors, water-well design consultants, government officials, and educators and students interested in the practical elements of the water-well industry. To be of maximum value to the diverse reader groups, highly technical words from geology, hydrogeology, chemistry, physics, engineering, and hydraulics have been used sparingly. Use of some technical words is necessary, and these generally are defined where they are first used in the text. A significant number of technical terms also are defined in the Glossary.

A Reference List is provided following the end of the text. This list is not comprehensive, but serves to indicate representative articles or texts that examine a particular subject in more detail. Specific technical information, manuals, and reports are provided as appendices on the DVD found at the back of the book.

To facilitate use of this book in countries that use Standard International units (the International System of Units is abbreviated "SI" in this text), most of the basic equations are presented in U.S. customary units of measure followed by the SI equivalent. Numerical values are given in both U.S. customary and SI units in most cases. Chapter 12, Groundwater Pumps, primarily uses U.S. customary units.

The driving forces behind the creation of the third edition have been Mr. Mike Mehmert and Mr. Thomas Hanna of Johnson Screens. Mr. William Rouse, President, Johnson Screens, also has fully supported the production of this edition.

Ms. Lisa Leroux, Weatherford Corporation (project management), and Ms. Gloria Hanson, Johnson Screens (document coordination and synthesis), have contributed significantly to the successful completion of this book. Ms. Amber Moran, a student at the Colorado School of Mines (Golden, CO), provided unit conversion and evaluations of equations.

The individuals who provided input or review of specific chapters are identified at the end of each chapter. The following individuals from within Johnson Screens provided technical review of the entire book.

- Mr. Don Baron
- Mr. Edd Schofield
- Mr. Al Smith
- Mr. Mike Mehmert
- Mr. Thomas Hanna

Particular recognition goes to Mr. Raymond Schreurs (Johnson Screens, retired); he provided invaluable review and comment of the book based upon his more than 50 years of experience in the water-well industry.

A special recognition goes to Ms. Lisa Joanis Teman, of All the Right Words (Morrison, CO), who provided copyediting, design, and production management services for the book. Her experience and professional insights were invaluable. CADD Services (Arvada, CO) provided exceptional services with respect to providing graphics.

I also would like to thank my partners at Engineering Management Support, Inc. (EMSI) for their support and encouragement.

I especially thank and wish to dedicate this edition to David A. Stephenson (PhD), President, Geological Society of America Foundation, who is both a mentor and a friend. His introductory course in hydrogeology—as well as the career opportunities he afforded me—were the impetuses for my interest in the field of groundwater.

Lastly, I want to recognize and acknowledge the patience, advice, and support provided by my wife, Renate Sterrett, throughout this project.

CHAPTER 2
Occurrence of Groundwater and Aquifer Types

Robert J. Sterrett, PhD, PG
Engineering Management Support, Inc.

Thomas M. Hanna, PG
Johnson Screens

This chapter emphasizes aquifer types, the occurrence of groundwater within the geologic media, and the movement of water. This book, however, does not discuss the hydrologic cycle and the distributions of precipitation, as there are several excellent texts that cover the subject in more detail (e.g., Fetter 2001).

To insure the successful production of groundwater, industry professionals must have a basic understanding of how groundwater occurs and moves, coupled with a rudimentary understanding of geology and chemistry. This chapter describes the flow of groundwater by using figures and several simple algebraic equations. The chemical properties of groundwater are provided in Chapter 5.

TYPES OF SUBSURFACE WATER

This chapter discusses the types of subsurface water, but it first provides a set of brief definitions. "Regolith" is a geologic term used to describe the loose and discontinuous blanket of fragmented and unconsolidated rock material overlying bedrock (Bates & Jackson 1984). Within the groundwater industry, the terms "soil" and "unconsolidated sediments" have been used synonymously. In the strictest definition, however, the term soil is used to describe the uppermost part of the regolith, where both chemical and physical weathering are most active. Soil is the geologic material that supports rooted plants. In engineering geology and geotechnical engineering, the term soil is equivalent to regolith and generally is applied to any non-cemented geologic material. To the geotechnical engineer, the term "consolidated" has a specific implication regarding the level of stress that the soil has experienced. Additionally, "consolidated" connotes that the geologic material is rock. This book uses the term "unconsolidated" or "soil" in place of "regolith."

The column of unconsolidated sediment might be only a few feet (meters) thick in mountainous terrain, and hundreds of feet (meters) in valley-fill deposits. Unconsolidated sediments can act as a storage medium for water and they can transmit water vertically and horizontally.

Water is introduced to the soil column by precipitation, stream flow, and other surface-water bodies, such as ponds. Once in the unconsolidated sediments, water exists in several different environments (Figure 2.1). This classification, proposed by Davis and DeWiest (1966), suggests that water occurs in two types of environments in the unconsolidated sediments: a zone of vadose water and a zone of phreatic water (saturated zone). This, however, does not mean that a vadose zone cannot exist in rock.

Variations of this classification system have been proposed by Heath (1982) and Assaad et al. (2003). The major difference is whether the capillary fringe is considered to be part of the saturated zone or the unsaturated zone. The pores within the capillary fringes can be completely filled with water and thus saturated, but (as discussed below) the water pressure is negative within the pores. Assigning the capillary fringe to the vadose zone therefore generally is acceptable. In the vadose zone, three separate types of water exist: soil water, intermediate vadose water, and capillary water.

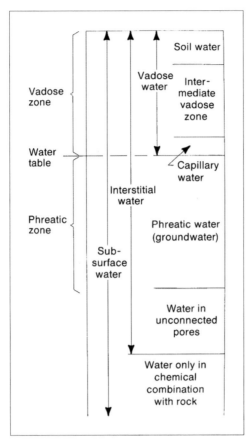

Figure 2.1. Classification of subsurface water (Davis & DeWiest 1966).

Soil water is particularly important to agriculture because it provides the water for plant growth. Water is lost from the soil-water zone by transpiration (water is absorbed by plants through the roots and then released into the atmosphere), evaporation, and percolation (the downward movement of water occurring when a soil's capacity to hold water is exceeded). Soils undergo wide variations in moisture content, from complete saturation (all openings are filled with water) to the occurrence of water in only a thin layer around individual soil grains. The depth of the soil-water zone varies from a few feet (or fractions of a meter) to hundreds of feet (meters).

Water is held in soils by both molecular attraction and capillarity acting against the force of gravity. Molecular attraction tends to hold water in a thin film on the surface of each soil particle. Capillarity holds water in the pores between soil particles. When the water-holding capacity of the capillary forces is exceeded, gravity causes the water to percolate downward.

The region immediately below the soil-water zone is called the intermediate zone. Although most water in this zone moves downward, some of it is retained but cannot be recovered except by applying a vacuum to soil. In humid regions, the intermediate zone can be quite thin or even can be absent. In arid climates only a small percentage of water passes completely through the intermediate zone to recharge the phreatic zone.

A capillary fringe lies at the bottom of the intermediate zone, and here groundwater is drawn upward by capillary forces. The thickness of the capillary fringe is dependent upon the average grain size of the geologic materials in that zone. A capillary zone might not exist where coarse-grained sediments are present; but water can migrate upward 10 ft (3 m) or more in fine-grained sediments. Fine-grained sediments often are completely saturated within the capillary fringe zone, and the physical forces acting on the fluid are the same as those operating below the water table (i.e., gravity). A well that is screened within the capillary zone will not yield water, however, because the interstitial pressures are negative; for water to move into a well, positive pressures are required.

The water table is at the bottom of the capillary zone, and it is the top of the saturated zone. The pressure of water at the water table is atmospheric. Water below the water table generally is called groundwater, although—strictly speaking—all water in the ground could be called groundwater. The region beneath the water table sometimes erroneously is referred to as the zone of saturation. This attribution is incorrect, because the capillary fringe directly above also can be completely saturated if the sediment is sufficiently fine grained that all pores are filled with water. To avoid such ambiguity, Davis and DeWiest suggest using the term "phreatic water," which is defined as water that enters freely into wells (Davis & DeWiest 1966). In this book the term "groundwater" refers to water that is below the water table. All other underground water is termed "subsurface water," and might not be available for extraction by flow to a well. An example is water that is in the vadose zone and is "perched." (Perched water is discussed elsewhere in this chapter.)

The bottom of the groundwater zone is difficult to delineate because it grades into a region where openings in the rocks are sparse and isolated. Water in these openings might not flow toward a well because individual pores are not connected. In areas of igneous rocks, the bottom of the groundwater zone might be less than 800 ft (250 m) deep; while in sedimentary rocks it can be more than 10,000 ft (3,000 m) deep. Below the zone of unconnected pores, water is chemically combined in rock-forming minerals; melting the rocks can release the water.

The groundwater zone can be visualized as a natural reservoir or system of reservoirs in unconsolidated sediments or rocks with a capacity equaling the volume of pores or openings that are filled with water. The thickness of the groundwater zone is governed by local geology, availability of pores or openings in soil and rock, recharge, and movement of water from areas of recharge toward points or areas of discharge.

It is nearly impossible to adequately summarize all types of geologic environments in which water can exist, but the list below provides some typical types of openings in consolidated and unconsolidated geologic materials.

- Intergrain pores in unconsolidated sand, gravel, and fine-grained sediment mixtures
- Joints (fractures) in fine-grained sediment such as silt and clay
- Joints (fractures) in metamorphic, igneous, and sedimentary rock
- Intergrain pores in shale
- Intergrain pores in sandstone and limestone
- Solution cavities in limestone
- Fractures formed during the cooling of basalt
- Gas-bubble holes and lava tubes in basalt
- Openings in fault zones

A more complete discussion of aquifer types is provided in Appendix 2.A.

AQUIFERS

An aquifer is a saturated geologic material that yields water in sufficient quantity to be economically useful. To be considered an aquifer, a geologic material must contain pores or open spaces (both of which often are called interstices) that are filled with water, and the interstices must be sufficiently connected (permeable) to transmit water toward a well at a useful rate.

Both the size of pores and the total number of pores in a geologic material can vary, depending on the types of sediment or rock and the geologic and chemical histories of the geologic formation. Individual pores in fine-grained sediment (such as clay) are extremely small, but the combined volume of the pores can be unusually large. The total pore volume (porosity) of recently deposited clay, for example, might exceed 60% (Kasenow 2002). Subsequent compaction of clay reduces the pore space considerably. In contrast, the porosity of a typical unconsolidated sand unit might be approximately 25%.

Although clay has a large water-holding capacity, water cannot move readily through its small open spaces because the pores are not well connected. This means that a clay unit under normal conditions does not yield significant quantities of water to wells, and therefore it is not an aquifer even though it might be water saturated. Clays that are in the process of compacting sometimes can yield useable quantities of water for a short time. Although the compaction of fine-grained sediments might yield water temporarily, the compaction largely is irreversible and can lead to subsidence of the land surface.

Geologic units that do yield some water but which usually do not produce enough to meet even modest demands are called aquitards. In reality, almost all geologic materials yield some water, and therefore are classified as either aquifers or aquitards. The term "aquifuge" generally refers to a geologic material which contains no interconnected openings or interstices, and which therefore neither absorbs nor transmits water (Bates & Jackson 1984). "Aquiclude" is another term that can be replaced by the word "aquitard." Research associated with nuclear waste disposal has shown that most geologic materials have some permeability (connection of pores) even if the value is extremely low. To avoid a theoretical discussion on the topic, this book uses only the terms "aquifer" and "aquitard."

In locations where there are no identified aquifers (in granites, for example) a geologic unit producing small quantities of water might be called an aquifer, whereas the same geologic unit in an area of abundant groundwater would be classified as an aquitard—this illustrates the ambiguity of the term "aquifer."

Another term frequently used is "water bearing," and it is preferred in some instances because there is no connotation regarding the volume of water that might be yielded by the geologic unit. To some people, the term "aquifer" evokes an image of flowing wells that discharge hundreds of gallons (liters) of water per minute. As noted, granite or clayey sand that produces only a few tenths of a gallon per minute could be considered to be an aquifer by some regulatory agencies in the United States. In this case, "water-bearing zone" seems more appropriate for describing the geologic material.

Energy Contained in Groundwater

Generally, water can exist in aquifers under two different pressure conditions. Where the upper surface of the phreatic zone is free to rise and decline, the water in such aquifers is unconfined. Unconfined aquifers also are referenced as water-table aquifers. The pressure measured at the water table is atmospheric or zero-gauge pressure.

Groundwater also can occur under confined conditions. Confined groundwater is isolated from the atmosphere by geologic materials of low permeability (aquitard), and the confined aquifer generally is subject to pressures that are higher than atmospheric pressure. Unconfined conditions exist, however, in recharge areas for confined aquifers. Figure 2.2 illustrates unconfined and confined groundwater conditions. Confined aquifers also are referred to as artesian aquifers, because the elevation of the water level in the aquifer is greater than the bottom of the confining unit. If the pressure in the confined aquifer is sufficient that the water-level elevation in a well is greater than the land surface, then the well is called a flowing artesian well.

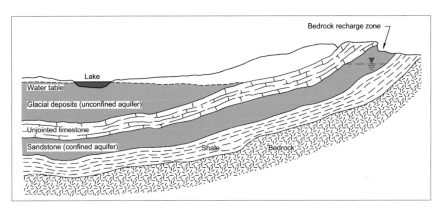

Figure 2.2. Groundwater exists underground in two primary environments: unconfined and confined.

To understand how groundwater moves, it is necessary to examine the forms of energy contained in groundwater. The total energy in a water mass consists of three components: pressure head, velocity head, and elevation head (energy derived from the elevation of the water body). The sum of these energy heads (H) is expressed by the Bernoulli equation (equation 2.1) presented below.

$$H = \frac{P}{\gamma} + \frac{V^2}{2g} + z$$

(2.1)

Where:

P = pressure;

γ = specific weight of water;

V = velocity of flow;

g = the acceleration of gravity; and

z = elevation above a certain datum.

Here, as noted, the units of head are length (L). The Bernoulli equation states that, under conditions of steady flow, the total energy of an incompressible fluid is constant at all positions along a flow path in a closed system.

The three terms of Bernoulli's equation, when expressed as energy per unit weight, are referred to as pressure head, velocity head, and elevation head. The pressure head (p/γ) represents the length of the water column in a well or piezometer; it is the work a fluid is capable of performing because of its sustained pressure. The velocity head ($V^2/2g$) is the energy component resulting from the movement of the water. The elevation head (z) is a latent form of energy; if the water is allowed to fall, elevation energy can be converted to velocity or pressure energy. As water moves, it loses part of its energy due to friction. This energy loss can be expressed by the following equation.

$$\frac{P_1}{\gamma} + \frac{V_1^2}{2g} + z_1 = \frac{P_2}{\gamma} + \frac{V_2^2}{2g} + z_2 + h_L$$

(2.2)

Where h_L is the loss of head energy caused by movement of the water from one point to another.

In most groundwater situations, the flow velocities are sufficiently low that the velocity energy component generally can be ignored when computing the energy contained in a groundwater system. The velocity terms in the Bernoulli equation therefore can be eliminated, resulting in equation 2.3.

$$\frac{P_1}{\gamma} + z_1 = \frac{P_2}{\gamma} + z_2 + h_L$$

(2.3)

Unconfined Aquifers

Atmospheric pressure is exerted upon the groundwater in an unconfined aquifer. Groundwater always flows from a position of higher total head to a location of lower total head, whether the aquifer is confined or unconfined. Situations where a flowing well occurs often are interpreted as a demonstration of confinement; however, flowing-well conditions can occur in an unconfined aquifer where a well is installed at sufficient depth in a groundwater discharge area to be able to intercept a higher potential. Figure 2.3 shows a well (D) that intercepts higher potentials with depth. This situation occurs in a groundwater discharge area. The opposite situation occurs in a recharge area; total potentials decline with depth. As noted in Figure 2.3 the water level in well B is less than the water table, thus water flows downward. The figure shows that the water level in well D is higher than the elevation in well C, thus water flows from well D toward well C. The water level in well D also is above the land surface, indicating flowing conditions (*see* Figure 2.3).

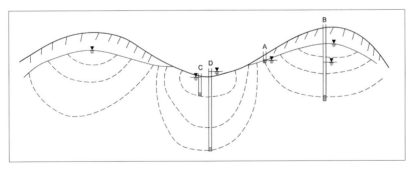

Figure 2.3. The water level in a well rises to the elevation of the hydraulic head represented by the potential at the intake end of the well. The water level in wells A and B is the same because both wells terminate on the same equipotential line (adapted from C. W. Fetter, Jr. 2001).

In some geologic settings, a local zone of saturation might exist at some level above the regional water table. This occurs where a stratum of low permeability within the vadose zone intercepts downward-percolating water and causes some of it to accumulate above the stratum. The upper surface of the subsurface water in such cases is called a perched water table. Perched water tables commonly occur where clay lenses exist; such as those found in thick sequences of glacial clay deposits (*see* Figure 2.4).

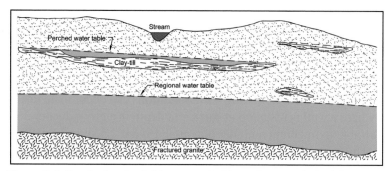

Figure 2.4. Perched water table supported by stringers of glacial clay till.

Under unconfined conditions the water table rises and falls. During periods of drought the water table can drop several feet (meters), as outflow to springs, streams, and wells reduces the volume of water held in storage. When precipitation begins again, aquifer recharge can be rapid.

Water levels in wells screened at similar depths in an unconfined aquifer can be contoured. The topography of the water table generally resembles the topography of the land surface, especially in regions that have humid climates. Contouring of water-level elevations in wells that are screened near the water table creates a water-table map or a potentiometric surface map representing the water table.

Confined Aquifers

When a well is drilled through an overlying low-permeability layer into a confined aquifer, water rises in the well to some level above the top of the aquifer. The water level in the well represents the confining pressure at the top of the aquifer. Confined pressure is defined as the vertical distance between the water level in the well and the top of the aquifer (bottom of the aquitard). This is equivalent to the hydrostatic head (or pressure head) expressed in feet (meters) of water.

The elevation to which water rises in a well that taps a confined aquifer is called its potentiometric level. Under confined conditions, the potentiometric surface is an imaginary surface representing the total potential (hydrostatic head plus elevation head) throughout all or part of a confined aquifer.

The hydrostatic pressure within a confined aquifer could be sufficient to cause the water to rise in a well above the land surface, thus creating a flowing artesian well. The static water level in this case is above the land surface and can be measured by capping the well near ground level and then measuring the pressure head with a pressure gauge. For every 1 pound per square inch (psi) (6.9 kilopascal (kPa)) of pressure measured, the water rises approximately 2.31 ft (0.7 m) above the gauge.

Just as in an unconfined aquifer, the potentiometric surface in a confined aquifer is able to rise and fall in response to the volume of water contained within the aquifer. When a well penetrating a confined aquifer is pumped, internal aquifer pressure is reduced and the weight of the overlying sediments compacts the aquifer. The pores in the aquifer remain saturated, however, as long as the potentiometric surface remains above the top of the aquifer. If the potentiometric surface of a confined aquifer falls below the top of the aquifer during pumping, then a partially unconfined aquifer is created.

Removal of water from the pores of an unconfined aquifer is easy to understand; water simply is drained from the aquifer's openings. The unconfined water is at atmospheric pressure, so the volume of water drained from the aquifer is that volume that exists in the pores minus the water that adheres to the particles making up the aquifer (and which therefore is not drained).

Conversely, the physical removal of water from a confined aquifer is more complex. Meinzer (1942) observed that more water could be removed from a well in a confined aquifer than was calculated to be flowing toward the well. Meinzer and other investigators concluded that the major sources of water from a well drilled in a confined aquifer are comprised of: (1) the water moving through the aquifer toward the well, (2) the water forced from the aquifer by compaction caused by the weight of overlying sediments, (3) water expansion resulting from reduced pressures in the aquifer, and (4) the water forced from surrounding aquitards by compaction of the aquitards. The compaction of aquitards and aquifers can lead to the subsidence at the land surface. There are many examples of land-surface subsidence due to the removal of fluids from confined aquifers (Poland, Lofgren, Ireland & Pugh 1973). Confined aquifers that lose or receive water from the surrounding formations are called leaky confined aquifers, and special mathematical methods have been devised to analyze them.

AQUIFER PROPERTIES

An aquifer performs two important functions: it stores water, and it transmits water. The interstices or openings of a water-bearing geologic material act as storage sites and are part of a network of conduits. Groundwater constantly moves through these conduits under the local hydraulic gradient, and rates of movement can vary from feet (meters) per year to feet (meters) per day.

Storage

Two important properties of an aquifer that are related to the storage of water are porosity and specific yield.

Porosity

The porosity of a water-bearing formation is the amount of open space within a specified volume of geologic material. It is defined as the volume of voids (open spaces) per total unit volume of geologic material. Porosity usually is expressed as a percentage of the bulk volume of the material.

$$\text{Porosity} = \eta = \frac{Volume\ of\ pore\ space}{Volume\ of\ bulk\ solid} \cdot 100 \qquad \textbf{(2.4)}$$

For example, if 1 ft^3 (1 m^3) of sand contains 0.3 ft^3 (0.3 m^3) of open space or pores, then its porosity is 30%. Typical porosities for some common materials are presented in Table 2.1.

There are two types of porosity, primary and secondary. Primary porosity includes the open spaces between grains; secondary porosity includes openings in rock or soil, such as fractures or solution channels. Nearly all of the porosity of sand or gravel is the open space between grains. Granite has very little open space between crystals, but can have significant fractures (secondary porosity) that contain water. Effective porosity is defined as the percentage of inter-connected pore space; it is less than total porosity. Although the volume of water contained in an aquifer is of interest, of more concern is how much water actually can be released from storage, per unit area of aquifer and per unit change in total head. Porosity represents the volume of water that an aquifer can hold, but it does not indicate how much water the aquifer can yield.

Table 2.1. Porosities for Common Consolidated and Unconsolidated Materials

Unconsolidated Sediments	η (%)	Consolidated Rocks	η (%)
Clay	45–55	Sandstone	5–30
Silt	35–50	Limestone/dolomite (primary & secondary porosity)	1–20
Sand	25–40	Shale	< 1–10
Gravel	25–40	Fractured crystalline rock	< 1–10
Sand & gravel mix	10–35	Vesicular basalt	10–50
Glacial till	10–25	Dense, solid rock	< 1

Specific Yield

When water is drained from a saturated material under the force of gravity, the material releases only part of the total volume stored in its pores. The quantity of water that a unit volume of unconfined aquifer provides by gravity drainage is termed specific yield (Figure 2.5). Additionally, specific yield and effective porosity for an unconfined aquifer are the same. Specific yields for certain rocks and sediment types are presented in Table 2.2.

Table 2.2. Representative Specific Yield Ranges for Selected Materials

Sediment	Specific Yield
Clay	1%–10%
Sand	10%–30%
Gravel	15%–30%
Sand & gravel	15%–25%
Sandstone	5%–15%
Shale	0.5%–5%
Limestone	0.5%–5%
(Walton 1970)	

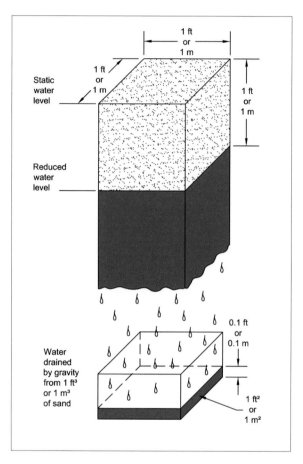

Figure 2.5. Specific yield of sand is illustrated in this diagram; its value is 0.1 ft^3 (m^3) per ft^3 (m^3) of aquifer material.

Specific Retention

Some water is retained in pores by molecular attraction and capillarity. The amount of water that a unit volume of aquifer retains after gravity drainage occurs is its specific retention. The smaller the average grain size of the geologic material, the greater the percent of retention; the more coarse-grained the sediment, the greater the specific yield in relation to the porosity.

The surface area for sand grains of differing sizes is shown in Table 2.3. Note the large increase in surface area for the fine-grained sediment; as the surface area increases, a larger percentage of the water in the pores is held by surface tension or other adhesive forces. Finer-grained sediments therefore have lower specific yields as compared to coarser sediments. Specific yield plus specific retention equals the porosity of an aquifer. Both specific yield and specific retention are expressed as decimal fractions or percentages.

Table 2.3. Total Surface Area of Grains in Samples Composed of Uniform Spheres

Diameter of Sphere (mm)	Number of Particles in a 1-mm Cube*	Approximate Surface Area (mm²)	
		One Particle	All Particles
1	1	3.1	3.1
0.062	$4.1 \cdot 10^3$	$1.2 \cdot 10^{-2}$	49
0.004	$1.7 \cdot 10^7$	$5.0 \cdot 10^{-5}$	850

* Cubic packing is assumed.

(Baver 1956)

Storage Coefficient

The storage coefficient is the volume of water taken into or released from storage, per unit change in head per unit area. In the case of an unconfined aquifer, the specific yield is equivalent to its storage coefficient, and storage coefficients for unconfined aquifers range from 0.01 to 0.30. Specific yields or storage coefficients for confined aquifers cannot be determined using standard laboratory techniques, because the aquifer materials are not dewatered during pumping.

Storage coefficients for confined aquifers are much lower than those for unconfined aquifers. Water released from storage in a confined aquifer primarily is obtained by compression of the aquifer and the expansion of the water when pumped. During pumping, the pressure is reduced in the confined aquifer but the aquifer is not dewatered. Typical storage coefficients for confined aquifers range from 10^{-5} (0.00001) to 10^{-3} (0.001). Figure 2.6 demonstrates how equal declines in the water table for unconfined aquifers and the potentiometric surface for confined aquifers produce significantly different volumes of water, consistent with the differences in storage coefficients described above.

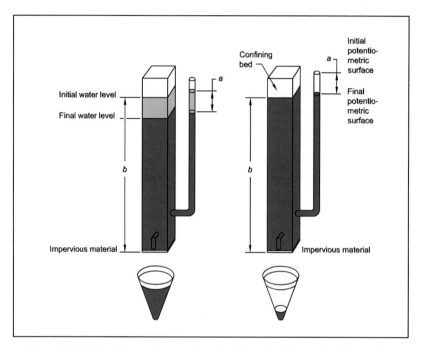

Figure 2.6. Unit prisms of unconfined and confined aquifers illustrating differences in storage coefficients. For equal declines in head, the yield from an unconfined aquifer is much greater than the yield from a confined aquifer (Heath & Trainer 1968).

Example

The following example illustrates some of the points presented above, and shows how the storage function of an aquifer permits the use of groundwater at a constant rate even though recharge of the aquifer could be intermittent.

If 1 ft³ (0.03 m³) of saturated sand under unconfined conditions has a porosity of 25% (0.25) and a specific yield of 10% (0.10), then its storage coefficient also is 10% and its specific retention is 15% (0.15). This means that 40% (0.10 ÷ 0.25) of the water residing in the aquifer is available for use.

If the aquifer extends over an area of 20 mi² (51.8 km²) with an average thickness of 40 ft (12.2 m), then the total volume of the upper 5 ft (1.5 m) of the aquifer is $2.8 \cdot 10^9$ ft³ ($7.9 \cdot 10^7$ m³) and it contains $7 \cdot 10^8$ ft³ ($2 \cdot 10^7$ m³) of water.

If the upper 5 ft (1.5 m) of the aquifer was drained by pumping, then the total yield would be about $2.8 \cdot 10^8$ ft³ ($7.9 \cdot 10^6$ m³). This quantity could supply five wells pumping 790 gpm (4,310 m³/day), 12 hours each day, for 736 days, or slightly more than 2 years. This pumping rate could be sustained by the groundwater stored in the upper 5 ft (1.5 m) of the aquifer in the total absence of any recharge to the aquifer during the 2-year period.

Hydraulic Conductivity

Hydraulic conductivity (K) is the property of a water-bearing geologic material that relates to its ability to transmit water at a standard temperature and density. This characteristic also is known as the coefficient of permeability. Permeability refers to the ease with which any fluid moves through a geologic material, therefore the term probably is applied more aptly to the property termed intrinsic permeability. Intrinsic permeability (k) is the ability of a geologic material to transmit a fluid. It is a function of the geologic material alone, and can be expressed as the following equation (2.5).

$$k = \frac{K\mu}{\rho g}$$
(2.5)

Where:

k = the permeability (units of length squared, L^2);

K = hydraulic conductivity (length/time, L/t);

μ = the dynamic viscosity of a particular fluid (mass (M)/$L \cdot t$);

ρ = the density of a particular fluid (M/L^3); and

g = the acceleration of gravity (L/t^2).

The notion of intrinsic permeability is used in the petroleum industry because fluids of different phases and densities (e.g., gas, oil, water) are analyzed using the rate of their movement through the porous medium.

Hydraulic conductivity is governed by the size and shape of the pores, the effectiveness of the interconnection between pores, and the physical and chemical properties of the water that is contained in openings. If the interconnecting tubes are small, as shown in Figure 2.7(A), then the volume of water passing from pore to pore is restricted and the resulting hydraulic conductivity is low. Conversely, in a coarse-grained sediment the connecting tubes are large relative to the pores and the hydraulic conductivity is high (Figure 2.7(B)). The fluid properties of water vary with temperature and chemistry (e.g., the total dissolved solids concentration), and hydraulic conductivity is defined on the basis of the viscosity and density of water at a particular temperature, generally 68°F (20°C), and a density of one gram per cubic centimeter (g/cm^3).

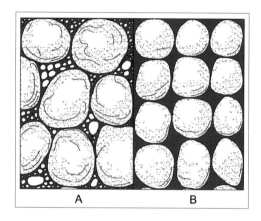

Figure 2.7. Hydraulic conductivity is affected by size of interconnections between pores in storage sites.

GROUNDWATER FLOW

Movement of groundwater takes place whenever a difference in total head exists between two points. Thus, water moves from locations of high total head to locations of low total head. Figure 2.8 shows a typical groundwater flow system for confined and unconfined aquifers. Water in confined aquifers can move from low-pressure areas to high-pressure areas. In Figure 2.8, at point (a) the water has high potential energy with low pressure energy. During its movement toward point (b), the potential energy (head) is transformed into pressure energy. At point (b) the potential energy is lower—but the pressure energy is higher—than at point (a). Total potential at point (b) is less than at point (a).

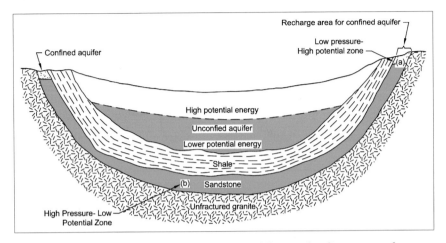

Figure 2.8. Groundwater can follow unusual flow paths; it can move from areas of low pressure toward areas of high pressure. This pressure energy is gained at the expense of available potential (head) energy.

Two basic types of flow occur in groundwater—laminar and turbulent—and one type always is more prevalent than the other. Experiments have shown that velocity determines which one of these flow regimes is present under a given field condition. Ordinarily, water moves so slowly through the ground that laminar flow takes place. In this condition the water particles tend to flow in ribbon-like patterns through the pore openings, although water moving in the center of the pores does move faster than the water that is closer to the walls (*see* Figure 2.9(A)). There is no intermixing of individual water layers. Occasionally, turbulent flow occurs near wells and other points where relatively large volumes of water must converge through constricted openings. In turbulent flow, individual water particles intermix and follow irregular paths through the pores (*see* Figure 2.9(B)).

Laminar flow is dominant at very low velocities but, at some point (at a Reynolds number of approximately 10), as velocity increases turbulent flow begins. The Reynolds number is a dimensionless number that is a ratio of inertial forces to viscous forces (Streeter & Wylie 1975). For groundwater flow, the Reynolds number relates the characteristic dimension of the flow space and the velocity, density, and viscosity of a moving fluid to determine whether laminar or turbulent flow exists (McWhorter & Sunada 1977).

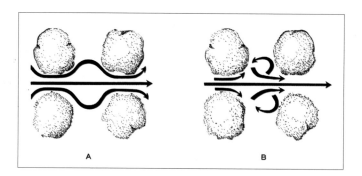

Figure 2.9. Schematic representation of laminar flow (A) and turbulent flow (B) in a granular deposit.

Henri Darcy, a French engineer, while attempting to estimate the volume of water that would flow through sand filters, conducted a series of experiments using a vertical pipe filled with sand (Darcy 1856). Darcy learned that the rate of flow through a column of saturated sand is proportional to the difference in hydraulic head at the ends of the column and is inversely proportional to the length of the column. The constant of proportionality that Darcy found that linked the parameters is hydraulic conductivity (K). This now is known as Darcy's law and is the basic equation describing the flow of groundwater.

$$\frac{Q}{A} = q = -K \frac{(h_1 - h_2)}{L} \tag{2.6}$$

Where:

Q = Flow rate (L^3/time);

A = Cross-sectional area perpendicular to groundwater flow (L^2);

q = the volumetric flow rate perpendicular to the direction of groundwater flow (L/t) (specific discharge or Darcy flux velocity);

$h_1 - h_2$ = the difference in hydraulic head (L);

L = the distance along the flow path between the points where h_1 and h_2 are measured; and

K = the hydraulic conductivity (L/t).

See Figure 2.10 for an illustration of the equipment used to measure hydraulic conductivity. The Darcy flux velocity assumes that the discharge occurs throughout the entire material cross section, despite the fact that solids comprise a large part of the cross-sectional area. Equation 2.21 (page 45, *infra*) is used to calculate the average linear groundwater velocity. The law provides a way to quantify the energy (head) required to move water through an aquifer.

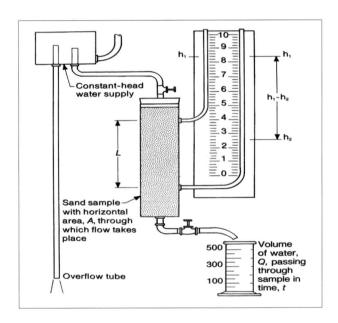

Figure 2.10. Diagram of a constant-rate permeameter used to estimate the hydraulic conductivity of sediments. Hydraulic conductivity is calculated by measuring the area of the sample, the rate of water flow, and the hydraulic gradient.

Energy is lost because of friction between the moving water and the confining walls of the pores. Equation 2.6 simply states that energy loss is proportional to the velocity of flow under laminar conditions—the faster the flow the higher the energy loss. Energy losses caused by the onset of turbulent flow near a well are discussed in Chapter 6.

The hydraulic gradient (I) is the difference in hydraulic head (h_1-h_2), divided by the distance (L) along the flowpath.

$$I = \frac{(h_1 - h_2)}{L}$$

(2.7)

Therefore the following is the case.

$$q = KI$$

(2.8)

From pipeflow, the discharge (Q, (L^3/t)) is equal to the flow velocity times the cross-sectional area (A, (L^2)).

$$Q = qA$$

(2.9)

Substituting the equivalent value of q from equation 2.8 results in the following.

$$Q = KIA$$

(2.10)

This form of Darcy's equation is used more frequently because Q (discharge of the aquifer) generally is the most important variable. Discharge is the quantity of flow per unit time, such as gallons per minute (gpm) or cubic meters per day (m³/day). The velocity of groundwater is more important in chemical transport studies. In the previous equations, K is the hydraulic conductivity of the porous medium. This value depends on:

- the size and arrangement of the particles in unconsolidated sediment;
- the size and character of the crevices, fractures, and solution openings in rock; and
- the density and viscosity of the fluid as determined by its temperature.

Hydraulic conductivity can change with any variation in these parameters.

The hydraulic conductivity indicates the quantity of water that can flow through a unit cross-sectional area of a porous medium per unit time, under a hydraulic gradient of 1 (100%) and at a specified temperature. A hydraulic gradient of 1 means that the head falls 1 ft (or 1 m) per unit of flow travel. For convenience, K is expressed as the flow (in ft³ or m³ per day) through a cross section of 1 ft² (or m²), under a hydraulic gradient of 1, at a temperature of 60° F (15.6° C).

$$1 \, K \, Unit = \frac{1 \, ft^3 \, of \, water \, at \, 60^{\circ}F \, / \, day}{1 \, ft^2 \left(-1 \, ft \, / \, ft\right)}$$

$$1 \, K \, Unit = \frac{1 \, m^3 \, of \, water \, at \, 15.5 \, ^{\circ}C \, / \, day}{1 \, m^2 \left(-1 \, m \, / \, m\right)} \tag{2.11}$$

The range in values of K generally is from 1 ft/day (0.3 m/day) to 1,000 ft/day (330 m/day) for aquifer materials (Figure 2.11).

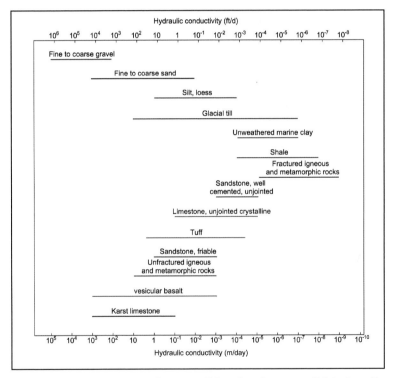

Figure 2.11. Typical *K* values for consolidated and unconsolidated aquifers (modified from Freeze & Cherry 1979).

As noted, the units of hydraulic conductivity are length and time, for example ft/day (m/day). Hydraulic conductivity also could be expressed in units of gallons per day per square foot (gpd/ft²), however this usage is not as common today as it was in the past.

The preliminary examination of groundwater flow establishes three important points.

1. The flow of groundwater from one point to another in an aquifer always is caused by a difference in head between the two points.
2. The difference in head reflects the frictional losses due to the resistance that develops in the pores of an aquifer during flow.
3. The hydraulic gradient is the loss in total head (ft or m) per unit length of travel through the medium.

Darcy's experiments show that flow in saturated sand varies directly with the hydraulic gradient. If the hydraulic gradient (head loss per unit length of travel) is doubled, then the rate of flow in a given cross section of porous medium also is doubled. Conversely, doubling of the flow rate requires doubling of the hydraulic gradient; however, ratios apply only to laminar flow. If turbulent flow is present then the flow rate does not change in direct proportion with the hydraulic gradient; doubling the hydraulic gradient might increase the flow rate by only 1.5 times instead of doubling it. This information is important to the understanding water-well hydraulics (*see* Chapter 6).

The slope of the water table or potentiometric surface is the hydraulic gradient under which groundwater movement takes place. The total flow through any vertical section of an aquifer can be calculated if the thickness of the aquifer, its width, its average hydraulic conductivity, and the hydraulic gradient are known.

The flow (q_i) through each unit incremental width (ft or m) of aquifer is as follows.

$$q_i = KbI \tag{2.12}$$

Where:

K = the hydraulic conductivity averaged over the height of the aquifer;

b = the aquifer thickness (ft or m); and

I = the hydraulic gradient.

Transmissivity

Theis (1935) pointed out the convenience of using the product of Kb as a single term to represent the transmission capability of the entire thickness of an aquifer. He introduced the term "coefficient of transmissibility," defining it as the rate of flow in gallons per minute through the vertical section of an aquifer one-foot wide and extending the full saturated height of an aquifer under a hydraulic gradient of 1. The term "transmissibility" still is in use, although it largely has been replaced by the word "transmissivity" (as used in this book). In the International System of Units (SI), transmissivity units are cubic meters per day per meter (m^3/day/m) or square meters per day (m^2/day). The temperature assumed in this definition is the ambient temperature of the groundwater in the aquifer. When the coefficient of transmissivity (T) is introduced in the Darcy equation, flow through any vertical section of an aquifer is expressed as shown in equation 2.13.

$$Q = TIw \qquad\qquad (2.13)$$

Where w is the width of the vertical section through which the flow occurs, and the other terms use their standard definitions.

Three general methods are used to estimate transmissivity: (1) using data collected during aquifer tests, (2) analyzing the hydraulic properties of aquifer material, and (3) making calculations based on laboratory tests. The first method is based on observation of the decline in groundwater levels during an aquifer test. There exists a set of equations that describe flow near wells, and that give the transmissivity value based on declines in water levels in wells or piezometers. These equations are discussed in Chapter 6.

The second method involves estimating hydraulic conductivities of the materials in an aquifer. The estimation is determined using a grain-size analysis of samples collected from the aquifer (cuttings or cores collected from boreholes). The transmissivity for an individual layer is estimated by multiplying the strata thickness by the hydraulic conductivity (K) value characterizing that layer. For a geologic unit consisting of multiple layers, the total transmissivity (T_t) is the sum of the transmissivity of each of the layers (I) (Fetter 2001).

$$T_t = \sum_{i=1}^{n} T_i \tag{2.14}$$

The third method involves the testing of samples from an aquifer using a permeameter (a tool similar to that shown in Figure 2.10). After measured quantities of water flow through the permeameter and the head loss is determined, the hydraulic conductivity then can be calculated. As is done in the second method described above, the hydraulic conductivity for all layers is summed to yield an overall transmissivity value.

Of these three methods, the transmissivity calculated from aquifer tests is the most representative of hydraulic conditions within an aquifer. Methods for collecting and analyzing aquifer test data are presented in Chapter 6. Transmissivity values obtained using the other two methods (presented above) are less representative, but can provide insight into the range of hydraulic conductivities for a particular unit.

Grain-Size and Hydraulic Conductivity

Hydraulic conductivity varies not only with porosity but also with the size, distribution, and continuity of pores. In most cases, the finer 10% to 20% portion of an unconsolidated aquifer controls the hydraulic conductivity of that material. Wells in geologic units consisting of coarse, unconsolidated sand or gravel have high yields because the pores or voids are large and well connected. In finer-grained sediments, the small pores offer more resistance to flow; therefore more water flows through coarser material under a given hydraulic gradient. The hydraulic conductivity is greater for the coarser material, even though the porosity can be the same for both sediments.

It is difficult to examine the effect of particle size on hydraulic conductivity without also discussing the sorting or grading of the sample, because the degree of uniformity of a mixture of fine to coarse material has a significant bearing on transmitting capacity. Sediment that consists of similar-sized particles is considered well sorted or uniformly graded, and well-sorted material has a higher porosity than does less-uniform or poorly sorted mixtures of coarse and fine sediments. In a poorly sorted mixture, porosity is reduced because the finer materials occupy openings between the coarser fragments. The result is a more-compact arrangement which reduces the volume of the void space. Even fine, well-sorted material has a higher porosity than that of mixtures of larger poorly sorted sediment. For geotechnical engineering it is important to note that a well-sorted (well-graded) sediment means that the material has a distribution of sediments across many grain sizes; the engineering definition of "well graded" is the opposite of that used by geologists.

Grain-size distribution is determined by passing the sediment sample through a series of sieves (see ASTM Standard D422-63 (2002) for a discussion of test procedures). The sieves normally are mounted in a device that vibrates both vertically and horizontally for a certain time, usually five to ten minutes per sample. The cumulative weight of the particles retained on each sieve then is plotted as a percent of the total sample weight against grain size (in (mm)). From this curve, the degree of sorting and the average grain size are calculated. Additional discussion regarding mechanical sieving is contained in Appendix 2.B (DVD).

Figure 2.12 shows plots of three sieve analyses of natural materials: beach sand, a mixture of glacial sands and gravels (glacial outrush), and a typical deposit from a slow-moving river (alluvial deposit). A grain-size distribution curve shows how much of the sample material is smaller or larger than a given particle size.

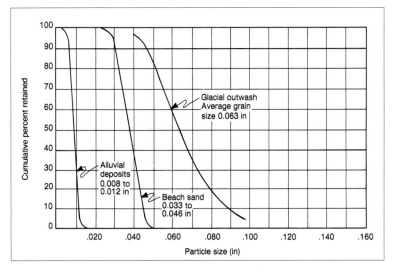

Figure 2.12. Sieve analysis for three naturally graded materials.

Figure 2.13 shows that 90% of the sample is larger than 0.009 in (0.23 mm) and 10% is smaller. The 40% retained size is 0.025 in (0.64 mm); 40% of the sample is coarser than 0.025 in (0.64 mm) and 60% is finer.

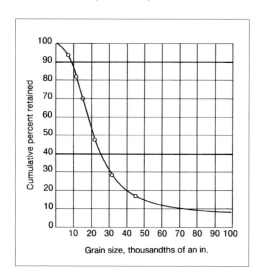

Figure 2.13. Plot showing the percent of the sample retained on each sieve. This plot illustrates grain-size distribution.

No single term adequately describes a sand or sand-gravel mixture because of the wide range of particle sizes. Intermediate size distributions (the particles which fall between the smallest and largest sizes) can change the shape of the distribution curve. Three elements explain a grain-size distribution curve: (1) sediment size, (2) slope of the curve, and (3) shape of the curve. As such, all three elements must be used to describe the grading of a sediment sample.

Sediment-Size Classification

Several different grain-size classifications have been developed for sediments, and each classification has been adopted for use in the specialized field that it seems to fit best.

The Wentworth scale developed in 1922 still is the basic particle-size classification used in the groundwater field. The United States Geological Survey (USGS) uses this classification but has taken one size range—0.26 in

(4 mm) to 2.5 in (64 mm)—and subdivided it. The Wentworth scale and USGS amendments are shown in Table 2.4.

Table 2.4. Grain-Size Classification

Wentworth Classification	Size Range	
	in	mm
Boulder	10.08 & larger	256 & larger
Cobble	2.52 to 10.08	64 to 256
Pebble*	0.16 to 2.52	4 to 64
Granule (very fine gravel)	0.08 to 0.16	2 to 4
Very coarse sand	0.04 to 0.08	1 to 2
Coarse sand	0.02 to 0.04	0.5 to 1
Medium sand	0.01 to 0.02	0.25 to 0.5
Fine sand	0.005 to 0.01	0.125 to 0.25
Very fine sand	0.002 to 0.005	0.063 to 0.125
Silt	0.0002 to 0.002	0.004 to 0.063
Clay	smaller than 0.0002	smaller than 0.004
* The USGS has subdivided the Pebble category as listed below.		
Very coarse gravel	1.26 to 2.52	32 to 64
Coarse gravel	0.63 to 1.26	16 to 32
Medium gravel	0.31 to 0.63	8 to 16
Fine gravel	0.16 to 0.31	4 to 8
(Krumbein & Pettijohn 1938)		

The sample in Figure 2.13 consists of medium and coarse sand, according to the USGS classification. Applying the same system to the four curves in Figure 2.14 to Figure 2.17 produces the following descriptions.

- ◆ Class-A curve: Fine sand
- ◆ Class-B curve: Fine and very coarse sand
- ◆ Class-C curve: Medium, coarse, and very coarse sand
- ◆ Class-D curve: Fine to very coarse sand and very fine gravel

Other Ways to Describe Sediment Size

The term "effective size" was developed by Allen Hazen (Filter sand studies 1893) and defined as the particle size where 10% of the sediment is finer and 90% is coarser. On all the curves shown in the figures below, the effective size is the 90% retained size. The effective size in Figure 2.14 (Class-A curve) is 0.003 in (0.08 mm). Another curve point index is the 50% size, shown in both Class-A and Class-B curves as 0.007 in (0.18 mm). The 50% size is the mean or average particle size for uniform (steep-slope) sediments. When the slope is flatter, however, as shown in the Class-D curve in Figure 2.17, the 50% size is inaccurate as an indicator of fineness or coarseness.

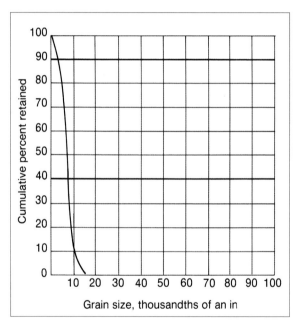

Figure 2.14. Class-A curve for fine sand.

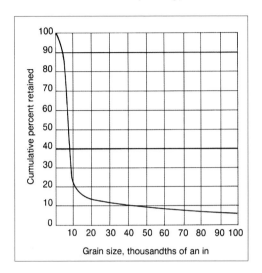

Figure 2.15. Class-B curve for fine and very coarse sand.

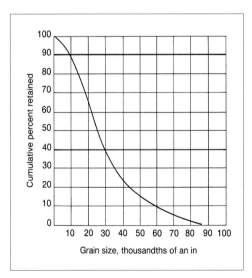

Figure 2.16. Class-C curve for medium, coarse, and very coarse sand.

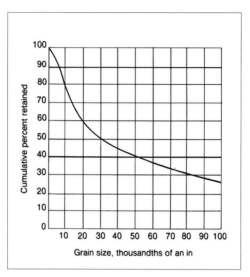

Figure 2.17. Class-D curve for fine to coarse sand and very fine gravel.

Slope and Shape of Curve

The uniformity coefficient describes the slope of the major portion of a grain-size distribution curve. Used extensively and developed by Hazen when he adopted the idea of effective size, the uniformity coefficient is defined as the 40% retained size of the sediment divided by the 90% retained size (equation 2.15).

$$UC = \frac{d_{40}}{d_{90}}$$

(2.15)

Lower values are more uniform, therefore practical application is limited to materials that are relatively uniformly graded and have coefficient values of less than 5. These attributes make such materials well suited for describing filter-pack materials.

Most granular sedimentary materials yield S-shaped curves (*see* Figure 2.14, Figure 2.16, and Figure 2.17). If gravel constitutes 15% (or more) of a sand-and-gravel mixture, then the S-shape is distorted (as shown by the "tail" configuration of the Class-D curve, Figure 2.17).

Table 2.5 presents a comparison of several sands. Hydraulic conductivity measurements were made using laboratory flow tests. Note that the effective size of the coarse sand is slightly more than 4 times that of the fine sand, whereas its hydraulic conductivity is about 18 times greater. Hazen (1893) observed that hydraulic conductivity varies in proportion to the square of the effective grain size. The values for the first two sands listed in Table 2.5 conform approximately to this ratio, because 4^2 equals 16 and the hydraulic conductivity ratio is about 18.

Table 2.5. Comparative Data for Filter Sands

	Fine Sand 0.008–0.01 in (0.2–0.3 mm)		Coarse Sand 0.033–0.04 in (0.84–1.17 mm)		Fine Gravel 0.046–0.093 in (1.17–2.36 mm)	
Effective Size	0.008 in	0.2 mm	0.034 in	0.86 mm	0.048	1.22 mm
Uniformity Coefficient	1.2		1.2		1.4	
Hydraulic Conductivity	540 gpd/ft²	22 m/d	9,600 gpd/ft²	391 m/d	13,000 gpd/ft²	591 m/d
Porosity	37%		37%		35%	

Hazen's rule, however, does not hold true for the third sediment listed. A ratio of the squares of the effective sizes of the fine gravel and the coarse sand is about 2, but the ratio of the hydraulic conductivity is only 1.4. The larger uniformity coefficient of the fine gravel reduces the impact of the greater effective size of the larger gravel and its influence on hydraulic conductivity. Generally, hydraulic conductivity increases with an increase in effective size, however other sediment characteristics tend to produce varying relationships between hydraulic conductivity and grain size.

Many researchers and others have attempted to calculate hydraulic conductivity on the basis of grain size and degree of sorting alone (Kasenow 2002). Studies have failed to find a simple relationship between sediment grading and hydraulic conductivity. Schafer (1971) developed an empirical equation to estimate the upper limits for hydraulic conductivity of unconsolidated material (a well-sorted sand) (equation 2.16 is an empirical equation and has no direct companion equation in SI units). In equation 2.16, the units of hydraulic conductivity used are gallons per day per square foot (gpd/ft²). To obtain hydraulic conductivity in ft/day, divide the result of equation 2.16 by 7.48 (the number of gal in 1 ft^3).

$$K = \frac{e^{2.99} \times d^{1.607}}{1 + \ln R}$$
(2.16)

Where:

$K =$ hydraulic conductivity (gpd/ft^2);

$e =$ base of the natural logarithm (2.71828);

$d =$ median diameter (thousandths of in); and

$R =$ range coefficient (which is the ratio of the 20% retained size to the 90% retained size from a sieve analysis of the sediment. The range of this parameter is approximately 2:1 or 3:1).

The Hazen formula as noted in Kasenow (2002) is written as follows.

$$K = (A)\,(\beta)\,\tau\,d_e^{\,2}$$
(2.17)

Where:

$K =$ hydraulic conductivity (L/T);

$A =$ coefficient that determines the units of K (for K in m/day, $A = 1$; for K in cm/sec, $A = 0.00116$);

$\beta =$ empirical coefficient that depends on the fraction of clay-sized particles within the porous media (for pure and uniform sands β ranges between 800 and 1200, and for clayey and nonuniform sands, β ranges between 400 and 800);

$d_e =$ effective grain diameter (L) of the porous medium (expressed in mm); and

$\tau = 0.70 + 0.03T$ (T = water temperature in degrees C).

An alternative is shown in equation 2.18.

$$\beta = 400 + 40(\eta - 26)$$
(2.18)

Where:

$\eta =$ percentage of porosity.

Effective grain diameter (d_e) most often is defined as d_{10}, which means that 10% of the sediment is finer and 90% is coarser. If hydraulic conductivity is expressed in cm/sec at a temperature of $T = 10°$ C and the coefficient β equals 860, then equation 2.17 is simplified as shown below.

$$K = (\text{cm/s}) = d_{10}^2 \text{ (mm)} \tag{2.19}$$

Equation 2.19 is applicable where the following conditions hold: the effective grain diameter is within 0.1 mm $< d_e <$ 3 mm, and the coefficient of uniformity is less than 5. Other methods to estimate hydraulic conductivity as a function of grain-size are described in Kasenow (2002). Figure 2.18 shows the relationship between grain size and hydraulic conductivity (K) as measured in ft/day (in U.S. customary units).

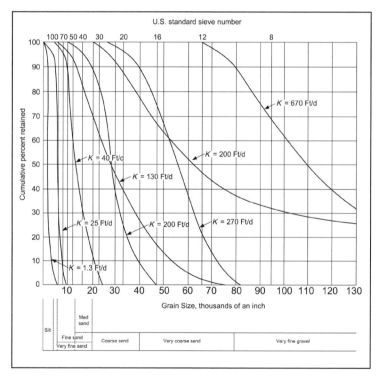

Figure 2.18. Relationship between grain size and hydraulic conductvity.

Permeameters

Modern permeameters are based on the apparatus used by Darcy in his experiments. A permeameter enables measurement of the rate at which water percolates through various types of earth materials. There are two types of permeameters, falling head and constant head. In a constant-head device, the hydraulic gradient is kept constant while the discharge is recorded (Figure 2.10). A description of protocols for this procedure is contained in ASTM Standard D2434. In a falling-head permeameter the hydraulic gradient decreases over time, therefore the discharge also decreases over time. Several tests usually are conducted, with each sample placed under varying hydraulic gradients to obtain an average hydraulic conductivity. The procedures for conducting falling-head tests are contained in ASTM Standard D5856.

Laboratory Permeameters

Use of a permeameter in a lab to estimate hydraulic conductivity is dependent on restoring the sample to in situ conditions. This often is a difficult task, especially for finer-grained sediment. The hydraulic heads also should be similar to those experienced in the field. Several problems can occur in attempting to determine hydraulic conductivity with a laboratory permeameter; for example trapped air within the sample can reduce the flow rate. Certain models of permeameters can drive air out by passing carbon dioxide gas through the sample, and the de-aerated water then is allowed to enter the testing chamber. Any air that remains in the system is absorbed readily by the de-aerated water, which also absorbs the carbon dioxide gas that was introduced. Combining these two procedures insures that no air remains in the sample chamber to impede the flow.

The packing of the grains presents a more difficult problem. Before a sample is collected, the arrangement of individual grains is quite dense because component particles have been compacted due to different geologic processes. Despite efforts to collect an undisturbed sample, every sample becomes at least partly disaggregated during its collection, transportation to the laboratory, and placement within the permeameter. As such, the original packing density must be reestablished if the measurements are to represent the percolation rates found in situ. Probably the best method for reestablishing the original packing of a sample is by using mechanical vibration; electrical vibrators are extremely useful for this purpose but hand jarring or tamping also tends to reduce the bulk of the sample. Additionally, it is possible to introduce water at a very slow rate into the sample chamber; as the water rises via capillarity, small particles migrate downward into the voids. Results obtained from laboratory permeameters can provide insight into the hydraulic conductivities of natural materials if samples are returned to field conditions.

Field Permeameters

Field permeameters generally are based on the falling-head principle, and can yield data about a wide variety of sediments and rock. Many field permeameters, however, do have various theoretical and practical limitations, including low-accuracy, complex equipment, and significant time and water requirements. With practice, however, water-well professionals can make reasonably accurate measurements using such instruments.

The Guelph Permeameter™ (developed at Canada's University of Guelph) can be used for a wide variety of geologic materials. This permeameter depends upon a constant head of water. When a constant well height of water is established in a cored hole in the soil, a "bulb" of saturated soil—with specific dimensions—is established rather quickly. This bulb is very stable and its shape depends on the type of soil being tested (Reynolds & Elrick 1985). Once the unique bulb shape is established, the outflow of water from the well reaches a measurable constant value. The rate of this constant outflow of water, together with the diameter of the well and height of water in the well, can be used to accurately assess the field-saturated hydraulic conductivity of the soil. It should be kept in mind that the hydraulic conductivity can be influenced by entrapped air. Additional discussion on the application of borehole permeameters is contained in Stephens (1996). Figure 2.19 shows the assembled Guelph Permeameter™ and Figure 2.20 shows the permeameter in its carrying case.

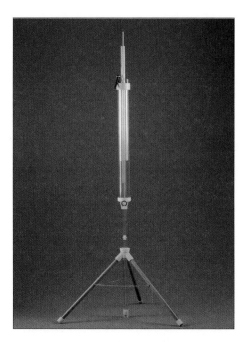

**Figure 2.19. Guelph Permeameter™ assembled
(Soilmoisture Equipment Corp.).**

**Figure 2.20. Guelph Permeameter™ in carrying case
(Soilmoisture Equipment Corp.).**

Groundwater Flow Velocities

Ordinarily, the rate of groundwater movement is of negligible interest to water-well professionals or others concerned primarily with yields from wells. Yields are directly affected by flow velocities, of course, but it is difficult to study velocity in an aquifer. An estimation of the groundwater flow velocity, however, is important to gaining an understanding of the transport of chemicals in groundwater. The ability to predict the rate at which a zone of impacted water can move downgradient from a source of chemicals is critical for designing groundwater remediation systems.

The average groundwater flow rate is estimated by combining Darcy's equation with the standard continuity equation of hydraulics. The continuity equation states that whatever goes into a system must come out. In Darcy's equation the hydraulic conductivity has the dimensional units of velocity. When the conductivity is expressed as feet (or meters) per day passing through one square foot (meter) of aquifer, this is the same as expressing the flow rate in terms of feet (meters) per day under the defined hydraulic gradient of 1. Multiplying this flow rate by the actual hydraulic gradient in the aquifer gives the apparent (or Darcy) velocity of groundwater movement in that aquifer.

$$\frac{Q}{A} = q = K\frac{(h_1 - h_2)}{L} \qquad\qquad (2.20)$$

The value of q in equation 2.20 has the units of velocity L/T, however it is not a true velocity. Actual groundwater flow velocities are greater than the equation indicates, because flow occurs only through the actual pore space and not through the entire cross section of the porous medium. Effective porosity is defined as the percentage of interconnected pore space (Domenico & Schwartz 1990). The average velocity of groundwater flow (V_a) can be calculated using the hydraulic conductivity, the hydraulic gradient, and the effective porosity, as shown in equation 2.21, where η_e equals the effective porosity of the porous medium.

$$V_a = \frac{\dfrac{K(h_1 - h_2)}{L}}{\eta_e} \qquad\qquad (2.21)$$

Note that the velocity calculated in equation 2.21 is only approximate and sometimes is referred to as the average linear velocity. In certain parts of an aquifer the interconnections between pores might be a nearly straight line in a downgradient direction, and elsewhere the water is forced to travel great distances to move rather short distances downgradient in the aquifer. Tortuosity is the term applied to the length of the sinuous path followed by a fluid particle, and is defined as the length of flow path divided by the overall length of sample. The arrival time of any chemical depends partly on the tortuosity of its flowpath through the aquifer.

Flow lines—lines of water movement—can be estimated by using water-elevation data from a minimum of three wells (Figure 2.21) that are screened at the same depth within the aquifer or below the water table. The heavy solid line shown in Figure 2.21 shows the flowpath taken by groundwater in the area. The calculated direction of groundwater flow is based upon the assumption that the 3 points define a plane and the slope of the plane defines a groundwater flow direction. It is important to note that groundwater flow moves in both horizontal and vertical directions. Nested wells (wells screened at distinct depths) provide information on vertical hydraulic gradients.

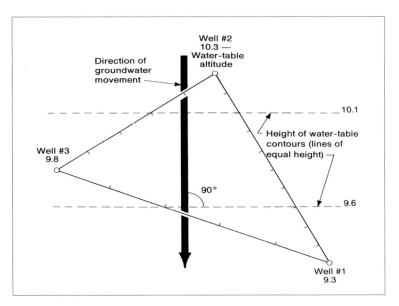

Figure 2.21. The direction of groundwater flow can be calculated by connecting a triangle linking the known potentiometric levels of 3 wells.

Measuring Groundwater Flow Velocities

The technology of measuring groundwater flow velocities has advanced significantly since the mid 1980s. Groundwater flow velocity can be measured by using a tracer or—within a well—by using borehole velocity meters or borehole dilution tests. An overview of tracing methods is provided by Leap and Kaplan (1988) and additional discussion is provided in Chapter 4.

SUMMARY

The successful development and protection of a groundwater resource depends upon the expertise of the water-well professionals involved and their understanding of the geology and topography of the site.

Some of the most basic information includes the following.

- ◆   The geologic characteristics of the aquifer usually indicate whether groundwater occurs in primary or secondary porosity.
- ◆   The topography of a site provides insight into whether the site is a groundwater recharge or discharge area.
- ◆   Understanding aquifer types and properties helps water-well professionals predict groundwater availability.

Possession of such rudimentary knowledge about the occurrence and movement of groundwater greatly enhance the probability of installation of a successful well.

ACKNOWLEDGMENTS

The authors wish to acknowledge the valuable comments and input provided by the reviewers of this chapter: Anthony D. Daus, PG, President and Principal Hydrogeologist, Geomatrix; and James Warner, PG, Principal, ERM. Mr. Raymond Scheurs, Johnson Screens (retired), also provided valuable insights.

CHAPTER 3
Subsurface Exploration and Hydrogeologic Logging

Thomas M. Hanna, PG
Johnson Screens

It increasingly is both more expensive and more difficult to find new sources of high-quality water. Groundwater investigations therefore must maximize the collection and use of data obtained from exploration or production-well drilling. This chapter focuses on subsurface exploration utilizing various drilling methods, examines a hydrogeologic classification system for water-well boreholes, and emphasizes information that can be gained from drilling exploration and production boreholes. This chapter does not discuss surface exploration methodologies or the use of hydrologic and topographic maps. Information on these topics is provided in Assaad et al. 2004, and Weight and Sonderegger 2001.

DRILLING TO OBTAIN FORMATION SAMPLES

Many different drilling methods have evolved to drill and complete wells in varying hydrogeologic environments. Exploratory drilling methods—with the primary purpose of collecting subsurface data—also have evolved. It is important to note that wells can be installed in boreholes drilled for exploration (e.g., using hollow-stem augers), but large-capacity water wells generally are not installed via such methods. Drilling methods that commonly are used to construct water-production wells (e.g., using reverse, direct mud rotary) are discussed in detail in Chapter 7.

The best way to understand the character of subsurface geologic materials is to obtain samples via drilling. Lithologic (geologic) logs document characteristic properties of the various geologic materials encountered in the borehole. Geologic samples collected during drilling consist of either cuttings produced by the action of the drill bit or cores collected using a variety of sampling methods. The collecting of representative samples is critical, because geologic samples commonly are relied upon in groundwater exploration for identifying aquifers, determining the size of the screen openings, and estimating a well's potential production capability.

The geologic information obtained by sampling can be supplemented by performing a suite of geophysical logs within the borehole (see Chapter 4 for additional discussion of this topic). Water production intervals can be assessed in a semi-quantified manner—without casing and well screen—by using certain drilling equipment to pump or inject water into and out of that interval. The responses of the interval to stresses can be used to infer hydrogeologic properties. It usually is best to combine two or more of these methods of investigation to verify the properties of the materials and their depths.

Different types of drilling methods have various advantages and disadvantages for providing hydrogeologic information. When conducting an exploration or test-well program, it is important to select the correct method of drilling to insure that proper data are collected. Table 3.1 provides a comparison of the different drilling methods and the relative quality of each method for obtaining hydrogeologic data. In Table 3.1, the units used in the last column are feet.

An example of the use of this table is in the case where a project requires that there be a relatively accurate determination of the water level, excellent geologic sample recovery, and a depth of exploration of 1,000 ft (305 m). To satisfy these requirements, the dual-wall air rotary drilling method probably would be selected.

Other considerations in the selection of a drilling method include cost, time, and the environment where the drilling is to occur. If in a residential area, for example, the environment probably is not conducive to the use of a casing hammer drilling rig.

Table 3.1. Relative Comparison of Common Drilling Methods for Hydrogeologic Drilling

Drilling Category	Drilling Method	Water-Level Data	Water Production Data	Geologic Sampling	Geophysical Logging	Sieve Analysis	Water Chemistry Data	Continuous Sample Collection Quality	Depth (ft)
Direct Circulation	Mud Rotary	P	P	F	E	F–G	P	G	> 3,000
	Air Rotary	E	E	G	G	F	F	P	1,500
	Casing Advancement Rotary	E	G	E	F[1]	G	F	P	1,000
Reverse Circulation	Flooded Reverse Mud Rotary	P	P	F	E	P	P	P	> 3,000
	Dual-Wall Flooded Reverse Mud Rotary	P	F	G	E	P	P	P	> 3,000
	Dual-Wall Percussion Hammer	G	G	G	F[1]	G	G	P	500
	Dual-Wall Air Rotary	E	E	G	G	G	F	P	1,500
Noncirculation	Roto-Sonic	G	F	E	F[1]	E	G	E	600
	Cable Tool	G	F	G	F[1]	G	G	P	1,500
	Hollow-Stem Auger	G	F	E	F[1]	E	G	E	150
	Direct Push	G	G	E	E[2]	E	E	E	100
	Wireline Core	G	F	E	F[1]	E	F	E	> 3,000

Key: E = Excellent; G = Good; F = Fair; P = Poor

1. Gamma logs can be conducted in boreholes drilled with these techniques.
2. Some direct push tools have geophysical logging tools built in, and provide excellent results.

The effectiveness of any of the drilling methods in obtaining a representative geologic sample is dependent on the formations being drilled and the drilling fluids used (if any). In materials comprised of consolidated rock, for example, the borehole probably will remain open and therefore can be drilled without using mud-based drilling fluids. Not using mud-based drilling fluids aids in the collection of representative samples. In locations where there are significant clay units, the clays can create a "natural" drilling fluid that masks water production and hinders the collection of representative geologic and water samples. A general description of the collection of samples is provided elsewhere in this chapter.

Rotary-Drilling Methods

In the rotary-drilling process—which includes all of the direct circulation, reverse circulation, mud-rotary, and dual-wall methods presented in Table 3.1—all of the drill cuttings are washed (to some degree) by the drilling fluids as they are transported upward from the bottom of the borehole. Drilling fluids carry up the sand grains that are fine and intermediate in size before transporting the coarse particles. The separated fractions must be combined as the sample is collected at the surface. The separation of different-sized particles can be minimized by properly controlling the weight and volume of the drilling fluid used, but separation cannot be eliminated entirely. When drilling in unconsolidated geological units it is important to avoid grinding the cuttings—or they could arrive at the surface much smaller than they were in their natural state, thus biasing the sample quality.

The choice of drilling fluid also affects the quality of samples. Bentonitic clays, when used as the drilling-fluid additive, tend to form part of the sample although there might be no clay present in the aquifer. Bentonitic drilling fluids also have high gel strength (discussed in Chapter 8); the drilling fluid gels, and suspended particles therefore do not drop out rapidly. This quality is essential when circulation is stopped and particles temporarily must be suspended in the borehole. High gel strength, however, keeps some of the cuttings—especially fine-grained particles—from settling during the short time that the fluid is circulated in the mud pit. Thus the collected and washed samples could exclude an important percentage of fine material.

Use of desanders and mechanical separating equipment located on the fluid discharge from the borehole might affect the representative nature of the sample that is collected. Samples should be collected before the drilling fluids enter the equipment, because a bias in sampling can impact the design of the screen. If the sizes of the openings for the well screen are based only on the coarser fraction of the sample, then the biased sample could result in a well that produces significant fine-grained materials (sand pumping).

Use of polymeric drilling fluids can improve the representativeness of the sample because drilling fluids made with such additives have low gel strength. Therefore, when circulation ceases, most of the fine-grained material settles as the drilling fluid passes through the mud pit. The various types of drilling-fluid additives are discussed in Chapter 8. The use of polymeric drilling fluids also has advantages when geophysical logs are to be run in the borehole. The drilling fluids help stabilize the borehole, keeping it open, and create a conductivity difference between the fluids in the aquifer and borehole, enhancing the response of electrical logs. See Chapter 4 for a discussion of borehole geophysics.

For projects that require intact samples from a small zone within a borehole drilled using mud-rotary methods, sidewall cores can be collected using oil field–type tools. Sidewall coring equipment primarily is used in consolidated formations. A sidewall coring-tool system consists of the downhole coring tool and a computer-based surface system that guides the coring operation (Baker Hughes 2006). The sidewall cores are drilled using a pivoting bit box (Figure 3.1). As the tool is lowered into the hole, the bit box remains in line with the tool body. Once it reaches the desired depth, the bit box is pivoted into the drill position to make contact with the wellbore wall. The maximum retrievable core length is drilled, brought to the surface, measured, and stored. The tool then can be repositioned for the next sample.

Wireline coring systems also have been developed for mud-rotary drilling. These systems obtain intact, undisturbed continuous core samples that are 5 ft (1.52 m) long. Appendix 3.A (DVD) provides more information on this type of coring system. Wireline coring systems used in mineral exploration are discussed elsewhere in this chapter.

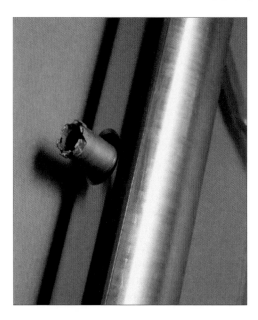

Figure 3.1. Sidewall coring tool (Baker Hughes Inc.).

Casing-Advancement Drilling

Rotary-drilling machines equipped with a casing driver can accomplish formation sampling (using air) in unconsolidated sediments, such as glacial boulder tills and alluvial deposits. The rig can be equipped with a downhole hammer to drill in bedrock. The depth to the water table usually can be detected using the casing-driver method, although the depth to which the casing can be driven for test-drilling operations might be limited in comparison with direct-rotary methods using a water-based drilling fluid. The casing-driver method insures that the samples are representative, because the casing follows the bit down the borehole and no sediment particles can fall from the borehole walls into the sample.

Dual-Wall Drilling with Air or Water

Using rotary-drilling rigs equipped with dual-wall drillpipe enables the recovery of continuous samples—if air or clear water is used as the drilling fluid. Cuttings immediately are pulled into the drillpipe, thus reducing erosion along the borehole and resulting in minimal contamination by overlying borehole materials. There also is negligible grinding of cuttings, resulting in the recovery of a higher percentage of coarse-grained sediment. The samples obtained by casing-driver method are more representative of the formation characteristics and depth of sample. For these reasons, test drilling using the casing-driver method now is used more frequently.

Geolograph

A geolograph is a specific type of drill-time log that is used on larger drilling rigs. The geolograph is used to record penetration rate (Figure 3.2), and is designed to automatically record the rate of penetration and depth during a drilling operation. The data often are displayed on a circular graph with a spiral curve indicating bit-rotation rate and depth.

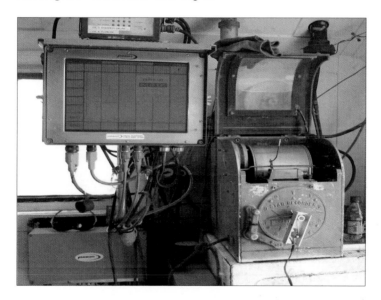

Figure 3.2. Geolograph, strip chart, and LCD (Layne Inc.).

A geolograph supplies useful information about the geologic materials encountered, because the character of the geological material largely determines the rate at which penetration proceeds. The drilling-time log is a record of the time required to drill a certain interval. The log is rendered as a curve or diagram that shows penetration time for each length of drill rod. Each significant change indicates a difference in the density of the geologic material being drilled.

Most drillers notice whether the rate of drill penetration increases or decreases, and then interpret these data in a relative way as to the density of the materials drilled. Their interpretations generally are based on experience. The value of a systematic record of the drilling time for each interval, however, sometimes is overlooked. The drilling-time log together with the borehole geologic log can be used to enhance the interpretation of subsurface conditions. Within a given borehole, penetration rates vary based on the density and composition of the geologic material, and the drilling method used (for example, using a tri-cone bit in clay is relatively slow). The impacts of composition are illustrated by the following example. A stiff, dry, non-expansive clay probably drills more easily than a wet expansive clay due to the "stickiness" of the expansive clay, assuming that the drilling techniques used are the same.

Factors other than formation density also affect the drilling rate, including the sharpness of the bit, diameter of the hole, type of bit, velocity of drilling fluids through the nozzles in the bit, speed of bit rotation, and weight on the bit. As a hole is deepened, additional drillpipe is added and the greater weight increases the penetration rate; this does not affect the usefulness of the drilling-time log. If hydraulic pulldown is required when drilling hard formations, the force applied should be recorded and taken into consideration when interpreting the geolograph. Carefully created time records have shown that—except for pulldown—none of the mechanical factors noted above influences drilling rate as much as the density of the formation drilled does.

Air Rotary Drilling Method Used to Evaluate Aquifer Production

Semi-quantitative data on aquifer production can be obtained during exploration drilling, especially if air rotary or air-hammer drilling methods are used. A log of groundwater production and temperature with depth can indicate locations of productive zones. Drilling with air enables short-term air-lift tests to be conducted. There typically are minimal costs associated with obtaining air-lift production data; a short-term air-lift aquifer test usually can be conducted during a few hours (2 or 3) of standby time. This program has been successful where air rotary drilling is used for groundwater exploration (Atkinson et al. 1989; see Appendix 3.B (DVD) for the complete paper).

Cable-Tool Drilling Method

The cable-tool drilling method occasionally is used for test drilling shallow boreholes or when drilling in cobbles, cavernous limestone, basalt, or dense tuff. Sampling unconsolidated materials using the cable-tool method presents relatively few difficulties, and the depth from which the samples are obtained can be measured accurately. The principal drawbacks of test drilling using this method is the comparatively slow rate of penetration, the need for driving casing when drilling, and potential for compacting the samples during drilling.

Collecting samples using the cable-tool method involves driving casing a short distance and then using a bailer to clean the cuttings out of the borehole. Compacted cuttings might have to be loosened and mixed by the drill bit before the material can be picked up by the bailer. The casing can be driven about 1 ft (0.3 m) in interbedded sand and clay—or several feet in thick sand—to isolate a sample. Heaving sand conditions complicate sampling and logging, and after a heave occurs there is no way to determine what part of a sand unit is represented by the material inside the bailer. In heaving-sand conditions, the upward flow of the sand tends to separate fine fractions from coarse fractions, thus biasing the collection of a sample.

EXPLORATION DRILLING METHODS

The following section discusses methods that are the best suited for hydrogeologic investigations. Methods such as sonic drilling, however, also can be used for drilling and completion of small-diameter wells (e.g., 2 in (51 mm), 4 in (102 mm)).

Sonic Drilling

Sonic drilling utilizes high-frequency mechanical vibrations to advance drilling tools through various geological formations, and the method is well suited for collecting core samples of unconsolidated formations. Coring usually is accomplished without the use of drilling fluids, except for the small amounts of fluid that are used to advance the outer casing.

The primary difference between a conventional drilling rig and a sonic-drilling rig is that the sonic rig has a specially designed hydraulically powered drill head or oscillator that generates adjustable high-frequency vibrational forces. The sonic head is attached directly to the core barrel, drillpipe, or outer casing, and sends the high-frequency vibrations through the drill rods to the face of the drill bit. The oscillator housing contains two eccentric, counter-rotating balance weights or rollers that are timed to direct the vibrational energy into the pipe (Figure 3.3).

The outer casing generally is advanced over the inner drill rods and core barrel, or after the core barrel has collected the undisturbed core sample and is pulled out of the borehole. In most situations, the outer casing can be advanced either without drilling fluids or with water, air, or a drilling fluid containing additives—depending upon the formation being drilled, the depth and diameter of the borehole, and the requirements of the project.

Advancement of the borehole and casing is achieved by fracturing, shearing, and displacement. Drilling through cobbles, boulders, rock, and construction debris requires the fracturing of the material using the inertial movement of the drill bit. Shearing takes place in dense silts, clay, and shales. Displacement of formation materials occurs when loose unconsolidated geologic materials are moved away by the vibrating drill bit.

The use of sonic drilling reduces the amount of cuttings created. Very few drill cuttings are brought to the surface—except the core sample itself—when the continuous dry-core method is used. As a result, in most cases the volume of drill cuttings generated is only 10% to 20% of the volume created when using hollow-stem auger, rotary, or cable-tool methods, however a large volume of core can be collected.

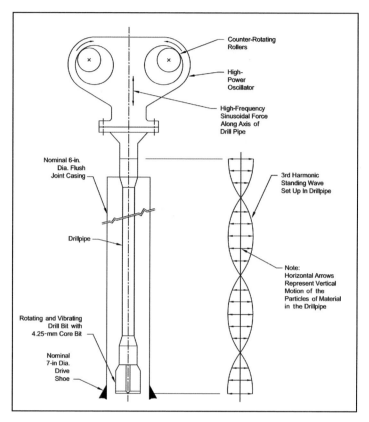

Figure 3.3. Schematic of sonic drilling (Ray Roussy, Sonic Drilling Ltd.).

Sonic drilling enables the collection of large-diameter, 3.5-in (89-mm) to 8-in (203-mm) continuous core samples from unconsolidated formations without the use of air, fluid, or additives, and with or without rotation.

Core samples can be obtained from the core barrel by extruding the sample into a continuous plastic sleeve (Figure 3.4) or another suitable container. Coarse-grained sediments such as cobbles and the surrounding matrix can be recovered by using the vibratory action of core barrels or split-spoon samplers. Such samplers can have an inside diameter of nearly 6 in (152 mm).

**Figure 3.4. Core sample being collected using sonic drilling
(Sonic Drilling Ltd.).**

If a continuous core is not required, then a sonic drill can be attached to conventional drillpipe and bits. Air is injected into the system to either blow the cuttings to the surface through a discharge system or push the cuttings into the formation. Significant drilling rates have been achieved in some geologic materials that are difficult to drill, such as cobbles and boulders, as compared to the rates of other methods. Sonic drills also can be configured for drilling and completion of wells angled to a nearly horizontal position (with minimal deviation).

In some situations, in-situ, vertical water-chemistry profiling data can be collected during drilling. The core barrel is advanced and then removed. A stainless-steel screen then is set at the bottom of the borehole with the lead rod and a K-packer (neoprene rubber seal), and the outer casing is vibrated back 5 ft (1.5 m), exposing the screen to the formation. A submersible pump and inflatable packer are installed and water is purged from the isolated zone (*see* Figure 3.5). The K-packer is attached to the upper end of the lead rod and prevents sediment from coming between the screen and drill casing. The interval below the inflatable packer is developed and purged, and a fresh sample of groundwater is collected. The water-sampling device then is retrieved via wireline.

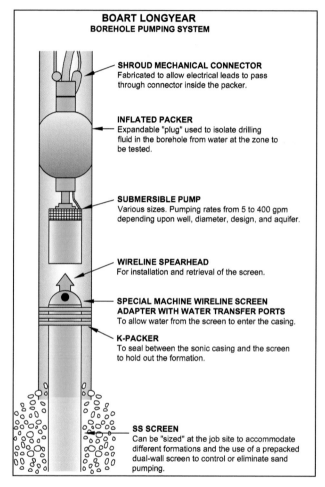

BOART LONGYEAR
BOREHOLE PUMPING SYSTEM

SHROUD MECHANICAL CONNECTOR
Fabricated to allow electrical leads to pass
through connector inside the packer.

INFLATED PACKER
Expandable "plug" used to isolate drilling
fluid in the borehole from water at the zone to
be tested.

SUBMERSIBLE PUMP
Various sizes. Pumping rates from 5 to 400 gpm
depending upon well, diameter, design, and aquifer.

WIRELINE SPEARHEAD
For installation and retrieval of the screen.

SPECIAL MACHINE WIRELINE SCREEN
ADAPTER WITH WATER TRANSFER PORTS
To allow water from the screen to enter the casing.

K-PACKER
To seal between the sonic casing and the screen
to hold out the formation.

SS SCREEN
Can be "sized" at the job site to accommodate
different formations and the use of a prepacked
dual-wall screen to control or eliminate sand
pumping.

**Figure 3.5. Boart Longyear borehole pumping system used with
sonic drilling techniques (Boart Longyear).**

Dual-Wall Percussion Hammer Drilling

The dual-wall percussion hammer drill rig is equipped with a single-cylinder
diesel-powered pile-driving hammer. The hammer advances dual-wall drillpipe
equipped with an open-face drill bit (Figure 3.6). As the pipe is advanced,

high-pressure filtered air is injected in the annulus of the dual-wall drillpipe. The air returns the cuttings from the rear of the cutting shoe to the surface through the center of the drillpipe. The cuttings are ejected through a cyclone unit mounted on the side of the drill rig.

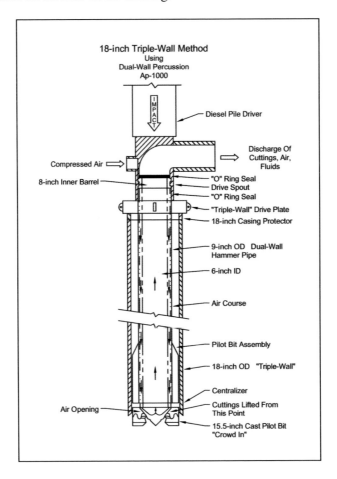

Figure 3.6. Dual-wall percussion hammer drilling method (Layne Environmental Services).

The dual-wall percussion hammer can be used to complete boreholes ranging from 6 in (152 mm) to 18 in (457 mm) in diameter. Wells can be completed inside of the drill string or driven casing so that there is minimal cross-contamination of soil or water samples during completion. In cases where wells larger than 4 in (102 mm) in diameter are required, an additional drillpipe or "triple wall" can be added to the drill string. The triple-wall drillpipe is simultaneously driven with the dual-wall drillpipe as the borehole is advanced.

The dual-wall percussion hammer method of drilling provides a variety of ways to collect geologic samples. The large center opening enables the return of materials that are nearly 6 in (152 mm) in diameter, and the collection of representative samples of cobble and larger-sized materials. Continuous samples can be collected using 2-in (51-mm) spilt-spoon samplers.

Water production information can be collected as the borehole is advanced, and air-lift tests on various intervals can be conducted to determine completion intervals for a well.

Hollow-Stem Auger Drilling

Hollow-stem augers commonly are used for relatively shallow groundwater exploration purposes in unconsolidated materials or in weathered or weakly cemented bedrock. Auger rigs (Figure 3.7) can be set up quickly, and the rate of penetration generally is rapid in many types of soft sediments. Geotechnical and exploration drillers have been using hollow-stem augers since the early 1950s. The flights for the hollow-stem auger are welded onto larger-diameter pipe with a cutter head mounted at the bottom (Figure 3.8). A plug is inserted into the hollow center of the cutter head to prevent soil from coming up inside the auger. This center plug has an attached bit that helps advance the auger. The auger flights are connected to the top-head drive unit.

Hollow-stem augers with outside diameters ranging from 6¼ in (159 mm) to 22 in (559 mm) and inside diameters of 2½ in (64 mm) to 13 in (330 mm) (Figure 3.8) have been used to drill water wells. The common outside diameters, however, are 6¼ in (159 mm) to 13 in (330 mm) with inside diameters ranging from 2½ in (64 mm) to 6 in (152 mm). Auger lengths usually are 5 ft (1.5 m) but on larger hollow-stem rigs, especially those equipped with carousel racks, the auger flights are 10 ft (3 m) long and are stored in 20-ft (6.1-m) sections. Holes as deep as 300 ft (91 m) have been drilled with 6¼-in (159-mm) diameter hollow-stem augers. More common depths in stable formations are 120 ft (36.6 m) using 6¼-in (159-mm) diameter hollow-stem augers, and 40 ft (12.2 m) using 12-in (305-mm) diameter hollow-stem augers.

Representative samples can be gathered using a variety of sampling methods as drilling proceeds with hollow-stem augers. Samples can be obtained from cuttings deposited at the top of the hole as the auger advances; however this method generally is unsatisfactory because the samples are mixed and the depth for the sample is not known accurately.

Figure 3.7. Continuous flight auger used to drill nominal 6-in (152-mm) borehole and complete 2-in (51-mm) well (AMS, Inc.).

Undisturbed samples from known depths can be obtained using the split-spoon method. The drill rods that hold the bottom plug in place are withdrawn from the borehole in long (10-ft (3-m)) sections. The sampler then is attached and the string reconnected and lowered into the borehole to retrieve the sample. The split spoon usually is driven 1 ft (0.3 m) to 2 ft (0.6 m) by a 140-lb (64-kg) hammer.

Another method is to use a core barrel that generally is advanced 5 ft (1.5 m) as the augers are advanced with the drilling rig. After retrieval, the sampler is opened and the sample contained inside is geologically logged. On some types of drilling rigs, the entire sampling apparatus is mounted on a wireline. Such units include a downhole hammer to drive the sampler.

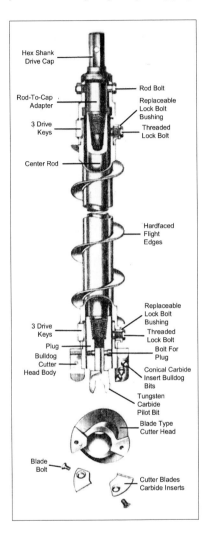

Figure 3.8. Typical hollow-stem auger (South Dakota State University).

The hollow-stem method is a fast and efficient means of drilling and completing small-diameter wells to moderate depths. Screens can be installed and filter packed without the use of casing or drilling fluids. Additional photographs of hollow-stem drilling equipment are contained in Appendix 3.C (DVD).

Direct-Push Drilling

Direct-push drilling methods (sometimes termed direct-push technology) use a combination of a hydraulically powered percussion hammer, a downward hydraulic push, and the static weight of the vehicle on which the system is mounted. These methods push a sampler into the ground by displacing soil to make a path for the tool, and therefore they do not generate drill cuttings. In favorable geologic conditions, using direct push enables subsurface investigations to be conducted to depths of approximately 120 ft (36.6 m). In most situations investigation depths are limited to 50 ft (15 m).

The outside diameters of boring and sampling tools can range from ¾ in (19 mm) to 3½ in (89 mm). Figure 3.9 shows sampling tools and Figure 3.10 is a photo of a direct-push rig. The inside diameter of well installations can range from 1½ in (13 mm) to 2 in (51 mm).

Direct-push technologies provide the following advantages (Geoprobe® 2007).

- Minimal disturbance of the ground surface; only a small-diameter hole is created.
- No cuttings are created, thus eliminating handling, containing, storing, sampling, analyzing, and disposing of potentially contaminated cuttings.
- Use of compact equipment.

Along with the actual probing equipment, there exists a wide variety of tools and options for additional subsurface investigations (Geoprobe® 2007), including:

- Probes for simultaneous measurement of volatile organic compounds and soil conductivity;
- Soil gas samplers;
- Electrical conductivity logging systems that measure lithologic changes in unconsolidated materials (resulting real-time data allows for the identification of high-yielding zones for groundwater or soil gas sampling);
- Groundwater samplers for collecting discreet samples during probing;
- Cone-penetration tools (CPT) to measure soil properties in situ; and
- Equipment to measure hydraulic conductivity in situ.

Additional information on direct-push technologies can be obtained from manufacturers such as AMS, Inc. or Geoprobe® Systems. Photographs of direct-push rigs and sampling equipment are contained in Appendix 3.D (DVD).

Figure 3.9. Probing equipment for direct-push system (Site Services, Inc.).

Figure 3.10. Nominal 1-in (250-mm) core sample collected using direct-push methods; note both the lack of cuttings and that there is no disturbance around the borehole (AMS Inc.).

Wireline-Core Drilling

The wireline method is used to drill relatively small-diameter core holes (Table 3.2) in bedrock. Unlike most types of drilling, the primary objective of core drilling is to retrieve a core sample. The resulting sample is a long solid cylinder of rock that geologists can characterize with respect to rock type, fracture density, and other attributes. This drilling method is used for mineral exploration, geotechnical work, and evaluation of fractured-rock masses.

Table 3.2. Common Wireline Core and Hole Dimensions

Size	Core Diameter		Hole Diameter	
	in	mm	in	mm
AQTK / AQTK-U	1.2	30.5	1.9	48.0
BQ / BQ-U	1.4	36.4	2.4	60.0
BQTK / BQTK-U	1.6	40.7	2.4	60.0
NQ / NQ-U	1.9	47.6	3	75.7
NQ2" / NQ2"-U	2	50.6	3	75.7
HQ / HQ-U	2.5	63.5	3.8	96.0
PQ	3.3	85.0	4.8	122.6

This sampling method yields a representative core sample of rock formations that can be evaluated for properties such as fracture density. A measure of fracture density and rock-mass strength is rock-quality designation (RQD). Rock-quality designation is based on measuring core-recovery percentage that incorporates only rock pieces that are greater than 4 in (102 mm) (Deere & Deere 1988). The optimal core diameter is 2 in (47.6 mm) (NQ Coring Equipment).

Rock-quality designation is defined as the following quotient.

$$RQD = \frac{Sum\ l}{l\ total} \cdot 100\% \tag{3.1}$$

Where:

Sum l = Sum of length of core segments longer than 4 in (10 cm); and

l total = Total length of core run.

From the RQD index, the rock mass can be classified as listed in Table 3.3.

Table 3.3. RQD Descriptions

RQD	Rock Mass Quality
< 25%	Very Poor
25% to 50%	Poor
51% to 75%	Fair
76% to 90%	Good
91% to 100%	Excellent

The following is an example of RQD calculations.

Total length drilled = 51.2 in (130 cm)

Total core recovered = 41 in (104 cm)

Core recovery = 41/51.2 (104/130) = 80%

Sum of core lengths greater than 10 cm = 28.1 in (71.5 cm)

RQD = 28.1/51.2 (71.5/130) = 55% (or fair quality, based on Table 3.3)

Wireline core holes can be drilled at angles that allow for investigations of areas that cannot be reached via vertical drilling, such as under buildings and dams.

A core drill string is a series of long connected hollow tubes (rods), with a barrel at the end that is connected to a special cutting bit at the bottom of the assembly. As the drill moves further into the formation, the drilling professional adds rods onto the end, thus lengthening the drill string. When the driller wants to remove core from a conventional core drill, the entire core barrel must be removed from the hole. This is time-consuming, because each rod must be removed to retrieve the core barrel.

When using wireline drilling, a core barrel can be removed from the bottom of the hole without removing the rod string. To remove the core, an overshot is lowered on the end of a wireline. The overshot attaches to the back of the core barrel inner tube, the wireline is pulled back, and the inner tube disengages itself from the barrel. Additional discussion of wireline sampling is contained in Appendix 3.E (DVD).

HYDROGEOLOGIC LOGGING OF BOREHOLES

Collection of hydrogeologic data from boreholes drilled for water wells is not consistent. Therefore, to provide a consistent approach to characterizing water-well boreholes, use of the Hydrogeologic Classification System for Water-Well Boreholes (HCSWB) is proposed.

The Hydrogeologic Classification System for Water-Well Boreholes (Hanna 2006) provides a methodology to identify and record consistent hydrogeologic data from water-well boreholes. The HCSWB was developed to establish a framework for creating uniform borehole logs that leads to consistent interpretation. It incorporates important aspects of geologic descriptions for distinguishing formation and aquifer characteristics, and documents important hydrologic characteristics that control groundwater flow. The HCSWB's uniform descriptions and identifiers also provide the basis for storing and sorting data in digital format; records in a database system can be sorted by the descriptors.

The two main parts of the HCSWB are a classification system and a Field Guide that enables quick identification of materials in the field (a copy is located at the back of this book). Figure 3.11 presents a flow chart showing the logging procedures and categories of the classification system.

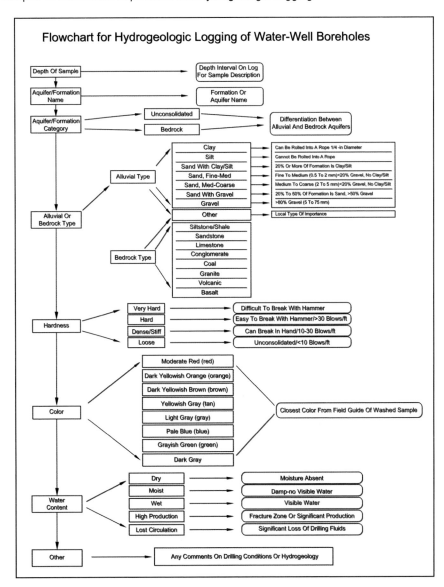

Figure 3.11. Flowchart of borehole logging
(Hydrogeologic Classification System for Water-Well Boreholes).

Sample Collection

The first step in creating a consistent hydrogeologic log is the collection of a representative sample for description. As discussed, the drilling method, the depth of the borehole, the penetration rate, and the type of drilling fluid have significant influences on the representativeness and quality of the sample. It is recommended that cuttings be logged in the field so that adjustments to the drilling program can be made as needed.

Prior to logging a borehole, the following steps should be followed and the necessary materials should be prepared.

- Gather logging materials (e.g., Field Guide, logging paper, computer).
- Establish a logging work area that is out of the way of the drilling operations.
- Collect samples in a consistent fashion and insure that they are representative of the interval penetrated. Figure 3.12 shows the collection of a sample using a sieve or strainer.
- Wash the samples and describe them when they are wet, for more-accurate color identifications. During the washing, care is required so that a significant amount of fines is not removed.
- In the logging work area, place samples on a sheet of plastic or on a board so that the cuttings can be easily distinguished from the ground they are placed upon and be stored until they are no longer needed (Figure 3.13).
- Recommended procedure is to log a series of samples together, as opposed to logging individual samples, because geologic transitions (e.g., fining upward depositional environments) can be noted and recorded.
- Mark the depth intervals clearly on the sample bags (Figure 3.14) or chip trays that store the cuttings.
- Send a representative sample of the cuttings from the interval to be screened to a lab for sieve analysis for screen slot selection.

It is important to note that using a strainer for sample collection can result in the loss of much of the sample, especially if the sample is fine grained. Another method involves the use of a bucket. Prior to drilling into the aquifer, drilling fluids are circulated until they are cleared of cuttings; then drill approximately 5 ft (1.5 m) into the aquifer and wait for returns. Additionally, measuring the uphole velocity enables determination of the time it takes to reach the surface at particular depths. Once the returns are estimated to be from the aquifer, the sample can be collected in a bucket placed under the discharge pipe.

Figure 3.12. Drilling professionals using a small sieve to catch samples of cuttings from a mud rotary drill rig.

Figure 3.13. Example of laying samples on a prepared surface for subsequent logging.

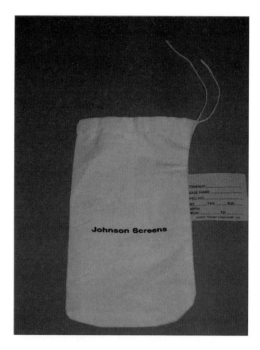

Figure 3.14. Sample bag.

Sample Description

Table 3.4 presents a sample of a borehole logged using the HCSWB. A simple spreadsheet that incorporates dropdown menus to insure uniformity is contained in Appendix 3.F (DVD). Borehole logs can be recorded using a computer logging program or handwritten field log. Because the identification system is standardized or menu driven, fewer notes are needed for creating a detailed log in the field. Standardization enables the use of electronic databases that can be used for storing and correlating borehole data. The elements of a detailed log are outlined in the following steps and an example of a computer-generated log (in U.S. customary units) is provided in Table 3.4. The following sections provide more detail on the logging process.

Table 3.4. Example of Borehole Log Using HCSWB and Database with Dropdown Menus

Well #1 U.S.A.							
Depth from / to (ft)	Forma-tion / Aquifer	Bedrock/ Uncon-solidated	Type	Hardness	Color	Water-Bearing / Fractured Bedrock	Other
0–5	Valley	Uncon-solidated	Sand, fine to med.	Loose	Dark yellowish (orange)	Moist	Moderately sorted
5–10	Valley	Uncon-solidated	Silt	Loose	Yellowish gray (tan)	Moist	
10–15	Valley	Uncon-solidated	Sand, med. to coarse	Loose	Dark yellowish (orange)	Wet	First water production
15–20	Madison	Bedrock	Lime-stone	Hard	Yellowish gray (tan)	Lost circulation	Rod drop 1 m
20–25	Denver	Bedrock	Siltstone/ shale	Dense/ stiff	Dark gray	Wet	Thin; interbedded with sandstone
20–25	Denver	Bedrock	Sand-stone	Hard	Dark yellowish (orange)	Wet	Interbedded with shale
25–30	Pierre Shale	Bedrock	Siltstone/ shale	Dense/ stiff	Dark gray	Wet	Slow drilling; clay balling on the bit
30–35	Challis	Bedrock	Volcanic	Hard	Dark yellowish (orange)	High production	Fractures
(© 2006 Johnson Screens)							

Depth

Record the depth interval for the description, which is the top and bottom of the depth interval being described. The length of the interval to be described depends upon the uniformity of the formation or aquifer and the level of detail required for each borehole. Typically samples are collected and described every 5 ft (1.5 m) to 10 ft (3 m) of depth.

Aquifer or Formation

The aquifer or formation should be identified by name. Formation names can be obtained from published data and generally are available from local, state, and federal geologic surveys. Important aquifers also have formal names which quite often duplicate the formation name (e.g., Denver Formation or Denver Aquifer). These names provide information that is helpful for understanding the extent and regional characteristics of the aquifer or formation. If the aquifer or formation name is not available then it can be omitted.

Unconsolidated Materials and Bedrock

The aquifer or formation should be identified as consisting of either bedrock or unconsolidated geologic materials. This information is the first descriptor providing information concerning bedrock and alluvial contacts that are important to many regulatory agencies for managing surface groundwater resources, and it is easy to identify on the log (see the example provided in Table 3.4).

Based on the identification of the formation as bedrock or unconsolidated materials, its general type can be identified. The Field Guide outlines the 7 types of unconsolidated materials and 8 bedrock types that represent the important hydrostratigraphic units.

Unconsolidated Materials

When describing the cuttings from an unconsolidated material, a better understanding of the water-yielding characteristics comes from a description of the smaller 20% fraction of the materials that influences the flow of water. In most cases, the finer 10% to 20% fraction (the d_{10} and d_{20}) of an unconsolidated formation influences the hydraulic conductivity of the material (Vukovic & Soro 1992). An example is a formation described as "sand and gravel." This designation indicates that at least 20% of the formation consists of sand-sized particles and, as such, has the transmitting capacity of a sand.

- ◆ **Clay:** Formations are classified as clays if the majority of the formation contains clay-sized particles and less than 10% of the formation is comprised of other materials such as sands or silts. Clays are easy to distinguish from silts because they can be rolled into ropes that are ¼-in (6-mm) in diameter (Figure 3.15).

Figure 3.15. Clays can be rolled into ropes ¼-in (6 mm) in diameter; silts cannot be rolled into ropes.

◆ **Silt:** Silts are similar in appearance to clays but cannot be rolled into ropes ¼-in (6 mm) in diameter. To be designated as silt, 10% or less of the formation should consist of coarser-grained materials.

◆ **Sand with clay or silt:** For a formation to have this designation, 20% or more of the sample is composed of clay or silt-sized material, and 80% or less of the sample should consist of sand and gravel. This designation is a mixture of materials that, at first, might seem to be permeable, however the clay and silt content reduces the hydraulic conductivity in comparison to that of a pure sand.

◆ **Sand, fine to medium:** For this designation, the smallest 20% or more of the sample is sand particles that range in diameter from 0.02 in (0.5 mm) to 0.08 in (2 mm). The remainder of the sample can be coarser-grained sands, but is comprised of less than 20% gravel-sized particles and essentially contains no silt or clay.

◆ **Sand, medium to coarse:** The smallest 20% of the formation's sand ranges from 0.08 in (2 mm) to 0.2 in (5 mm) in diameter. Less than 20% of the formation can be gravel with almost no silt and clay (Figure 3.16).

Figure 3.16. Using the Field Guide to identify and describe medium- to coarse-grained sand.

- **Sand and gravel:** For a formation to have this designation, the smallest 20% to 50% of the sample consists of sand-sized particles that range in diameter from 0.08 in (2 mm) to 0.2 in (5 mm), and more than 50% of the formation is gravel sized.
- **Gravel:** The finest 20% or more of the sample is larger than 0.2 in (5 mm) in diameter. This designation also includes gravel mixed with cobbles or boulders. Less than 5% of the sample is comprised of sand-sized particles.

Bedrock

Describing bedrock cuttings can be difficult when in the field. Subtle differences—such as between siltstone and shale or metamorphic and igneous rocks (especially granites)—can be difficult to determine from borehole cuttings. Evaluating cuttings along with other descriptors, however, such as hardness, fractures, and formation or aquifer identification provides additional detail, especially if rock cores are available.

Rock types have been grouped into general categories that easily can be identified in the field from cuttings. Quite often, groundwater flow in bedrock is a function of secondary permeability. The presence of fractures is noted under "Water Content."

- **Siltstone and shale**: Siltstone and shale are very fine–grained sedimentary rock formations; slate is the metamorphic equivalent. The degree of induration (density) is a function of depth of burial. Shales and siltstones generally are considered aquitards and barriers to groundwater flow.

- **Sandstone:** Sandstone is the consolidated equivalent of sand, and this type of formation can have primary and secondary permeability. Quartzite is the metamorphic equivalent of sandstone and, due to its hardness, forms good marker beds.

- **Limestone:** Carbonate rock aquifers consist of limestone, dolomite, and marble (the metamorphic equivalent of limestone). The yield of carbonate aquifers can vary greatly from confining layers to prolific water producers due to secondary permeability that is the result of fracturing and dissolution of the limestone. Carbonate borehole cuttings often can be identified in the field by their reaction to weak acids (e.g., 10% hydrochloric acid), which make them effervesce.

- **Conglomerates:** Conglomerate is the rock equivalent of a sand and gravel deposit. Conglomerates can be excellent marker beds for stratigraphic interpretation. Like sandstones, conglomerates can have both primary and secondary permeability.

- **Coal:** Coal can be a good aquifer depending on the amount of fracturing and the presence of sandstone interbeds. In some areas coal is important for noting areas of potential poor water quality or the presence of methane gas. Coal serves as a distinct marker bed for establishing stratigraphic sequences.

- **Granite:** Granites are intrusive igneous crystalline rocks. The colors of granites are a function of the mineral content, and crystal size is a function of the rock's cooling history. Granites generally are low-yielding formations that produce water through fractures. Very often these rocks act as barriers to groundwater flow.

- **Volcanic:** Volcanic rocks are extrusive formations (e.g., andesites, rhyolites) and exclude basalts (which are identified as separate hydrogeologic classifications). Volcanic rocks generally are finely crystalline, and groundwater flow is through fractures. Similar to granites, the color of a rock is indicative of its mineral type. Volcanic formations generally can act as barriers to groundwater flow.

+ **Basalts:** Basalts can have significant secondary permeability, and in some areas they are important aquifers. Basaltic aquifers form in layers of varying permeability determined by flow events. The flows tend to have permeable zones that develop at the top and bottom. Basalt flows commonly are interbedded with debris flows or lava tubes that can be high–water production zones.
+ **Other:** This category can be used to add any rock type that might aid in describing cuttings.

Hardness

Hardness is a relative term that has been defined in the field of engineering geology but has not been defined adequately in the water-well industry. The term "hardness" is useful to assess drilling penetration rates and to assist in correlation of rock units. Often, the density and to some extent the hardness of an unconfined geologic unit are assessed using a Standard Penetration Test (STP). The STP consists of driving a standard-sized tube into an unconsolidated sediment using a 140-lb (64-kg) hammer falling 30 in (76.2 cm), and recording the number of hammer blows required to drive the tube a distance of 1 ft (30.5 cm) into the geologic unit. The number of blows (N) is termed the "blow count" (Perloff & Baron 1976).

+ **Very hard:** Cuttings or core that are difficult to break with hammer.
+ **Hard:** Cuttings or core that are easy to break with a hammer or that require more than 30 blows/ft using an SPT.
+ **Dense/stiff:** Cuttings that can be broken by hand using no tools or that require 10 to 30 blows/ft.
+ **Loose:** Cuttings that are unconsolidated or require fewer than 10 blows/ft.

Color

Color provides information that can be used to correlate different formations. Red and orange can indicate oxidation or the flow of oxygenated water though the formation. The colors presented in the Field Guide are the most common colors occurring in the field. If the exact color is not depicted on the card then the closest color match should be selected.

Water Content

Notations on water content are influenced by the drilling method and whether fluids were used to drill the well. Water-content data helps identify water-production zones and the position of the water table (Figure 3.17). Following are the descriptors used for water content.

- **Dry:** No moisture in cuttings
- **Moist:** Cuttings are damp but have no visible water
- **Wet:** Cuttings have visible water
- **High production:** Locations of fractures or coarse-grained materials that yield significantly more water than do adjacent geologic materials
- **Lost circulation:** Zone of significant loss of drilling fluids or cuttings, indicating a highly permeable zone

If the borehole is drilled with a heavy drilling fluid and the water content of the samples cannot be determined, then this data column should be left blank.

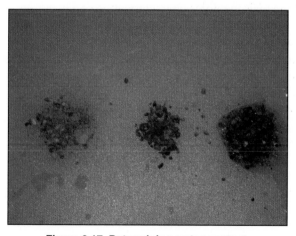

Figure 3.17. Determining water content.

Other

The other areas of the log can be used for any additional comments that enhance description of the formation or aquifer. This facilitates modifications of the borehole log for a particular application. A drilling professional can include descriptions of such things as angularity or roundness of the sediment grains, organic content, drilling conditions, or any other information that augments the log.

Frequently in sedimentary aquifers there are thin, interbedded materials such as clays and sands that have bedding smaller than the sample interval, or the cuttings are returned to the surface in a mixed sample. These interbed aquifers can be described on two lines that describe the same depth interval as shown in Table 3.4 for the depth interval of 20 ft to 25 ft.

Water-Level Data

An important part of hydrogeologic logging is determining (1) where water first is encountered, (2) the zones of significant production, and (3) the degree of confinement of the aquifers. If water-level data are an important part of the exploration program, then a drilling method that minimizes or eliminates the introduction of drilling fluids should be selected.

As part of the hydrogeologic characterization of a borehole, a good practice is to measure the water levels at different intervals during the drilling of the borehole. In any drilling program, there are points when this can be done without delaying the drilling, such as at the end of a shift, during breaks, or any other time when the drilling process has stopped (e.g., when mechanical breakdowns occur). During a break in drilling, the water level should be allowed to recover for between 5 min and 10 min as the borehole starts to fill with water. This is especially important if the borehole is being drilled using air rotary method. Fluids constantly are removed from the borehole during drilling, and sufficient time should be allowed for water levels to recover.

If obtaining moisture data is important, then the drill cuttings should be inspected carefully and the moisture content noted on the borehole log. In such cases, discreet core samples should be collected.

Well-Log Software

A demonstration version of WellMagic—a well-log software package developed by Geographic Insights—is included as Appendix 3.G (DVD). This program systematically creates well logs and well-completion reports. The HCSWB is incorporated into the software and lithologies can be cataloged with drilling, well-completion, and pump-installation data. The program also manages many other facets of the well-drilling business including estimating, accounting functions, work orders, and scheduling. It also tracks well and pump maintenance.

WellMagic typically is customized for specific locales (either the United States or international) to reflect the requirements of the specific governmental agencies as well as to incorporate the governmental boundaries (e.g., counties, provinces, towns). The data records in the program can be searched easily for such information as customer, address, and invoice.

Some sample data are included with the program, enabling a user to evaluate the program and its operation. All screens are accessed from the Screens Menu and reports are found in the Reports Menu at the top of the page. To close any screen or report, simply click the small "X" found at the upper-right corner of the screen; clicking the large "X" closes the program completely. Instructions appear with each screen or tab, and online help is available from the Help Menu.

SUMMARY

This chapter describes the strengths and limitations of hydrogeologic sample collection for various drilling methods. Drilling methods and fluids can influence the representativeness of the samples, and water-well professionals should be aware of such influences. Drilling methods should be selected based on the anticipated geologic media, target depths, types of samples needed, and well diameter (if applicable). Representative hydrogeologic samples are important for designing appropriate well screens, and a drilling method capable of obtaining core samples should be used if a sieve analysis is to be conducted.

The HCSWB method and Field Guide enable groundwater professionals to make detailed, concise, and consistent logs based on the cuttings from water-well boreholes. The HCSWB allows for observations of water production capabilities from geologic units, and such notations often are omitted in water-well borehole logs.

ACKNOWLEDGMENTS

Mr. Ray Roussy of Sonic Drilling Ltd., Mr. Thomas Dalzell of AMS, Inc., and Mr. Mark Scharenbroich of Layne-Western Company, Inc. contributed sections to this chapter.

Valuable reviews of this chapter were provide by: Mr. Raymond Schreurs, Johnson Screens (retired); Mr. Marc H. Silva, PG, Principal, Central Valley Environmental, Inc.; Mr. Richard Schramm, Chairman, Schramm Inc.; and Mr. Tom Downey, President, Downey Drilling Inc.

CHAPTER 4
Borehole Geophysics

John Jansen, PhD
Ruekert/Kielke, Inc, Aquifer Science and Technology Division

James J. LoCoco, CPG
Mount Sopris Instrument Co., Inc.

A comprehensive suite of borehole geophysical methods has been used for many years to measure physical properties of geologic materials around a borehole, formation fluid, and well-construction materials. Downhole tools directly measure—or enable the drawing of inferences about—several properties, including: aquifer lithology and thickness; porosity; density; water quality (temperature, pressure, conductivity, pH, dissolved oxygen, oxidation-reduction potential, and the concentrations of nitrate, ammonia, and chloride); borehole diameter and deviation; flow within the borehole; and mineralogy.

Borehole geophysical methods are particularly useful when the drilling method used provides altered formation samples or when it is not obvious from which depth the sample originated (as is the case in mud rotary drilling, especially in deeper wells). Other applications include determining productive intervals of a borehole, the physical condition of a well, and the water quality in distinct intervals of the well. In fractured rock aquifers, oriented borehole-wall imagery can help establish geometry and hydraulic importance of individual fractures and fracture systems. In well fields, geophysical logs are used to estimate lateral extent of aquifer facies, aquifer compaction over time, and aquifer recharge.

Geophysical well logging for groundwater applications is a broad field of study, and only a brief introduction is provided in this chapter. New and more sophisticated logs are introduced regularly. In the past, these logs were used almost exclusively in the petroleum industry; the emergence of powerful field computers, however, has made many of these logs much easier to acquire and interpret. As the logs have become more accessible these tools are becoming increasingly available to the water-well industry, either from logging contractors and manufacturers or from rental-equipment outlets.

The discussion of logging methods presented in this chapter covers a few widely used methods that are listed in Table 4.1; it is, however, far from complete and doubtlessly excludes some new methods that have come into common use after this book's publication. Several excellent references currently are available and provide more detailed information, and some of these are listed in references section at the end of this book. Although not comprehensive, this list provides a good overview of the existing references regarding the science and application of common logging methods.

Many different downhole measurements commonly are used in the groundwater industry, and some require specific borehole conditions. Natural–gamma ray logs, for example, can yield information in any borehole condition, including in metal-cased or PVC-cased holes, fluid-filled holes, and holes containing air. Other measurements, such as the commonly used resistivity and spontaneous potential, require a fluid filled open borehole. The radius of investigation for most borehole geophysical measurements typically is only a few inches to a few feet around the borehole. Due to the small scale of the measurement, borehole methods tend to produce excellent vertical resolution. The combination of high resolution and greater accuracy make most calibrated borehole methods suitable for quantitative measurements and small-scale correlation of stratigraphic properties.

Table 4.1. Log-Selection Criteria

Log Type	Varieties & Related Types	Properties Measured	Potential Applications	Required Borehole Conditions	Limitations
Acoustic Tele-viewer	Acoustic caliper	Acoustic reflectivity of borehole wall	Location, orientation & character of fractures & solution openings; strike & dip of bedding; casing inspection	Fluid-filled & 3-in to 16-in diameter	Heavy mud or mud cake attenuate signal; slow logging
Acoustic Velocity	Compensated wave form; cement bond	Compressional wave velocity; flexural waves; tube waves	Porosity; lithology; fracture location; character; cement bond; permeability estimates	Fluid-filled & uncased, except cement bond	Does not detect secondary porosity; cement bond & wave form require expert analysis
Caliper	Oriented, 1-, 2-, 3-, 4-arm high-resolution bow spring	Borehole or casing internal diameter	Borehole-diameter corrections to other logs; lithology; fractures; borehole volume for cementing	Any conditions	Deviated holes limit some probes; significant resolution difference between tools
Electrical Conduc-tivity	EM	Formation conductivity	Lithology; grain size	Fluid-air non-conditioned	Cannot be used in metal casing
Flow	Spinner; radioactive tracer; brine tracer; thermal pulse	Flow of borehole fluid	Flow within borehole; location & apparent hydraulic conductivity of permeable interval	Fluid filled	Spinners require faster velocities; must be centralized
Fluid Conduc-tivity	Resistivity	Most measure resistivity of borehole fluid	Quality & flow of borehole fluid; location of contaminant plumes	Fluid filled	Accuracy varies; requires temperature correction
Gamma	Gamma spectral	Gamma radiation from natural or artificial radioisotopes	Lithology (can be related to clay & silt content/permeability); spectral identifies radioisotopes	Any borehole conditions, except large diameter or several strings of casing & cement	None

Log Type	Varieties & Related Types	Properties Measured	Potential Applications	Required Borehole Conditions	Limitations
Gamma-Gamma	Compensated (dual detector); omni-directional	Electron density	Bulk density; porosity; moisture content; lithology	Optimum results in uncased borehole; qualitative through casing or drill stem	Severe borehole-diameter effects, unless combined with caliper
Multi-Electrode Resistivity	Normal; focused; guard	Resistivity of rock & saturating fluids	Quantitative data on salinity of interstitial water; lithology	Uncased borehole filled with conductive fluid	Normal logs provide inaccurate values and thicknesses in thin beds
Neutron	Epithermal; thermal; compensated activation; pulsed	Hydrogen content	Saturated porosity; moisture content; activation analysis; lithology	Optimum results in uncased borehole; can be calibrated for casing	Borehole-diameter & chemical effects
Optical Televiewer	None	Scanned image of borehole wall	Fracture aperture and orientation; borehole condition; bedding and stratigraphic structures	Clear fluid or clear air	Cloudy water or dusty air reduces image quality; mudded boreholes obscure view of formation
Single-Point Resistance	Conventional; differential	Resistance of rock, saturating fluid & borehole fluid	High-resolution lithology; fracture location by differential probe	Uncased borehole filled with conductive fluid	Not quantitative; substantial borehole-diameter effects
Spontaneous Potential	None	Electric potential caused by salinity differences in borehole and interstitial fluids	Lithology; shale content; water quality; bed boundaries	Uncased borehole filled with conductive fluid	Salinity difference needed between borehole fluid and interstitial fluids; correct only for NaCl fluids
Temperature	Differential	Temperature of borehole fluid near sensor	Geothermal gradient; flow within borehole; location of injected water; correction of other logs; curing cement	Fluid filled, can be used in air-filled boreholes	Accuracy and resolution of probes varies
(adapted from W. S. Keys 1989)					

THE BOREHOLE ENVIRONMENT

The process of drilling and constructing a well modifies the formation located around the borehole. These changes can have significant effects on the physical properties of the formation and formation fluids in the zone around the well that is measured by most logging methods. Different drilling methods and well-construction processes have different impacts. To be able to properly interpret geophysical well logs it is important to understand the changes occurring in the borehole environment.

Figure 4.1 presents an idealized representation of the borehole environment in which logging measurements are made. The borehole is filled with fluid that can be air, water, or drilling mud, therefore—for any investigation of the formation to be conducted—the logging method must penetrate the fluid. Fluids have varying physical properties that affect measurements made by logging tools. The face of the borehole often is covered with a skin of drilling fluid and cuttings, or covered by a mud cake if the well was drilled using mud.

Formations immediately adjacent to the borehole wall typically are flushed with drilling fluids that displace the natural fluids. This zone is called the invaded zone. For wells completed across multiple hydrostratigraphic units, formation fluid from the zone having the highest head typically displaces the formation fluid in the zones with lower head. In some wells, the invasion of the low-head units can consist of many thousands of gallons (liters) and extend several feet (meters) into the formation. Beyond the invaded zone is the transition zone, where the mixing of formation fluid and invading fluid occurs. The next zone—called the un-invaded zone—is relatively undisturbed and is filled with the fluid of the native formation. The distance to the un-invaded zone might be only a few inches (centimeters), such as for mud rotary wells drilled with good mud programs, or could be many feet (meters), such as for wells drilled by air rotary in coarse-grained, unsaturated zones. If borehole-fluid properties differ from formation-fluid properties, multi-point resistivity logs can map borehole invasion profiles enabling inferences to be drawn about formation hydraulic conductivity.

In its simplest form, a logging system consists of a winch with cable, a recording system, and a downhole sensor. Older logging systems collected analog data on strip charts. The downhole sensors or tools were several inches in diameter and required multiple-conductor cable. These systems often were difficult to operate and the tools did not fit down small-diameter holes. New systems acquire digital data using slimline downhole tools, enabling the use of lighter single-conductor cable, smaller winches, notebook computer–based acquisition systems, and much easier processing and presentation of log data. The move to slim downhole tools means that logs can be run in holes that have diameters of less than 2 in (51 mm) and, in larger production wells, tools can be slipped past pumps to log the well while pumping is in progress.

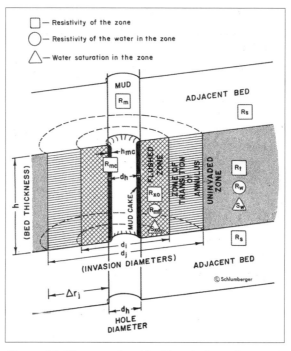

Figure 4.1. Diagram of an ideal borehole environment (Schlumberger Well Services).

Some typical water-well logging systems are shown in Figure 4.2, Figure 4.3, Figure 4.4, and Figure 4.5. Modern logging sondes (tools) contain multiple sensors and make all measurements simultaneously. A very common downhole digital (combination) tool widely used in the groundwater industry collects what is considered a typical electrical log, or e-log suite, with a single pass down the borehole. Logs collected by these combination tools include natural-gamma, SP (spontaneous potential), SPR (single-point resistance), fluid temperature/resistivity, and multi-spaced resistivity, most commonly with electrode spacing of 8 in (20.3 cm), 16 in (40.6 cm), 32 in (81.3 cm), and 64 in (62.6 cm). This suite usually is sufficient for making general interpretations of formation lithology and water quality and, in some cases, hydraulic conductivity when sufficient resistivity electrode spacings are acquired and interpreted correctly.

Figure 4.2. Portable mini–groundwater logger.

Figure 4.3. Groundwater logger in the field.

**Figure 4.4. Typical small-truck groundwater-logging system
(Mount Sopris Instruments).**

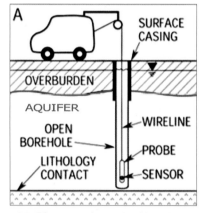

Figure 4.5. Diagram of standard logging system.

For ease of presentation, in the following sections logging methods are grouped by their method of action, common application, or other properties. Methods are grouped into electrical logs, natural-gamma logs, porosity logs, borehole-imaging logs, flow meters, well-construction logs, and geochemical logs.

ELECTRICAL LOGS

The electrical log is the oldest logging method, and it also still is one of the most useful. Electrical logs measure the electrical properties of the formation, interstitial fluids, and borehole fluid. With proper interpretation, these logs can classify formation lithology, estimate aquifer thickness, determine formation fluid salinity, and identify permeable zones.

Most electrical logs employ one or more electrodes mounted on a downhole sonde with an uphole ground or reference electrode. Electric logs only can be obtained in the fluid-filled (water or drilling mud) uncased portion of a borehole. Figure 4.9 (below) illustrates the electrode arrangements for several common sondes. Other methods use radio-frequency electromagnetic waves to measure the electrical properties of the formation by electromagnetic induction. Induction tools can be run in boreholes filled with air or freshwater drilling fluids or in boreholes cased with non-metallic casing. Electrical logging tools make nearly instantaneous measurements, so logging speeds of 20 ft/min (6 m/min) to 50 ft/min (15 m/min) often are used. Vertical sampling in groundwater applications typically ranges from 0.1 ft (3 cm) to 0.5 ft (15 cm), and is user-configurable in most systems.

Most electrical logs measure electrical resistivity, which is the mathematical inverse of electrical conductivity. Resistivity is a material constant that is a function of the aquifer matrix material, the formation porosity, and the conductivity of the formation fluid. Figure 4.6 illustrates the relative resistivity of various types of formations.

Dry material tends to have higher resistivity than does saturated material. Sand or sandstone units that contain freshwater generally have a higher resistivity than that of clay or shale. Permeable formations that contain salty or brackish water have lower resistivity values. Carbonates such as limestone or dolomite tend to have very high resistivity and lower natural gamma, unless they contain significant shale fractions.

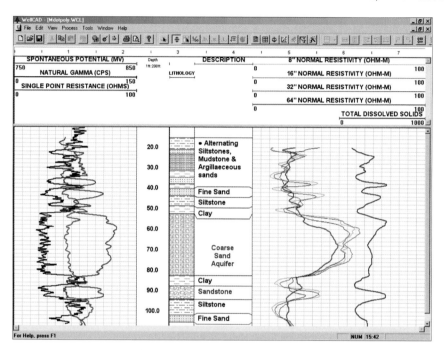

Figure 4.6. Geophysical logging run through a clay-sand sequence. Typical groundwater well logs include natural gamma (black–left track), SP (red–left track), single-point resistance (blue–left track), and at least two investigation resistivity depths (four spacings in the log–right track).
Total dissolved solids can be estimated using theses logs (right track), along with borehole-fluid temperature and mud data
(Mount Sopris Instruments).

The effects of invasion of the borehole fluid into the formation also must be considered. In a new well that is being drilled using the mud rotary method, considerations include the conductivity of the drilling mud, the depth of invasion of the mud into the formation, and the thickness of the filter cake on the borehole walls. When properly interpreted, these parameters can help identify permeable zones with high water-production potential.

In existing wells that are completed as an open borehole across multiple aquifers, the invasion of water from the highest-head aquifer into the other aquifers must be taken into account. If a well has not been pumped for a period of days or weeks, thousands to millions of gallons (liters) of water might have invaded some aquifers and displaced the native formation water. Extensive purging of a well often is necessary before representative formation water is present in the zone of investigation.

Spontaneous Potential Log

The spontaneous potential (SP) or self-potential log is the simplest and oldest geophysical well log. The log requires only a fluid-filled uncased borehole with a single downhole electrode wired through a voltmeter to a grounded electrode on the surface. Figure 4.7 presents a schematic representation of the electrode arrangement for a SP log. Spontaneous potential is measured in millivolts and responds to electrochemical and electrokinetic potentials at bed boundaries (Figure 4.8). In practice, SP logs usually are acquired simultaneously with resistivity logs.

Figure 4.6 illustrates the typical SP (red log–left track) response of various formation types. Spontaneous potential responds to the difference in resistivity between the formation fluid and the borehole fluid. For a borehole filled with freshwater or freshwater mud, shale units cause the log to deflect to the right. This typically establishes what is known as the shale baseline. Permeable sand units filled with fluid that is fresher than the borehole fluid cause a deflection to the right of the shale baseline. Permeable sand units filled with fluids that are more saline than the borehole fluid cause a deflection to the left of the baseline.

Spontaneous potential logs often are useful for boreholes drilled by mud rotary methods. In boreholes that are not drilled with mud or in completed water wells, however, the borehole fluid typically consists of formation fluid and there is no resistivity contrast between the two fluids. This results in a small to negligible SP response to permeable units. In practical terms, SP logs of many water wells are almost flat, and little information can be obtained from the log. If SP logs are good, then bed-boundary responses and the SP deflection in aquifers can be used to estimate water-quality parameters (Jorgensen 1989).

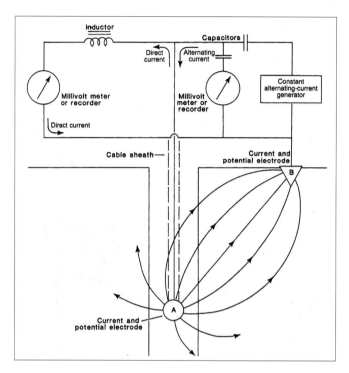

Figure 4.7. Schematic drawing of spontaneous potential (left) and single-point resistance (right) circuit electrode-log configuration.

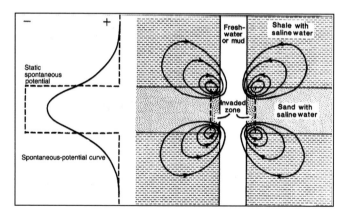

Figure 4.8. Detailed drawing of spontaneous potential effect.

Resistance Log

A resistance log is a log that was widely used in water wells in the past, but which largely has been replaced by resistivity logs. Resistance logs commonly are called single-point resistance (SPR) or point-resistance logs. (See the blue log in the left track of Figure 4.6.) This log type only can be run in the fluid-filled uncased portion of a borehole. Single-point resistance logs measure the resistance (in ohms) between a downhole electrode and a grounded surface electrode by passing a constant current through the formation between the electrodes. The measured resistance has a depth of investigation of only a few inches (centimeters) into the formation, and is strongly influenced by the resistivity of the borehole fluid. The resistance is not a material constant and is not equivalent to a resistivity measurement. Additionally, although the SPR log no longer is an industry norm, it does have excellent vertical resolution and can be a useful indicator of the depth of the contact between two beds.

Resistivity Log

Another more common and more useful form of electrical log is the resistivity log. Resistivity logs only can be run in fluid-filled uncased boreholes; and some logs can be run in wells with plastic screens. The most common form is called a normal (galvanic) resistivity log. As Figure 4.9 shows, normal resistivity tools use a single downhole current electrode and multiple downhole potential electrodes to make resistivity measurements at different electrode spacings that penetrate to different depths into the formation.

The closest electrode spacing, commonly called the shallow tool, primarily measures the resistivity of the borehole fluid and formation a few inches (centimeters) from the borehole wall, but it has the highest vertical resolution. The longer electrode spacings, called the mid or deep tools, make measurements that are influenced by more-distant portions of the formation. As mentioned above, common electrode spacings are 8 in (20.3 cm), 16 in (40.6 cm), 32 in (81.3 cm), and 64 in (162.6 cm). The longest spacing, called the long normal tool, commonly makes a measurement that penetrates several meters into the formation, and is an indicator of R_t, true formation (aquifer) resistivity.

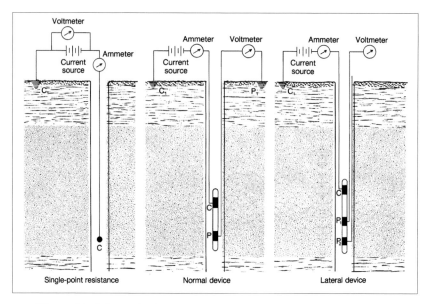

Figure 4.9. Schematic drawing of common resistance configurations.

Multiple spacings are used to make measurements of the depth of invasion of drilling mud. This is of importance primarily for water wells drilled by mud rotary. A difference in resistivity between the deep and shallow tools in a mud rotary hole can indicate a permeable zone that allowed drilling mud to invade the formation to a greater depth than surrounding units. In most water wells, the shallow investigation measurements (due to their higher vertical resolution) are used to estimate the depth of an interface, and the deeper measurements are used to make more representative measurements of the formation resistivity independent of the borehole fluid. Closer examination of the normal resistivity logs through the aquifer in Figure 4.6 indicates variations in permeability as the difference in resistivity values at the different electrode spacings.

The potential gradients produced by a resistivity logging tool across an interface are not uniform, and geometric factors can create errors in the thickness and resistivity measurements of thin beds. Normal resistivity logs always show resistive beds to be thinner—by a thickness equal to the electrode spacing—than they actually are. For beds that are greater than approximately three times the electrode spacing, the measured resistivity is unaffected by adjacent beds. For beds that are relatively thin, corrections should be made to obtain true resistivity.

For resistive beds that are thinner than the electrode spacing and which are between two conductive beds, the response of the resistive bed is lower than that of the conductive beds. This phenomenon, known as reversal, can be detected when the short tools read higher resistivity than the long or mid tools. See the reversals at 37 ft and 44 ft in Figure 4.6. A bed with a thickness equal to the electrode spacing produces a nearly flat response; this sometimes is referred to as "critical thickness." Correction charts can be obtained from logging companies or from experienced geophysicists, if accurate measurements of the thickness and resistivity of a thin bed are critical.

Figure 4.10 illustrates how the thickness of a resistive bed relative to the electrode spacing affects the log response. Example A shows a reversal in resistivity caused by a thin bed. Example B illustrates a bed at the critical thickness causing a flat response. Example C shows a thick bed displaying the true resistivity, but with an apparent thickness that is less than the true thickness of the unit.

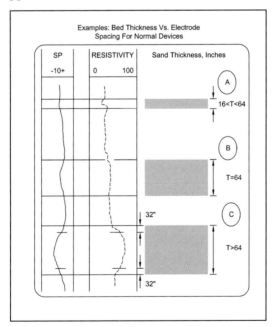

Figure 4.10. Illustration showing the thickness of a resistive bed relative to electrode spacing.

Several tools with shorter electrode spacings have been developed, and they use additional current electrodes to focus the current density deeper into the formation. This provides better resolution of thin beds and improves log response in boreholes where the formation resistivity is much higher than the borehole fluid. Examples of focused electrical logs are the lateral log and guard electrode log. Electrode geometry creates a distinct current distribution. Focused logs can produce complex responses across formation contacts that are difficult to interpret and cannot be compared to those of other tools. The tools typically are longer and they have a larger diameter, making them more difficult to use and more expensive. Consequently, focused logs are used much less extensively for examining water wells than they are for petroleum industry–related wells.

Another useful feature of resistivity logs is the ability to provide an indication of the water quality in a formation. In general, the resistivity of a formation varies inversely to the total dissolved solids (TDS) of the formation fluid. All other factors being equal, the resistivity of a sand unit increases as the TDS decreases. A synthetic TDS log calculated from resistivity is shown in Figure 4.6. It is possible to make quantitative estimates of the salinity of the formation fluid using normal resistivity measurements. Several methods have been used, but most are based on Archie's equation that relates measured resistivity to fluid resistivity and a formation factor (Archie 1942). Archie's empirical formula is given in equation 4.1.

$$r_e = a\eta^{-m}S^{-n}r_w \qquad\qquad\qquad (4.1)$$

Where the variables are as follows.

- r_e = resistivity of formation at 100% saturation
- η = porosity
- S = fraction of pores containing water
- r_w = resistivity of water
- a, n, m = constants
- $n \approx 2$
- $0.5 \leq a \leq 2.5$
- $1.3 \leq m \leq 2.5$

The formation factor can be derived empirically using the estimated porosity and standard values for the variables in the equation. Accurately estimating the formation factor can be difficult without performing calibration using other wells. In basins where the formation factor is not known precisely, TDS values calculated from resistivity logs should be viewed with caution. When sufficient data are available from other wells to empirically derive a reliable formation factor, accurate water-quality measurements can be made from the log data. Estimates of fluid salinity from resistivity logs are not reliable in formations with appreciable clay content or in fracture-controlled aquifers. This method often is simplified by calculating a formation factor (F, unitless) (equation 4.2).

$$r_w = r_e / F \qquad\qquad\qquad\qquad\text{(4.2)}$$

Induction Log

Induction logs have become more commonly used in the water-well industry in the last several years. Induction logs use radio-frequency electromagnetic waves to induce eddy currents in the formation around the tool. One or more receiver coils in the tool measure the magnetic field created by the eddy currents. The measured magnetic field is directly related to the electrical conductivity of the formation; hence, these tools measure formation conductivity. Measurements typically are reported in conductivity units of mhos per meter or millimhos per meter, which is the mathematical inverse of ohm-meters. Figure 4.11 is a schematic drawing of a typical induction tool.

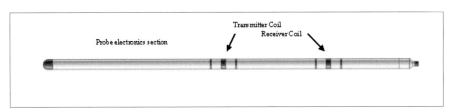

Figure 4.11. Schematic drawing of a typical one transmitter–one receiver electromagnetic induction tool (Mount Sopris Instruments).

Induction tools have been used in the petroleum industry for decades. These tools tended to be expensive, which had limited their use for water wells. The development of a small slimline tool in the 1980s enabled induction logging to come into common use in the water-well industry.

Such tools have several advantages over electrode tools. Induction logs can be run in boreholes filled with air or another fluid. Data can be collected either in open holes or through non-metallic casing such as PVC or fiberglass. Slimline induction tools generally are not focused and have a limited depth of investigation—typically less than one yard (one meter) into the formation. The method is most sensitive to conductive formations and loses sensitivity in high-resistivity units. Induction tools typically are not able to detect small changes in resistivity when formation resistivity values exceed a few hundred ohm-meters.

NATURAL–GAMMA RAY LOG

Most geologic units contain low levels of naturally occurring radioactive material. The most significant radioactive materials in natural formations are potassium 40, uranium 238, uranium 235, and thorium 232. Of these, potassium 40 is by far the most abundant and is a common constituent of clay minerals. When these radioactive elements decay, they release gamma-ray radiation that can be measured in a borehole.

Natural–gamma ray logs (also called gamma logs) measure the gamma-ray radiation emanating from the formation adjacent to a borehole. Higher levels of gamma-ray emissions typically are associated with the higher abundance of clay minerals in shale or clay layers that could be significant confining units. Conversely, low levels of gamma radiation are taken as an indicator of low clay-mineral content and commonly are used to identify clean sandstone or sand units. Limestone or dolomite units have low gamma emissions unless they contain a significant clay-mineral fraction.

A few exceptions to these generalizations are worth noting. Some permeable sand units—over time—build up uranium salts from groundwater flow, and these salts cause high gamma emissions despite the low clay content of the sand. These so-called "hot sands" often are used in the petroleum industry as indicators of permeable zones, but can be misinterpreted as shale zones. Some multiple-aquifer wells precipitate barite (barium sulfate) on the borehole wall, due to the mixing of sulfate-rich water with barium-rich water in the borehole. The precipitated barite sorbs radium and other dissolved radionuclides and can form a cake on the borehole or casing walls that is a strong gamma emitter.

Natural–gamma ray logs are a common and very useful tool for many water-well projects. They often are part of a combination tool and are considered part of a standard e-log suite. Gamma logs are obtained in boreholes filed with air or another fluid. These logs also are run in open holes, screened wells, and cased holes (including those with steel casing). Gamma logs often are used to delineate stratigraphy in the cased portion of a well that has no other well logs. A slight (10% to 20%) reduction in the magnitude of the response of the formation often is noted when logging in cased wells, especially if the annular space is grouted. Although gamma logs have also been used to determine whether wells have grout seals behind the casing, this often provides misleading results because sodium bentonite grout that frequently is used in wells has low potassium content and does not produce a strong gamma signal.

Figure 4.6 shows the typical response of a gamma log to various formations. Some gamma tools are calibrated in standardized American Petroleum Institute (API) units, and others measure gamma emissions in units of counts per second (CPS). Counts per second is the raw output from all gamma tools measuring relative gamma intensity. The CPS response of some gamma-logging tools can be only half of what the response is in API units, and other tools can have greater counts. Response depends on the volume of the scintillation crystal (sensor) inside the tool. A few borehole models in the United States (and around the world) have known API values. Users can place gamma tools in the model and then calibrate their own tools to output API units (Fink 1978).

Gamma logs are influenced by several factors in addition to the intensity of emission of the formation, including the borehole fluid, well construction, logging speed, and hole diameter. Borehole correction charts are available to standardize the response of a gamma log and enable direct comparison of formations in wells of different diameters.

Gamma logs commonly are run at speeds of 10 ft/min (3 m/min) to 20 ft/min (6 m/min), although slower speeds might be necessary to make detailed measurements in low-radioactivity formations, in large-diameter wells, or through casing. In the groundwater industry, vertical sampling usually is conducted at between 0.1 ft (3 cm) to 0.5 ft (15 cm). In very large wells it is common to offset the tool and place it closer to one wall of the borehole to increase the sensitivity. It is also possible to drag a gamma tool over an outcrop or road cut to determine the characteristic response of a unit of interest—but it must be understood that the outcrop response is approximately half the response of the same unit when it is in a borehole.

Gamma tools measure gamma rays striking the sensor from a spherical volume around the tool, so the formation closest to the tool has the strongest contribution to the response. Typically, the formation within 6 in (15 cm) to 12 in (30 cm) produces 90% of the tool's response. Because of the multi-directional response, gamma logs do not produce sharp breaks at formation contacts. As a result, the thickness of a bed could be picked at the point of inflection of a gamma peak. Additionally, the response of units of thickness that are less than about two times the depth of investigation never will reach full intensity. Tables for correcting the thickness and amplitude of thin units on gamma logs are available from logging companies or consultants.

A specialized form of the natural–gamma ray log is the spectral–gamma ray log. The spectral–gamma ray log measures gamma intensity across a spectrum of energy, typically from about 1 to 3 MeV (million electron-volts). The total gamma count rate (CPS) is divided up into counts per second at many different energies. Decaying radioactive elements emit gamma rays in characteristic energies. The relative abundance of several radioactive isotopes can be determined by analyzing the gamma-ray spectrum signature. This is particularly useful when it is important to distinguish uranium- and thorium-rich units, such as uranium-rich hot sands, from potassium 40–rich shale units. Spectral–gamma ray logs are common in mineral exploration and in some geochemical investigations, but have not found common application in the water industry unless, for example, groundwater systems are found to have elevated levels of uranium.

POROSITY LOGS

Several logging methods are used to estimate formation porosity. These tools have proven to be very useful in identifying productive intervals in oil wells and, to a lesser degree, in water wells. Porosity is an important property in hydrologic studies but it generally is not as important as permeability or hydraulic conductivity, which is a related—but by no means equivalent—property. Many highly porous formations, such as clay units, have low permeability. Many very permeable formations, such as fractured carbonates, have low porosity. Other methods of directly measuring permeability, such as aquifer tests and flow meters, have been found to be more practical and reliable for water wells. As long as limitations are kept in mind, however, porosity logs can be useful tools in groundwater projects.

Although formation porosity and hydraulic conductivity can be estimated using resistivity and SP logs, some of the most useful downhole tools used to estimate porosity require the use of an active radiation–source downhole. In the United States, these sources only may be handled by an operator licensed by the Nuclear Regulatory Commission or an Agreement State. This greatly increases the complexity, cost, and risk of running these logs. Many U.S. states forbid the use of active-source porosity tools in water wells unless the operator holds specific permits. Well owners also often are reluctant to place radioactive sources into sources of potable water. Although the risk of contamination usually is small, the consequences of a lost tool can be significant. As a result, porosity tools that incorporate a radioactive source are not used as extensively in the water-well industry as they are in the petroleum industry (where the tools are used at greater depth in units that tend to contain non-potable brine and other fluids). Several methods of cross-plotting different types of porosity log data are used for wells where multiple porosity tools have been used. These cross-plot porosity methods overcome the limitations of individual porosity logging methods, provide more accurate porosity measurements, and can be used to determine the lithology of the formation.

Neutron Log

Neutron tools directly measure the presence of hydrogen, which corresponds to porosity of saturated formations and moisture content in unsaturated formations. These tools are used in open holes or through casing (including steel casing or drill rod). Although neutron logs could be among the most useful logs for groundwater studies, the need for a radioactive source limits the utility of these logs. Prompt neutron activation, which does not use an active radioactive source, could find its way to the groundwater industry in the future but, at the time of this writing, it is cost prohibitive.

Neutron logging tools use a small pellet of radioactive americium 241–beryllium to bombard the formation with fast neutrons. Neutrons are captured in the formation when they collide with hydrogen ions. In groundwater studies the primary hydrogen source is water, making the tool a direct indicator of the presence of water. Raw tool output is CPS, but the logs can be plotted in units of percent neutron porosity when calibrated correctly. A quick field check for 100% porosity would be the tool's response in a large water barrel; the tool reacts to the bound water in shale units and shows these units as very porous. Although shale units are very porous they have very low permeability, which can lead to erroneous interpretations. The hydrogen atoms in any hydrocarbons present also produce a strong response that results in erroneously high porosity readings. Figure 4.12 illustrates the operation of a neutron tool.

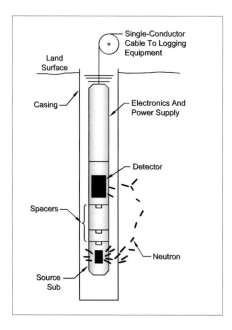

Figure 4.12. Schematic drawing of a neutron tool.

Two styles of neutron detectors are used. The older-style neutron-gamma tools measure secondary gamma rays emitted during neutron capture by hydrogen atoms; newer-style neutron-neutron tools measure thermal neutrons that have been slowed by collisions with hydrogen atoms before returning to the detector. Some petroleum tools use a pad and decentralizing arm to keep the source immediately adjacent to the borehole wall. Many water wells have a larger diameter than the pad tools are designed to log, and extensions are added to the caliper arm to enable the tool to function. Most water-well tools use a source centered in the borehole. The depth of investigation typically is about 6 in (15 cm) to 1 ft (30 cm), but can reach outside the borehole approximately 2 ft (60 cm) in low-porosity units, depending on source-to-detector spacing. Washouts in a fluid-filled borehole result in erroneously high porosity readings because the tool reads the higher water content of the enlarged borehole. Pad-type tools reduce this problem by forcing the tool against the borehole wall across the washout; however even pad tools cannot fully compensate for large washouts or rough borehole surfaces.

Gamma-Density Log

Gamma-density tools, also called gamma-gamma tools or density tools, bombard the formation with gamma rays from a cesium 137 or cobalt 60 source. In many modern tools, the source and detector are located in a pad that is forced up against the borehole wall by a caliper arm. Some tools use two detectors above and below the source to compensate for irregularities on the borehole wall. Older-style tools do not have a caliper arm or pad for the source and detector. When using these tools, a separate caliper log is essential for interpreting the log because the tool is very sensitive to washouts and variations in the borehole diameter. Density tools can be run in cased or uncased holes. The depth of investigation typically is 5 in (13 cm) to 6 in (15 cm), depending on the source-to-detector spacing. If the gamma rays must pass through casing, cement, or mud, however, then the depth of investigation could be attenuated. Figure 4.13 is a simple drawing of a density tool in a borehole.

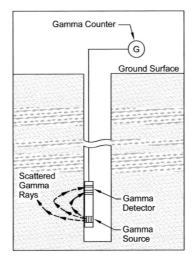

Figure 4.13. Schematic drawing of a single-source-to-detector gamma-gamma tool.

Gamma detectors (usually a scintillation detector and photo-multiplier tube) count gamma rays that are scattered back to the tool, primarily by a process called Compton Scattering. The amount of back-scattered gamma rays is a function of the electron density of the formation, therefore the tool indirectly is measuring the bulk density of the formation. When a matrix density (or grain density) is assigned—typically either a sandstone or a carbonate density—the formation porosity is calculated by the deviation of the formation bulk density from the matrix density. The log output usually is presented as bulk density and percent porosity based on a specific matrix density.

Sonic Log

A sonic log, also called an acoustic log, uses sound waves to estimate the porosity of the formation. This tool does not use a radioactive source, so it does not face the same regulatory obstacles or present the same risks as the neutron log or gamma-density log. Sonic porosity logs are collected in fluid-filled uncased boreholes only. A cement-bond log is a version of the sonic log that is used to measure the integrity of the bond between a casing and the cement grout. Cement-bond logs are discussed in this chapter in the section entitled Well-Construction Logs.

Figure 4.14 is a schematic drawing of a sonic log tool. The tool transmits a high-frequency acoustic pulse that is partitioned at the borehole surface into transmitted and reflected energy. A portion of the transmitted energy is critically refracted and travels along the wall of the borehole at the acoustic velocity of the formation. The critically refracted wave radiates energy back into the borehole and is measured by the acoustic receiver (detector). This process is directly analogous to a seismic-refraction survey used for surface geophysical methods.

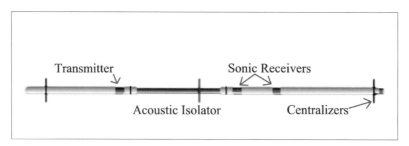

Figure 4.14. Schematic of a single-transmitter, dual-receiver sonic tool (Mount Sopris Instruments).

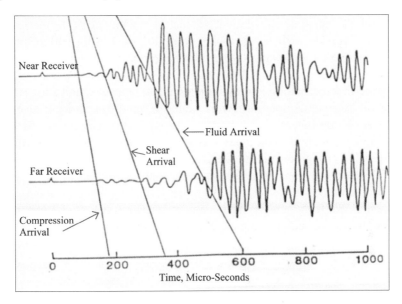

**Figure 4.15. Sample acoustic waveforms from near receiver and
far receiver, showing compressional and shear arrivals
(Mount Sopris Instruments).**

The transit time for acoustic energy traveling to each receiver is measured in (and usually recorded in) μSec/ft (μSec/cm). Acoustic velocity of rock is much higher than that of borehole fluid, so the first wavelets to reach the sonic receiver are the critically refracted energy that travels along the borehole wall. The transit time for water depends on salinity, but ranges from 189 μSec/ft (6.2 μSec/cm) in brines to 208 μSec/ft (6.8 μSec/cm) in freshwater. Sandstone aquifers can have transit times ranging from 54 μSec/ft (1.8 μSec/cm) to 100 μSec/ft (3.3 μSec/cm). Modern instruments often use multi-detectors to compensate for the variations in the orientation of the tool in the borehole or in the borehole diameter.

The log output is plotted as delta-t (Δt) (or transit-time)—the travel time between the transmitter and receiver—usually in units of microseconds, along with a VDL (variable density log), which is a time versus amplitude plot measured with borehole depth. Delta-t is used to calculate the acoustic velocity of the formation. The porosity of the formation is calculated by comparing the formation velocity to the velocity of the rock matrix, assuming no porosity.

To make an accurate calculation, the matrix velocity of the formation must be known. Typically, when processing sonic log data, a formation matrix—either sandstone or carbonate—is specified and porosity is calculated relative to the selected matrix velocity. This means that the porosity of a carbonate unit is not plotted correctly for a log run with a sandstone matrix, and a log run with a carbonate matrix does not plot correct values for sandstone units. It is common to plot a sonic log twice—using both sandstone and carbonate matrixes—for wells that penetrate both rock types. The measurement is subject to error if the borehole wall is rough or if large washouts are present.

A full waveform sonic tool records time versus amplitude of the waveform energy at each receiver, as shown in Figure 4.16. Full waveform sonic tools, when combined with density data, enable measurement of the mechanical properties of the formation, such as shear modulus.

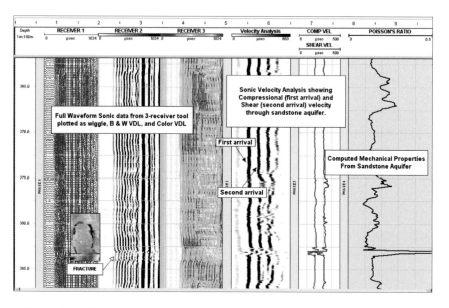

Figure 4.16. Three-receiver full waveform sonic log through sandstone aquifer showing compressional and shear wave velocities, and Poisson's ratio (Mount Sopris Instruments).

BOREHOLE IMAGING LOGS

Several logging methods have been developed to image a borehole and determine its physical condition. These methods are designed to find washouts, cavities, fractures, hole deviation, or other obstructions. A variety of tools are available to achieve specific objectives under different borehole conditions. These tools include downhole cameras, caliper tools, acoustic televiewers, optical televiewers, and downhole surveying tools. In recent years, high-resolution tools have been developed, and these can image fine details such as individual sand grains.

Downhole Televising Log

Under favorable conditions a downhole televising log is perhaps the most versatile and useful logging tool available. A downhole camera is lowered into the well and the data is displayed in real time on a monitor with a depth display. Simple cameras provide forward-looking fish-eye views of the borehole. Many newer cameras provide high-resolution color images using forward-looking fish-eye views and side-looking views, with a variable depth of focus that can be rotated 360 degrees. Under ideal conditions a side view can image individual sand grains on the borehole wall or look into fractures or voids in the formation.

For a televising log to work, the borehole must contain clear fluid— either water or air. It frequently is necessary to pump a well for several hours or to flush it with clear water so the camera is able to capture a clear image. Flocculants have been used with some success to precipitate suspended material prior to logging when it is not practical to pump or flush a well. Although televising logs provide some of the highest-resolution images of the borehole most tools do not make an orientated image of the well, so the strike of fractures and other features cannot be determined.

Borehole televising logs can be used to:

+ Inspect a casing or casing seat,
+ Examine the condition of a borehole,
+ See fractures and voids,
+ Find the location and position of debris in the well,
+ View formation contacts and small-scale stratigraphic features such as cross bedding,

- Measure the depth to water,
- Identify zones of cascading water,
- Inspect mineral scale and biofilm deposits,
- Find zones of loose or incompetent rock,
- See sand-producing zones while pumping is in progress,
- Direct fishing operations,
- Inspect for well damage, and
- Make comparisons.

In some cases, flow within the borehole can be observed by watching the motion of fine particles or by observing motion of the camera due to turbulent flow. Televising logs often are run as the first log of a logging suite to identify any obstructions in the well that might affect subsequent logging. Figure 4.17 shows a caliper tool that became stuck on a ledge and snarled in logging cable that accidentally was allowed to spool into the hole. The televising log enabled fabrication of a fishing tool to successfully remove the caliper tool.

Figure 4.17. A downhole camera's still image of a caliper tool lodged in a wellbore (Ruekert & Mielke, Inc.).

Acoustic Televiewer

Acoustic televiewers produce high-resolution images of the borehole wall by utilizing a rotating high-frequency transducer to scan the hole and produce acoustic amplitude and time images. The associated acoustic amplitude is proportional to rock hardness and is divided into colors, creating an image of the borehole wall. This type of tool also has a built-in three-axis magnetometer and accelerometer, which insures that the images are oriented properly. Standard log formats show the borehole wall from 0 to 360 degrees on the horizontal axis and show depth on the vertical axis. Figure 4.18 illustrates the principle of the acoustic-televiewer measurement.

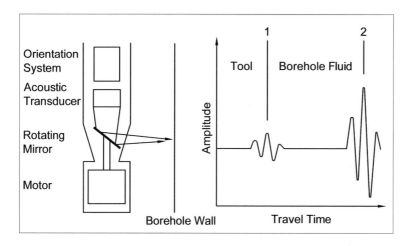

Figure 4.18. Principle of acoustic-televiewer measurement (Mount Sopris Instruments).

Acoustic-televiewer logs are used to map fractures and to plot strike and dip. Processing packages are available and can use the log data to quickly calculate the strike, dip, and aperture of fractures. Although the tool can make high-resolution measurements of fractures, the effects of the drilling process on the fractures must be considered when applying the results to the rock mass around the borehole. The acoustic televiewer requires a fluid-filled hole, but the logs can be run in mud and turbid water. Water can be added to artificially raise the water level for logging purposes.

Optical Televiewer

An optical televiewer produces an optical image of the borehole wall by using a high-resolution digital camera focusing on a cone-shaped mirror (both are mounted along the axis of the borehole, along with external lighting) to produce a digitized 360-degree scan of the hole. The log produces an image of the borehole wall in true color. Standard log formats show the borehole wall from 0 to 360 degrees on the horizontal axis and depth on the vertical axis. Figure 4.19 shows how the light head and mirror work together to produce unwrapped, true-color borehole wall images. The tool requires a clear borehole, filled with either air or clear water. Mineral scale or biofilm formation on the borehole wall obscure the formation image of many older wells.

Optical televiewer logs often are used to map fractures and plot their strike and dip, as well as to image small-scale stratigraphic features. Processing packages are available to quickly calculate the strike, dip, and aperture of fractures or dipping interfaces. The data also can be plotted as a cylinder that can be rotated to provide a virtual core of the volume contained by the borehole wall. Drill core recovery is poor in most fracture zones, therefore the virtual core from the optical televiewer data might provide the most complete image of a cored interval, and can be very useful in filling in data from lost core intervals.

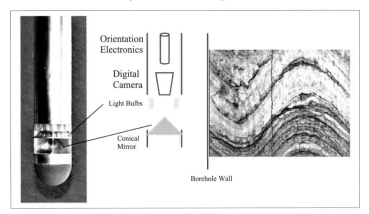

Figure 4.19. Diagram of an optical televiewer with sample output (Mount Sopris Instruments).

Note how the acoustic imagery in Figure 4.20 shows calcite infilling (dark areas on image), but optically the calcite is more difficult to visualize.

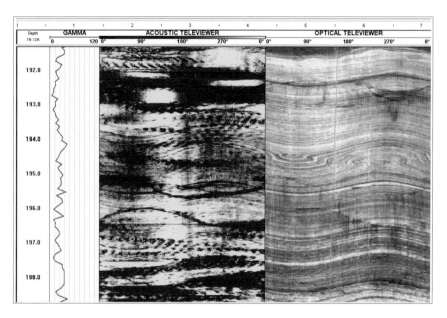

Figure 4.20. Comparison of optical televiewer (right track) and acoustic televiewer (left track) through sandstone with calcite lithology (Mount Sopris Instruments).

Caliper Log

The caliper log is one of the simplest logging measurements to perform. A spring-loaded tool is lowered to the bottom of a well. Once on the bottom, the tool's arms are extended and press against the borehole wall. As it is pulled up the borehole the tool measures the borehole's diameter.

Simple caliper tools use one or two arms to measure diameter. Two-arm caliper tools tend to rotate to place the arms across the maximum diameter of the hole. This can provide erroneous measurements in elliptically shaped holes or irregularly shaped washouts. Some tools have three arms to force the tool to measure the average diameter of the borehole rather than the maximum, and such tools sometimes are used to estimate borehole volume. Other tools use four arms to provide independent measurements in two planes; these often are called XY caliper tools. Many four-arm caliper tools use a compass to measure the orientation of the tool. The data from these tools can be plotted to show the change in diameter in two planes with a calculated average diameter, and also can be processed to provide an orientated image of the borehole shape at any depth. Such XY caliper tools are useful when the volume of the borehole must be known more precisely or when the shape of the hole is critical for setting a casing or passing a tool string. If the arms of the caliper are too long, however, much of the detail can be lost.

Logging speeds of 10 ft/min (3 m/min) to 20 ft/min (6 m/min) are common, but speed depends upon the need for resolution for small variations in borehole diameter (such as fractures), and concerns regarding snagging the tool. Caliper tools are among the most likely tools to become stuck in a well, and for that reason it usually is not wise to run the caliper tool as a first pass in a well of unknown integrity. Figure 4.21 shows a typical caliper logging tool.

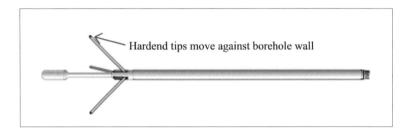

Hardend tips move against borehole wall

Figure 4.21. Three-arm caliper logging tool (Mount Sopris Instruments).

Figure 4.22 shows a caliper log trace along with the volume of cement for various intervals.

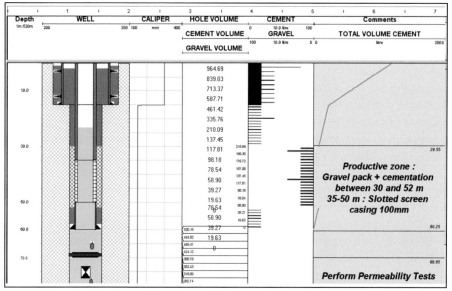

Figure 4.22. Well-completion plot with caliper (green log, middle track), cement volume, and comments (Mount Sopris Instruments).

Alignment Logs

Several tools have been developed to measure a borehole's deviation from vertical. These logs generally are called alignment logs, directional logs, or downhole surveying logs. The simplest of these logs uses cameras or perforating devices to mark the deviation of the tool from a horizontal target at a given depth. A series of readings is taken by lowering fresh targets to different depths and plotting the cumulative deviation from vertical in two horizontal axes from each reading. More-sophisticated tools use compasses, three-axis magneto-meters/accelerometers, or gyroscopes to continuously measure the deviation of the tool in two horizontal axes as the tools is moved up or down the borehole. It is important to note that magnetic tools do not function inside steel casing. Gyroscopic tools do function in casing, but are used less commonly and generally are more expensive.

FLOW METERS

Several logging tools have been developed to measure flow in a borehole. These tools can be used to measure ambient flow between units in a non-pumping well or to measure the relative water production within a pumping well. Existing flow meters handle flow velocities within distinct velocity ranges, so it often is necessary to use different types of flow meters for the non-pumping logs and the pumping logs of the same well. Several specialized flow meters are in various states of development, and include the colloidal borescope, electromagnetic flow meters, several types of tracer tools, and others. These tools might have utility for specific applications, however they are not yet widely available and are not examined in this chapter.

It is important to remember that the tools only measure fluid velocity; the borehole diameter must be considered when converting flow velocity to flow volume. For irregular boreholes it is necessary to have an accurate caliper log to make these conversions. It often is impossible to make accurate flow readings in large washouts or cavities, due to both the difficulty in measuring the diameter accurately and the turbulent flow conditions that can exist in these areas. In practice, it is better to measure flow in smoother portions of the hole above and below a major washout or fracture, and then use the difference between the measurements to determine the flow from the zone of interest.

The flow profile varies across the borehole diameter, with the highest velocities existing in the center of the borehole. Measuring flow velocity next to the borehole wall produces erroneously low values. It is important to use centralizers or standoffs to keep the flow meter off the borehole wall and as close as possible to the center of the hole.

Most flow meters produce output in relative units such as counts per second rather than gallons (liters) per minute or cubic inches (centimeters) per second. It therefore usually is necessary to calibrate the meter output with known flow rates to be able to quantify the readings. When logging a well while pumping, it often is possible to take a reading only a short distance below the pump—especially if the pump is inside the casing—and to then assign the meter reading to 100% of the pump discharge. Using the well diameter, the meter reading can be converted to a flow velocity. Flow-meter readings at other depths can be linearly scaled to this value to convert the readings to flow velocity. The borehole diameter from the caliper log then can be used to convert the velocity profile to a flow-rate profile of the well. When logging non-pumping wells, normally it is possible to troll the tool at a known speed through a portion of the well with uniform diameter and low flow velocity, such as inside the casing. The speed of the logging tool and the flow-meter reading then can be used to calibrate meter output to flow velocity.

A method has been developed (Paillet 2001, 2000) to use flow-meter data to calculate interval transmissivity and interval head. This requires flow-meter data at two different head conditions, such as pumping and static, or two different steady-state pumping rates. The method has proven to be very useful in identifying major water-producing zones as well as thief zones in multiple-aquifer wells.

Temperature Log

One of the simplest flow meters is the downhole temperature log (Figure 4.23). The tool consists of a temperature sensor, usually a thermistor or thermocouple, used to measure the change in borehole-fluid temperature with depth. Many tools include a borehole-fluid conductivity sensor (described in the next section). If collected when the borehole is at ambient equilibrium, temperature anomalies adjacent to fractures or porous media can be hydraulically important.

Due to the geothermal gradient, the temperature of the subsurface typically increases with depth. Moving fluids carry heat much more efficiently through the formation matrix than thermal conduction does, therefore flowing water disrupts the geothermal gradient in a borehole. Abrupt shifts in fluid temperature indicate water leaving or entering the borehole. Zones of flat thermal gradients indicate vertical flow within the borehole, where water of constant temperature is flowing up or down the wellbore. Zones of uniform thermal gradient generally indicate stagnant water in equilibrium with the geothermal gradient of the formation. Temperature logs also can be used to detect rapid recharge events in some aquifers or, if they are run within the first 24 hours after grouting, can detect curing cement located behind a casing.

Temperature-log data frequently are plotted as the temperature versus depth or as the differential temperature, which emphasizes small thermal anomalies independent of the geothermal gradient. Temperature logs are often run under both non-pumping and pumping conditions in a well to determine the change in flow within the well under different head conditions. When logging a non-pumping well, the passage of the logging tool can stir the water column and disrupt the thermal stratification in the well. It therefore is advisable to run the

temperature log first and to make the measurements on the tool's initial pass
down the well. Logging speeds of 10 ft/min (3 m/min) to 20 ft/min (6 m/min)
are common. When logging downward, the tool can become lodged in the well
causing cable to "ball up" in the hole. To prevent snagging a tool in the well, it
is important to check the cable tension regularly; although this can be difficult
in deep wells when the cable spooled down the well weighs more than the tool.

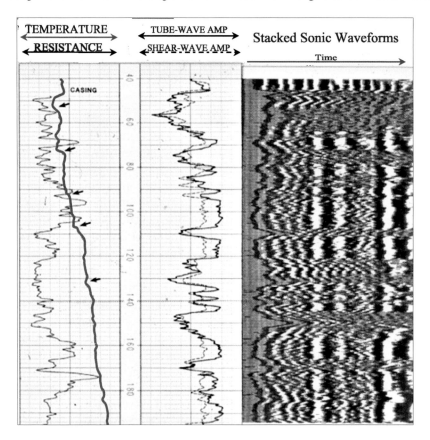

**Figure 4.23. Temperature log (red) shows anomalies at flow zones (indicated with
arrows) (Mount Sopris Instruments).**

Borehole-Fluid Conductivity Log

Borehole-fluid conductivity logs measure the electrical conductivity of the borehole fluid independent of the resistivity of the formation or formation fluid. Fluid electrical conductivity (FEC) is the mathematical inverse of electrical resistivity, and is proportional to the total dissolved solids (TDS) concentration of the fluid. Borehole fluid conductivity logs can measure small variations in conductivity that indicate slight changes in the TDS of the borehole fluid caused by water of different quality entering or leaving the borehole.

These logs usually are run simultaneously with temperature logs, and available tools can measure FEC, temperature, pressure, oxidation-reduction potential, and dissolved oxygen concurrently in one pass down the borehole. Interpreting the two logs together allows more potential flow zones to be detected than either log can show when used alone. The conductivity measurement essentially is simultaneous, therefore the logging speed is determined by the response of the temperature sensor and the degree of agitation of the water column that can be tolerated.

As with the temperature log, the passage of the logging tool can stir the water column and disrupt the conductivity stratification in the well. It therefore is advisable to run the borehole fluid conductivity log first and to make the measurements on the tool's initial pass down the well. Like the temperature log, borehole fluid conductivity logs often are run under both non-pumping and pumping conditions in a well to determine the change in flow within the well under different head conditions.

Spinner Log

A spinner log is a simple flow meter that uses an impeller with a rotation counter to measure the flow of fluid across the tool. Figure 4.24 shows a typical spinner logging tool set-up at municipal-water well site. Spinner logs usually are run by trolling the tool up and down the borehole at two or three constant speeds, enabling the operator to estimate interval-specific flow. Modern geophysical logging systems allow users to log at near-constant speeds while sampling at any depth interval. It is possible to log both up and down the hole at the same speed and then average the readings to isolate the apparent flow caused by the motion of the tool from changes in flow in the well. Static readings are recorded by stopping the tool at a specific depth and observing impeller movement. When making static readings it often is necessary to wait a few minutes to allow the tool to stabilize, due to slight rocking in the well that can occur when a tool is stopped.

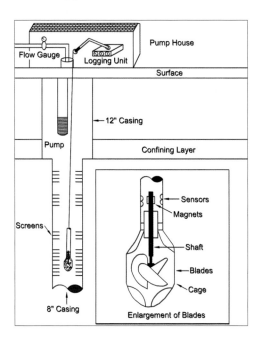

Figure 4.24. Example flow-meter logging set up at municipal water-well site (Mount Sopris Instruments).

Spinner tools are mechanical devices, so there is a small but unavoidable amount of friction and inertial mass in the impeller. As a result, a minimum amount of flow is needed to overcome this resistance and cause the impeller to turn. The stall velocity of each tool is different, but it typically is from 4 ft/min (1.2 m/min) to 7 ft/min (2.1 m/min) in the static mode. It is common for the flow velocities to be too low to turn the impeller in large-diameter wells or in wells that are not being pumped. If the tool is trolled up or down the well, then the motion of the tool through the fluid overcomes the resistance of the impeller and causes it to turn. Once the impeller is turning, smaller changes in flow can be detected; however in low-flow environments spinner tools might not have adequate sensitivity to make meaningful measurements. As a general rule, the higher the flow rate, the more accurate a spinner tool becomes. If flow velocities are lower than about 10 ft/min (3 m/min) then other flow meters, such as the heat-pulse flow meter, are more suitable. Figure 4.25 presents some typical spinner flow-meter data that have been converted to interval flow and interval hydraulic conductivity.

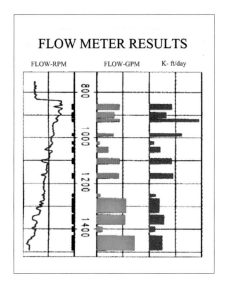

Figure 4.25. Spinner flow-meter log from a constant-diameter, steel-cased, multi-screened municipal groundwater production well. The log in the left track is the spinner flow-meter log with calculated flow in GPM (green histograms) and hydraulic conductivity, *K*, in feet per day (Mount Sopris Instruments).

Heat-Pulse Flow Meter

Heat-pulse flow meters are capable of measuring very low flow rates. Readings are taken at specific depths while the tool is kept stationary. The tool uses a small heating element to create a pulse of heated water. Thermistors located above and below the heating element take continuous readings of temperature after the initiation of the heat pulse. The flow velocity is calculated by recording the time required for the temperature pulse to reach either the upper or lower thermistors, through an orifice having a known diameter. Figure 4.26 is a schematic drawing of a heat-pulse tool.

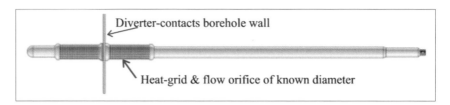

**Figure 4.26. Schematic drawing of a heat-pulse tool
(Mount Sopris Instruments).**

Heat-pulse tools can measure flow in the range of 0.02 gpm (0.08 ℓ/min) to 1.5 gpm (5.7 ℓ/min) very accurately. Flow diverters typically are used to channel the flow through the tool and to increase the sensitivity of the tool. It is customary to take several readings at each depth and use the average for the velocity measurement. The diverters might not fully direct the flow into the tool in large-diameter holes. In such cases, the measurements are relative flow-velocity data that must be calibrated (similar to what is done with spinner log data) to provide flow measurements. Heat-pulse flow meters have been made to measure horizontal flow. These tools are not common, however, and are needed for only a limited number of groundwater investigations.

Fluid Displacement Log

Very high–resolution flow profiles can be made using a specialized logging method known as a fluid displacement log. To run a fluid displacement log, the borehole fluid is replaced with a low-conductivity fluid by slowly pumping deionized water into the top of the water column while pumping the borehole fluid from the bottom of the well at the same rate. When the entire water column in the well has been replaced with deionized water, the well is periodically logged with a borehole fluid temperature and conductivity tool (BHFTC). As formation fluid enters the borehole, the BHFTC log shows an increase in conductivity and might show a temperature change in the intervals where the water is entering the well. The conductivity profile changes over time, as more of the formation fluid enters the well and displaces the deionized water. The influx of the water can be monitored as the more-conductive formation water moves through the borehole. Intervals where water is leaving the well are observed as zones where the conductivity of the water column either decreases or does not change.

The change in conductivity over time is modeled using a multiple aquifer well function to identify producing intervals, thief zones, and flow rates. Fluid displacement logs can be made under non-pumping conditions, or they can be made under pumping conditions by continuously injecting deionized water at a fraction of the pumping rate to slow the rate of change in the pumping-water profile. Although fluid-displacement logs provide very high–resolution flow profiles, data acquisition is complicated and relatively expensive, therefore use of this method has been limited.

WELL-CONSTRUCTION EVALUATION LOGS

Several logs have been developed to evaluate the construction of a well, identify casing perforations, and find defects behind casing. These tools are particularly useful in evaluating wells that do not have construction documentation or when casing failure is suspected.

Well-construction logs include cement-bond logs, magnetic flux density logs, and several more-specialized logs (such as oxygen activations logs that can find flow behind casing). Most of the specialized logs only are used occasionally in water wells and are not discussed in this chapter.

Cement-Bond Log

The cement-bond log (CBL) is a modified version of the sonic porosity tool that measures the coupling between the casing and cement grout. As when using the sonic log method, the borehole must be filled with fluid when using this tool. The CBL is run inside casing, however, therefore it is possible to use a packer to temporarily seal the bottom of the casing and then to fill it with water to allow the full casing to be logged.

Cement-bond logs display the sonic wave as a variable-density log with time increasing to the right and depth increasing downward. The shaded areas represent the positive portion of the wave form and the unshaded areas represent the negative portion of the wave. When steel casing is strongly bonded to cement, most of the sound energy is carried by the cement behind the casing. The signal from the casing is weak and the recorded waveform has a slower arrival time (displaced to the right). For steel casing that is poorly grouted, most of the sound waves are carried by the casing and the casing can oscillate freely (or ring). This causes a strong initial signal from the casing and a distinct displacement of the signal to the left (faster arrival time). Figure 4.27 presents a sample CBL that illustrates a typical response of both well-bonded and poorly bonded casing. Cement-bond logs can be run in PVC casing to evaluate the integrity of bentonite grout; however the acoustic velocity of PVC casing is slower than that of grout. Consequently, faster arrivals indicate the presence of grout in PVC wells.

Complementary to CBL logging, advanced techniques using acoustic tele-viewer tools can be used to image both the inside and the outside of the steel casing, as shown in Figure 4.27. Casing thickness can be determined by the re-cording of travel time and amplitude of the entire acoustic televiewer wavetrain. Casing joints, pits, scraps, cracks, and other features can be visualized. Trained professionals typically perform acoustic televiewer logging and data processing.

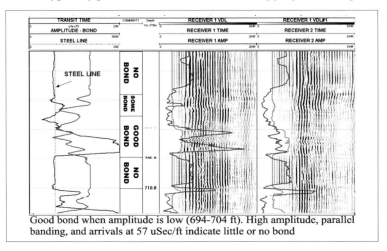

Good bond when amplitude is low (694-704 ft). High amplitude, parallel banding, and arrivals at 57 uSec/ft indicate little or no bond

Figure 4.27. Cement-bond log (CBL) through 8-in casing well in Edwards Limestone aquifer, central Texas (U.S.A.) (Mount Sopris Instruments).

Cement-bond logs measure the response of the full circumference of the borehole. The signal from well-grouted portions of the well circumference can swamp the signal from small areas of poorly bonded casing. Consequently, a grout defect must affect a significant fraction of the well circumference to be reliably detected by a standard CBL log. Small defects or continuous channels or cracks can be missed easily. A modified version of the CBL, called a seg-mented cement-bond log, also is available. The segmented CBL uses multiple pads with sonic logging tools pressed against the borehole at regular intervals around the well. Each pad evaluates the casing bond of a small portion of the circumference of the well. Segmented cement-bond logs can detect smaller defects in the grout behind the casing, including thin channels or cracks. Newer acoustic televiewer tools can be deployed to measure casing thickness in old water wells, enabling investigators to make decisions about well integrity.

Magnetic Flux Density Log

A magnetic flux density log can measure the degree of corrosion of steel casing. The tool magnetizes the casing and logs its magnetic flux density. When the iron in steel corrodes, the magnetic susceptibility decreases significantly and the magnetic field is disrupted in the corroded area. Commercially available tools can detect corrosion pits in casing, estimate the degree of penetration of the corrosion pit, and indicate whether the pit is on the inside or the outside of the casing. Magnetic flux density logs have been used to evaluate the integrity of old casing and to find perforations that allow contaminated water to infiltrate the casing. Such logs also have been used in combination with segmented cement-bond logs prior to beginning well-rehabilitation projects, to determine if old, poorly grouted casing can be safely pulled from a well and replaced with full-diameter grouted casing.

GEOCHEMICAL LOGS

Logging tools with ion-specific electrodes have been developed to make direct measurements of several geochemical properties of the borehole fluid. Tools are available to directly log the pH and oxidation-reduction potential (ORP) in a borehole. Other tools log the concentration of specific ions such chloride, fluoride, and nitrate. Although these logs can be powerful tools for specific applications, the normal limitations of mixing within the borehole and the invasion of low-head zones must be considered when designing and interpreting geochemical logging studies.

In addition to the ion-specific electrode tools, downhole samplers have been developed to collect water samples from specific depths in the water column in a well. The samplers have solenoid-operated valves that can be opened from the surface to allow a sampling chamber to fill, and then be closed to prevent mixing as the sampler is withdrawn. Most tools collect a single water sample of about 1 quart (liter) per logging trip. A few available tools can collect multiple samples in separate chambers on a single trip.

Downhole samplers typically are used to collect samples from selected depths from a well during pumping. Often the sampling depths are chosen as the result of comprehensive logging suites, including the use of flow meters. The water samples should be collected while pumping—after extensive purging has been completed to remove invaded fluids—and representative formation fluid be obtained from all intervals. The pumping rate should create enough drawdown to overcome the largest head difference between hydraulic zones in the well. Downhole water sampling has been used to identify zones producing elevated levels of radium, barium, sulfate, and total dissolved solids (TDS), as well as other water-quality problems.

DESIGNING A LOGGING PROGRAM

The key to a successful logging project is a properly designed logging suite. Although many applications are routine, some projects require significant expertise and experience. A few notable basic concepts that can help in the design of logging projects are listed below.

- Clearly define the project objective
- Determine the condition of the borehole
- Assemble the project team
- Design the logging program
- Get a good contract in place and insure that it specifies responsibility for lost or stuck tools

LOG INTERPRETATION: THE STANDARD E-LOG SUITE

Well logging is most useful in its ability to measure multiple physical parameters of the formations adjacent to the borehole. Simultaneous interpretation of multiple measurements provides the most information about the hydrologic properties of the formations. One of the most common collections of logs—generally called a standard electric-log suite or e-log—consists of one or more electrical logs and the natural–gamma ray log.

Figure 4.6 presents the output of a typical e-log. The standard printout shows the resistivity log output as three traces on the right half of the chart. The three traces generally are a short, mid, and long normal resistivity log. By convention, the deeper-looking logs are plotted with dashed lines and the shallow log is plotted with a solid line, however newer hardware has made it more convenient to use different colors for different logs instead of using dashed lines. A trace showing the estimated TDS of the formation water from the electrical logs has been added to Figure 4.6. The left half of the plot usually contains the gamma log and the SP or SPR log (if one was collected), and can include a track showing logging speed.

Grouping all of the logs on a single plot enables quick evaluation of the response of a formation. Using the resistivity logs and the gamma log, for example, allows shale and clay layers to be quickly identified by the low resistivity and high gamma counts, and distinguishes them from saltwater sand units (identified by low resistivity and low gamma response). Carbonates usually are identified by very high resistivity values with low or erratic gamma counts. The shape of the gamma and resistivity logs can be used to identify characteristic patterns such as fining upward or coarsening upward sequences that can indicate the depositional environment or assist in correlating units between wells.

It is easy to include multiple digital well-logging files on a single plot by using spreadsheets and plotting software. Such plots often are more useful than the typical format of a standard e-log suite, and allow easy comparison of the response of a formation to multiple logs, as the following example demonstrates.

Figure 4.28 is a plot of a series of logs that were run to identify the source of saline water entering a well and to determine whether the well could be reconstructed to improve water quality. The well was constructed as an open-hole completion in a thick sandstone aquifer. The well originally produced water with 600 ppm TDS. After approximately 20 years of service as a municipal well, the water's TDS levels had risen to between 1,000 ppm to 1,400 ppm.

The well was logged after purging for three weeks at 73 gpm (2,830 ℓ/min) to remove any invasion into low-head intervals. The purging time was longer than necessary due to several failures of the purge pump. The logging suite included long and short normal resistivity, natural gamma, borehole fluid temperature and conductivity, and spinner and heat-pulse flow meters. The logs were collected while pumping at the purge rate immediately after the well was deemed to be adequately purged.

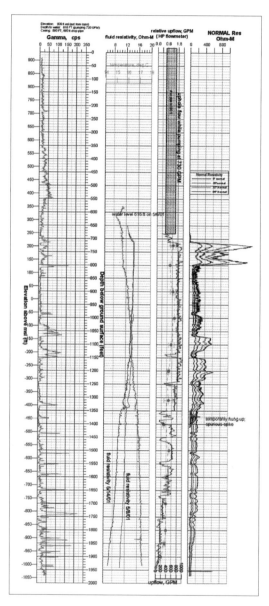

Figure 4.28. Multiple-log output from a water-quality study (Ruekert & Mielke, Inc.).

The gamma log identified thick sandstone units in the lower portion of the well. The sandstone was generally clean, however it contained several thin shale units that could be used as confining units to form a seal in the formation if a portion of the hole were to be isolated. Particularly important was a shale unit located between about 1,740 ft (530 m) and 1,750 ft (533 m).

The borehole fluid temperature and conductivity log showed that the water entering the lower portion of the borehole was warmer and had lower resistivity—and therefore higher TDS—than the water entering the shallow portion of the borehole. The log was repeated a few days later after extended pumping. The resistivity of the borehole fluid of the lower portion of the well was lower than the initial log, which indicated that the well had not been fully purged during the initial logging run.

The flow-meter logs indicated that approximately 75% of the well production was originating from above a depth of 1,750 ft (533.5 m). The long and short normal resistivity log indicated that the sandstone unit had a typical resistivity of about 240 ohm-meters, but dropped to about 80 ohm-meters below 1,820 ft (554.9 m) deep. The gamma log showed that the shale content of this interval was no different than the higher resistivity portion of the sandstone, which indicates higher TDS formation water. The TDS of the formation water was calculated using the resistivity log data. The formation water above 1,500 ft (457.3 m) contained about 870 ppm TDS. Below 1,900 ft (579.3 m), the TDS of the formation water was 2,300 ppm.

The well was backfilled with sand and cement to a depth of about 1,740 ft (530.5 m). The TDS of the water produced by the well was reduced to 500 ppm with a loss in specific capacity of 25%. After 5 years of regular service, the water quality and capacity of the well have not changed.

Figure 4.29 presents the log data from a borehole flow log conducted as part of a groundwater-contamination study in a carbonate aquifer. The logging suite consisted of a borehole fluid temperature and conductivity log and heat-pulse flow meter conducted under non-pumping (static) conditions and a spinner log and heat-pulse flow log conducted while pumping the well at 20 gpm (77.5 ℓ/min) (dynamic condition). Due to small contrasts in the conductivity and temperature of the water in the aquifer, the borehole fluid temperature and conductivity log did not clearly define flow zones; however the flow-meter data detected strong downflow in the wellbore under non-pumping conditions. The downward flow provided a pathway for contaminated groundwater to move from fractures in the shallow portion of the aquifer to fractures in the deeper part of the aquifer. When pumping, the thief zones in the lower aquifer became the major water-producing fractures, returning some of the contaminated water to the well. Similar results were obtained in the logs of several other wells in the area. The log data demonstrated that the wells were serving as conduits for the migration of contaminants between two isolated fracture zones.

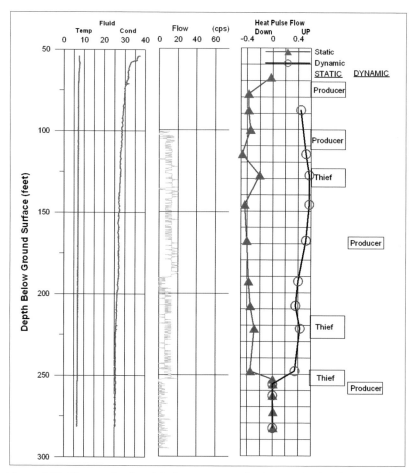

Figure 4.29. Flow-meter log data from a groundwater-contamination study in a carbonate aquifer (Ruekert & Mielke, Inc.).

As noted, there is a variety of tools and methodologies for investigation of the subsurface using geophysical techniques. Additional information regarding downhole tools is contained in Appendix 4 (DVD).

ACKNOWLEDGMENT

James B. Fink (PhD), President, hydroGEOPHYSICS, Inc., was the reviewer for this chapter. His valuable insights are gratefully acknowledged.

CHAPTER 5
Groundwater Chemistry

Andrew Nicholson, PhD
Geomega

INTRODUCTION

Understanding and interpreting groundwater chemical analyses are important adjuncts to the exploration, production, and use of groundwater. Chemical contaminants can create health or environmental effects that make water unsuitable for use or require that it be treated. The presence of specific substances in groundwater can create conditions that promote scale formation or biofouling and inhibit water production. The chemical composition of groundwater also can be used to track sources of groundwater to support the exploration and development of water-well production. This chapter provides a brief overview of groundwater chemical issues as background. Appendix 5.A (book) contains a compilation of common water-quality issues associated with groundwater production, and can be used as a cross-reference for sections of this chapter.

Groundwater wells lie at the interface between two chemical regimes—the groundwater aquifer, and the surface sampling, collection, and distribution systems. These two regimes have different temperatures, pressures, and oxygen contents. The transition between the two regimes can change water chemistry, resulting in fouling, chemical precipitate formation, promotion of bacterial growth, and facilitation of chemical corrosion or occlusion of well materials.

Groundwater chemistry therefore must be understood in the context of the in-situ chemistry of the aquifer, the chemical changes that might occur during groundwater production, and the ultimate quality of the water produced.

CHEMICAL PROPERTIES OF GROUNDWATER

Groundwater contains dissolved chemical species, and suspended compounds also might be present. The species are composed of molecules of chemicals, which are comprised of atoms of the specific elements. These chemical species primarily are inorganic and usually have either a negative or positive charge. The term "inorganic" applies to all substances other than compounds containing carbon and hydrogen bound together—the primary building-block compounds of living things, petroleum products, and plastics. Carbon dioxide gas and carbonate species are inorganic compounds because the carbon is not bound to hydrogen; these are discussed below in the section on alkalinity and pH.

Positively charged species are called cations and the negatively charged species are termed anions. In most waters usually only a few chemical species make up the majority of the charges in the water—these ions are referred to as the water's major ions. The most common major cations in water are sodium, calcium, magnesium, and potassium. The most common anions are chloride, sulfate, and carbonate. These major ions impart important properties to groundwater, including its specific conductance, salinity, and hardness.

Groundwater differs from surface water in several respects; for example, groundwater tends to contain more dissolved constituents as it flows through the aquifer and interacts with the aquifer's minerals. Groundwater also might have higher or lower dissolved gas concentrations, because it often is under greater pressures than are surface waters. The temperature of groundwater tends to be relatively constant through all seasons. Typically, shallow groundwater is at a temperature similar to the average annual ambient air temperature of the specific location, although geothermal and artesian processes might create local temperature differences. Because groundwater is not in contact with the land surface and the atmosphere, groundwater can be anoxic and can have a composition that changes when the groundwater is exposed to the atmosphere through pumping or via a spring.

UNITS OF MEASUREMENT IN ANALYSES

All chemical analyses reports indicate the units of measure used. Most chemical analyses are expressed in units of mass per volume, such as milligrams per liter (mg/ℓ) or micrograms per liter (μg/ℓ). Because most dilute waters have a density near 1 kilogram per liter (kg/ℓ), 1 mg/ℓ usually is equal to 1 mg/kg (water's density varies slightly with temperature, so this is strictly true only at 39°F (3.89°C)), which is also equivalent to 1 part per million (ppm). Thus, the units ppm and mg/ℓ are used interchangeably with regard to water analyses. Similarly, 1 μg/ℓ is equivalent to 1 μg/kg in dilute waters, which is equivalent to 1 part per billion (ppb). Note that these interconversions are only applicable in dilute waters and normal temperatures, and are not applicable to water with high salinity (including seawater) where the density of water is greater than 1 kg/ℓ.

The terms moles, molarity, and molality, which are units of measurement based on the number of molecules present, often are used by chemists. One mole of a compound is equal to $6.02 \cdot 10^{23}$ atoms of a compound (also known as Avogadro's Number). Therefore the molecular weight of a compound is the mass of one mole of the compound in grams.

Chemists also refer to the units of equivalents, which are based on the number of positive or negative charges present. Equivalents are particularly useful in evaluating whether a water analysis is complete, and are used to determine whether the water is charge balanced. To convert from mg/ℓ to millimoles/ℓ, divide the concentration (mg/ℓ) by the molecular weight of a compound (the sum of atomic weights of a molecule). To determine the milliequivalents per ℓ (meq/ℓ) for a compound, divide the molecular weight by the valence (charge) of the ions. Appendix 5.B (DVD) contains a compilation of chemical conversion factors to aid in the performance of these calculations.

In evaluating the units of a particular measurement, it sometimes is important to state the chemical basis of the unit. For example, phosphorus in water usually occurs as the phosphate ion (PO_4^{3-}). Phosphate analyses can be reported as "PO_4^{3-}" (in which case all of the PO_4^{3-} including the attached oxygen is included as the basis of the analyses) or as "P" (in which case only the phosphorus is the basis for analyses). These two measurements can be converted by using the ratio of molecular weights of P and PO_4^{3-}. These types of measurement unit issues can be important to consider in the analyses of nitrate, nitrite, ammonia, sulfate, alkalinity, and acidity.

CLASSES OF COMPOUNDS AND ANALYSIS

For this introduction to groundwater chemistry, the analyses discussed are divided into different groups.

- **Physical properties of groundwater** include temperature, specific electrical conductance, specific gravity, and turbidity.
- **Conservative elements** include sodium (Na^+), potassium (K^+), lithium (Li^+), chloride (Cl^-), fluoride (F^-), and bromide (Br^-). Additionally, the secondary chemical property of salinity is included with these elements because salinity often is controlled by their presence (especially that of sodium and chloride).
- **Dissolved gases,** frequently oxygen (O_2), carbon dioxide (CO_2), hydrogen sulfide (H_2S), methane (CH_4), and ammonia (NH_3). These are dissolved in groundwater and can be exsolved as bubbles when groundwater undergoes temperature and pressure changes during production, potentially impacting groundwater chemistry. The behaviors of specific gases are discussed in the sections relevant to each compound.
- **Radionuclides;** radioactive elements and the associated radio-activity also are regulated in groundwater. These elements include both natural and anthropogenic sources of radiation.
- **Reactive major elements** include the chemical compounds calcium (Ca^{2+}), magnesium (Mg^{2+}), aluminum (Al^{3+}), silica (SiO_2), sulfate (SO_4^{2-}), phosphate (PO_4^{3-}), carbonate (CO_3^{2-}), and hydrogen ions (H^+). The secondary chemical property of hardness is included in this group of compounds. These compounds comprise a large portion of the dissolved content of most potable groundwater, but they can undergo chemical reactions that have many repercussions, including corrosion, scale formation, and gas exsolution and bubble formation, Water with elevated calcium and magnesium is termed "hard," and hardness can affect water's suitability for some domestic and industrial uses.
- **Redox-sensitive elements and compounds** include iron (Fe), manganese (Mn), hydrogen sulfide (H_2S), and nitrogen compounds (including nitrate (NO_3^-) and ammonia (NH_3)). Each substance reacts very differently in oxygen-rich environments (surface

waters, water-distribution systems, water-treatment plants, some groundwater) and in oxygen-poor environments (sediment pore water, deep groundwater, groundwater contaminated with organic compounds). Elevated levels of these compounds can create problems in groundwater production due to chemical precipitates, biofouling, taste, odor, and color.

- ◆ **Trace elements** are the elements found at low levels; they often have important water-quality implications due to their toxicity.
- ◆ **Organic compounds;** organic chemicals can either occur naturally or be man made. Specific organic compounds which can cause severe health effects often are tightly regulated in groundwater.

Physical Properties of Groundwater

The physical properties of groundwater—specifically its temperature, suspended solid composition (turbidity), and specific gravity—often reveal some important characteristics of the water or of the well producing it.

Temperature

Groundwater temperature is a fundamental property of aquifers. Near-surface groundwater generally has an almost constant temperature, which ordinarily is close to the mean annual air temperature. Geothermal heat increases groundwater temperatures about 3.6°F (2°C) per 328 ft (100 m) of depth, beginning at approximately 96 ft (30 m).

Temperature is a property of water that can be determined relatively easily, but it often is measured inaccurately. Temperature can be measured either directly in wells via downhole devices, or at the surface upon collection of the sample. Measuring temperature at the surface must be done quickly (within a minute, and sooner in very hot or very cold conditions) to ensure that equilibration with the surface temperature does not affect the measurement. Additionally, water temperatures in wells might be stratified somewhat differently from the temperature of surrounding groundwater. During sampling, an accurate groundwater temperature only can be determined by pumping the well for a period of time and tracking the temperature of produced water until it stabilizes. The United States Geological Survey (USGS) (Radtke, Kurklin & Wilde 2005) in its sampling guidance suggests that temperature measurements taken from bailed water samples are not accurate and should not be reported. This underscores the importance of both rapid sample analysis and clear reporting of the measurement methods.

Temperature is a vital property of water because thermal changes during pumping can trigger gas exsolution and mineral precipitation. Temperature itself also is a good parameter to evaluate when either sampling standing water in a well or pulling in water from the surrounding aquifer. It therefore is important to use great care when gathering data on this most simple but sensitive field measurement.

Turbidity

Turbidity is the measure of the relative clarity of a water sample. In groundwater, high turbidity usually is due to the presence of suspended material. Turbidity is measured using a turbidimeter, an optical device that measures the scattering of light though a water sample. This instrument is readily available as a compact, field-ready, battery-powered unit, and enables immediate field analysis of turbidity. Turbidity is measured in Nephelometric Turbidity Units (NTU), which are based on the scattering of light in a water sample relative to the scattering of light from a known standard suspension of formazin.

In a properly constructed well, turbidity of the water produced generally should be low (less than 10 NTU) and should be consistent after extended pumping. Turbidity in well waters can arise from particulates mobilized from the aquifer or well-construction materials during well installation and initial pumping, or from the formation of chemical precipitates within a well. Poorly developed wells can have high turbidity if drilling fluids and fine-grained sediment from the formation are not removed adequately.

Water with high turbidity generally is undesirable as drinking water, and can create fouling and clogging problems in other applications. Water samples with high levels of turbidity often have elevated levels of other trace constituents, particularly metals and organic matter.

Like temperature, turbidity in water can be affected by time. The solids in the water can settle as a sample sits, and this decreases turbidity. Alternatively, iron and manganese in water samples can react with atmospheric oxygen to produce particulate phases that can increase turbidity after sample collection.

Specific Electrical Conductance

Specific electrical conductance (EC) is a measure of water's ability to conduct an electrical current. Current flows in ionized or mineralized water because the ions are electrically charged and move in response to a charged field. The more ions present in the water, the greater the water's ability to conduct electricity.

Specific electrical conductance is defined as the conductance of a cubic centimeter of any substance compared with the conductance of the same volume of water. Chemically pure water has a very low electrical conductance, indicating that it is a good insulator. The addition of dissolved mineral and inorganic material increases the conductance of the water. The dissolved constituents in groundwater are termed total dissolved solids (TDS).

Electrical conductance is a relatively easy and stable method for analysis of water, and can be used to estimate the dissolved constituent concentration. The unit of measurement for conductance is the mho, which is the inverse of ohm (the unit commonly used to express electrical resistance). Values of specific conductance for groundwater are reported in millionths of mhos per cm (μmhos/cm), or in microsiemens per cm (μS/cm).

In most dilute groundwaters the specific conductance varies almost directly with the amount of dissolved ions, but also is dependent on the actual dissolved constituents in the water. For example, 100 mg/ℓ of sodium chloride (NaCl) gives water a specific conductance that is higher than for 100 mg/ℓ of calcium bicarbonate ($Ca(HCO_3)_2$). Table 5.1 provides conductance values for solutions of these two mineral salts. To be comparable, conductance measurements must be performed at the same temperature.

Table 5.1. Conductivity of Two Salt Solutions

Specific Conductance at 77°F (25°C), Micromhos		
Concentration of Dissolved Salt in mg/ℓ	NaCl	$Ca(HCO_3)_2$
50	93	62
100	187	125
200	370	250
400	750	500
(Driscoll 1986)		

Figure 5.1 shows the strong correlation between TDS and specific conductance. As a result, the concentration of dissolved salts can be estimated on the basis of electrical conductivity measurements. For most groundwater, the specific conductance (in μmhos/cm) multiplied by a factor of 0.55 to 0.75 gives a reasonable estimate of the dissolved solids (in mg/ℓ). For the values shown in Figure 5.1, the specific conductance multiplied by a factor of 0.55 to 0.63 gives the dissolved-solids concentration. The multiplication factor for saline waters usually is greater than 0.75, and for acidic water it can be much lower. Estimation of total dissolved solids from conductivity measurements is convenient because conductivity can be determined quickly in the field using fairly simple equipment and procedures.

Specific conductance is a useful parameter in the development and sampling of wells. During pumping its stability is a good indicator that water content is not changing and that aquifer water, rather than standing water within a well, actually is being pumped.

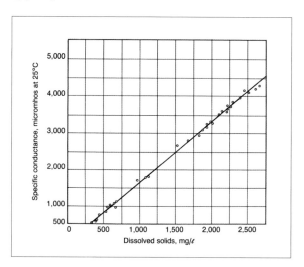

Figure 5.1. Dissolved solids concentration compared with specific conductance shows a constant ratio between conductance and mineral content of water taken from Gila River at Bylas, AZ (U.S.A.), in a 12-month period (Hem 1992).

Water that has relatively high specific conductance can corrode iron and steel, even though other properties of the water might not indicate a corrosion problem. Specific conductance reflects activity of the electrically charged ions, therefore it follows that the higher the conductivity the greater the potential for electrochemical action. The importance of this statement as it relates to the long-term success of wells becomes clear in the well design discussion found in Chapter 9, and the discussion of maintenance found in Chapter 13.

Specific Gravity

Specific gravity is a measure of the density of water. Groundwater generally has a specific gravity near 1 g/ml, with some variation depending on temperature and the presence of dissolved constituents. Groundwater having high levels of dissolved constituents, however, can have specific gravity of greater than 1. The most common water having high specific gravity is seawater, which can have a specific gravity between 1.02 g/ml and 1.03 g/ml; this is enough to create density stratification when seawater intrudes groundwater in coastal zones. In sites with industrial contamination and in oil and gas fields, specific gravity also is important because liquid phases that do not mix with water either float on top of the water table (as is common with many petroleum hydrocarbons) or sink to the bottom of the aquifer (as is common with chlorinated solvents or concentrated brines).

Conservative Elements

The elements sodium (Na^+), potassium (K^+), lithium (Li^+), chloride (Cl^-), fluoride (F^-), and bromide (Br^-), generally do not react with many other compounds in groundwater, and thereby are conserved in the water. These elements tend to move at the same velocity as groundwater and can be used to trace groundwater flow. The concentration of these compounds and properties is controlled primarily by the simple dilution and evapoconcentration of waters. These chemicals generally do not present health hazards unless the concentrations are very high (with the possible exception of fluoride), but elevated concentrations can make water nonpotable and limit its uses, and also can cause well corrosion. In many waters, these elements make up the bulk of dissolved constituents present.

Salinity and Total Dissolved Solids

Salinity and total dissolved solids are interchangeable terms that refer to the total concentration of dissolved substances in water. Salinity commonly is used in reference to seawater, and to groundwater and surface water that are near oceans, while TDS more typically is used to express the total dissolved concentrations of elements found in most groundwater.

Salinity generally is measured in parts per thousand (or per mil ‰) and TDS is expressed in mg/ℓ. Seawater has a salinity of approximately 35‰ (35,000 mg/ℓ), and freshwater generally has a salinity of less than 0.5‰ (500 mg/ℓ). Water having salinity of between 0.5‰ and 35‰ is considered brackish. Salinity and TDS commonly are used to assess the general quality of water. Because salinity also is easily correlated for particular water compositions to specific conductance (SC), an SC measurement often is the first indicator of salinity or TDS. The U.S. EPA has developed a secondary drinking-water standard for TDS of 500 mg/ℓ.

Sodium

The element sodium (Na^+) and its salts all are highly soluble in water. Once it is leached from rocks or sediments, sodium remains in solution except at very high concentrations that approach saturation of sodium chloride. Sodium is by far the most abundant metallic ion in seawaters, averaging about 10,000 mg/ℓ. The usual concentration of sodium ions in groundwater is 10 mg/ℓ to 100 mg/ℓ (Hem 1992). The solubility of sodium is so high that it does not precipitate to form scale and plug wells.

Sodium, however, is retained by clay mineral surfaces, affecting both soil salinity and the productivity of agricultural lands irrigated with high-sodium waters; it therefore is monitored carefully in irrigation waters. Sodium salts can affect crop production because crop roots—especially in the upper root zone—have great difficulty extracting enough water and nutrients from saline solutions. Soil permeability can be reduced significantly by the buildup of salts in the soil zone, resulting in reduced crop production. Sodium toxicity also can be problematic for maintaining good crop yields.

Of particular consequence is the ratio of sodium to calcium and magnesium. When sodium-rich water is applied to soil, some of the sodium is taken up by clay and the clay releases calcium and magnesium to the water. This reaction—called base exchange—alters the physical characteristics of soil and even can lead to crop-growth retardation. A clayey soil that takes up sodium becomes sticky and slick when wet, and has low permeability.

If irrigation water contains calcium and magnesium ions sufficient to equal or exceed the sodium ions, then enough calcium and magnesium is retained on clay particles to maintain good tilth and permeability. Such waters serve well for irrigation, even though the total mineral content might be quite high.

The importance of sodium led to the adoption of a method to measure the effect of sodium ions. In 1954, the United States Salinity Laboratory proposed that the sodium effect be calculated by the sodium adsorption ratio (SAR) method. The SAR is calculated using the following equation.

$$SAR = \frac{Na}{\sqrt{\dfrac{Ca + Mg}{2}}} \tag{5.1}$$

Here, the water analysis gives the Na, Ca, and Mg in milliequivalents per liter (meq/ℓ). Development of excess sodium in soils results from irrigation water that has a high SAR value (18 or greater). Values that are less than 10 indicate little danger of a sodium problem. See Appendix 5.C (DVD) for a discussion of this analysis method. Appendix 5.C (DVD) also presents a convenient soils classification system that has been developed on the basis of the sodium adsorption ratio and the conductivity of the irrigation water.

Under ordinary conditions plants take up little of the dissolved minerals from irrigation water. Most minerals carried by the water remain either in the soil or dissolved in the unused portion of the water. Repeated irrigation can result in the accumulation of too great a quantity of mineral salts—destroying the productivity of the irrigated soil. Some means of leaching salts from the soil therefore must be found.

Under favorable water-quality conditions, irrigation can be conducted successfully if management practices include:

- Irrigating frequently to maintain an adequate soil-water supply for the crop;
- Planting crops that can tolerate an existing or potential salinity problem;
- Using extra water routinely to satisfy leaching requirements;
- Changing the irrigation method to one that allows better salt control; and
- Modifying specific practices.

An analysis of the initial water quality can suggest effective management practices but—as a standard part of the irrigation management system—water quality must be monitored annually to detect changes that could affect yields.

Sodium does not contribute to the hardness of water. In fact, it commonly is used in ion-exchange-based water softeners to replace the hardness-causing Ca^{2+} and Mg^{2+} ions in solution. The presence of sodium commonly is an indicator of water-quality issues. Elevated sodium often is seen in coastal areas, where the pumping of groundwater brings in nearby seawater. Elevated sodium also can be a product of salt introduced by highway deicers or the disposal of saline oil-field brines.

Chloride

Chloride (Cl^-) is the predominant negatively charged ion in seawater and has an average concentration of about 19,000 mg/ℓ. Although very little chloride exists in crystalline rocks, the weathering of these rocks does contribute minute amounts to rivers and streams. Chloride found in groundwater typically ranges from 6 mg/ℓ to 15 mg/ℓ (Tardy 1971).

Rainwater that falls in coastal regions generally contains more chloride than that which falls farther inland. Mairs (1967) demonstrated that the chloride concentration of lakes in Maine (U.S.A.) decreases from about 10 mg/ℓ near the coast to less than 1 mg/ℓ at 150 mi (241 km) inland. Other data suggest that atmospheric chloride contributes about 0.4 mg/ℓ to the total chloride content of inland surface waters. Additionally, some chloride comes from the weathering of rocks. In local settings, however, chloride also can result from industrial activity. Abundant chlorides in groundwater also can indicate seepage from certain types of sewage facilities. Human wastes generally are high in chloride content. Once these wastes are deposited in sewage lagoons or septic tanks, chloride often moves into the groundwater system; and because it is not absorbed by soil, chloride can travel great distances.

Chloride in groundwater also can originate from seawater intrusion in coastal areas. When wells near the coast are pumped continuously, ocean water can intrude into the freshwater aquifer, increasing both salinity and chloride concentrations.

Water that contains less than 150 mg/ℓ chloride is satisfactory for most purposes. A chloride content of more than 250 mg/ℓ generally is unacceptable for a municipal water supply, and water containing more than 350 mg/ℓ is objectionable even for most irrigation and industrial uses. Water containing

500 mg/ℓ chloride frequently has a disagreeable taste. Animals can drink water that has much more chloride; cattle, for example, safely can drink water that has chloride concentrations as high as 3,000 mg/ℓ to 4,000 mg/ℓ.

Fluoride

In groundwater, fluoride (F⁻) generally is present only in low concentrations. Fluoride is derived from the dissolution of fluorite (CaF_2) (a common mineral found in igneous rocks), the weathering of apatite and mica minerals, and the evapo-concentration of lower-fluoride waters. Volcanic or fumarolic gases can contain fluoride and, in some areas, these could be the source of fluoride in groundwater.

It is important to know the amount of fluoride in water that is consumed by children. Excessive fluoride causes mottling of tooth enamel and, because fluoride affects tooth density, teeth also can become brittle. These defects are more evident in children who drink too much fluoridated water while their permanent teeth are forming.

Although too much fluoride can harm teeth, minute amounts are quite beneficial. In many parts of the United States, public health laws require the addition of fluoride to public water supplies. The usual recommended fluoride content is 0.7 mg/ℓ to 1.2 mg/ℓ.

Potassium, Lithium, and Bromide

Potassium (K^+), lithium (Li^{2+}), and bromide (Br⁻) are found at much lower concentrations in groundwater, relative to the other less-reactive elements. The most common of these elements is potassium, as it is a product of the weathering of the feldspar minerals. Potassium is highly mobile and almost never is sorbed or precipitated in natural groundwater. It does precipitate in some moderately soluble aluminum-iron sulfate minerals in low-pH, high-sulfate waters.

Lithium and bromide are present at low levels in most groundwaters (less than 1 mg/ℓ). Their low native concentrations and high mobility in groundwater, however, enable them to be used in tracer tests to assess groundwater flow paths. Bromide could be a concern in groundwater, as it can react to create potentially harmful by-products in water-treatment systems during the disinfection of drinking water.

Dissolved Gases

All groundwaters are infused with certain amounts of dissolved gases, and their presence in substantial quantities critically affects the use of water. The most common dissolved gases include oxygen, hydrogen sulfide, carbon dioxide, nitrogen, and ammonia; and, of this group, the first three gases listed have the greatest significance for groundwater and its development. The solubility of gas decreases as temperature increases. The solubility also increases with increasing pressure. Dissolved gases can cause corrosion of well casings and well screens, and also can impact the deposition of incrusting materials because of pressure changes near wells. Dissolved gases typically occur in concentrations of 1 mg/ℓ to 100 mg/ℓ (the specific chemistry of many of these gasses is discussed below).

The pumping of groundwater wells and a reduction in the pressure confining the water causes the release of gasses from the solution. The chemical changes associated with this pressure drop can result in scale deposits, particularly in wells completed in limestone and dolomite aquifers. As shown in Figure 5.2, the velocity of water must increase as it moves from an area that is away from a pumping well (cylinder A1) to an area nearer the well (cylinder A2). The same volume of water must pass through both (theoretical) cylinders, therefore the velocity of groundwater flow results in a corresponding decrease in pressure. The pressure thus decreases near the well as the water velocity increases.

The decrease in pressure is especially significant within 3 ft (0.9 m) to 6 ft (1.8 m) of the well. Reduced pressure in this zone leads to the release of carbon-dioxide gas, causing the pH to rise and magnesium and calcium to form carbonate scale. Depending on the hydraulic characteristics of the well and surrounding formations, scale deposition can cause serious losses in well efficiency or actual loss of the well within as few as 1 to 3 years. The benefits of high–open area screens include reducing the potential of mineral scale deposition, and the degassing of water in the aquifer and well.

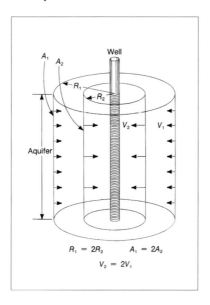

Figure 5.2. As water moves toward a well its velocity varies with its distance from the well.

Radionuclides

Isotopes of some elements naturally break down in the environment, through alpha (a), beta (β), or gamma (γ) radiation, to produce other elements. The primary sources of radiation in the environment are:

- The decay of naturally occurring uranium (and its daughter products) producing radioactive isotopes of uranium (U), thorium (Th), radium (Ra), and radon (Rn);
- The decay of the by-products of nuclear fission, including materials from atomic explosions, nuclear power–related accidents, or nuclear-waste producing radioactive isotopes of plutonium (Pu), americium (Am), neptunium (Np), uranium (U), thorium (Th), strontium (Sr), radium (Ra), and radon (Rn); or
- The products of research, medical, and industrial radioactivity applications producing a variety of esoteric isotopes (depending on the specific process).

A detailed description of these decay processes is beyond the scope of this chapter, but the overall processes are important to understand. Many elements have several different isotopes (each element has the same number of protons in its atomic nucleus, but each different isotope has a different number of neutrons in its nucleus). Isotopes are either stable (non-radioactive) or unstable (radioactive). Various isotopes of an element can demonstrate nearly identical chemical behavior, but also can have differing radioactive properties.

A radioactive isotope of an element decays at a known rate (defined by that isotope's half-life, which is the time it takes for one half of the total quantity of the isotope present to decay). These decays might occur over many sequential steps with intermediate isotopes each having its own half-life before the decay is ended by formation of a stable isotope. The isotopes with the longest half-lives persist and more likely are present, and those with the shortest half-lives only are present at very low levels. For example, ^{238}U decays to stable ^{206}Pb in a series of 14 steps. The half-lives of the sequential steps range from 100 microseconds (μs) to 10^9 years, therefore only ^{234}Th, ^{234}U, ^{230}Th, ^{226}Ra, and ^{222}Rn generally are of environmental importance (Langmuir 1997). Naturally elevated levels of uranium decay–derived isotopes generally are highest in pegmatitic and granitic regimes.

Radiation can affect human health, and accumulated radiation exposure can cause leukemia, birth defects, mental retardation, and malignant tumors. To monitor radionuclides in water, total radiation (gross alpha and beta particles) is measured. Additionally, the specific concentration of different radioactive elements (especially uranium) also can be measured. The U.S. EPA has developed drinking-water criteria for gross alpha particles, gross beta particles, and total uranium present.

Reactive Major Elements

pH and Acidity

The primary indicator of whether water is acidic or basic is its pH. Because pH controls the solubility and mobility of many inorganic compounds in water, it is a key factor in the corrosiveness of waters and can be the determining variable of the suitability of using specific water. The pH level is perhaps the single most important measure of water chemistry.

Technically, pH is the negative logarithm of the activity of the hydrogen ion (which is the primary acid in water) in solution.

$$pH = -\log_{10}[H^+] \tag{5.2}$$

In short, water dissociates naturally to form hydrogen (H^+) and hydroxide (OH^-) ions in solution.

$$H_2O \leftrightarrow H^+ + OH^- \tag{5.3}$$

Acidic solutions contain an excess of H^+ that is balanced by a negatively charged ion, and basic solutions contain an excess of OH^-. In all natural waters, the activity (which can be simplified in dilute waters to be essentially equal to concentration) of H^+ multiplied by the value of OH^- is equal to a constant of 10^{-14}.

Most waters have a pH of between 1 and 14, with the exceptions being highly concentrated industrial and laboratory solutions. A neutral pH is 7, an acidic pH is less than 7, and alkaline or basic pH is greater than 7. Because pH measurement uses a logarithmic scale, a change of 1 pH unit indicates a significant change (a factor of 10) in the acid content of a solution.

Another indicator of the acid content of a solution is its acidity measurement. Acidity is the capacity of water to react with hydroxyl ions (e.g., base). It is operationally defined as the amount of base required to raise the pH of water to 8.2. Although pH is a measure of the reactivity of the acid in water, acidity is a measure of the total amount of acid contained. Rainwater and a concentrated solution of a weak acid, for example, might have the same low pH. It might take a much larger quantity of base to raise the pH of the acid solution, however, as compared to that needed for dilute rainwater. Acidity is measured using either meq/ℓ or the units of mg/ℓ $CaCO_3$, and is a useful measure to analyze when determining whether to raise the pH of water in a treatment system.

Alkalinity

The alkalinity of a water is the capacity for the solutes it contains to react with and neutralize acid (Hem 1992). In other words, it is the neutralizing capacity of a water. In most waters, alkalinity primarily is a function of the amount of carbonate present in solution. Alkalinity does not measure an actual concentration, but rather it is a measure of the capacity of water. This capacity commonly is translated into the carbonate concentration in water, but this assumption should be applied cautiously for waters with high pH, phosphate, borate, ammonia, or organic content. These constituents can add alkalinity to groundwater. Like acidity, alkalinity usually is reported in units of either meq/ℓ or of mg/ℓ $CaCO_3$ (mg/ℓ $CaCO_3$ is one fiftieth of meq/ℓ).

In practice, alkalinity is determined by titrating water (adding acid) until it reaches a predefined pH endpoint. Hydroxide alkalinity is defined as the amount of acid required to reduce a water's pH to 9.3, carbonate alkalinity is the amount of acid required to lower a water's pH to 8.3, and bicarbonate alkalinity is the amount of acid required to lower a water's pH from 8.3 to 4.4. Total alkalinity is the sum of these 3 alkalinities. This distinction is important because the carbonate ion (CO_3^{2-}) is the dominant carbonate species above pH 8.3 (Figure 5.3), and the bicarbonate ion (HCO_3^-) dominates at pH of between 8.3 and 4.4 (see Figure 5.3). Below a pH of 4.4, carbonate is present in water as carbonic acid (H_2CO_3).

Carbonate

The carbonate ion in solution has a complex chemistry that is fundamental in controlling many chemical processes in groundwater. As discussed, the pH values that define alkalinity provide a basis to identify the 3 general pH zones of carbonate behavior (CO_3^{2-}, HCO_3^-, H_2CO_3, and dissolved CO_2 gas) (*see* Figure 5.3).

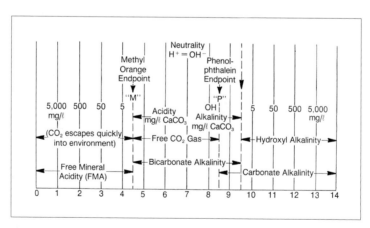

Figure 5.3. Acidity and various types of alkalinity and their pH ranges (adapted from Kemmer 1979).

Carbonic acid has a pH of less than 4.4, and is the dominant carbonate species present in water. One primary source of carbonic acid is carbon dioxide (CO_2) from the atmosphere, where CO_2 accounts for approximately 0.04% of air. Carbon dioxide dissolves into water and then forms carbonic acid, as shown in the following equation.

$$CO_2 + H_2O \leftrightarrow HCO_3^- + H^+ \qquad \text{(5.4)}$$

The amount of carbonic acid in the water depends on the partial pressure of carbon dioxide in the air in equilibrium with the groundwater. Therefore, at depth, where pressures are higher, or in environments where high levels of CO_2 are present, more carbonic acid is present in the water. The opposite reaction also can occur. If water is brought from a high-pressure, high-CO_2 environment to a lower-CO_2 environment, the CO_2 exsolves from the water and forms bubbles. The most common example of this reaction is seen when opening a can of a carbonated beverage. Once carbonic acid is present in water, it acts as an acid and dissociates to form hydrogen and bicarbonate ions as noted in equation 5.5.

$$H_2CO_3 \leftrightarrow HCO_3^- + H^+ \qquad \text{(5.5)}$$

The extent of the reaction depends on the pH of the system. At a pH of less than 4.4 this reaction occurs only minimally, and at a pH greater than 4.4 the reaction favors the right side of the equation, although some carbonic acid always is present in the system. The net result of these reactions is that carbon dioxide in the atmosphere acts as a weak acid. Waters with no source of carbonate other than the atmosphere (e.g., rainwater) are slightly acidic due to atmospheric CO_2—the theoretical pH of pure water in equilibrium with atmospheric CO_2 is 5.65. The most important point to understand about the reaction of atmospheric CO_2 with water is that adding CO_2 gas to water makes the water more acidic, and CO_2 gas exsolving from water raises the water's pH.

Carbonate has a pH of between 4.4 and 8.3, and is dominantly present as HCO_3^-. If any acid is added to the system, it is neutralized by the HCO_3^- and forms carbonic acid—the reverse reaction of that shown in equation 5.6. If any base (i.e., OH^-) is added to the system, then the HCO_3^- reacts with it and forms the carbonate ion CO_3^{2-}.

$$HCO_3^- + OH^- \leftrightarrow CO_3^{2-} + H_2O \qquad \text{(5.6)}$$

At a pH of between 4.4 and 8.3, HCO_3^- can act both as an acid and a base. Due to the presence of HCO_3^-, the system is buffered (resists changes in pH) until the HCO_3^- is consumed.

At a pH of more than 8.3, carbonate is present as CO_3^{2-}, and only consumes acid. When the pH is greater than 8.3, many carbonate minerals—such as calcite ($CaCO_3$), the primary mineral in limestone—become much more insoluble and tend to precipitate.

It is important to note, however, that even at a pH of more than 8.3 the amount of carbonic acid present in a water still is controlled by the partial pressure of CO_2 in the air in equilibrium with that water. The reactions that the carbonate ion undergoes often ultimately control the pH of the system. For example, a water in equilibrium with calcite and atmospheric CO_2 has a theoretical pH of 8.4.

In groundwater systems, it is common to have carbonate ions present due to the interaction with the minerals in the aquifer material. Because of the elevated pressures and subsurface sources of CO_2, it also is common to have elevated levels of dissolved "free" CO_2 present in the water. The "free" CO_2 exsolves as water is pumped from a well, resulting in an increased pH of the water during water production. If the groundwater is near saturation with any minerals in the system, then this increase in pH might cause the precipitation of minerals within wells and water-collection systems, resulting in scale formation. Scale formation is enhanced by high alkalinity and high hardness.

Hardness, Calcium, and Magnesium

Water hardness historically was based on the observation that some waters produced soapsuds and others more effectively rinsed soap. The waters that didn't produce suds also typically created more insoluble scum in bathtubs and sinks. These properties commonly result from calcium and magnesium in groundwater binding with the soap molecules and inhibiting their surfactant properties. Hardness also can negatively affect the taste of water. For some metals that are toxic to fish, however, elevated hardness mitigates the toxic effects. Many governing agencies therefore adjust surface-water quality standards based on the hardness of the surface-water body. Note that these adjustments are not applicable to humans or to drinking-water supplies.

Hardness is defined as the sum of the amounts of calcium and magnesium present in water. Water having a hardness of less than 50 mg/ℓ is considered soft. A hardness of 50 mg/ℓ to 150 mg/ℓ is not objectionable for most purposes, but the amount of soap needed to reduce the calcium and magnesium increases with the mineral content. Laundries and other industries using large quantities of soap generally find it cost effective to reduce hardness to about 50 mg/ℓ, but find that further softening of municipal water is not economical.

Numerical values for hardness have meaning only in a relative sense. An individual living in New England (U.S.A.)—where waters normally contain only small amounts of dissolved solids—might consider water with 100 mg/ℓ hardness to be very hard. In contrast, residents of U.S. states such as Iowa, Minnesota, or Nebraska might consider water having 100 mg/ℓ hardness to be soft.

Calcium and magnesium can contribute to incrustation that develops when hard water undergoes changes in temperature and pressure. This type of incrustation results from a change in the solution chemistry that facilitates the precipitation of carbonate or sulfate minerals. Changes in water pH, temperature, or pressure, or the addition of water-treatment reagents all could trigger such scale-formation issues. The problem of scale deposits in teakettles, for example, is familiar and generally causes little concern. Scale deposits in large evaporators (such as cooling towers) and in water wells can lead to complete operational failure.

Saturation Index

The primary chemical indication of whether minerals will precipitate is the saturation index. When a water is at equilibrium with a mineral, the concentrations of the ions raised to the power of each molar abundance in the mineral multiplied together are equal to the solubility constant (K_{sp}). The formation of fluorite (calcium fluoride) can be shown by the following equation.

$$Ca^{2+} + 2\ F^- \leftrightarrow CaF_2\ (solid) \tag{5.7}$$

At equilibrium and 25°C, the following equation then is satisfied.

$$K_{sp} = [Ca^+][F^-]^2 = 10^{-10.5} \tag{5.8}$$

Where [Ca^+] and [F^-] are the activities of calcium and fluoride in solution. Note that these are the activities of the ions, not their absolute concentrations. In dilute solutions, activities can be almost the same as concentrations, but in more concentrated waters with more complex chemistry, the activities are altered by the formation of complex ions in solution.

The saturation index is based on the solubility product.

$$SI = \log\left[\frac{IAP}{K_{sp}}\right] \tag{5.9}$$

Where the IAP (ion activity product) is the product of ions measured in solution raised to power of their numbers in the mineral formula (e.g., $[Ca^+][F^-]^2$ for fluorite). At equilibrium the saturation index equals 0. If the saturation index is greater than 0, the solution is supersaturated and minerals can precipitate. If the saturation index is less than 0, the water is undersaturated and minerals can dissolve. The assumption of the saturation index is that waters are at equilibrium. Kinetic factors can inhibit mineral dissolution or formation, but the saturation index does indicate the direction the system will go (towards precipitation or dilution).

In the fluorite example, either increasing the concentration of calcium (by evaporation or adding calcium-rich water) or increasing the F⁻ activity (through fluoridation) will result in the saturation index being greater than 0 causing fluorite to precipitate.

To accurately calculate the saturation index, it is important to have a water analysis that contains all the major ions in solution. The most straightforward method is to use geochemical models that perform the calculations.

Langelier Saturation Index

The saturation index is the most rigorous method for calculating the tendency of minerals to precipitate, and to accurately perform calculations it requires a complete water analysis. Carbonates are the primary scale-forming minerals in wells (*see* Chapter 13), and carbonate mineral precipitation is controlled by known processes. The Langelier Saturation Index (LSI) was developed to enable empiric prediction of the potential of scale formation, with less data—only temperature, pH, calcium hardness, and total dissolved solids (TDS) are required.

The LSI is calculated from the difference of the pH of the solution and a calculated Langelier pH (pH_s).

$$LSI = pH - pH_s \qquad (5.10)$$

The pH_s is calculated from a series of terms to account for the total TDS of a water (A), the temperature of the water (B), a calcium hardness term (C), and an alkalinity term (D).

$$pH_s = (9.3 + A + B) - (C) + (D) \qquad (5.11)$$

Where:

$A = (Log_{10} [TDS (mg/\ell] - 1) / 10;$

$B = -13.12 \times Log_{10} (T(°C) + 273) + 34.55;$

$C = Log_{10} [Ca+2 \text{ as } CaCO_3] - 0.4;$ and

$D = Log_{10} [\text{alkalinity as } CaCO_3].$

If the LSI is greater than 0, waters can precipitate scale, if it is more than 1 it is likely for waters to precipitate scale. Conversely, if the LSI is less than 0, waters likely will not scale precipitate carbonate scale.

Ryznar Stability Index

The Ryznar Stability Index is an empirical method for predicting scaling tendencies of water based on a study of operating results with water of various indices. The Ryznar Stability Index is defined by the following equation.

$2pH_s - pH = pH_s - \text{Langelier's Saturation pH}$ (5.12)

The Ryznar Stability Index often is used in combination with the Langelier Saturation Index to improve the accuracy in predicting the scaling or corrosive tendencies of a water. The following table illustrates the use of this index.

Table 5.2. Ryznar Stability Index and Tendency of Water

Ryznar Stability Index	Tendency of Water
4.0 to 5.0	Heavy scale
5.0 to 6.0	Light scale
6.0 to 7.0	Light scale or corrosion
7.0 to 7.5	Corrosion significant
7.5 to 9.0	Heavy corrosion
9.0 and greater	Corrosion is intolerable

Sulfate

Sulfate (SO_4^{-2}) in groundwater can be derived from several sources, including the evaporite minerals gypsum (hydrous calcium sulfate, $CaSO_4$-$2H_2O$) and anhydrite (calcium sulfate, $CaSO_4$), the infiltration of surface waters that have undergone significant evaporation, or the oxidation of pyrite (iron sulfide) or other sulfide minerals. Additionally, seawater has relatively high levels of sulfate (approximately 1,400 mg/ℓ), therefore sulfate could be elevated in near-coastal aquifers due to either seawater intrusion or the deposition and infiltration of salt spray.

Sulfate has few health effects but elevated levels can impart a bitter taste to drinking water. It also might act as a laxative for some people who are not accustomed to drinking water with elevated sulfate levels. The U.S. EPA therefore has developed a secondary drinking-water standard of 250 mg/ℓ for sulfate.

Sulfate also can react with concrete to degrade its quality over time. If high levels of sulfate are present, the appropriate concrete to be used in construction of wells or other water-management infrastructure must be selected carefully.

Phosphorus

Phosphorus (P) primarily is found in groundwater in the form of phosphate ions (PO_4^{3-}) although, as an essential nutrient to plant growth, it also is present in organic forms. It is derived from the weathering of minerals such as apatite, a phosphate-bearing mineral in igneous and some sedimentary rocks. Phosphorus also can be found in groundwater due to releases of sewage or fertilizer. Phosphorus generally is found in low concentration in groundwater (less than 1 mg/ℓ). Where phosphate is present at elevated levels, it adds additional alkalinity to the water.

Silica

Silicon (Si) is the second-most abundant element in the earth's crust (oxygen is the most abundant). Silicon in combination with oxygen is called silica (SiO_2). The common mineral quartz, in its many varieties, essentially is pure silicon dioxide. Silicon and oxygen combine readily with many other major elements such as potassium, magnesium, sodium, iron, calcium, and aluminum to create a broad range of rock-forming minerals.

Silica is not readily dissolved by water. Nevertheless, warm groundwater sometimes contains as much as 100 mg/ℓ of silica, and silica concentrations of 20 mg/ℓ are common. The origin of silica in groundwater is attributed to the chemical weathering of silicate minerals. Temperature, the rate of water movement through the rock, and the presence of natural acids such as carbonic acid affect weathering and the degree to which silica dissolves in a specific water.

Silica does not contribute to the hardness of water. It is, however, an important constituent of the incrusting material or scale formed by many groundwaters. As deposited, the scale commonly is calcium or magnesium silicate. Silicate scale is not easily dissolved by acids or other chemicals that are used for chemical treatment of wells. Therefore silica-rich water to be used in boilers must be treated in advance, using adsorption or ion-exchange techniques.

Redox-Sensitive Elements and Compounds

About 20% of the earth's atmosphere is composed of oxygen, which creates oxidizing conditions. Many chemical and biological processes consume oxygen, however, and oxygen has a limited solubility in water. Therefore, looking inward from the surface of the earth into the groundwater shows that oxygen concentrations rapidly decrease and the environment becomes more reducing. A familiar example of this is the difference between the water at the surface of a lake and the often smelly conditions associated with the sediment at the bottom of the lake. The anoxic environment of the sediments is characterized by the presence of different bacteria, and commonly has associated elevated levels of methane and hydrogen sulfide in the sediment pore water. The differences between these two environments is due to both biologically mediated and abiotic oxidation-reduction reactions, commonly referred to as redox reactions.

Changes in oxygen content have little chemical effect on some redox-independent elements—such as Na, Cl, and Ca—but can have major impacts on the chemistry of other elements. This different chemistry is particularly evident in the context of water wells, where water is moved rapidly from the subsurface reducing environment to oxygenated surface conditions. This change in environment can promote well corrosion, clogging, scale formation, and bacterial fouling of wells. Therefore, when dealing with the redox-sensitive constituents of dissolved oxygen (O_2), Eh (a voltage measurement, defined below), iron (Fe), manganese (Mn), sulfide (S^{2-}), methane (CH_4), and nitrogen compounds and their chemistries must be considered in relation to the relevant redox conditions.

Dissolved Oxygen

Humans and all other aerobic organisms require oxygen. In short, food is oxidized to produce energy. Because oxygen is readily consumed by oxidation processes, the deeper the groundwater, the more likely it is to not contain any oxygen. The oxygen concentration of groundwater at depths greater than 100 ft (30.5 m) to 150 ft (45.7 m) generally is less than 1 mg/ℓ.

The solubility of oxygen in near-freezing water (32°F or 0°C) is about 10 mg/ℓ. Solubility of oxygen in water decreases with higher temperatures and becomes almost 0 at its boiling point. Oxygen content can increase in groundwater due to elevated pressure. Water in a pneumatic tank or in a well where the air-lift pumping method is being used, for example, can contain more than 10 mg/ℓ of oxygen.

It is difficult to accurately measure dissolved oxygen (DO) in water produced from a well, because the sample becomes contaminated with oxygen the instant it comes in contact with the atmosphere. Further, if the pumping or bailing process causes the water level in the well to drop significantly, then air can be entrained in the water during sample collection, thus contaminating the sample. It therefore is important to sample dissolved oxygen from well water using a dissolved oxygen electrode in a flow-through cell, and measure the sample's dissolved oxygen before the sample encounters the atmosphere.

Elevated dissolved oxygen in groundwater can promote corrosion in wells. Pure water—highly demineralized water containing no dissolved gases (e.g., oxygen, carbon dioxide)—is not corrosive to metals. If dissolved oxygen is present, however, a corrosion potential exists because the dissolved oxygen can react with the reduced metals in the steel of the well. Water with dissolved oxygen corrodes metals more rapidly when the pH is low. Water that has some dissolved oxygen and a relatively high electrical conductance (caused by total dissolved solids), however, is corrosive even though the pH can be 8 or greater. Susceptible metals include iron, steel, galvanized iron, and brass. The rate of corrosion tends to increase directly with temperature, but the amount of oxygen in solution decreases with higher temperature.

Dissolved oxygen might cause water to attack galvanized iron and some types of brass as rapidly as it would attack black iron. The galvanized zinc is oxidized and washed away much more rapidly than if the water was free of oxygen. Dissolved oxygen also removes zinc from brass alloys, leaving the metal porous and weakened. Iron-oxide scale accumulates on the inner surface of iron pipes when iron dissolved into solution by acidic water combines with dissolved oxygen to form the insoluble oxide, and an oxide film then deposits on the corroded surfaces. The scale occupies a larger volume than did the original metal, and the pipe gradually fills with scale and its capacity is reduced. One study shows that, over a period of 20 to 30 years, water mains lose carrying capacity at the rate of 1% to 2% per year (Driscoll 1986).

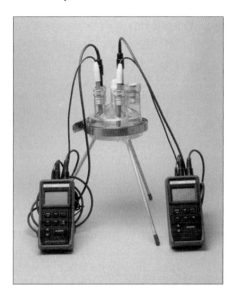

Figure 5.4. A flow-through cell measuring specific conductivity, pH, Eh, and dissolved oxygen.

Oxidation-Reduction Potential

Oxidation-reduction potential (ORP), or redox, is a measure of the electrical potential of the aquifer, and can be quantified using an electrode and reported as a voltage (known as an Eh). Oxidation-reduction potential also is a measure of the oxidation state of groundwater. A highly negative measurement is indicative of anoxic (reducing) conditions. Conversely, a large positive measurement generally means that the water is oxic. Reducing conditions can be highly corrosive. The description of the underlying theory behind this measurement, however, is beyond the scope of this chapter. It is a common measurement used in field characterization of waters, where an electrode's response is measured against a standard reference solution (such as Zobell's or a pH-buffered hydroquinone solution). Measured Eh values in groundwaters range from 0.82 volts to -0.042 volts, at a pH of 7.0 (Hem 1992), and the lower the measured Eh, the more reducing the system.

Unfortunately, kinetic and disequilibrium factors often add variability to electrode-measured Eh values—even the most careful measurements might produce erroneous values. Despite this variability, however, electrode-measured Eh values are useful in characterizing the redox state of a system when compared to other data about the system. Knowing the oxidation state of groundwater is useful in determining whether certain chemical species might be present.

As with dissolved oxygen measurements, ORP measurements must be taken using water samples that have not been in contact with air, in wells being pumped in a fashion that does not entrain air into water samples, such as through a flow-through cell. Information on ORP measurement is found in Hem (1992), and in Nordstrom and Wilde (2005).

Iron

Most water supplies contain some iron (Fe) because iron is abundant in rocks and is somewhat soluble under anoxic conditions. The iron content of water is important because small amounts seriously affect water's usefulness for some domestic and industrial purposes. In groundwater, concentrations of 1 mg/ℓ to 5 mg/ℓ are common. Standards created by the U.S. EPA state that the iron content of drinking water should not be greater than 0.3 mg/ℓ, because iron in water stains plumbing fixtures, stains clothes during laundering, incrusts well screens, and clogs pipes. Some industrial plant processes cannot tolerate more than 0.1 mg/ℓ of iron.

Iron is found dissolved in groundwater in one of two valence states, Fe^{2+} or Fe^{3+}. (Metallic iron in steel is termed "zero valent" and has no charge (Fe^0).) Ferrous iron (Fe^{2+}) is moderately soluble and can be found at levels of up to 200 mg/ℓ in groundwater with near-neutral pH. Ferrous iron reacts rapidly with oxygen or other oxidants (either abiotically or in a bacterially mediated process) to form Fe^{3+}, as shown, for example, in equation 5.13.

$$4Fe^{2+} + O_2 + 4H^+ \rightarrow 4Fe^{3+} + 2\,H_2O \qquad (5.13)$$

Ferric iron (Fe^{3+}) generally is insoluble in water and, unless the pH is low (less than 4), it precipitates rapidly to form a ferric hydroxide precipitate.

$$Fe^{3+} + 3H_2O \rightarrow Fe(OH)_3\,(solid) + 3H^+ \qquad (5.14)$$

When iron-containing groundwater is aerated, iron becomes insoluble and precipitates. The precipitates that are formed by this process often are very small and can foul water-collection, water-storage, and water-treatment systems. It often is difficult to settle out these precipitates due to their light, fluffy nature.

Iron-bearing waters also encourage the growth of iron bacteria, such as *Crenothrix, Gallionella,* and *Leptothrix.* These growths form so abundantly in water mains, recirculating systems, and wells, that they have a marked clogging effect. Their growth rate in wells can be so rapid that the water supply can be shut off almost completely only months after a well first is put into operation. Iron bacteria rapidly can change soluble Fe^{2+} into insoluble Fe^{3+} which is deposited in the sheaths of the organisms and in the voids of sand. The sheaths, developed as the bacteria multiply, create a gel-like slime that can seriously clog water-bearing formations and the openings in well screens. These large gelatinous masses also occasionally can break loose and further clog a system.

When the iron content of water is naturally high, treatment for removal is the ultimate solution. In cases where the iron and carbon dioxide content of groundwater are moderately low and there is no treatment, problems might be minimized by avoiding aeration. Iron that already is oxidized can be removed by using slow and rapid sand filters (Fair, Geyer & Okun 1958).

Although iron precipitates in wells can create problems, these same precipitates often are used in water-treatment systems to remove undesirable trace elements from water. The iron precipitates have a great affinity to sorb many ions from solution. Therefore oxidation and settling of high-iron waters also might reduce concentrations of other non-desirable elements in groundwater.

Iron in water extracted from a well might be either naturally present in the aquifer or be a by-product of corrosion of well materials. Water might dissolve iron upon contact with metal well casings, pump parts, screen, and piping. The more corrosive the water (low pH or high oxygen content), the more metal it can dissolve. Water standing in a well that has not been pumped recently can have higher iron content than the natural waters in the surrounding aquifer. The air in the well casing can react with the iron in the groundwater to form fine-grained iron hydroxides that can be disturbed with the onset of pumping. In sampling water, therefore, the pump should be operated long enough to ensure a non-turbid formation sample, and operated slowly enough to minimize the amount of turbulence in the well. When the water is completely clear, the sample should be collected as close to the pump discharge as possible and before the water has come into contact with air.

Manganese

Manganese (Mn^{+2}) resembles iron in its chemical behavior and occurrence in groundwater but it is less abundant than iron (Kemmer 1977). Manganese is found less commonly in water, and its concentration generally is much lower than iron—although, in deep wells, manganese can reach concentrations as high as 2 mg/ℓ to 3 mg/ℓ. Drainage or wastewater from mines and metallurgical operations commonly contain abundant manganese.

Manganese in water is as objectionable as the presence of iron, and it is relatively soluble in most waters. It occurs as soluble Mn^{2+} and reacts with carbonate in groundwater to form insoluble manganese hydroxide, and forms carbonates when it reacts with atmospheric oxygen. When it reacts with oxygen it becomes Mn^{3+} and forms black, insoluble oxide and hydroxide minerals such as manganite ($MnOOH$), and causes stains that are more difficult to remove than those caused by iron. To avoid such staining, secondary drinking-water regulations limit manganese concentrations to 0.05 mg/ℓ.

Manganese bicarbonate precipitates out of solution as a black, sooty deposit when carbon dioxide is liberated from the water near a well. Manganese bicarbonates virtually can cement a poorly designed well screen in the ground, and can clog well screens. Slime-forming bacteria (most of the same species as iron bacteria except for *Gallionella*) also can cause oxidation of manganese compounds and can form an insoluble residue.

Hydrogen Sulfide

Groundwater that contains dissolved hydrogen sulfide (H_2S) gas is easily recognized by its rotten-egg odor. As little as 0.5 mg/ℓ of hydrogen sulfide in cold water is noticeable, and the odor from 1 mg/ℓ definitely is offensive. Water containing small amounts of hydrogen sulfide forms a weak acid and usually is corrosive.

The primary source of H_2S in groundwater is production by sulfate-reducing bacteria (*see* Chapter 13). Conditions favorable for bacteria growth include absence of oxygen, fairly high sulfate content, and the presence of some organic compounds to provide energy for the bacteria. These bacteria gain energy from the oxidation of organic compounds and, in the process, take oxygen from the sulfate ions. Reduction of the sulfate ions produces hydrogen sulfide gas that easily can be absorbed by the water.

Nitrogen

Unlike most other elements in groundwater, nitrogen (N) compounds are not derived primarily from the minerals in rocks that make up the groundwater reservoir. Instead, nitrogen enters groundwater from biological or anthropogenic sources of nitrogen. Several nitrogen compounds are found in groundwater: nitrate (NO_3^-), nitrite (NO_2^-), and ammonia (NH_3). In water analyses these species are reported as either the complex ion or as equivalent molecular nitrogen (N); 1 mg/ℓ of nitrogen equals 4.5 mg/ℓ of nitrate.

Nitrogen enters the ground from several sources. Certain plants (such as alfalfa and other legumes) fix atmospheric nitrogen and transfer it to the soil where it then is used by plants. Some of the surplus nitrogen, however, is removed in solution by downward-percolating soil water. Other sources of soil nitrogen are decomposing plant debris, animal waste, and nitrate fertilizers. Nitrogen also can enter the ground from sewage discharges on land or from sewage lagoons. Additionally, many industrial-waste chemicals contain high concentrations of nitrogen. Natural nitrate concentrations in groundwater range from 0.1 mg/ℓ to 10 mg/ℓ (Davis & DeWiest 1966). Concentrations can reach 600 mg/ℓ or greater when enrichment from nitrate fertilizers or stockyard runoff occurs. Nitrogen also can be present in reducing groundwaters as ammonia. While ammonia itself generally is not toxic, in surface-water systems it can be oxidized to nitrate or nitrite, which both have greater toxicity.

High nitrate concentrations in well water are a cause for concern. They originate from either direct discharge of contaminated surface water into a well or via natural infiltration by contaminated surface water. Excessive nitrogen in well waters can indicate leakage from cesspools, stockyards, sewage lagoons, and from the overuse of agricultural chemicals in sandy soils. Unfortunately, localized contamination of groundwater from these sources is common in many agricultural areas. Moreover, a high nitrate content can be considered an indicator—and thus a warning—that an aquifer should be tested for harmful (pathogenic) bacteria which can accompany contamination from these sources. Nitrate contamination is particularly troublesome in karstic regions where water movement through solution openings is rapid and allows for little attenuation (dilution) of the containment.

The safe nitrate limit for domestic water is set at 45 mg/ℓ by the U.S. EPA, and this is equivalent to 10 mg/ℓ of elemental nitrogen (N). Nitrate in concentrations greater than 45 mg/ℓ is unacceptable in domestic water supplies.

Methane Gas

Methane gas (CH_4) is generated by methanogenic bacteria under very reducing conditions. These bacteria reduce organic compounds to produce CO_2 and CH_4. In general, methane is found in locations containing high levels of organic matter, such as bog sediments, landfills, petroleum-hydrocarbon contaminated groundwater, and certain types of coal deposits. Its presence is an indicator of highly reducing conditions.

Trace Elements

Trace elements generally are found at low levels that do not constitute a major portion of the total ions of the water in a well, but they often are important in governing the use and toxicity of waters. Some elements are toxic (either to humans or organisms in the environment) and therefore regulations mandate very low allowable levels (parts per billion or lower). Most trace metals are found in low concentrations in groundwater for two reasons: (1) they are not abundant elements in the earth's crust; and (2) they generally are insoluble, and therefore are not found in elevated concentrations in water except under extreme conditions of low or high pH.

Because of their low solubility, many of these elements often are found in soils and sediments at more than 1,000 times the typical concentration. As noted, it therefore is important to ensure that water samples collected for trace-element analysis have a low turbidity, because particulate composition can create an apparent elevation in metals composition.

Many trace elements have relatively simple chemistries in that there is only one chemical form that is present and relevant to environmental chemistry. Elements with straightforward chemistry and one redox state include lead (Pb), nickel (Ni), copper (Cu), zinc (Zn), cadmium (Cd), and silver (Ag). These elements tend to precipitate as sulfide minerals when hydrogen sulfide is present, and commonly sorb to hydrous iron oxide precipitates under more-oxidizing conditions. They therefore tend to have low mobility and rarely are found to move any great distance in groundwater.

Other trace elements, however, have more-complex chemistries. Such elements can be present in a number of redox states, can react with organic compounds, or have other behaviors that complicate the interpretation of their fate and transport in groundwater. These elements include arsenic (As), selenium (Se), antimony (Sb), chromium (Cr), and mercury (Hg).

Arsenic

Arsenic (As) is a trace element that recently has received a great deal of scrutiny due to its toxicity at low concentrations and its common occurrence in groundwater and drinking-water supplies. In the Bengal Delta, on the

India-Bangladesh border, it is estimated that approximately 40 million people are drinking water that has arsenic concentrations greater than 50 $\mu g/\ell$, and that this practice is causing widespread illness. This arsenic-rich groundwater is produced from more than 4 million wells in the region (Smedley 2003; Kinniburgh et al. 2003). This enrichment of arsenic is due to its tendency to be mobilized under reducing conditions.

Selenium

The chemistry of selenium (Se) is similar in some respects to that of sulfur, but selenium is a significantly less-common element. Selenium can have an adverse impact on livestock and wildlife, and the exposure route is through the consumption of vegetation that bioconcentrates selenium. Thermodynamic data show that, above a pH of 6.6 in aerated water, the stable form of selenium is the anion selenite, SeO_3^{-2} (Hem 1970). Under mildly reducing conditions, however, the equilibrium species is elemental selenium that has low solubility and thus is unavailable to plants. The presence of selenium in elevated concentrations could be natural or could be a product of human activity, such as agricultural runoff.

Antimony

Antimony (Sb) is a chemical element that is a metalloid. It resembles a metal in its appearance and physical properties, but does not chemically react as a metal does. The toxicity of antimony is highly dependant upon its chemical form and oxidation state, with +III compounds exerting greater toxicity than +V compounds. Antimony compounds show toxic properties similar to those of arsenic. Like arsenic, the mobility of antimony appears to be highly dependent on its oxidation state; however, conflicting data currently exists and more research is needed. In mineralized areas, antimony should be analyzed in water samples.

Chromium

The toxicity and mobility of chromium in groundwater is highly dependent upon its redox state. Chromium (VI) (often referred to as hexavalent chromium) is found as CrO_4^- which is highly mobile and toxic, but rarely is found in nature and almost always is a by-product of industrial processes. In contrast, Cr^{3+} generally is insoluble and non-toxic.

Mercury

Mercury (Hg) generally is immobile and found at low concentrations in groundwater. Bacteria and other organisms, however, can convert mercury from inorganic mercury to a methylated, organic mercury species. Methylated mercury is a potent neurotoxin and can bioaccumulate in ecological systems, resulting in serious environmental consequences, therefore water-quality standards for the discharge of waters to the surface-water environment are very stringent. Depending on the chemical species of mercury, measurement increments can be as small as parts per trillion. Such low regulatory limits mandate stringent sampling requirements to avoid cross-contaminating samples (Bloom & Crecelius 1983).

Organic Compounds

Organic compounds primarily are derived from industrial waste. In general, these compounds have low water solubility and can have toxic effects even at relatively low levels. Organic releases to water tend to make groundwater more reducing and degrade its quality through both the addition of toxic constituents into water and a reduction in the aesthetic qualities of the water.

Many organic compounds (including most petroleum products) are liquids that are lighter (less dense) than water. When present in groundwater, they therefore tend to float on top of the water table and form a discrete layer of material, often referred to as light non-aqueous phase liquid (LNAPL). This material can release contaminants into groundwater over long periods of time. Because this material floats on water, however, it can be addressed by a variety of methods such as air sparging, skimming, chemical oxidation, and simple excavation for shallow problems.

For petroleum-related plumes, the primary constituents of interest are benzene, toluene, ethylbenzene, and xylene compounds (BTEX). In some areas, methyl-tert butyl ether (MTBE) in gasoline also has been released into groundwater. The MTBE compound is unique among this group of compounds because it has a relatively high water solubility, high toxicity, and is not as easily attenuated in groundwater as compared to other organic compounds.

Some halogenated solvents such as trichloroethylene (TCE), tetrachloroethylene (PCE), and trichloroethane (TCA) are more dense than groundwater, and therefore can sink through the aquifer when released to the environment, and form dense non-aqueous phase liquids (DNAPLs). These DNAPLs create unique problems because they can sink to great depths in the aquifer, can have variable depths, and serve as potential long-term sources of contaminants.

The other general class of organic contaminants is insoluble anthropogeneic products such as pesticides, polyaromatic hydrocarbons (PAHs), and polychlorinated biphenyls (PCBs). These compounds are derived from chemical manufacturing and use, and from agricultural runoff. In general, the solubility of these compounds is low and they are present at low levels in groundwater. The regulatory limits for many of these compounds, however, also are low.

Some groundwater contains elevated amounts of natural organic matter. While this material generally is non-toxic on its own, it could create aesthetic problems. Furthermore, natural organic matter can react with disinfection agents (e.g., chlorine) in drinking water–treatment processes to form potentially hazardous disinfection by-products such as trihalomethanes, haloacetic acids, and n-nitroso-dimethylamine (NDMA).

GROUNDWATER SAMPLING METHODS AND HANDLING

Given the issues described in this chapter, it is clear that collecting a representative groundwater sample often is not a straightforward process. The key issues include:

   ◆   Ensuring that the sample collected is from the surrounding aquifer
       rather than from standing water in the well;
   ◆   Collecting a non-turbid sample to avoid artificially measuring
       elevated trace-element composition; and
   ◆   Collecting sensitive parameters (such as T and pH) at the wellhead
       before the sample interacts with the surface environment.

Groundwater samples traditionally were collected with pumps or bailers. The sampler purged 3 well volumes of water from the well and then collected the sample. In properly developed wells that easily produced water, this method provided generally reproducible results. In wells with poor production, high turbidity, or other issues, however, these techniques often resulted in poor-quality water samples.

Environmental sampling professionals have begun using low-flow techniques (Puls & Barcelona 1996). Groundwater is sampled with low-flow bladder pumps or peristaltic pumps (where groundwater is shallow). Field parameters such as pH, Eh, specific conductivity, and temperature are measured continuously at the wellhead in a flow-through cell system before the sample comes into contact with air. The well is purged only as long as needed to allow for these parameters to stabilize, and then water samples are taken. Low-flow techniques allow for collection of water samples without many of the previously described difficulties. Low-flow techniques can be significantly faster to implement, generate smaller amounts of purge water, and can reduce overall sampling costs. Many governmental agencies have issued guidance documents on groundwater sampling. Appendix 5.D (DVD) is a groundwater sampling manual that was issued by the Wisconsin Department of Natural Resources (U.S.A.).

Most chemical parameters of water samples are analyzed in an off-site analytical laboratory. An adequate sample volume must be placed in bottles appropriate for the analyte being measured, and many analytes require special preservation and handling. The samples almost always must be shipped under cool conditions. Some regulatory agencies require that samples be analyzed within a specific amount of time (the holding time) to prevent sample concentrations from changing due to chemical or physical effects. For example, bacterial activity can result in a change in the concentration of biologically active compounds.

Holding times for biological parameters often are very short (less than 2 days). Generally, metals samples are put into high-density polyethylene (HDPE) plastic bottles and preserved with nitric acid, and have a generous hold time (more than 1 month). Anion samples are put into HDPE plastic bottles with no preservative and have a limited hold time (less than 1 month). Samples for organic compounds are put into glass bottles and have a relatively short hold time (less than 2 weeks) before they must be extracted (the initial step of the analysis) in the laboratory. Organic samples for volatile organic constituents are put in special zero-head-space bottles with septum tops. In practice, the best source of information on the appropriate bottles, preservatives, and hold times is the analytical laboratory performing the analyses.

Groundwater samples must be handled meticulously to insure that accurate representative results are achieved. As discussed, particulates from well-construction materials and the surrounding aquifer might be present in a groundwater sample. If present, this material is analyzed with the rest of the sample, potentially creating an overestimation of the actual chemical concentrations in groundwater. A common practice for preventing this is to filter samples prior to performing any analyses. Sample filtration must be done during sample collection, before the sample interacts with the air. Interaction with the atmosphere and the degassing of CO_2 can cause carbonate, iron, and manganese hydroxide precipitates to form. Filtering a sample containing these post-collection precipitates results in an underestimation of the chemical concentrations present and of any trace constituents sorbed. Many regulatory agencies therefore take the conservative position that results obtained from filtered samples are unacceptable unless further work shows that sample filtration is more indicative of the actual water conditions.

Most workers use a 0.45 μm filter size to define the cutoff point between dissolved and precipitate phases in water. Many companies offer high-capacity in-line 0.45 μm filters or filter holders that allow sample filtration immediately upon sample recovery and prior to samples being exposed to the air. For some analyses (particularly iron and radio nuclides), the mobility in groundwater of colloidal mineral particles of less than 0.45 μm might be important. If this is the case, then ultrafiltration using smaller particle-sized filters might be necessary to accurately characterize transport in groundwater systems.

Field Measurements

Most chemical parameters are best measured in the field immediately upon sample collection. It is important to measure several chemical parameters in the field—when the sample is freshest—including parameters that are measured in a flow-though cell (temperature, dissolved oxygen, Eh, pH). It is important to conduct analyses of sulfide and the speciation of iron (Fe(II)) in the field if these constituents are being measured, because they can change rapidly with the exposure to oxygen.

It often is useful to measure analytes in the field to assess water quality or guide further sampling efforts using colorimetric kits (e.g., battery-powered models), specific ion electrodes, field titration kits, field test strips, or more-complex field instruments. When using these kits it is important to recognize the potential interferences and limitations of the analyses. The decision to use field analysis is guided by how likely it is that a constituent will change after sample collection, the convenience of gathering information immediately, the difficulty of analyzing the parameter in the field, the difficulty of shipping the sample to the laboratory, and the greater control of analyzing samples in a laboratory. Often, analyses conducted in the field are confirmed by an off-site analytical laboratory that has conducted analyses of part of the sample.

DATA ANALYSIS

After groundwater data are collected, they should be interpreted to evaluate the quality of the analyses and the nature of the groundwater being produced by a specific well. One important step is evaluating the charge balance as a check on groundwater analytical quality. If the positive ions are equal to the negative ions (plus or minus 20%), it suggests that a groundwater analyses likely is accurate.

Evaluating the charge balance of acidic waters (pH less than 4) requires caution, because the calculated charge balance could be up to 30% inaccurate due to the nature of the pH measurement and the presence of bound H^+ ions in solution. Charge balances for acidic waters should be checked after the water has been speciated in a geochemical model. If the charge balance of water is inaccurate, then the chemical analyses all must be evaluated carefully to insure that important ions are measured and there are no other issues with the quality of the analytical data.

The ions present in groundwater also can provide insight into baseline conditions for a well, and can be used to track changes in water chemistry. If a producing water well is near an ocean shore, for example, then it is important to track the proportion of sodium and chloride in the well water because it could be a sign of seawater intrusion. Changing the ionic character of a water-well chemistry might indicate the presence of different hydrochemical water types entering a well, which can aid in interpreting hydrologic source and water-rights issues.

As a better understanding of the interaction between groundwater and aquifer materials has evolved, the techniques for displaying water-quality data have become more complex and instructive. Several different graphical presentation methods are available for evaluating water analyses and are common components of many hydrologic and geochemical data evaluation software packages. Six common techniques used to portray chemical analyses of natural waters are discussed below.

Table

The simplest technique is to place the data into tables indicating the specific ions present and their relative or absolute concentration.

Bar Graph

Collins (1923) presented the first graphical method in which the concentration of individual ions, both cations and anions, were indicated by color or patterns on a bar graph (this method still is used by the USGS). The area extent of a particular color (ion) indicated the milliequivalents of that ion compared to the others present in the water sample (Figure 5.5). The water should be charge balanced and the columns should be of equal height. In reality, however, usually the amounts of cations and anions are not equivalent, and the heights of the respective bars differ.

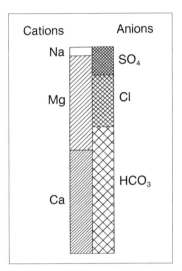

Figure 5.5. Analysis of a water sample presented using the graphical method developed by the USGS.

Pie Chart

Pie charts show both the individual ions present in a water sample and the total milliequivalents per liter (ℓ) (Figure 5.6). The scale for the radius of the circle—and thus the area—represents the total ionic concentration, whereas subdivisions of the circle represent the proportions for individual ions.

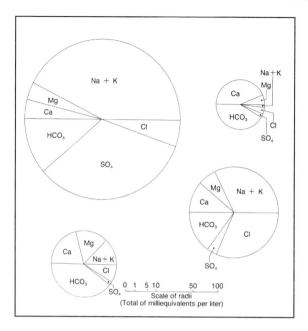

Figure 5.6. Four analyses represented by circular diagrams subdivided on the basis of percentage of total milliequivalents per ℓ (Hem 1992).

Trilinear Diagram

Trilinear diagrams are used widely to depict chemical data. This method, proposed independently by Piper (1944), shows the relative concentrations of the major cations (Ca^{+2}, Mg^{+2}, and K^+) and anions (CO_3^{-2}, HCO_3^{-2}, Cl^-, and SO_4^{-2}) (Figure 5.7). Cations are plotted on the left triangle and anions on the right triangle. To use this method, Na is combined with K, and CO is combined with HCO_3.

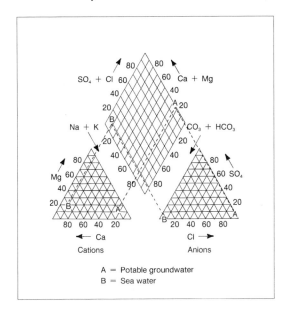

Figure 5.7. Chemical analyses of water represented as percentages of total equivalents per liter on the trilinear diagram developed by Piper (1944).

The numbers along the sides of the triangle indicate the percentage of the specific ion in the sample. Thus, the relative concentrations of 3 ions or ion groups can be shown in each triangular diagram. If only 1 cation is present, the concentration point falls on an apex of the triangle (100%). If only 2 of the 3 ions are present, the concentration point falls on one side of the triangle. If all 3 ions are present, then the point falls within the triangle.

The diamond-shaped diagram above the cation and anion triangles can be used to present both anion and cation groups as a percentage of the sample. This point is found by extending the cation point parallel with the magnesium leg into the upper diagram. Similarly, another extension is made from the point in the anion triangle parallel with the sulfate leg into the upper diamond. This point indicates the relative composition of the water sample in regard to the cation-anion pairs that correspond to the four sides of the diamond-shaped area. Ideally, the relative percentages of both cations and anions should be 50%. Many chemical analyses cannot be conducted with the required accuracy, however, and inevitably one of the ion groups will appear to be larger than the other on a percentage basis.

Pattern Analysis

Another graphical procedure was developed to depict water chemistry. Stiff (1951) devised a simple pattern analysis that can be used to trace similar formation waters over large areas. The scale is used as a guide to plot the ion concentrations for a specific water sample. When the points are connected, the resulting pattern provides a pictorial representation of the water sample. Two typical samples are plotted in Figure 5.8. Once a pattern for a certain ground-water has been established, it is a simple matter to compare patterns as the water moves toward different hydrogeologic environments.

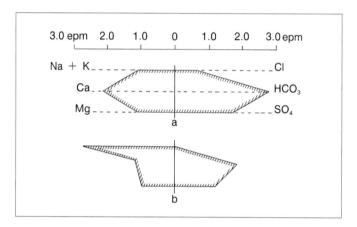

Figure 5.8. Pattern analysis developed by Stiff (1951) can be used to trace similar formation waters over large areas.

After the analytical data have been entered into a table or another database, it is common practice to compare the data to drinking-water criteria (Appendix 5.E (DVD)) for specific use.

Chemical Modeling

Chemical modeling is one method of analyzing complete sets of chemical data (all major anions and cations are measured). Models use the results of chemical analyses to calculate the distribution of chemical species in the water and calculate the minerals that might be in equilibrium with the water. The models convert chemical parameters that are based on activity (e.g., pH, Eh) or capacity (e.g., alkalinity, acidity) to actual chemical masses in solution. Models are useful tools for assessing whether water is near equilibrium with a scale-forming mineral; deciding whether a gas is expected to exsolve from a water, determining the effects of a water reacting with oxygen or water treatment compounds, and otherwise evaluating how water chemistry could change during groundwater production and distribution.

Examples of chemical models include PHREEQC, which was developed by the U.S. Geological Survey (Parkhust 1988), MINTEQA2, developed by the U.S. Environmental Protection Agency (Allison, Brown, and Novo-Gradac 1991), and the Geochemist's Workbench®, developed by the University of Illinois (Bethke 1998).

SUMMARY

Groundwater chemistry is a critical consideration in the water-well industry. An understanding of groundwater chemistry is useful in the planning, drilling, design, and maintenance of water wells. These topics are discussed in other chapters of the book. The major element chemistry often controls the possibility of well fouling and maintenance needs. Trace-element chemistry can affect the suitability of groundwater for its intended use. Therefore, it is essential to evaluate the groundwater chemistry within the well during development, testing, and operation of the well.

ACKNOWLEDGMENTS

Mr. David A. Bird, Senior Geochemist, Colorado Division of Reclamation, Mining and Safety, and John H. Schneiders, PhD, CPC, Principal Chemist, Water Systems Engineering Inc., provided valuable comments to this chapter; their efforts are greatly appreciated.

CHAPTER 6
Aquifer-Test Data Collection and Analysis

Robert J. Sterrett, PhD, RG
Engineering Management Support, Inc.

OVERVIEW

Various texts interchangeably use the terms "pumping tests" and "aquifer tests" to describe a variety of hydraulic tests and, in practice, groundwater professionals also generally use the terms interchangeably. For consistency, in this chapter the term "aquifer testing" covers all types of tests conducted to assess the performance of the well-aquifer system and the aquifer itself. Pumping tests—as defined in this chapter—are conducted to assess the capabilities of the pump, and such information can be obtained from pump manufacturers.

Aquifer testing includes tests used to estimate the performance characteristics of a well (screen and aquifer in the immediate vicinity of the well), and also to determine the hydraulic properties of the aquifer. For a well-performance test, flow rate and drawdown are recorded within the pumping well to enable calculation of the specific capacity (which is equal to flow divided by drawdown). These data provide a measure of the productive capacity of the completed well. Specific-capacity data collected periodically over the operational life of the well provide insight as to whether blockage of the screen or aquifer is occurring. Specific-capacity data also provide information needed for selection of pumping equipment.

The primary purpose of aquifer testing is to provide data from which aquifer properties, such as transmissivity and storage coefficient, can be calculated. Aquifer tests also are used to assess the impacts of boundaries on well production. The results of aquifer tests provide fundamental input data that can be used in calculations that predict drawdowns in an area (due to pumping).

Pumping a well lowers the water level in both the well and the surrounding geologic materials. The change (drop) in water level from the static or pre-pumping level is termed "drawdown." The greatest drawdown occurs at the pumping well and dissipates as distance from the well increases. Under ideal conditions, the distribution of drawdown around the pumping well assumes a conical shape—often referred to as a cone of depression. Figure 6.1 provides a diagram of the processes associated with pumping a well, and also shows the static water level (SWL) and pumping water level (PWL).

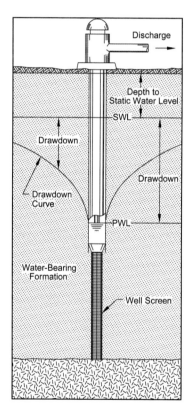

Figure 6.1. Processes associated with pumping a well.

A common type of test is the constant-rate aquifer test, which consists of pumping a well at a specific rate for a length of time and recording the drawdown in both the pumping well and in nearby observation wells at specific times. A constant-head variable-rate test commonly is run when a naturally flowing well in a confined aquifer is shut-in long enough for the head to recover, and then the well is opened and allowed to flow.

Step-drawdown tests commonly are conducted prior to undertaking a long-term constant-rate test, and are used to assess a long-term pumping rate and to estimate laminar versus non-laminar well losses within the aquifer and well. A step-drawdown test also is useful in assessing the appropriate pump for the well. These types of tests are described in more detail in this chapter.

Measurements required for aquifer tests include the:

- Static water levels just before the test is started;
- Time since the pump started;
- Pumping rate;
- Pumping levels or dynamic water levels at various intervals during the pumping period in both the pumping well and observation wells (if installed);
- Time of any change in discharge rate;
- Time the pump stopped; and
- Water levels during recovery.

Measurements of water levels after the pump was stopped (recovery) are extremely valuable for verifying the aquifer properties calculated during the pumping phase of the test. Most hydraulic testing of water-supply or irrigation wells is conducted in the pumping well without the use of an observation well or piezometer to measure drawdown occurring as a result of pumping. Single-well tests can lead to erroneous interpretations of aquifer characteristics due to head losses occurring within the pumping well. As is discussed in this chapter, the use of an observation well for measuring water levels is very advantageous.

This chapter emphasizes constant-rate, variable-rate, and step-drawdown tests because they are the most common types of aquifer tests conducted using large-capacity wells and aquifers having high transmissivity.

This chapter only provides an overview of concepts of delayed yield and boundaries. Single-well tests (or "slug tests") are not discussed because they primarily are used to test small-diameter wells installed in geologic materials that have relatively low to moderate hydraulic conductivities. Some excellent references on slug tests or aquifer testing include Butler (1998) and Kruseman and de Ridder (1992).

CONDUCTING AN AQUIFER TEST

Prior to performing an aquifer test, the following topics should be addressed.

- Objectives of testing
- Budget
- Site logistics (access, discharge of water)
- Availability and types of equipment for pumping and measurements of flow rates and water levels
- Conceptual hydrogeologic model of site based on available background information and geologic exploration

The objectives and associated budget should determine the type of test to be performed. If the objective of testing merely is to assess the type of pump to be installed in a well, for example, then a step-drawdown test that spans the probable range of pumping rates could suffice. Conversely, if the objective is to assess the long-term impacts to water levels in a fractured bedrock terrain due to mining, then aquifer tests might have to be conducted for several weeks and water levels measured in multiple observation wells or piezometers that are distributed around the proposed mine. The availability of flow and water-level measuring equipment, together with the number of field personnel available, dictate the frequency and accuracy of measurements.

It cannot be overemphasized that background hydrogeologic information should be used to synthesize a conceptual hydrogeologic model of the area. The conceptual model should include comprehensive information about recharge and discharge areas; locations and thicknesses of aquifers and aquitards; preliminary estimates of hydraulic properties based on background literature and experience; and the locations of boundaries (such as surface-water bodies and changes in stratigraphy). The conceptual hydrogeologic model influences the length of test (i.e., a test performed under confined conditions generally is shorter than one done in unconfined conditions). The locations and design of observation wells also are influenced by the conceptual model. For example, the impacts of boundaries on pumping can be assessed by placing observation wells between the pumping well and the suspected boundary.

Estimates of the magnitude and timing of drawdown can be made based upon information obtained from the drilling and development of the well through the use of air-lift tests. Air-lift tests are discussed in Appendix 6.A (DVD). Geologic data obtained from drilling and sampling in conjunction with estimates of hydraulic properties from air-lift tests can be used to refine the preliminary conceptual hydrogeologic model. Calculations can be made based upon the model and then used to design the aquifer test and to determine expected drawdown. Using the estimates of drawdown, the type of water-level measurement device and timing of measurements can be established. As noted, considerations of equipment used are based on budget constraints and data requirements for each project. Prior planning and experimentation with equipment by the field personnel during preliminary testing can eliminate potential errors that could occur during the actual aquifer test.

Aquifer tests do not produce accurate data unless the tests are conducted by systematically and accurately recording the duration, flow rates, and water levels over time. Certain preliminary steps should be taken to assure the reliability of test data recorded during the actual aquifer test. Before a constant-rate test is to be performed, for instance, a step-drawdown test can be conducted in the pumping well to assess the following.

- Maximum anticipated drawdown (for most aquifer tests, a major portion of the drawdown occurs in the first few hours of pumping)
- The volume of water produced at certain pumping rates and drawdown
- Flow measurement methods
- Whether the discharge from the pump is piped far enough away to avoid recharge
- Whether the observation wells are located so that they exhibit sufficient drawdown to produce usable data

The quality of drawdown data recorded during a constant-rate aquifer test depends on the following.

- Maintaining a constant flow rate during the test
- Accurately measuring the drawdown in the pumping well and in one or more properly placed observation wells, if installed
- Recording drawdown measurements at appropriate time intervals

- Determining how changes in barometric pressure and other loadings or stresses affect drawdown data
- Continuing the test for sufficient time for its objectives to be met

Maintaining Discharge

It is vital that uninterrupted drawdown data be obtained once the constant-rate aquifer test commences. As such, the pump and power unit should be capable of operating at a constant rate for the length of the test. In cases where the observation wells must be located at considerable distances from the pumped well, or where it is critical to assess boundary conditions, the pump must be capable of operating for at least several days or even weeks. Pump failure during the test can significantly complicate the analysis.

The pumping rate should be measured accurately and recorded periodically. Control of the pumping rate during testing requires both a device for accurately measuring the discharge of the pump and a convenient means for adjusting the rate to keep it as nearly constant as possible. A valve in the discharge line of the pump provides the best control. The discharge pipe and the valve should be sized so that the valve is from one-half to three-fourths open when pumping at the desired rate. Minor changes in motor or pump output cause less fluctuation of the discharge when the pump is working against the back pressure or head developed in a partially closed valve. Changing the pumping rate by controlling the pump speed (in the case of a turbine pump) generally is unsatisfactory, and using a valve—such as a gate valve (Figure 6.2)—is preferred for adjusting the flow rate.

Figure 6.2. Gate valve (Danfoss Flomatic Corp.).

Flow Measurement Methods

Calibrated Container

A simple and accurate method for determining the pumping rate is to observe the time required to fill a container of known volume or calibrated container. If it takes 30 sec to fill a 55-gal (0.2-m³) barrel, for example, then the pump is delivering 110 gpm (600 m³/day). This method is practical only for measuring relatively low pumping rates, however, and requires near-constant attention.

Flow Meter

A commercial water meter is more reliable for measuring large discharges. On a totalizing flow meter, the dials or digital readout on the meter show the total volume discharged through the meter up to the time of observation. Subtracting two readings taken at a set time apart gives the pumping rate. This meter perhaps is the easiest apparatus to use. Its only disadvantage is the unavoidable delay in obtaining values at the start of the test, when the pumping rate is being adjusted to the desired level.

Instantaneous readings can be made using instantaneous flow meters (Figure 6.3). To obtain accurate readings, an inline flow meter must be located in a straight section of pipe. It is recommended that a minimum of 10 pipe diameters upstream and 5 diameters downstream of the meter be straight and have no obstructions.

Figure 6.3. In-line flow meter (Kobold, Inc.).

Orifice Weir

A circular orifice weir is a device commonly used to measure the discharge rate from a high-capacity pump. Figure 6.4 shows a typical orifice weir.

The orifice is a round hole—with clean, square edges—in the center of a circular steel plate. The plate must be 1/16 in (1.6 mm) thick around the circumference of the hole; it is fastened against the outer end of a level discharge pipe so that the orifice is centered on the pipe. The end of the pipe must be cut squarely so that the plate is vertical. The bore of the pipe should be smooth and free of any obstruction that could cause abnormal turbulence. The discharge pipe must be straight and level for a distance of at least 6 ft (1.8 m) before the water reaches the orifice plate. The piezometer (manometer or transducer) tube must be placed exactly 24 in (610 mm) from the end of the pipe. The pipe wall is tapped midway between top and bottom with a ⅛-in (3.2-mm) or ¼-in (6.4-mm) hole that is exactly 24 in (0.6 m) away from the orifice plate.

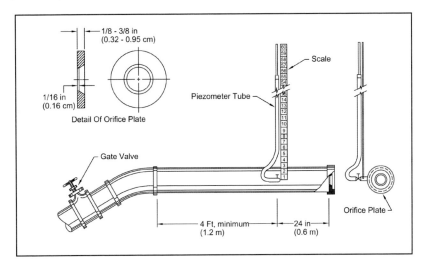

Figure 6.4. Diagram of a circular orifice weir.

A piezometer (manometer) tube or transducer is fitted to this small hole to measure the water head (pressure) in the discharge pipe. The piezometer consists of a clear plastic tube 4 ft (1.2 m) to 5 ft (1.5 m) long. One end is connected to pipe fittings that are tapped into the hole in the discharge pipe. The nipple, which is screwed into the tapped hole, must not protrude inside the pipe. A scale is fastened to a support so that the vertical distance from the center of the discharge pipe up to the water level in the piezometer tube can be measured. The water level in the piezometer tube indicates the pressure head in the approach pipe when water is being pumped through the orifice. A sensitive pressure transducer also can be used in place of the piezometer. For any given size of orifice discharge pipe, the rate of flow through the orifice varies with the pressure head as measured in this manner. Appendix 6.B (DVD) provides more information on orifice weirs.

Weirs and Flumes

Another method used to measure flow from a well is the placing of a constriction in a discharge channel originating at the well head. In most cases the flow from the pumping well can be channelized. A calibrated constriction placed in the channel changes the level of the water in or near the constriction. The rate of flow through or over the constriction is a function of the water level behind the constriction. The water-level measurement near the constriction is used to calculate the discharge, and it is important to know the dimensions of the constriction.

Two types of constricting structures—weirs and flumes—can be used to measure flows (Figure 6.5). Each type has its advantages and can provide discharge measurements to a sufficient accuracy. Selecting which type to use depends on criteria such as cost, sediment retention potential, ease of installation, site configuration, flow rates, and accuracy requirements.

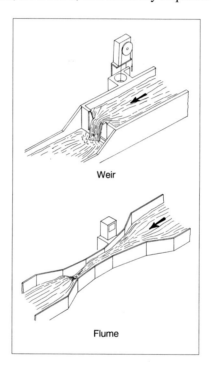

Figure 6.5. Weirs and flumes are the two primary types of constricting structures (Instrumentation Specialties Co. 1979).

A weir is a vertical baffle that restricts the total flow of water in an open or closed channel, and is a simple device to use to measure flow. The weir crest is either the bottom of the notch or the level to which water must rise before it can spill over the weir. Weir crests are constructed either including a notch (weir with end contractions) or without a notch (weir without end contractions). If the weir is contracted at the ends and bottom, then the ends of the weir should be no closer to the sides of the channel than two times the head of the weir. Additional discussion and diagrams of flow measurements using weirs are contained in Appendix 6.C (DVD).

A flume is a device used to measure flow in open channels. It is constructed so that a restriction in the channel causes the water to accelerate, producing a corresponding change (drop) in the water level (Figure 6.5). The head then can be related to discharge. Smaller flumes are ideal for measuring discharges from wells. All flumes used for measuring discharges from wells should have the following characteristics (Grant 1979).

- The flume should be located in a straight stretch of the channel (no bends immediately upstream).
- High approach velocities should be avoided; water should be free of turbulence and waves.
- Flow is restricted in a flume, therefore the channel upstream should have banks high enough to contain the flow.
- The channel approaching the flume should be regularly shaped so that flow is well distributed in the approach channel.
- Excessive submergence of the flume throat caused by backwater downstream should be avoided because it reduces the accuracy of discharge measurements.

Several types of flumes have been developed. A common flume for measuring flows is the Parshall flume (Parshall 1950). More information regarding the Parshall flume is contained in Appendix 6.D (DVD).

Another type of flume has come into use because its construction is simpler than that of the Parshall flume, and it can operate satisfactorily under both free-flow and submerged conditions. This type of flume is called a cutthroat flume because it does not have a throat with parallel walls (*see* Figure 6.6). The cutthroat flume has a flat floor, so it can be placed on a channel bed or inside a concrete-lined channel (Skogerboe et al. 1973). This type of flume is an ideal discharge-measuring device for use by water-well professionals because of its low cost and high accuracy. Appendix 6.E (DVD) contains additional information on cutthroat flumes that are practical for measuring well yields.

Flumes offer several advantages as compared to weirs. The most important of these is the self-cleaning capacity of flumes compared with that of sharp-edged weirs. Head losses through a flume also are much less than through a weir, therefore if the available head is limited then flumes are more desirable.

Flumes can function over a wide range of discharges and still require only a single upstream head measurement. Collapsible cutthroat flumes provide a rapid and reliable means to measure flow rates and also require minimal setup time. Figure 6.6 shows a collapsible cutthroat flume installed in a stream.

Figure 6.6. A collapsible cutthroat flume (Baski, Inc.).

MEASURING DRAWDOWN IN WELLS

Observation Wells and Piezometers

Drawdown measurements should be made in both the pumping well and appropriately placed observation wells or piezometers (if the budget allows for the installation of observation wells). The accuracy of water-level data taken from the pumping well usually is less reliable due to turbulence created by the pump and also because of well losses. The resulting water-level drawdowns usually are not representative of drawdown in the aquifer. As such, at least one observation well should be used when practicable. Observation wells should be of sufficient diameter to allow accurate and rapid measurement of water levels. Examples include 1-in (25-mm) to 2-in (50-mm) diameter wells. Many transducers can be placed in 1-in (25-mm) casings. Small-diameter wells are best, because the volume of water contained in a large-diameter observation well can cause a time lag in drawdown changes. Using large-diameter production wells as observation wells should be avoided, and the data collected from such wells should be evaluated with care.

The length of the screens recommended to be installed in observation wells depends on the objectives and budget of the aquifer test. Generally, fully penetrating observation wells are preferred. Partially penetrating observation wells produce measurements that are skewed by the effects of partial penetration and the vertical anisotropy of the aquifer (the ratio of vertical to horizontal hydraulic conductivity). In a stratified formation, the cone of depression becomes distorted by the spatially varying hydraulic conductivity. Distortion of the cone of depression and the effects of partial penetration extend from the pumped well a distance equal to 1 or 2 aquifer thicknesses divided by the square root of the vertical anisotropy ratio. Using fully penetrating observation wells and a pumped well that penetrates most or all of the aquifer thickness eliminates the complicating effects of partial penetration.

An exception to this is the situation where the aquifer test is intended to help quantify the vertical anisotropy ratio of the aquifer. In this case, a partially penetrating pumped well is required, along with partially penetrating observation wells—some completed in the upper portion of the aquifer and some completed in the lower portion (Schafer 1998). Schafer's 1998 paper is contained in Appendix 6.Q (DVD).

As a practical matter, in very thick aquifers fully penetrating wells might be too costly to install or could create vertical conduits that enable unwanted vertical groundwater or contaminant migration. In these cases it might be necessary to perform the investigation using partially penetrating wells. Under these circumstances, the analyst must both recognize the limits imposed on the well design and account for the effects of partial penetration.

For unconfined aquifers, observation wells and piezometers should be placed no farther than 100 ft (30.5 m) to 300 ft (91 m) from the pumped well. For thick confined aquifers that are stratified, observation wells should be placed within 300 ft (91 m) to 700 ft (214 m) of the pumped well. If the well is screened across the entire thickness of the aquifer then observation wells can be placed closer to the pumping well. Locating the wells too far away is not good practice because the aquifer test must be continued for a longer time to produce sufficient drawdowns at the most distant points, and small measurement errors could be a significant percentage of the total drawdown in the observation well. Boundary effects also might not be noticed. Boundary effects are discussed in subsequent sections of this chapter.

Screens for observation wells should be installed at about the same depth as the central portion of the screen in the production well. This is especially important if a short screen is used in the pumping well (resulting in partial penetration), because the distribution of drawdown is more distorted. If the recommended procedure is followed, then the reduction in pressure or water level at the observation well usually occurs within moments of this occurrence in the pumping well (assuming that the observation well is the proper distance from the pumped well). Observation wells occasionally are terminated in strata above or below that tapped by the pumped well, to assess the hydraulic inter-connection between the geologic units. Naturally, the response of these observation wells to pumping can be delayed significantly, depending on the degree of hydraulic connection. Additional discussion on this topic can be found in Kruseman and de Ridder (1992).

The appropriate number of observation wells to be used depends upon the amount of information desired and upon the funds available for the test program. The data obtained by measuring the drawdown at a single observation well enables calculation of the average hydraulic conductivity, transmissivity, and storage coefficient of the aquifer. If two or more observation wells are placed at different distances, then the test data can be analyzed using both the time-drawdown and the distance-drawdown relationships. If possible, observation wells should be located at logarithmically spaced distances from the pumping well. This spacing arrangement is based upon analytical procedures discussed in this chapter. Use of as many observation wells as conditions and budget allow is recommended because the hydraulic conductivity can vary in one or more directions away from the pumping well. Observation wells placed radially from the pumping well should indicate directional differences in drawdown that results from differences in transmissivity.

Before beginning the aquifer test, a complete program for depth-to-water measurements should be established. It is not necessary to make the measurements in all the wells simultaneously. Watches and transducers or dataloggers that are used for timing the measurements, however, should be synchronized so that the time of each reading can be referenced to the time that pumping is started.

Previously, water levels generally were measured using a chalked tape. Although this methodology is acceptable there are other, more efficient, techniques. One of the most common tools used to measure water levels is an electric water-level sounder (or meter) (Figure 6.7). The water-level meter uses a probe attached to a permanently marked polyethylene tape fitted on a reel, and is powered by a battery. The probe at the bottom of the tape incorporates an insulating gap between electrodes (Figure 6.8). When contact is made with water the circuit is completed, activating a buzzer or light. The water level is determined by taking a reading directly from the tape at the top of the well casing or borehole.

Figure 6.7. An electric sounder consists of an electrode, a two-wire cable, and a light which indicates a closed circuit when the electrode touches water (Solinst®).

An air line also can be used to measure water levels in a well. An air line works on the principle that the air pressure required to push all the water out of the submerged portion of the tube equals the water pressure of a water column of the same height. Additional discussion regarding air lines is contained in Appendix 6.F (DVD).

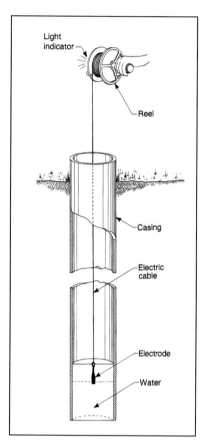

Figure 6.8. Diagram of a water-level measurement device.

Advances in microchip technology have enabled the development of pressure transducers combined with data loggers that can be placed in the pumping or observation wells. These automatic data loggers can be programmed to record water levels over a wide variety of time intervals. The water-level data then can be downloaded from the datalogger to a computer for analysis. Figure 6.9 shows a transducer, and additional information is contained in Appendix 6.G (DVD).

Figure 6.9. A transducer for measuring water levels (Solinst®).

Prior to conducting an aquifer test, background water-level trends should be recorded, at least for several days and preferably for a week. Background water-level trends then can be used to adjust the measured water levels taken during the test so that water-level changes induced by the pumping can be analyzed. It is also important to have a "background" well in which water levels can be measured before, during, and after the test to assess any trends in water levels that are unrelated to the aquifer test. The background well should be located in the same hydrostratigraphic unit as the pumping well, but be sufficiently distant so that water levels are not impacted by pumping. Water-level corrections are discussed in more detail elsewhere in this chapter.

During an aquifer test, water levels in the pumping well and observation wells must be measured multiple times and with an accuracy of at least 0.01 ft (0.3 cm). Water-level measurements should be made within brief intervals during the first few hours of the beginning of the test because water levels decline rapidly. As the test continues, the time intervals between measurements can be lengthened. Table 6.1 and Table 6.2 provide a recommended range of intervals for the pumped well and observation wells. The actual number of measurements that can be taken depends upon the number of available personnel and measuring devices. If electronic data loggers are used then readings can be made more frequently because data storage generally is not an issue. Water levels in wells that are equipped with transducers periodically should be checked manually (e.g., with a water-level meter) in case a failure of the transducer has occurred.

Table 6.1. Recommended Time Intervals for Measuring Drawdown in the Pumped Well During a Aquifer Test

Time Since Pumping Started (or Stopped)	Time Intervals Between Measurement
0–5 min	0.5–1 min
5–15 min	1 min
15–60 min	5 min
60–120 min	20 min
120 to termination of test	60 min

Table 6.2. Recommended Time Intervals for Measuring Drawdown in the Observation Wells During an Aquifer Test

Time Since Pumping Started (or Stopped)	Time Intervals Between Measurement
0–2 min	Approx. 10 sec
2–5 min	30 sec
5–15 min	1 min
15–50 min	5 min
50–100 min	10 min
100 min to 5 hr	30 min
5 hr to 48 hr	60 min
48 hr to 6 days	Every 8 hr
6 days to shutdown of pumping	Once per day
(adapted from Kruseman and de Ridder 1992)	

Where turbulence is a problem in a pumping well, a transducer provides a better means to measure drawdown, especially if the transducer is located in an access pipe that is inserted into the well.

Early test data are extremely important, and as much information as possible should be obtained in the first 10 min of pumping for every observation well that is located near the pumping well, because as the cone of depression moves outward from the well it might encounter heterogeneities which cause either acceleration or deceleration of drawdown with increasing time. Any unusual event (i.e., the pump stopping, the weather changing, a train passing) should be noted on a water-level measurement form, along with the time the event occurred. An example of an aquifer-test form is contained in Appendix 6.H (DVD).

Ideally, aquifer tests should be continued until equilibrium is reached; that is, until the cone of depression stabilizes. In practice, however, this rarely is possible. In confined aquifers, the cone of depression spreads rapidly because dewatering (drainage) does not take place, only a pressure reduction is occurring outward from the well. Thus, a maximum of 24 hr usually is sufficient to run an aquifer test in a confined aquifer. To obtain sufficient information for unconfined aquifers, 72 hr usually is required to dewater the materials within the cone of depression because of the slow downward percolation of water in many stratified deposits. This process is termed "delayed yield." The duration of the test can be reduced if equilibrium conditions are established before 24 hr (for a confined aquifer) or 72 hr (for an unconfined aquifer) have elapsed.

It is recommended that preliminary drawdown data be plotted during the course of the aquifer test. Anomalies in the data should become apparent and necessary adjustments can be made so that the subsequent data are more useful. Plotting the data also indicates when equilibrium conditions have been reached. In this case, the pumping portion of the test can be shortened without losing necessary data.

Barometric change, tidal change, and surface loadings can influence drawdown data, especially in a confined aquifer. A barometric pressure change of 1 in (25.4 mm) of mercury, for example, can result in a rise or fall of up to 1 ft (0.3 m) in the potentiometric surface for confined aquifers that have high barometric efficiency. Barometric efficiency refers to the difficulty with which changes in atmospheric pressure are delivered through the overburden and aquifer materials to the pore space in the aquifer. For example, 100% barometric efficiency means that changes in atmospheric pressure cause no change in the pore-water pressure, and a barometric efficiency of 0 means that any change in the barometric pressure causes an equivalent change in the pore-water pressure within the aquifer. Given this potential influence, it is recommended that the nature and time of any weather changes be recorded on the water-level measurement form. Unusually high or low oceanic tides also can affect drawdown data in wells located near coastlines. Appendix 6.I (DVD) provides more information regarding corrections to water-level data.

Recovery Data

Recovery water-level data should be collected to verify the accuracy of water levels collected during the extraction phase of the test. Often the recovery water-level data from a pumping well are more reliable than pumping data, because turbulence induced in the pumping well is eliminated. Recovery water-level measurements should be recorded with the same frequency as measurements taken during the pumping portion of the aquifer test.

AQUIFER-TEST ANALYSIS

Steady-State Flow in Confined and Unconfined Aquifers

Thiem Equation

In a confined aquifer, the rate of discharge by a pumping well under steady-state (time-invariant) conditions is predicted by the Thiem (1906) equation (equation 6.1). Note that the equations can be solved using consistent units for length (*L*), time (*t*), head (length (*L*)).

$$Q = \frac{2\pi T(h_2 - h_1)}{ln(r_2 / r_1)} = \frac{2\pi Kb(h_2 - h_1)}{ln(r_2 / r_1)} \tag{6.1}$$

Where:

Q = pumping rate (L^3/t);

T = transmissivity (L^2/t);

K = hydraulic conductivity (L/t);

b = aquifer thickness (L);

r_1, r_2 = radial distances of two observation wells from the discharging well (L); and

h_1, h_2 = steady-state water-level elevations (heads) in the two observation wells (L).

As noted on Figure 6.10, the heads are measured from the base of the aquifer in this example. The function *ln* in equation 6.1 is the natural logarithm. Figure 6.10 shows the various parameters listed in equation 6.1. Note that the pumping well can be used as an observation well; however, due to well losses, the drawdown probably is greater than that in the adjacent aquifer. Figure 6.10 shows drawdown in a well that is 100% efficient.

The Thiem equation is based on the following important assumptions.

- The aquifer is confined with infinite areal extent.
- The aquifer is homogeneous and isotropic, with uniform thickness.
- The potentiometric surface is horizontal prior to pumping.
- The pumped well is fully penetrating (screened or open over the full thickness of the aquifer) and discharges at a constant rate.
- Flow in the aquifer is horizontal and laminar.
- Drawdown in the aquifer has reached a steady state (is constant over time).

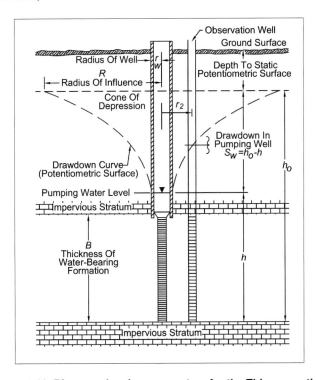

Figure 6.10. Diagram showing parameters for the Thiem equation.

The Thiem equation shows that the yield of a well is directly proportional to the transmissivity of an aquifer. An increase in T by a factor of 2 results in a doubling of the discharge rate.

The Thiem equation can be rewritten in terms of drawdown as follows.

$$Q = \frac{2\pi T(s_1 - s_2)}{\ln(r_2 / r_1)}$$ (6.2)

Where s_1 and s_2 are steady-state drawdowns (*L*) measured in two observation wells.

Drawdown is given by the following.

$$s = h_0 - h$$ (6.3)

Where:

$h_0 =$ head prior to pumping (*L*); and

$h \;=$ steady-state head (*L*).

If drawdown data only are available from an observation well and the pumped well, then the Thiem equation is expressed as shown in equation 6.4.

$$Q = \frac{2\pi T(s_w - s_2)}{\ln(r_2 / r_w)}$$ (6.4)

Where:

$s_w =$ drawdown in the pumped well (*L*); and

$r_w =$ radius of the pumped well (*L*).

Equation 6.4 assumes that the pumped well is 100% efficient; therefore well losses might limit the use of this equation.

In an unconfined aquifer, a modified version of the Thiem equation can be used by assuming Dupuit (1863) conditions.

$$Q = \frac{2\pi T(s'_1 - s'_2)}{\ln(r_2 / r_1)}$$ (6.5)

The Dupuit (or Dupuit-Forchheimer) theory assumes that groundwater flow is horizontal with no vertical flow resistance, and that the flow velocity is proportional to the slope of the water table. The theory further assumes that the slope of the water table is very small and therefore drawdown due to pumping also is very small relative to aquifer thickness.

Rewritten in terms of drawdown in an unconfined aquifer, equation 6.5 is rendered as shown below.

$$Q = \frac{2\pi T(s_1' - s_2')}{\ln(r_2 / r_1)} \tag{6.6}$$

Where the corrected drawdown is given by the following.

$$s' = s - s^2 / 2b \tag{6.7}$$

The foregoing equations can be used to compute the discharge rate of a well when the hydraulic conductivity (K) and thickness (b) of an aquifer are known in conjunction with steady-state water levels in two observation wells. Alternatively, by pumping a well at a constant discharge rate (Q), K of a confined aquifer can be determined by rearranging equation 6.1.

$$K = \frac{Q \ln(r_2 / r_1)}{2\pi b(h_2 - h_1)} \tag{6.8}$$

Rearranging equation 6.2 enables the determination of K from drawdown measurements.

$$K = \frac{Q \ln(r_2 / r_1)}{2\pi b(s_1 - s_2)} \tag{6.9}$$

Similarly, rearranging equation 6.5 enables the determination of K in an unconfined aquifer as follows.

$$K = \frac{Q \ln(r_2 / r_1)}{\pi (h_2^2 - h_1^2)} \tag{6.10}$$

The steady-state assumption appears to be a severe restriction on the use of the Thiem equation; however Butler (1988) has shown that the Thiem equation can be applicable to late-time data from an aquifer test even when heads in individual observation wells are declining with time. After a sufficient period of pumping has elapsed, the shape of a pumping cone of depression reaches a pseudo-steady state; consequently, the Thiem equation still can be used to determine the hydraulic conductivity of an aquifer from water levels measured in observation wells.

The example below, expressed in U.S. customary units, demonstrates how equation 6.9 can be used. The example is based on data for a confined aquifer 150-ft thick, pumped at a constant rate of 200 gpm (38,500 ft^3/day) for a sufficiently long period such that drawdown is not changing appreciably with time. The drawdown in the pumped well ($r = 0.5$ ft) is 25 ft; in an observation well located 200 ft away, the drawdown is 2.5 ft. Equation 6.9 can be used to compute the hydraulic conductivity of the aquifer as shown below.

$$K = \frac{Q\ln(r_2/r_1)}{2\pi b(s_1 - s_2)} = \frac{(38,500)\ln(200/0.5)}{2\pi (150)(25 - 2.5)} = 10.9 \text{ ft/day}$$

In the United States, values of hydraulic conductivity are expressed as feet per day (ft/day) or gallons per day per foot squared (gpd/ft^2). To convert ft^2/day to gpd/ft, multiply the value in ft^2/day by 7.48 gal/ft^3. Likewise, transmissivity can be expressed as ft^2/day or gpd/ft. In this chapter transmissivity is expressed using both units.

Transient Flow in Confined Aquifers

Theis Method

Applying principles from the study of heat conduction, Theis (1935) was the first to derive equations that account for unsteady (transient) drawdown around a pumping well. The introduction of the Theis equation was a major advance in the study of well hydraulics. Countless studies have relied on this method for the evaluation of groundwater resources. The original work by Theis also spawned subsequent research into more-complex well configurations and aquifer geometries. An excellent reference that discusses these more-complex situations is Kruseman and De Ridder (1992).

The following assumptions apply to the Theis equation.

- The aquifer is confined with infinite areal extent and no vertical leakage or recharge.
- The aquifer is homogeneous and isotropic with uniform thickness.
- The potentiometric surface prior to pumping is horizontal.
- The pumped well has an insignificantly small radius, fully penetrates the aquifer (screened or open over the full thickness of the aquifer), and discharges at a constant rate.
- Flow in the aquifer is horizontal and laminar.
- Drawdown changes with time.

The Theis equation for flow to a well in a confined aquifer is as follows.

$$s = \frac{Q}{4\pi T} \int_{u}^{\infty} \frac{e^{-x}}{x} dx \qquad\qquad (6.11)$$

Where:

$u = r^2 S / 4Tt$;

x = a dummy variable of integration;

Q = pumping rate (L^3/t);

T = transmissivity (L^2/t);

S = storativity (- (dimensionless));

s = drawdown at observation well (L);

r = radial distance between pumping and observation wells (L); and

t = time.

Note that any set of consistent units can be used with equation 6.11. The integral in equation 6.11 commonly is known as the Theis well function, and is designated by $W(u)$. The following infinite series can be used to compute $W(u)$.

$$W(u) = \int_{u}^{\infty} \frac{e^{-x}}{x} dx = -0.5772 - \ln u + u - \frac{u^2}{2 \cdot 2!} + \frac{u^3}{3 \cdot 3!} - \frac{u^4}{4 \cdot 4!} + \ldots \qquad (6.12)$$

Therefore equation 6.11 can be written in the following compact form.

$$s = \frac{Q}{4\pi T} W(u) \qquad\qquad (6.13)$$

An extensive table of values for the Theis well function for selected values of u is provided in Appendix 6.J. (DVD). It is recommended that water-well professionals have a copy of this table available for use in the field.

When the aquifer coefficients T and S are known, the Theis equation can be used to compute drawdown in a confined aquifer for a given Q, r, and t.

Example

A confined aquifer has a transmissivity of 50,000 ft^2/day (or 374,000 gpd/ft) (in U.S. customary units) and storativity of $5 \cdot 10^{-4}$. A pumping well that fully penetrates the aquifer discharges at a constant rate of 100 gpm (545 m^3/day). To compute the theoretical drawdown in an observation well located 100 ft

(33 m) from the pumped well after 1 day of steady pumping, first compute the value of u as follows.

$$u = \frac{r^2 S}{4Tt} = \frac{(100)^2(0.0005)}{4(50,000)(1)} = 2.5x10^{-5}$$

The table for the Theis well function provided in Appendix 6.J (DVD), shows that, for this value of u, the corresponding value of $W(u)$ is 10.0194. Before computing drawdown using equation 6.13, the pumping rate first must be converted to consistent units. In this case, consistent units are feet and days.

$$(100 \text{ gpm})(1440 \text{ min/day})(ft^3/7.481 \text{ gal}) \approx 19,250 \text{ ft}^3/\text{day}$$

The drawdown in the observation well then can be computed as follows.

$$s = \frac{Q}{4\pi T}W(u) = \frac{(19,250)}{4\pi(50,000)}(10.0194) = 0.31 \text{ ft}$$

Thus, for the given aquifer properties, drawdown in the observation well is predicted to be 0.31 ft after one day of pumping.

When the aquifer coefficients, T and S, are known, equation 6.13 can be used to solve for drawdown directly. When the aquifer properties are not known it is possible to determine them by conducting an aquifer test. To estimate unknown T and S values from measured values of s and Q, the Theis equation can be used to find a solution to what is known as the "inverse problem." Theis devised a graphical method based on type-curve matching to determine T and S from field data. More recently, computer software based on optimization techniques (sometimes referred to as automatic curve matching) can be employed to estimate T and S. Programs such as AQTESOLV™ (software created by HydroSOLVE, Inc. © 2006) combine traditional graphical curve matching with automatic curve matching to estimate aquifer properties from aquifer-test data.

To apply the graphical method of determining T and S devised by Theis, perform the following steps using drawdown data from an aquifer test measured in an observation well located 400 ft (121.9 m) from the pumped well (Table 6.3). The pumped well discharged at a constant rate of 500 gpm (2,725 m³/day).

Table 6.3. Drawdown Measurements in an Observation Well 400 ft (121.9 m) from a Pumped Well

Time Since Pump Started	Drawdown (s)		Time Since Pump Started	Drawdown (s)	
min	ft	m	min	ft	m
1	0.16	0.05	24	1.58	0.48
1.5	0.27	0.08	30	1.70	0.52
2	0.38	0.12	40	1.88	0.57
2.5	0.46	0.14	50	2.00	0.61
3	0.53	0.16	60	2.11	0.64
4	0.67	0.20	80	2.24	0.68
5	0.77	0.23	100	2.38	0.73
6	0.87	0.27	120	2.49	0.76
8	0.99	0.30	150	2.62	0.80
10	1.12	0.34	180	2.72	0.83
12	1.21	0.37	210	2.81	0.86
14	1.30	0.40	240	2.88	0.88
18	1.43	0.44			

A "type curve" with values of $W(u)$ plotted as a function of $1/u$ on double logarithmic (log-log) graph paper (Figure 6.11) is used in this analysis.

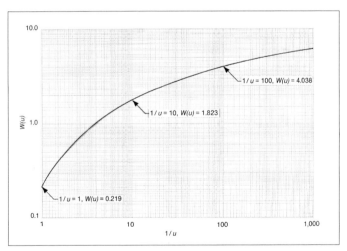

Figure 6.11. Type curve for graphic solution of Theis nonequilibrium equation shows values of $W(u)$ well function of u, corresponding to values of $1/u$. Curve is plotted on logarithmic graph.

Using log-log graph paper of the same scale as the type curve, prepare a plot of drawdown measured in an observation well as a function of elapsed time since the start of pumping (Figure 6.12).

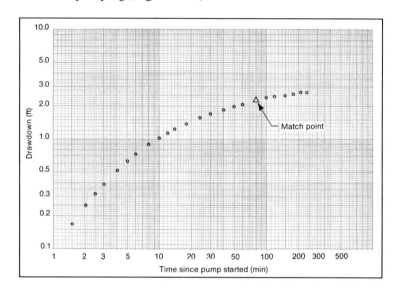

Figure 6.12. Plot of data provided in Table 6.3, on logarithmic graph.

With the graph of the data placed over the type curve, adjust the position of the data to match the type curve while simultaneously ensuring that the axes of both plots remain parallel (Figure 6.13). After achieving a satisfactory match between the data and the type curve, select an arbitrary match point where the two plots overlap (Figure 6.13). The match point can be any convenient point on the graph (that is, where u equals 100 or s equals a whole number). Often, the point is selected in the center of the area of best overlap, as shown in Figure 6.13.

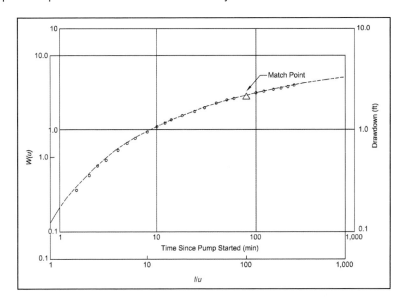

Figure 6.13. Diagram of plotted point representing aquifer-test data superimposed on the type curve. Match point chosen for 1/u = 100.

The match point values (the asterisk (*) is the value at the match point) from the field data plot are $t^* = 83$ min and $s^* = 2.3$ ft. On the type curve plot the corresponding match point values are $W(u)^* = 4.038$ and $1/u^* = 100$ (Figure 6.13). Use the match point values (t^*, s^*, $W(u)^*$, and $1/u^*$) to solve for T and S. The flow rate, Q, is 500 gpm or 96,250 ft³/day.

$$S = \frac{4Tt^* u^*}{r^2} = \frac{4(13,450)(0.0576)(0.01)}{(400)^2} = 1.94 \cdot 10^{-4} \, \text{lay}$$

Note that these equations for determining T and S assume consistent units for all values.

It is evident from equation 6.13 that s is directly proportional to Q for constant t, r, T, and S. Thus, when s is known for a given Q, drawdown at any Q can be calculated. If Q is doubled, for example, then drawdown also is doubled.

Cooper-Jacob Method

Cooper and Jacob (1946) noted that when the value of u in the Theis well function is small, equation 6.12 can be approximated as follows.

$$W(u) \approx -0.5772 - \log u \tag{6.14}$$

Using this approximation for $W(u)$, equation 6.11 can be reformulated as follows.

$$s = \frac{2.303Q}{4\pi T} \log \frac{2.25Tt}{r^2 S} \tag{6.15}$$

The symbols represent the same quantities as given in equation 6.11. Note that the log function in the above equation is the common or decimal logarithm.

Equation 6.15 becomes valid when time (t) is sufficiently large and distance to the observation well (or radius of pumping well) (r) is sufficiently small. Different criteria have been proposed for what constitutes a sufficiently small value of u. According to Kruseman and De Ridder (1992), the error resulting from equation 6.14 is less than 2% when values of u are less than 0.05.

From equation 6.15, it is apparent that drawdown varies linearly as a function of log t or log t/r^2 (Figure 6.14). Therefore a plot of s versus t, or s versus t/r^2, on semilogarithmic (semilog) graph paper forms a straight line when the value of u is small. In most instances, it far easier to match a straight line to field data than to match a type curve; consequently, fitting a straight line with the Cooper-Jacob method generally is preferable to matching the Theis-type curve.

To use the Cooper-Jacob method, first use semilog graph paper to plot values of time horizontally on the logarithmic axis and values of drawdown vertically on the linear (arithmetic) axis; then identify late-time data, forming a straight line on the plot, and draw a line over it.

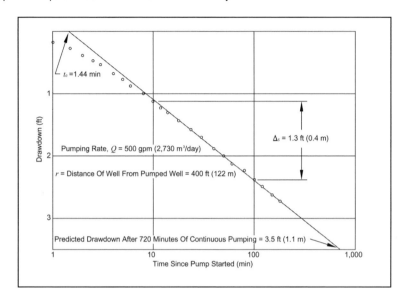

Figure 6.14. Plot of data from Table 6.3 on semilogarithmic graph.

Except for the data for the first 10 min of the test, most of the data fall on a straight line. The transmissivity of the aquifer is determined using the following equation.

$$T = \frac{2.303Q}{4\pi\,\Delta s}$$

(6.16)

Where:

T = transmissivity (L^2/t);

Q = pumping rate (L^3/t); and

Δs = the change in drawdown given by the straight line over one log-cycle time (L).

In the example, Δs is 1.3 ft between 10 min and 100 min. Given a pumping rate of 500 gpm (96,244 ft³/day), transmissivity is computed as follows.

$$T = \frac{2.303(96,244)}{4\pi(1.3)} = 13,570\,ft^2\,/\,day$$

The result compares favorably with the earlier estimate of T from the Theis type-curve analysis.

Compute the storativity of the aquifer using the following formula.

$$S = \frac{2.25Tt_0}{r^2}$$

(6.17)

Where:

T = transmissivity (L^2/t);

t_0 = the intercept of the straight line on the x-axis (time); and

r = radial distance from pumped well to observation well (L).

In the example, t_0 is 1.44 min or 0.001 day. Given $r = 400$ ft, the storativity is computed as follows.

$$S = \frac{2.25(13,570)(0.001)}{(400)^2} = 1.91 \cdot 10^{-4}$$

The above estimate of S agrees with the Theis curve matching result.

The Cooper-Jacob equation shows that s is directly proportional to Q assuming constant values of t, r, T, and S. Once s is known for a given Q, the calculation to predict drawdowns for different pumping rates is straightforward.

The Cooper-Jacob equation also can be used to make quick predictions of drawdown in an aquifer, given estimates of T and S. To do so, first extend the straight line on a semilog plot to extrapolate drawdowns beyond the time period of a aquifer test (Figure 6.14). Next, use equation 6.15 to compute s for any value of t/r^2 given values of T, S, and Q. Using the previous example, the drawdown at 5 days is predicted as indicated below.

$$s = \frac{2.303(96,244)}{4\pi(13,570)} \log \frac{2.25(13,570)(5)}{(400)^2(1.91 \cdot 10^{-4})} = 4.81 \text{ ft}$$

Predictions of this sort assume no recharge to—or discharge from—the aquifer (e.g., precipitation, boundaries, wells, or vertical leakage).

Distance-Drawdown Analysis

The Cooper-Jacob (1946) relationship shows that drawdown (s) varies with the log t/r^2 or with the log of distance. Using this relationship, a semilog distance-drawdown graph can be constructed. Simultaneous drawdown measurements in at least 3 observation wells, each at a different distance from the pumped well, are needed to construct a distance-drawdown graph (Figure 6.15). If drawdowns in the same 3 wells are plotted on a semilog diagram, in theory the drawdown curve becomes a straight line, as shown in Figure 6.16. Points representing drawdown in other observation wells farther away from the pumped well fall a little below the straight line in Figure 6.16, because at some distance from the pumped well u is greater than 0.05. If u is greater than 0.05, then the straight-line relationship of s to log r no longer holds.

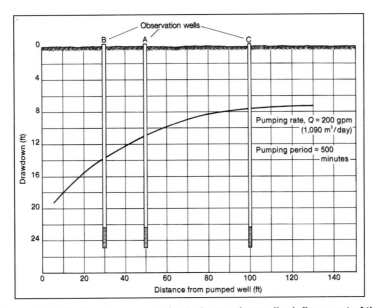

Figure 6.15. Plotting drawdowns for 3 observation wells defines part of the cone of depression.

The semilog plot of the cone of depression (distance-drawdown diagram) simplifies application of the distance-drawdown relationship. The straight line can be extended to the left, to the right, or to intermediate points between the observation wells to determine the effect of pumping at any distance from the pumped well. As noted, however, the *u* value must remain less than 0.05. At sufficiently great distances from the pumped well, *u* is greater than 0.05, and the extrapolated drawdown values are invalid when using the semilog approach. For a more general extrapolation, it is necessary to plot drawdown versus the reciprocal of the distance squared on a log-log graph and perform Theis curve matching. Drawdown at any distance from the pumped well then can be extrapolated along the fitted Theis type curve.

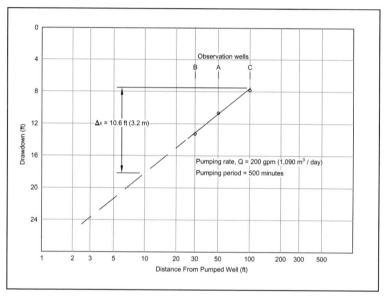

Figure 6.16. Trace of the cone of depression plotted on semilogarithmic graph paper becomes a straight line. Drawdown in each observation well was measured 500 minutes after start of the aquifer test.

Transmissivity

An arrangement of equation 6.16 enables calculation of transmissivity from the distance-drawdown diagram. The slope of the straight line is used in a manner similar to the procedure for use of the time-drawdown diagram. The equation for this method is expressed in U.S. customary units in equation 6.18, and in SI units in equation 6.19. Note that in U.S. customary units transmissivity can be reported in ft²/day or in gallons per day per foot (gpd/ft).

$$T = \frac{528Q}{\Delta s} \tag{6.18}$$

Where:

T = transmissivity (gpd/ft);

Q = pumping rate (gpm); and

Δs = slope of distance-drawdown graph expressed as the change in drawdown in feet, between any two values of distance on the log scale with a ratio of 10.

In SI units the equation is as follows.

$$T = \frac{0.366Q}{\Delta s} \tag{6.19}$$

Where:

T = transmissivity (m²/day);

Q = pumping rate (m³/day); and

s = slope of distance drawdown graph expressed as the change in drawdown in meters, between any two values of distance on the log scale with a ratio of 10.

For the example shown in Figure 6.16 the results are as follows.

$$T = \frac{528 \cdot 200}{10.6} = 9,960 \, gpd \, / \, ft \qquad T = \frac{0.366 \cdot 1090}{3.2} = 125 m^2 \, / \, d$$

Storage Coefficient

The storage coefficient can be obtained from the distance-drawdown diagram by using the following equations. In U.S. customary units the equation is rendered as follows.

$$S = \frac{0.3Tt}{r_o^2} \tag{6.20}$$

Where:

  S = coefficient of storage;

  T = transmissivity (gpd/ft);

  t = time elapsed since pumping started (days); and

  r_0 = intercept of extended straight line at zero drawdown (ft).

In SI units, the equation is expressed as follows.

$$S = \frac{2.25Tt}{r_o^2}$$

(6.21)

Where:

  S = coefficient of storage;

  T = transmissivity (m²/day);

  t = time elapsed since pumping started (days); and

  r_0 = intercept of extended straight line at zero drawdown (m).

From Figure 6.16, the value of r_0 is 500 ft (152 m), T is 9,960 gpd/ft (124 m²/day), and t is 500 min (0.347 day). Results are shown below, in both U.S. customary and SI units.

$$S = \frac{0.3 \cdot 9,960 \cdot 0.347}{(500)^2} = 4.1 \cdot 10^{-3}$$
U.S. customary units

$$S = \frac{2.25 \cdot 124 \cdot 0.347}{(152)^2} = 4.2 \cdot 10^{-3}$$
SI units

Thus the aquifer storage coefficients can be calculated using data from the following two relationships obtained via an aquifer test.

- Rate of lowering of the water level at any place within the cone of depression on the time-drawdown diagram
- Shape and position of the cone of depression at any given time on the distance-drawdown diagram

These calculations are independent of each other, so the result from one can be used to check the result of the other.

HYDROGEOLOGIC BOUNDARIES AND IMAGES

The discussion of the Theis equation and its Jacob modification is based upon the assumptions that the aquifer is uniform in thickness, isotropic, homogeneous, and of infinite areal extent, and that no recharge occurs. A basic understanding of geology indicates that these assumptions seldom are applicable in the field; however it is up to the analyst to determine when the assumptions are valid in a particular case. This section presents basic understandings of boundaries and image theory. Bear (1979) and Kresic (1997) provide a more in-depth discussion on this topic.

Recharge

The assumption that an aquifer receives no recharge during the pumping period is one of the fundamental conditions upon which the nonequilibrium formulas are based. Therefore, all water discharged from a well is assumed to be taken from storage within the aquifer. This situation must occur because, as pumping continues, drawdown increases and the cone of depression expands. This fundamental concept makes it possible to calculate the transmissivity from the time-drawdown data, employing the Cooper-Jacob modification of the Theis equation. Assuming no recharge during pumping also permits extension of the time-drawdown curve at its initial slope to predict drawdowns at future times. The time-drawdown curves presented in this section represent well performance during periods of no recharge. If an aquifer test is performed while recharge reaches the aquifer, the time-drawdown graph from the aquifer test reflects the recharge.

Figure 6.17 shows a time-drawdown graph for a pumped well operating under conditions of no recharge. The well was pumped at a constant rate of 350 gpm (1,910 m³/day) and the drawdown measurements were obtained at various intervals during 360 min of pumping. The points plotted on semilogarithmic paper define a straight line with a slope, or Δs value, of 9.3 ft (2.8 m) per log cycle of time. As shown previously, the future drawdown in this well for any period of continuous pumping at 350 gpm can be estimated by extending the straight line. The drawdown corresponding to 5,000 min of continuous pumping is 73.3 ft (22.3 m) in this case.

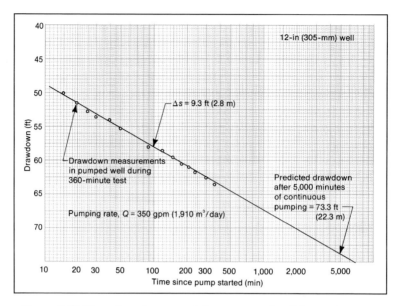

Figure 6.17. Time-drawdown graph for a pumped well (no recharge to aquifer) can be extended to predict drawdown for a period of continuous pumping longer than the test itself.

This method enables easy determination of the anticipated pumping level and the pump setting required to provide adequate submergence for the pump bowls. A safety factor can be applied to the calculated pumping level to offset changes in well performance resulting from incrustation or from interference effects if other wells later are constructed nearby.

Continuous pumping means operating 24 hr per day, with no opportunity for recovery of the water level. A well that is pumped for only part of each day does not show the same cumulative drawdown after 7, 30, or 90 days as would be predicted by a time-drawdown graph such as Figure 6.17. A well that is pumped on a cycle of 12 hr on and 12 hr off benefits from recovery of the water level during the 12-hr idle period.

If insufficient recharge takes place while the pump is off, then the water level does not fully recover to the original static level. Each time pumping is resumed drawdown starts from a new level, which is slightly below the level at the start of the previous pumping period.

Drawdown stabilizes when recharge within the zone of influence of the pumping well equals the rate of discharge of the well. No further lowering of the water levels will occur as pumping continues at a constant rate. The time-drawdown curve then becomes horizontal, as shown in Figure 6.18.

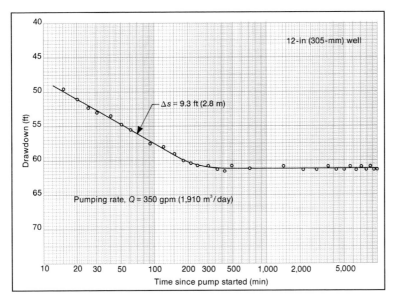

Figure 6.18. When recharge to the aquifer occurs within the zone of influence of the well, the slope of the time-drawdown curve flattens. The horizontal leg indicates that recharge equals well discharge after 240 min of pumping.

The first part of the curve illustrated in Figure 6.18 shows that the cone of depression was enlarging during the first 240 min of pumping. After 240 min, the cone of depression (or area of influence of the well) encountered a source of recharge. In the second part of the curve, the rate of recharge within the area of influence was sufficient to equal the rate of pumping, resulting in stabilized water levels throughout the area of influence. Recharge generally occurs gradually; it does not occur instantaneously. Recharge could be from a lake or river located in only a part of the cone of depression. After the recharge boundary is encountered, the drawdown increases slowly in areas away from the recharge source until equilibrium is established.

Sometimes the recharge rate within the cone of depression is lower than the pumping rate of the well. Although this changes the slope of time-drawdown curve, the second part might not become horizontal. Thus, the slope becomes flatter than the initial slope and indicates that the cone of depression is enlarging more slowly than during the first part of the pumping period (Figure 6.19). Future drawdown in a well can be predicted by extending the straight line of the second leg of the curve and reading the drawdown indicated for a particular time in the future.

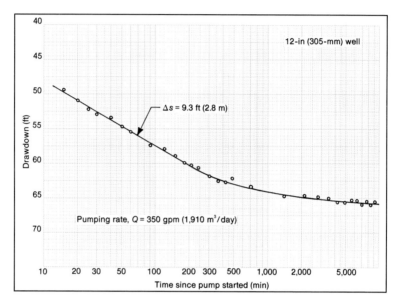

Figure 6.19. Recharge rate is somewhat less than the pump discharge; thus, the second part of the drawdown curve does not become horizontal.

The calculation of transmissivity (T) of a water-bearing formation should be made from Δs that is based on the first part of the time-drawdown curve. A value for transmissivity based upon the second slope of the graph is not used in analyzing the aqufier test data because recharge is occurring. If recharge is not occurring then the change in slope could indicate a physical change in the aquifer. The aquifer might thicken in one or more directions away from the well, for example, causing reduction in the slope of the time-drawdown curve. The hydraulic conductivity of the aquifer has not changed, only the volume of water available for withdrawal. Thus, the second Δs does not represent the true hydraulic conductivity of the primary aquifer sediments; it represents a geologic boundary within the radius of influence. Similarly, if a zone of higher hydraulic conductivity is encountered within the cone of depression, the time-drawdown curve flattens somewhat. Considerable variation in aquifer thickness and hydraulic conductivity violates two of the assumptions inherent in the Theis methodology. The time-drawdown curve reflects this departure from idealized conditions.

Recharge from a River

Equilibrium conditions that stabilize the cone of depression around a pumping well could develop in several general situations. One of these is when an aquifer is recharged from a river or lake. Figure 6.20 illustrates this situation after equilibrium has been reached.

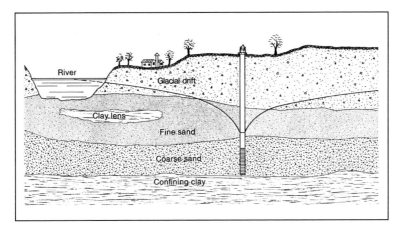

Figure 6.20. Cone of depression expanding beneath a riverbed creates a hydraulic gradient between the aquifer and river, and can result in induced recharge to the aquifer from the river.

During the early part of the pumping period, the cone of depression does not extend to the river and no recharge is evident. The pumping level in the well goes down as pumping continues, which is shown by the first part of the draw-down curve in Figure 6.18. When the cone of depression intersects a river channel, a hydraulic gradient develops between the groundwater in the aquifer and the water in the river. If the streambed is hydraulically connected with the aquifer, then river water percolates downward through the previous streambed under the influence of the hydraulic gradient. Thus, the river recharges the aquifer at an increasing rate as the cone of depression enlarges. When the rate of recharge to the aquifer equals the rate of discharge from the well, the cone of depression and the pumping level become stable. This condition corresponds to the horizontal part for the drawdown curve in Figure 6.18, and the situation shown in Figure 6.20.

Extension of the drawdown curve in Figure 6.18 shows that the predicted drawdown after 5,000 min of continuous pumping is 61.2 ft (18.7 m). Recharge to the aquifer in this case reduces the drawdown 12.1 ft (3.7 m) from the values shown in Figure 6.17 after the same period of continuous pumping.

Image Wells

When an aquifer has finite dimensions, analysis of the data by the Theis or Cooper-Jacob methodologies is not possible; however, this difficulty can be addressed through images. Imaginary wells or streams sometimes can be used at various locations to duplicate the hydraulic effects on the flow system caused by the physical boundary. Use of the image essentially is equivalent to substituting the physical boundary with a hydraulic one. The following descriptions provide an insight into how images are used.

An aquifer boundary formed by a low-permeability barrier such as a fault or a low-permeability geologic material (e.g., unfractured granite) that prevents the flow of water is termed a low-flow or no-flow boundary. Conversely, a geologic or hydrologic feature that allows for recharge to the aquifer (in the case of a surface-water body) or a highly transmissive zone is a recharge boundary or a line source. Although most geologic boundaries do not occur as abrupt discontinuities, it is possible to treat them as such (Ferris et al. 1962). When possible, it is convenient for the purpose of analysis to substitute a hypothetical image system for the boundary conditions of the real system.

If during an aquifer test the water levels in the aquifer are controlled by a perennial stream, then the physical situation can be represented as shown in Figure 6.21(A) If the stream stage is not lowered by the flow to the extraction well, then there is established a boundary condition and no drawdown along the stream. For most field situations it can be assumed that the stream is fully penetrating the aquifer and is equivalent to a line source at a constant head.

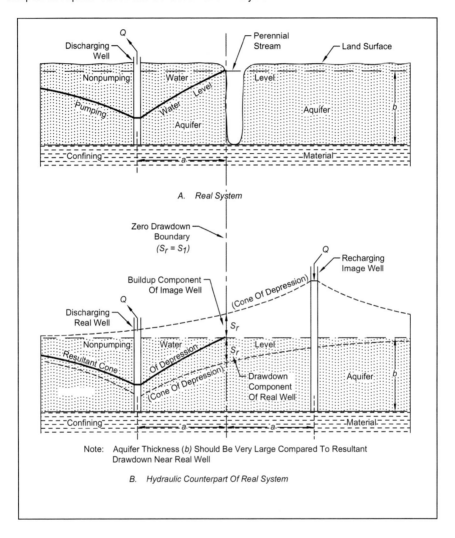

Figure 6.21. Idealized section views of a discharge in a well in (A) a semi-infinite aquifer bounded by a perennial stream, and the equivalent hydraulic system in (B) an infinite aquifer.

An image system that satisfies the above-described boundary condition (Figure 6.21(B)) allows a solution of the real problem through use of the Theis non-equilibrium methodology. Note in Figure 6.21(B) that an imaginary recharging well has been placed at the same distance as the real well from the line source, but on the opposite side. Both wells are situated on a common line perpendicular to the line source. The imaginary recharge well operates in the same manner as the real well, and returns water to the aquifer at the same rate that it is withdrawn by the real well. The resulting drawdown at any point on the cone of depression the real region is the algebraic sum of the drawdown caused by the real well and the buildup produced by its image.

An idealized section through a discharging well in an aquifer bounded on one side by an impermeable barrier is shown in Figure 6.22. It is assumed that the irregularly sloping boundary can be replaced by a vertical boundary, occupying the position shown by the vertical dashed line in Figure 6.22(A). The hydraulic condition imposed by the vertical boundary is that there can be no groundwater flow across it. No water is contributed to the discharging well. The image system that satisfies this condition and permits a solution of the real problem by the Theis equation is shown in Figure 6.22(B). An imaginary discharging well has been placed at the same distance as the real well from the boundary but on the opposite side, and both wells are on a common line perpendicular to the boundary. At the boundary the drawdown produced by the image well is equal to the drawdown caused by the real well. The resultant drawdown at any point on the cone of depression in the real region is the algebraic sum of the drawdowns produced at that point by the real well and its image.

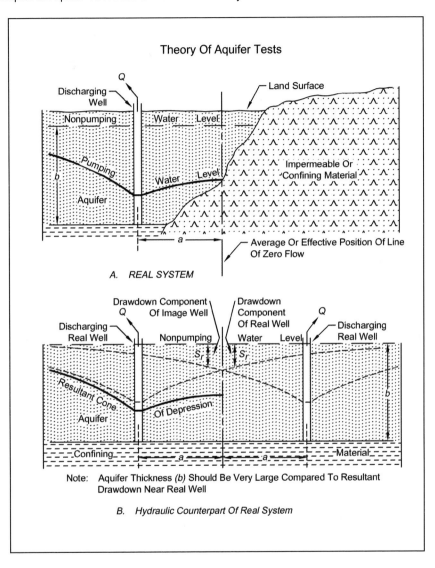

Figure 6.22. Idealized section view of a discharging well in a semi-infinite aquifer bounded by an impermeable formation, and the equivalent hydraulic system.

Vertical Infiltration (Vertical Recharge)

Another situation leading to equilibrium conditions is when vertical recharge occurs throughout the area of influence around a pumping well. An example is a well completed in an unconfined aquifer where all the material in the vadose zone from the ground surface to the water table is permeable sand. Assume that infiltration is from rain falling within the cone of depression of the well. When the quantity of water percolating to the water table within that circle equals the discharge from the well, the cone of depression stops spreading and the pumping levels within the well and the aquifer become stable.

Slow Drainage

The more common type of recharge producing equilibrium conditions is vertical leakage from saturated layers above an aquifer tapped by a production well. The upper strata of saturated material might have considerably lower hydraulic conductivity than the deeper material in which the well terminates. The difference in hydraulic conductivity between the upper and lower strata could be so great that the upper material is not considered to be part of the aquifer. When the area of the cone of depression covers a large area, the total vertical seepage from the upper material—even though it has a relatively low hydraulic conductivity—can equal the well discharge and thus bring about equilibrium in the pumping level. This situation also could develop in lenticular formations in which only the lower part of the formation is screened.

In unconfined conditions, slow drainage within the cone of depression can affect the validity of early time-drawdown data. Figure 6.23 shows the effect on the drawdown curve. Typically, the effect of slow drainage lasts only a matter of hours before the slope of the drawdown line reflects true aquifer characteristics.

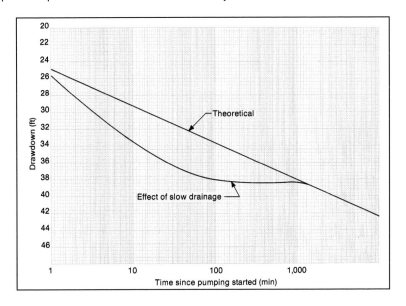

Figure 6.23. Time-drawdown curve showing the effect of slow drainage on the early part of the curve.

This phenomenon is caused by the great difference between the horizontal and vertical hydraulic conductivity in some sediments, and the severely limited hydraulic conductivity of sediments overlying many aquifers. In glacial drift, for example, layers of rather coarse sand or gravel commonly lie between thin layers of silt or clay. Water can flow freely in a horizontal direction, but vertical flow is greatly retarded. When pumping begins, the amount of vertical water movement toward the screen is relatively small but, as time passes and the cone of depression widens, a larger percentage of the water moves toward the well vertically, thereby reducing the slope of the time-drawdown.

It is important to recognize the effects of slow drainage because the curve might otherwise suggest that a recharge boundary has been encountered after a few minutes of pumping. Actually, the true transmissivity can be calculated only after several hours of pumping. Earlier transmissivity values might seem appropriate for a particular aquifer, but the storage values will be much lower than expected. Often the storage coefficients are similar to those encountered in a confined aquifer. Abnormally low values are clear indications of slow drainage. Thus, early data in slow drainage situations do not indicate true aquifer conditions.

Vertical Leakage

Like slow drainage, vertical leakage can distort the time-drawdown curve, but it occurs later. Vertical leakage occurs when an aquifer is confined geologically by two aquitards. During pumping, reduction in head within the cone of depression can cause leakage from the aquitards that are located above and below the aquifer.

Detailed analyses of leakage effects on aquifers have been developed by a variety of researchers, and Kruseman and deRidder (1992) provide a variety of analytical procedures to assess the impacts of leakage. Figure 6.24. shows distortion of the Jacob curve by vertical leakage. In complex geologic situations, computer modeling can be used to assess the effects of leakage and other boundary conditions. The use of computer models for the analysis of aquifer tests also is discussed in this chapter.

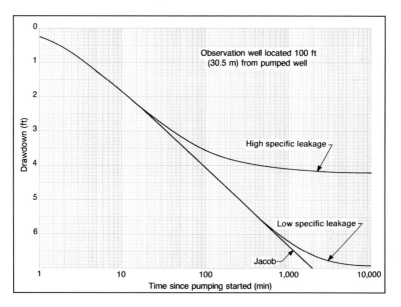

Figure 6.24. Drawdown graphs showing both low and high specific leakage.

Wellbore Storage

The mathematics of the Theis equation represents the pumped well by a line source which implies an insignificantly small well radius. As a consequence of this assumption, the Theis equation ignores water stored within the casing of the pumped well as a source of water during pumping. Casing (or wellbore) storage has its greatest influence at the outset of pumping. As the time of pumping progresses, however, this source of water is depleted and the well derives increasingly more water from the aquifer.

Papadopoulos and Cooper (1967) developed an equation that accounts for wellbore storage, and reported the time required to deplete wellbore storage as shown in equation 6.22.

$$t > \frac{250 r_c^2}{T} \tag{6.22}$$

Where:

t = time since start of pumping;

r_c = casing radius (L); and

T = transmissivity (L^2/t).

The criterion given in equation 6.22 indicate that the period affected by wellbore storage is shorter in small-diameter wells and in high-transmissivity aquifers. Equation 6.22 is applicable only to wells that are 100% efficient and fully penetrating.

Graphical methods also are useful for determining the period influenced by wellbore storage. On a log-log plot, the wellbore storage effect results in early-time drawdown data plotting with a unit (1:1) slope. A more useful approach to assessing wellbore is found in Schafer (1978) (a copy of this paper is contained in Appendix 6.Q (DVD)).

Schafer (1978) suggested that, in many instances, early aquifer test data might not fit Jacob's modification of the nonequilibrium theory, and that calculations based on this early Δs value have erroneous results. These early data reflect the removal of water stored in the casing because, when pumping begins, the water in the casing is removed first. As the water level in the casing falls, water from the surrounding formation begins to enter the well. Gradually, a greater percentage of the well's yield comes from the aquifer. The Δs value is higher during the time required to exhaust the casing storage, which gives an erroneously low transmissivity value in the early stages of the aquifer test. Figure 6.25 shows data from a typical aquifer test in which casing storage has distorted the early part of the time-drawdown curve.

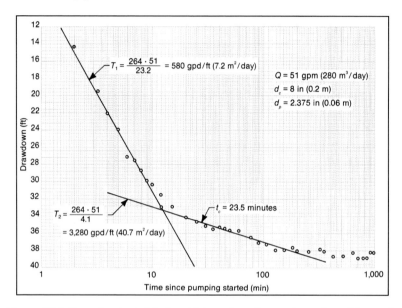

Figure 6.25. Pumping test data in which casing storage has altered the early part of the time-drawdown plot.

Before the effect of casing storage on aquifer test data was recognized, the flattened portion (or second part) of the drawdown curve might have been mistaken as an indication of aquifer recharge. The duration of the effect of casing storage varies greatly from well to well, depending on the casing diameter and specific capacity. In general, the storage effect lasts longer for wells that have large diameters and low specific capacities.

Papadopulos and Cooper (1967) and Ramey et al. (1973) present equations that modify the early part of the Jacob and Theis curves by taking into account casing storage (Papadopulos-Cooper equation for determining t_c is shown in Figure 6.26). These equations indicate the critical time after which casing storage no longer contributes to the yield of a well. Presumably, drawdown data collected after this time represents the true physical conditions within an aquifer. Unfortunately, these equations only can be used if the transmissivity and well efficiency are known in advance of the aquifer test.

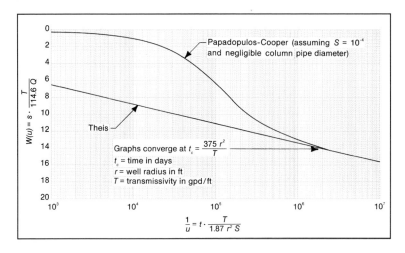

Figure 6.26. Graphic representation of the Papadopulos-Cooper equation which takes into account casing storage.

Schafer suggested that the critical time can be calculated using the following equations (6.23 as U.S. customary units; 6.24 as SI units).

$$t_c = \frac{0.6(d_c^{\ 2} - d_p^{\ 2})}{Q/s} \tag{6.23}$$

Where:

t_c = time (min) when casing storage effect becomes negligible;

d_c = inside diameter of well casing (in);

d_p = outside diameter of pump pipe (in); and

Q/s = specific capacity of the well in gpm/ft of drawdown at time t_c.

$$t_c = \frac{0.017(d_c^{\ 2} - d_p^{\ 2})}{Q/s} \tag{6.24}$$

Where:

t_c = time (min) when casing storage effect becomes negligible;

d_c = inside diameter of well casing (mm);

d_p = outside diameter of pump pipe (mm); and

Q/s = specific capacity of the well in m³/day/m of drawdown at time t_c.

Estimating a representative transmissivity value depends on being able to identify the difference between a casing storage effect and a recharge boundary encountered early in the aquifer test.

Example

Assume that it is unknown whether the aquifer-test data presented in Figure 6.26 represents boundary conditions or casing storage. If an iteration using equation 6.23 is performed (throughout, equation 6.24 also can be used), it is possible to estimate whether the change in the slope of the curve is caused by a casing storage effect or if it instead represents a recharge boundary. If the change in slope is caused by a casing storage effect, then the time of the change can be predicted using equation 6.23.

Equation 6.23 requires that the drawdown at time t_c be known; thus, there appear to be two unknowns, s and t_c. Initially, however, any drawdown value s_1 can be chosen and a trial t_c value can be calculated. Using the trial value of t_c and the time-drawdown graph, a new drawdown value (s_2) is obtained and can be used in equation 6.23 to calculate a second trial value of t_c. This procedure is repeated two or three times until the calculated value for t_c does not change significantly between iterations. Using this equation does not require knowledge of either the transmissivity or well efficiency.

To use equation 6.23, an initial drawdown value is selected and a t_c value is calculated. Assume, for example, that the initial s is 20 ft and values for the remaining parameters are listed in Figure 6.25 in U.S. customary units; the estimated t_c then is calculated as follows.

$$t_c = \frac{0.6((8)^2 - (2.375)^2)}{51/20} = 13.7 \text{ min} \qquad\qquad \textbf{(6.25)}$$

At 13.7 min, the drawdown is 33 ft (read from time-drawdown graph, Figure 6.25). Another calculation is made using 33 ft instead of 20 ft, resulting in a t_c value of approximately 22.7 min. The drawdown at 22.7 min is 34.2 ft. Substituting this value in equation 6.23 leads to a t_c of 23.5 min. Note that the change in the t_c value between the last two iterations is only 0.8 min—a small value. The three iterations using equation 6.23 suggest that the casing storage effect becomes negligible at approximately 23 min. Thus, the initial slope (Figure 6.25) provides an erroneous T value. Any predictions of the well's performance instead should be based on the T value calculated using the latter part of the curve. If the change in slope was caused by a boundary effect, then the time of the change in slope could not be predicted by applying equation 6.23, and instead the initial T value must be used to predict well performance.

Casing and Filter-Pack Storage

In some filter-packed wells, the static water level intersects the filter pack and can be close enough to the well screen to enable rapid drainage of the filter pack when the pump is started. In such cases, the storage effect is increased by the volume of water that can drain from the filter-pack storage.

$$t_c = \frac{0.6\left[(d_c{}^2 - d_p{}^2) + S_y(D_W{}^2 - d_o{}^2)\right]}{Q/s}$$ (6.26)

Where:

d_c = inside diameter of well casing (in);

d_p = outside diameter of pump pipe (in);

S_y = short-term specific yield of filter-pack material (typically 20%);

D_w = diameter of the borehole (in); and

d_o = outside diameter of well casing (in).

If water draining from the filter pack contributes to the storage effect, this equation should be used in lieu of equation 6.23 for computing t_c.

Partial Penetration

To understand partial penetration, consider a well with a screen or open interval of length L in an aquifer of thickness b. A well is "fully penetrating" when its dimensionless screen length L/b is equal to unity. When L/b is less than 1, the well is "partially penetrating."

In an ideal confined aquifer, flow to a fully penetrating pumping well is horizontal throughout the aquifer and no vertical flow occurs. When a pumping well partially penetrates an aquifer, however, convergence of flow toward the well screen results in vertical flow gradients that increase in magnitude as distance from the well decreases (Figure 6.27). Thus, the drawdown in a pumped well that partially penetrates an aquifer is greater than that of a fully penetrating well, due to the head loss associated with the convergence of flow. Vertical flow gradients produced by partial penetration extend beyond the pumped well and can affect the drawdown response in nearby observation wells.

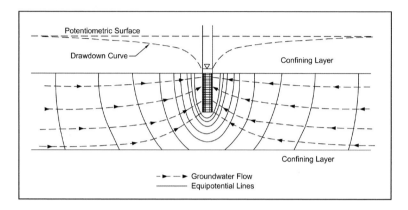

Figure 6.27. When the intake section of a well partially penetrates a confined aquifer, flow lines deviate somewhat from the radial flow pattern associated with a fully penetrating well.

The Theis and Cooper-Jacob equations considered thus far both assume that the wells are fully penetrating. Hantush (1961; 1964) considered the effects of partial penetration on wells in confined and leaky confined aquifers. Hantush showed that the partial penetration effect becomes negligible when observation wells are sufficiently distant from the pumped well.

$$r > 1.5b / \sqrt{K_z / K_r} \qquad\qquad\qquad (6.27)$$

Where:

r = radial distance from the pumped well (L);

b = aquifer thickness (L);

K_z = vertical hydraulic conductivity in the aquifer (L/t); and

K_r = radial hydraulic conductivity in the aquifer (L/t).

According to Hantush, the Theis or Cooper-Jacob equations can be applied to partially penetrating wells to determine the transmissivity and storativity of a confined aquifer when the criterion in equation 6.27 is satisfied. An example (using U.S. customary units), is a 50-ft confined aquifer having an estimated hydraulic conductivity anisotropy ratio $K_z/K_r = 0.5$. Using equation 6.27, the predicted effect of partial penetration becomes negligible when r is greater than 150 ft.

It also is true that the partial penetration effect reaches a constant maximum after sufficient time has elapsed. Hantush (1961) showed that the correct semilog slope occurs after the following time criterion is met.

$$t > bS / 2K_z \qquad\qquad (6.28)$$

Where:

t = time elapsed since pumping began;

b = aquifer thickness (L);

S = storage coefficient; and

K_z = vertical hydraulic conductivity in the aquifer (L/t).

According to Hantush, the Cooper-Jacob equation can be applied to partially penetrating wells to determine the transmissivity of a confined aquifer when the criterion in equation 6.28 is satisfied. For a 50-ft confined aquifer with an estimated storativity of 0.0005 and vertical hydraulic conductivity of 0.1 ft/day, for example, equation 6.28 enables a prediction that drawdown data in partially penetrating wells can be analyzed using the Cooper-Jacob equation when the time since pumping began exceeds 0.125 days or 180 min.

The criteria given in equations 6.27 and 6.28 enable the equations for fully penetrating wells to be used to analyze aquifer-test data. For data not meeting these criteria, the Hantush equation (1961; 1964)—which explicitly accounts for partially penetrating wells in confined aquifers—can be used. Type curves for the Hantush equation are a function of the penetration depths of the pumping and observation wells, in addition to the transmissivity and storativity of the aquifer. Tabulated values for selected pumping and observation well depths are available in Reed (1980), and Kruseman and De Ridder (1992). For other cases not available in tabulated form, computer programs are available for determining the well function for the Hantush equation (e.g., Reed 1980) as well as commercially available software packages (e.g., AQTESOLV™). Additional discussion on partial penetration is contained in Appendix 6.K (DVD).

Well Efficiency and Well Loss

Well efficiency is defined as the theoretical drawdown divided by the actual drawdown. Appendix 6.L (DVD) provides additional discussion regarding well efficiency. The following example (in U.S. customary units) defines and calculates the efficiency of a well.

A 12-in pumping well discharges at a constant rate of 200 gpm (38,500 ft³/day) from a confined aquifer that has a transmissivity of 10,000 ft²/day and storativity of 0.0005. Using the Theis formula supplied in equation 6.11, the theoretical drawdown in the pumped well after one day is computed as follows.

$$u = \frac{r^2 S}{4Tt} = \frac{(0.5)^2 (0.0005)}{4(10,000)(1)} = 3.125 \cdot 10^{-9}$$

$$s = \frac{Q}{4\pi T} W(u) = \frac{(38,500)}{4\pi (10,000)} (19.0) = 5.82 \text{ ft}$$

This calculation assumes that the well is fully penetrating and 100% efficient (i.e., no additional drawdown occurs in the well due to sources of well loss such as friction, turbulence, or reduced permeability in the vicinity of the wellbore). If the actual drawdown measured in the pumped well during the same period is 7.5 ft, then the efficiency of the well is computed as follows.

$$efficiency = \frac{theoretical\ drawdown}{actual\ drawdown} \cdot 100 = \frac{5.82 \text{ ft}}{7.5 \text{ ft}} \cdot 100 = 78\%$$

The factors contributing to excess drawdown in wells (inefficiency) can be grouped into two classes. One class is comprised of factors primarily related to choices made in the design of wells; the other class includes factors related to construction. The following is a summary of the factors in the two classes.

Design Factors

- Using a well screen that has insufficient open area creates entrance velocities that are too high, resulting in greater-than-normal entrance (head) losses.
- Choosing a well screen that has poor distribution of screen openings causes excessive convergence flow near the individual openings, and this can produce more drawdown than necessary (*see* Figure 6.28).
- Using a screen that results in partial penetration of the aquifer distorts the flow pattern for some distance around the well (*see* Figure 6.27). In such cases, flow to the well screen includes major

vertical and the main horizontal components. Vertical hydraulic conductivity generally is lower than horizontal hydraulic conductivity, therefore considerable head losses result from the vertical flow. Although extra drawdown might result, in many instances a shorter well screen can be used due to other design considerations. The effect of screen length is discussed in Chapter 9.

◆ Selecting improperly sized filter packs or those made from angular or plate-like materials can restrict flow into a well screen. Particle shape and size, and grain-size distribution all affect the hydraulic conductivity of the pack.

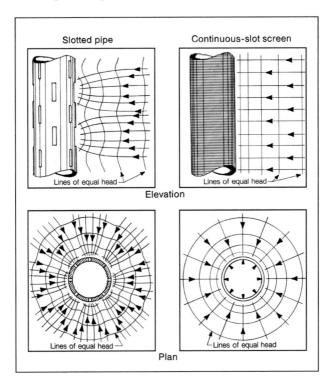

Figure 6.28. Flow nets around screen devices. Water approaches openings along the lines indicated by arrows. Flow lines for slotted pipe converge to individual slots; flow lines for continuous-slot well screens are less distorted.

Construction Factors

- Inadequate development of a well can leave drilling fluid and small particles in the aquifer around the screen, reducing the original hydraulic conductivity. Developing wells can be very difficult when screens with insufficient open area or poor distribution of slot openings are installed. Additional discussion regarding well development is contained in Chapter 11.
- Placement of the well screen at a depth that does not correspond to the best water-yielding stratum can lead to excess drawdown.

ANALYSIS OF RECOVERY DATA

Analyzing water-level recovery data provides a means of checking results obtained with time-drawdown analyses. Values obtained from analysis of the recovery record can be used to validate the calculations based on the pumping record.

During an aquifer test, measurement of the recovery of water levels in wells monitored should continue after pumping stops. When pumping stops, well and aquifer water levels rise toward their pre-pumping levels, and recording the rate of recovery enables calculation of values for transmissivity and storage. The time-recovery record therefore is an important part of an aquifer test. The time-drawdown measurements taken during the pumping period and the time-recovery measurements taken during the recovery period provide two different sets of information from a single aquifer test. In all cases, water levels should be measured in the pumped well and in each observation well during the recovery phase of the test.

Recovery data can be analyzed as described below only when the pumping portion of the aquifer test is conducted at a constant rate. Recovery measurements following a variable-rate test, such as a step-drawdown test, are difficult to analyze. The exact time of starting and stopping the pump must be recorded, in addition to any changes in pumping rate and the time that each incident occurs.

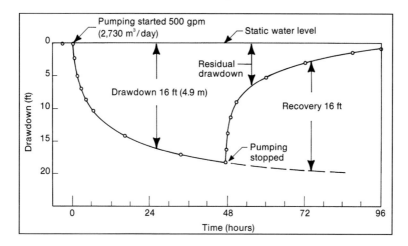

Figure 6.29. Typical drawdown and recovery plots for a well pumped for 48 hr at a constant rate of 500 gpm (2,730 m³/day), followed by a 48-hr water-level recovery period.

Figure 6.29 shows how water levels in a well change over time. The left half of the diagram corresponds to the pumping period and the right half to the recovery period. The recovery curve nearly is an inverted image of the drawdown curve. The shape of each curve is determined by the physical characteristics of the aquifer.

The points plotted for the recovery curve (right half of Figure 6.29) represent the residual drawdown in the well during the recovery period. Each point represents the difference between the original static water level and the depth to water at a given instant during the recovery period.

The hydraulic theory of well and aquifer performance assumes that water-level changes during the recovery period are the result of input from a theoretical recharge well. If such a well injects water into the aquifer at the same rate the real well pumps it out—with both wells working simultaneously after a given instant—then the recovery curve is similar to that depicted in Figure 6.29. The rise in water level (because of the imaginary recharge well) is the vertical distance between an extension of the time-drawdown curve and the actual time-recovery curve.

Recovery therefore is the difference between the measured water level in an observation well at a given time after pumping stops and the level to which the water would have dropped if pumping had continued until that instant. When defined in this way, the degree of water-level recovery at any time after the end of the pumping period theoretically is equal to—but opposite of—the drawdown during the same pumping period.

Example

A 6-in (152 mm) test well and an observation well 50 ft (15.2 m) away are used for an aquifer test. After pumping the well at 200 gpm (1,090 m³/day) for 500 min, the pump is stopped and water-level measurements are made during the first 390 min of the recovery period.

Table 6.4 shows the depth-to-water measurements in the observation well and the residual drawdown for time intervals measured from both the beginning of the aquifer test and the beginning of the recovery period. These intervals are defined as t and t', respectively. The ratios of the two time periods (t/t') also are shown in the table.

Figure 6.30 shows the recovery curve plotted for the observation well. Extension of the preceding drawdown curve indicates the drawdown that would have occurred if pumping had been continued beyond the pumping period. The water-level recovery for various time intervals is the vertical difference between the curves in this diagram. Values are provided in Table 6.4.

Table 6.4. Residual Drawdown and Calculated Recovery in the Observation Well

Time Since Pump Started (t)	Time Since Pump Stopped (t')	Ratio	Depth to Water		Residual Drawdown (s')		Drawdown (s) from Pumping Curve		Calculated Recovery ($s - s'$)	
min	min	(t/t')	ft	m	ft	m	ft	m	ft	m
500	0	—	18.60	5.67	10.60	3.23	10.60	3.23	0.00	0.00
501	1	501.00	18.55	5.66	10.55	3.22	10.60	3.23	0.05	0.01
502	2	251.00	18.50	5.64	10.50	3.20	10.60	3.23	0.10	0.03
503	3	168.00	18.40	5.61	10.40	3.17	10.61	3.23	0.21	0.06
504	4	126.00	18.09	5.52	10.09	3.08	10.61	3.23	0.52	0.15
506	6	84.00	17.72	5.40	9.72	2.96	10.62	3.24	0.90	0.28
508	8	64.00	17.22	5.25	9.22	2.81	10.63	3.24	1.41	0.43
510	10	51.00	16.64	5.07	8.64	2.63	10.64	3.24	2.00	0.61

Time Since Pump Started (*t*)	Time Since Pump Stopped (*t'*)	Ratio	Depth to Water		Residual Drawdown (*s'*)		Drawdown (s) from Pumping Curve		Calculated Recovery (s - s')	
min	min	(*t/t'*)	ft	m	ft	m	ft	m	ft	m
520	20	26.00	15.27	4.66	7.27	2.22	10.67	3.25	3.40	1.03
530	30	17.70	14.50	4.42	6.50	1.98	10.70	3.26	4.20	1.28
540	40	13.50	13.63	4.16	5.63	1.72	10.73	3.27	5.10	1.55
560	60	9.35	12.95	3.95	4.95	1.51	10.80	3.29	5.85	1.78
590	90	6.55	12.01	3.66	4.01	1.22	10.96	3.34	6.95	2.12
650	150	4.33	10.80	3.29	2.80	0.85	11.15	3.40	8.35	2.55
710	210	3.38	10.70	3.26	2.70	0.82	11.35	3.46	8.65	2.64
770	270	2.85	10.06	3.07	2.06	0.63	11.56	3.52	9.50	2.89
830	330	2.51	9.96	3.04	1.96	0.60	11.76	3.59	9.80	2.99
890	390	2.28	9.60	2.93	1.60	0.49	11.95	3.64	10.35	3.15

Note: Static water level is 8 ft (2.44 m).

Average pumping rate during preceding pumping period was 200 gpm (1,090 m³/day).

The recovery curve plotted in Figure 6.30 can be analyzed using either the Theis (1935) corollary to the non-equilibrium equation (presented below) or Jacob's (1946) modification of the non-equilibrium equation. As shown, the time-drawdown curve for the pumping period becomes a straight line on a semi-logarithmic diagram. The same simplification can be used for the time-recovery plot, where the horizontal scale represents the logarithm of time during the recovery period and the vertical scale represents water-level recovery (*s – s'*).

Data from Table 6.4 plotted in this way are shown in Figure 6.31. The result is similar to a time-drawdown plot for the pumping phase of the same aquifer test. Theoretically, the drawdown and recovery plots should be identical if the aquifer conditions conform to the basic assumptions of the Theis equation.

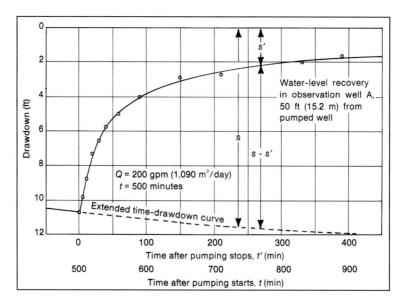

Figure 6.30. Residual-drawdown curve from piezometer, with extended time-drawdown curve (on arithmetic scales) showing how calculated recovery is determined at any instant during the recovery period. Producing well pumped 200 gpm (1,090 m³/day) for 500 min.

The time-recovery plot for the pumped well is more accurate than its time-drawdown plot because the residual-drawdown measurements are more accurate. During the recovery period, water-level measurements taken within the pumping well can be made without the effects of turbulence, vibrations, or well losses within the pumping well. The time-recovery data measured in a piezometer can be analyzed in the same manner as that used for the pumping-well data.

In an analysis of the time-recovery plot, the slope is of primary interest. Two factors determine the slope of the straight line in Figure 6.31. One is the average pumping rate during the preceding pumping period, the other is the aquifer transmissivity.

In Figure 6.31, the slope of the straight line is expressed numerically as the change in the water-level recovery per logarithmic cycle. It is designated using $\Delta(s - s')$. Its value in Figure 6.31 is 5.2 ft (1.6 m), which is the recovery during the period from 10 min to 100 min after pumping stopped.

The next step is to calculate the transmissivity of the aquifer from the following equation (given in both U.S. customary and SI units).

$$T = \frac{264Q}{\Delta(s - s')} \qquad \text{in gpd/ft} \qquad\qquad \text{U.S. customary} \qquad \textbf{(6.29)}$$

$$T = \frac{0.183Q}{\Delta(s - s')} \qquad \text{in m}^2\text{/day} \qquad\qquad \text{SI}$$

Figure 6.31 shows the value of T to be about 10,200 gpd/ft (127 m²/day). The values for T calculated from drawdown and recovery data should agree.

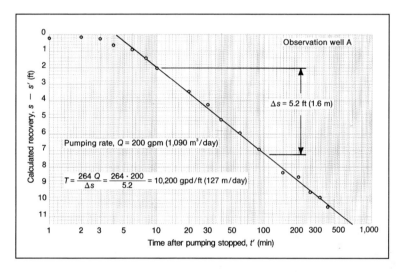

Figure 6.31. Time-recovery plot for observation well becomes a straight line when plotted on a semilog diagram (similar to the time-drawdown diagram for the preceding pumping period).

The commonly used method of plotting the data permits direct use of the residual drawdown without calculating the recovery from an extension of the time-drawdown plot. It can be shown that the residual drawdown is related to the logarithm of the ratio t/t' as follows (mathematical development of this relationship is given in Appendix 6.M).

$$s' = \frac{264Q}{T}\log\frac{t}{t'} \qquad\qquad \text{U.S. customary} \qquad \textbf{(6.30)}$$

Where T is in gpd/ft and Q is gpm.

$$s' = \frac{0.183Q}{T} \log \frac{t}{t'} \qquad\qquad \text{SI}$$

Where T is in m²/day and Q is in m³/day.

This equation shows that when values of s' are plotted against corresponding values of t/t' on semilogarithmic graph paper; a straight line can be drawn through the plotted points. Figure 6.32 shows the data from Table 6.4 plotted on a semilog diagram, with s' indicated on the vertical arithmetic scale and t/t' on the horizontal logarithmic scale. The transmissivity then is calculated using the following equation.

$$T = \frac{264Q}{\Delta s'} \qquad\qquad \text{U.S. customary} \qquad\qquad \mathbf{(6.31)}$$

$$T = \frac{0.183Q}{\Delta s'} \qquad\qquad \text{SI}$$

Figure 6.32 (below) shows that during the recovery period time increases toward the left in this method of plotting, as compared with the time-drawdown and time-recovery plots in which time increases toward the right.

Use of the residual-drawdown plot (Figure 6.32)—instead of the recovery plot (Figure 6.31)—might be preferable for calculating transmissivity. The method used for a residual-drawdown plot provides an independent check on the results calculated from the pumping period. The method used for a recovery plot depends upon extension of the time-drawdown plot through the recovery period; thus the drawdown plot itself determines the values used in the recovery plot, and any inaccuracies in the drawdown plot are projected into the recovery plot.

If no observation well is available for measurement, then the recovery data from the pumped well provides an acceptable basis for calculating the transmissivity of the aquifer. In this case, the residual-drawdown plot (Figure 6.32) should be used.

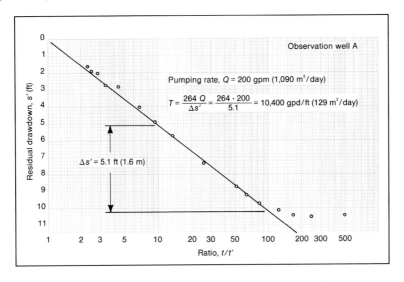

Figure 6.32. Residual-drawdown plotted against the ratio t/t' becomes a straight line on semilog graph and enables calculation of transmissivity as shown. Time during recovery period increases toward the left in this diagram.

VARIABLE-RATE TESTS

Constant-head, variable-rate tests are used when a flowing well in a confined aquifer is shut-in long enough for the head to recover, and then the well is opened and allowed to flow for some period. A similar situation occurs in tunneling or mining projects when the tunnel is below the water table. An exploratory corehole is advanced away from the tunnel and a packer-piping assembly is inserted into the corehole and the piping, equipped with a valve, is shut-in. When the static pressures are achieved the valve is opened and, in many cases, the flows decline with time.

Straight-line solutions to address constant-head, variable-flow rates were developed by Jacob and Lohman (1952). For large values of time (t) and sufficiently small values of u, $W(u)$ again can be closely approximated by $2.30 \log_{10} 2.25Tt/r^2S$. The following equation (rendered in both SI and U.S. customary units) was developed by Jacob and Lohman (1952).

$$T = \frac{2.30}{4\pi\Delta(s_w / Q) / \Delta\log_{10} t / r_w^2}$$ U.S. customary   **(6.32)**

$$T = \frac{2.30}{4\pi s_w (\Delta 1 / Q) / \Delta\log_{10} t}$$ SI

The following example was taken from Lohman (1979). A well was shut-in for several days; the static head just prior to the test was 92.33 ft above the measuring point. The data from the test are shown in Figure 6.33. The s_w/Q data were derived by dividing 92.33 ft by the flow rate at a particular time.

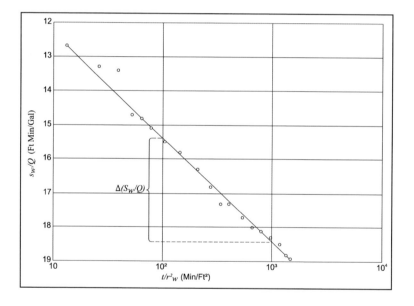

Figure 6.33. Semilogarthmic plot of *sw/Q* versus *t/r_w²* for a constant-head, variable-rate test.

From the values of $\Delta(s_w/Q)$ per log cycle of t/r_w^2 obtained from Figure 6.33, transmissivity (T) can be calculated using equation 6.32.

$$T = \frac{(2.30)(1.44 \times 10^3 \min day^{-1})}{(4\pi)[(18.4 - 15.38) ft \cdot gal^{-1} \min](7.48gal / ft^3)}$$

$$T = 11.7 \text{ ft}^2 \text{ day}^{-1}$$

DIAGNOSTIC FLOW PLOTS

Diagnostic flow plots (e.g., radial flow, linear flow, bilinear flow, and spherical flow plots) commonly are used in the analysis of well tests in the petroleum industry. These plots also can be used to improve the interpretation of aquifer-test data.

Table 6.5. Useful Diagnostic Plots for Analyzing Aquifer Tests

Plot Type	Axes
Radial	s vs. log t and log s vs. log t
Linear	log s vs. log $t^{1/2}$

Diagnostic flow plots can help identify the following conditions.

- **Wellbore storage.** A radial flow plot with log-log axes can help identify wellbore storage effects in a pumped well. Early-time data exhibiting a unit slope on this plot type are indicative of wellbore storage.

- **Infinite-acting aquifer.** A radial flow plot with log-linear axes can help identify radial flow in an infinite-acting aquifer (i.e., late-time data plotting as a straight line). Late-time behavior on a semi-log plot is the basis for the Cooper-Jacob straight-line method of analysis.

- **Linear flow to a fracture.** A linear flow plot with log-log axes can help identify linear flow conditions to a fracture. Early-time data exhibiting a unit slope on this plot type are indicative of linear flow to a single fracture with infinite conductivity or uniform flux along the fracture.

For additional information on diagnostic flow plots (e.g., flow to a fracture, other flow conditions), see Horne (1995).

STEP-DRAWDOWN TESTS

The equations developed to calculate aquifer parameters are based on the assumption that laminar flow conditions exist in the aquifer during pumping. If the flow is laminar, then drawdown is directly proportional to the pumping rate. Turbulent flow occurs in some wells—especially those producing from fractured rock—when they are pumped at a sufficiently high rate. Under turbulent conditions, the linear relationship between drawdown and pumping rate no longer holds. Figure 6.34 shows the total drawdown (s) in a well. Well loss is the difference between the theoretical drawdown and the actual draw-down in the well. The losses include linear and nonlinear components. In Figure 6.34 total drawdown (s) in a well has four components.

$$s = s_1 + s_n + s_e + s_w$$

Where:

s = total drawdown in a well (L);

s_l = head loss due to viscous drag as water moves through the aquifer with low velocity in the laminar flow region (L);

s_n = head loss due to a non-laminar flow in the aquifer in the high-velocity region in the in the immediate vicinity of the well (L);

s_e = head loss as the water exits the aquifer into the wellbore (L); and

s_w = head loss as the water flows within the wellbore to the pump intake (L).

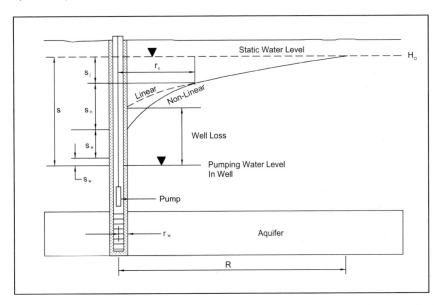

Figure 6.34. Components of drawdown in a well (HCItasca, Inc.).

When turbulent flow occurs, the specific capacity declines—often dramatically—as the discharge rate is increased. When this happens, it is useful to have a means of computing the turbulent and laminar drawdown components to be able to make proper judgments concerning the optimum pumping rate and pump-setting depth.

The step-drawdown test was developed to examine the performance of wells having turbulent flow (Jacob 1946). In a step-drawdown test, the well is pumped at several successively higher pumping rates and the drawdown for each rate—or step—is recorded. The entire test usually is conducted in one day, and calculations are simplified if all the pumping times are the same for each discharge rate. Usually 4 to 6 pumping steps are used, each lasting approximately 1 hr. The data from a step test can be used to calculate the relative proportion of laminar and turbulent flow occurring at selected pumping rates. A discussion of the approach to analyze turbulent versus laminar components of drawdown is contained in Appendix 6.N (DVD). Appendix 6.N also provides a discussion on a method to obtain an estimate of transmissivity from a measure of specific capacity.

In sum, the step-drawdown test can be used to calculate the following.

◆ Specific capacity of the well at various discharge rates. This information can be used to select optimum discharge rates. The length of time the test is run, however, might not be sufficient to encounter boundary effects. Therefore, the actual long-term specific capacity at a certain discharge can be different than originally calculated from the step-drawdown data. Slow drainage also can distort the discharge data in highly stratified aquifers.

◆ Percentage of total head loss attributable to laminar flow (however this percentage must not be confused with the true hydraulic efficiency of the well).

◆ Transmissivity and storage-coefficient values for the aquifer from time-drawdown and distance-drawdown graphs plotted from data for one of the constant-rate steps of the step test.

ANALYSIS OF AQUIFER TESTS USING NUMERICAL CODES

As discussed in this chapter, the standard method of analyzing aquifer-test data is using the type-curve or straight-line methods. Type-curve and straight-line methods of analysis both have a number of drawbacks, including the fact that it generally is not possible to use a consistent approach to evaluate all of the data collected during the aquifer test. Aquifer geometries and boundary conditions also in many cases cannot be represented accurately (Spiliotopulos & Andrews 2006).

Complex aquifer test conditions can be analyzed using numerical models. In the past, the synthesis and calibration of a numerical model often was very labor intensive. Graphical user interfaces (GUIs) for numerical models, such as MODFLOW (Harbaugh et al. 2000) and PEST (Doherty 2005), have made it possible to rapidly analyze aquifer-test data without the limitations of the type-curve methods (Spiliotopulos & Andrews 2006). Additional discussion on the use of numerical codes to analyze aquifer tests is provided in Appendix 6.O (DVD).

SUMMARY

Constant-rate, variable-rate, and step-drawdown aquifer tests offer methods for obtaining aquifer parameters such as transmissivity and storage coefficient. The hydraulic conductivity values determined from aquifer-test data are more accurate than hydraulic conductivities calculated on the basis of field samples tested in a laboratory, because samples rarely are representative of the undisturbed formation. Additionally, aquifer tests utilizing observation wells provide more-representative values for aquifer parameters than do single-well tests (e.g., slug tests), because a larger volume of aquifer is stressed. The aquifer test measures the performance of the aquifer over a larger volume of aquifer.

In addition to estimating hydraulic conductivity, transmissivity, and coefficient of storage, aquifer-test data can be used to estimate interferences between wells at various spacings and rates of pumping other than those employed in the test itself. Under some conditions, aquifer-test data also can indicate what drawdown might be expected from long-term pumping at different discharge rates, the presence of boundaries that limit the extent of the aquifer, and the existence of recharge sources—which might not be otherwise apparent based on observations of land features.

In many cases, aquifer-test data can be interpreted in more than one way. Even in the best-controlled of tests, data could be confusing unless all hydraulic and geologic factors are taken into account. A goal of aquifer-test design should be that the test be as simple as possible, to include the fewest deviations from the theoretical basis of the analysis. Wells should be fully penetrating, for example, and pumping rates should be constant. Analysts must be able to identify unreliable data so that the calculated values for transmissivity and storage coefficient correctly predict aquifer performance. An analyst also should review the test data in terms of a conceptual hydrogeologic model for the site. Figure 6.35 shows the relative components of an aquifer test and the potential impact on analysis. As shown in Figure 6.35, early-time data can be impacted by wellbore storage effects, whereas late-time data can be impacted by hydraulic boundaries.

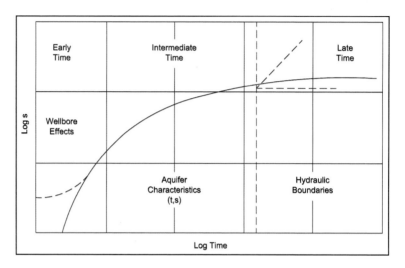

Figure 6.35. Components of a constant-rate test (HCItasca, Inc.).

Appendix 6.P (DVD) provides a number of examples of aquifer tests and interpretations of the data. Analysis of aquifer-test data requires an appreciation of all the factors that can affect the drawdown data. Such consideration chiefly comes from understanding the hydrogeology of the site, the assumptions inherent to the analytical methods, and the practical aspects of conducting the test. The accuracy of the data-collection methodologies also must be recognized when analyzing the data. The person performing the analysis must be able to visualize the physical nature of the aquifer and how it deviates from the basic assumptions upon which well-hydraulic equations are based. The limitations of hydraulic equations and the hydrogeologic nature of the aquifer system always must be kept in mind while analyzing aquifer-test data. Importantly, water-well professionals also must determine what data are valid for inclusion in the analysis to meet the objectives of each test.

ACKNOWLEDGMENTS

Mr. Glenn M. Duffield, President, HydroSOLVE, Inc., and the developer of AQTESOLVE™ (software used for the analysis of aquifer and slug tests), provided some text discussing the basic analysis of aquifer tests; his contributions are greatly appreciated.

The following individuals provided valuable reviews and comments on the chapter and its appendices.

- Mr. David Schafer, President, David Schafer & Associates
- Mr. Raymond Schreurs, Chief Hydrogeologist (retired), International Operations, Johnson Screens
- Charles B. Andrews (PhD), President, S.S. Papadopoulos & Associates, Inc.
- Lee C. Atkinson (PhD), President, HCItasca, Inc.

CHAPTER 7
Well-Drilling Methods

Mike Mehmert
Johnson Screens

This chapter discusses drilling methods that are appropriate for installing water wells. (For a discussion of which methods are most appropriate for sampling, see Chapter 3.) A variety of drilling methods exists due to the occurrence of a wide range of geologic conditions—from hard rock (e.g., granite, dolomite) to unconsolidated sediments (e.g., alluvial sand, gravel). Specific drilling methods are dominant in certain areas because they are effective and provide cost advantages. No single drilling method is best for all geologic conditions, and the methods and equipment capabilities vary as widely as the application requirements can.

Also described in this chapter are basic drilling principles, some applications, and the practical limits of major drilling methods for various geologic conditions. Additionally, a master table (Table 7.2) that summarizes the advantages and disadvantages of each drilling method is included at the end of this chapter.

DIRECT CIRCULATION METHODS

Air and Mud Rotary Drilling

The direct rotary drilling method was developed to increase drilling speeds and to enable drillers to reach greater depths in most formations (Figure 7.1). A borehole is drilled by rotating a bit attached to the lower end of a string of drillpipe. Cuttings are removed by continuous flow of air or other fluid in the annular space between the borehole and drillpipe. At the surface, settling pits or mechanical equipment extract the cuttings, allowing clean drilling fluid to be recirculated downhole. When using air drilling, cuttings are deposited on the ground or in a collection system and the circulating air goes into the atmosphere.

Figure 7.1. Tophead drilling rig (Schramm, Inc.).

Two drilling methods use air as the primary drilling fluid—direct air rotary and downhole air hammer. In air rotary drilling, air alone lifts the cuttings from the borehole. A compressor provides air that is piped to the swivel hose connected to the top of the kelly or drillpipe. When forced down the drillpipe, the air escapes through small ports at the bottom of the drill bit thereby lifting the cuttings and cooling the bit. The cuttings are blown out through the top of the borehole and collect at the surface around it. Injecting a small volume of water or a water and surfactant (foam) mixture into the air system controls dust, lowers the temperature of the air, and cools the swivel.

Use of air drilling is practical only in semi-consolidated or consolidated materials. It is the preferred flushing medium, however, because penetration rates are greater, no cleaning of the flushing medium is required before its re-introduction into the borehole, and no coating of the borehole occurs.

Air and mud rotary rigs use two different methods to rotate the drill string, either a table-drive or a tophead drive. On tophead rigs (*see* Figure 7.1), rotation is provided by a hydraulically driven gearbox which travels up and down the mast. The drill string is connected directly to the rotation unit therefore a kelly is not required. Tophead rigs provide excellent control of the drill string during penetration and retraction. A table-drive rig supplies power to the drillpipe through a kelly bushing located on the table (Figure 7.2). The components of the direct-rotary drilling machine are designed to serve two functions simultaneously: operation of the bit and continuous circulation of the drilling fluid. Both functions are indispensable in cutting and maintaining the borehole.

Cuttings are ground finely enough that the uphole velocity of the air is sufficient to lift them to the surface. Foam enhances the lifting capacity of the air which enables larger cuttings to be removed, thus increasing the drilling rate and reducing air loss to the formation. Suggestions for appropriate uphole velocities and the use of various drilling-fluid additives can be found in Chapter 8.

Drilling bits similar to those designed for drilling with water-based fluids also can be used when drilling with air. Field tests of various bit sizes have shown that the penetration rate often is faster and the bit life is longer when air is used (as compared with the use of water-based drilling fluids). Figure 7.3 lists the formations drilled effectively by carbide- and steel-tooth bits in air rotary drilling.

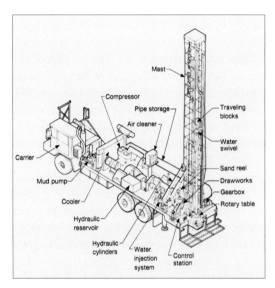

Figure 7.2. Schematic diagram of a truck-mounted direct rotary rig, illustrating the important operational components.

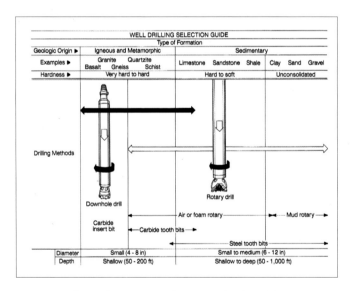

Figure 7.3. Guide for the use of bit types in air-drilling systems.

In direct circulation rotary drilling, generally two types of bits are used—the drag bit and the roller-cone bit. Drag bits (Figure 7.4) have short cutting blades that are faced with durable metal and are cleaned and cooled by jetting drilling fluid down the faces. These bits cut rapidly in sand, clay, and some soft-rock formations, but they do not work well in coarse gravel or hard-rock formations.

Figure 7.4. Drag bits are used in rotary drilling for fast penetration in unconsolidated or semi-consolidated sediments (Torquato Drilling Accessories).

A special type of drill bit—polycrystalline diamond compact (PDC)—has synthetic diamond discs on the cutting faces. These bits can drill formations that are too soft or too sticky for conventional diamond bits, and formations that are too hard for conventional drag bits and which previously were drilled using tricone roller bits or downhole hammer (DTH) bits (*see* Figure 7.5).

Figure 7.5. Photograph of a PDC bit (Torquato Drilling Accessories).

Roller-cone bits perform a crushing and chipping action, making it possible to drill harder formations. The number of teeth on each roller cone used depends on the difficulty of the drilling—the bit should have more teeth on each cone as a rock becomes harder and more difficult to drill. The rollers commonly have either hardened-steel teeth (Figure 7.6) or tungsten-carbide inserts of varied shape, length, and spacing. Roller bits are available to cut materials ranging from soft clays to particularly dense and abrasive formations such as dolomite, granite, chert, basalt, and quartzite. For drilling particularly dense or abrasive formations, roller cones that have carbide buttons (instead of teeth) are used. These are termed button bits (Figure 7.7).

Figure 7.6. Roller-cone or other cone-type bits are preferable for drilling into consolidated rock.

Figure 7.7. Button bit (Atlas CopCo).

When borehole enlargement is necessary, reamers (Figure 7.8) and under-reamers are used. A reamer is used to straighten, clean, or enlarge a borehole. Underreaming enlarges the borehole beneath the casing with a bit that can be expanded at the desired depth, so that a larger hole can be drilled. Underreaming often is practical when use of a filter pack is desired but drilling the entire borehole at the larger diameter is cost-prohibitive. Utilizing pre-pack screens, such as the Johnson Screens Muni-Pak™, is becoming a popular option in place of performing underreaming. (See Chapter 9 for a discussion of Muni-Pak™ screens.)

Figure 7.8. Roller-cone borehole reamers.

A conventional drill string consists of the bit, drill collar(s), and the drillpipe; table-drive rigs also include the kelly (Figure 7.9), but no kelly is used on a tophead rig. Both tophead and table-drive rigs also can use stabilizers or reamers in the drill string. Selection of the bottom-hole assembly depends on the physical conditions of the geologic materials. Drill collars are heavy-walled drillpipe used to add weight and stiffness to the lower part of the drill string to facilitate borehole straightness and optimum penetration rate. Table 7.1 presents representative data (in U.S. customary units) on recommended sizes of drill collars. Such stabilizers are important for maintaining a borehole's straightness.

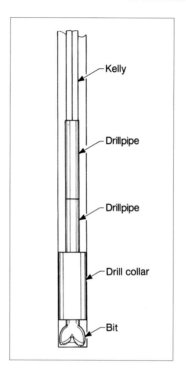

Figure 7.9. Typical drill string for a direct rotary rig operation.

Table 7.1. Ideal Size Range for Drill Collars

Hole Size (in)	Casing Size to be Run (OD in)	Calculated Ideal Drill-Collar Range (in)		API Drill-Collar Sizes Which Fall in the Ideal Range (in)
		Min	Max	
6⅛	4½	3.87	4.75	4⅛, 4¾
6⅛	4½	3.75	4.87	4⅛, 4¾
6¾	4½	3.25	5.12	3½, 4⅛, 4¾, 5
7⅞	4½	2.12	6.12	3⅛, 3½, 4⅛, 4¾, 5, 6
	5½	4.22	6.12	4¾, 5, 6
8⅜	5½	3.72	6.50	4⅛, 4¾, 5, 6, 6¼, 6½
	6⅝	6.40	6.50	6½
8½	6⅝	6.28	6.72	6½, 6¾
	7	6.81*	6.75	6¾
8¾	6⅝	6.03	7.12	6¼, 6½, 6¾, 7
	7	6.56	7.12	6¾, 7

Hole Size (in)	Casing Size to be Run (OD in)	Calculated Ideal Drill-Collar Range (in)		API Drill-Collar Sizes Which Fall in the Ideal Range (in)
		Min	Max	
9½	7	6.81	7.62	6, 6¼, 6½, 7, 7¼
	7⅝	7.50	7.62	7⅝[†]
9⅞	7	5.43	8.00	6, 6¼, 6½, 6¾, 7, 7¼, 7¾, 8
	7⅝	7.12	8.00	7¼, 7¾, 8
10⅝	7⅝	6.37	8.50	6½, 6¾, 7, 7¼, 7¾, 8, 8¼
	8⅝	8.62[*]	8.50	8¼
11	8⅝	8.25	9.62	8¼, 9, 9½
12¼	9⅝	9.00	10.12	9, 9½, 9¾, 10
	10¾	11.25[*]	10.12	10
13¾	10¾	9.75	11.25	9¾, 10, 11
14¾	11¾	8.75	12.00	9, 9½, 9¾, 10, 11, 12[†]
17½	13⅜	11.25	13.37	12[†]
20	16	14.00	14.75	14[†]
24	18⅝	15.50	16.75	16[†]
26	20	16.00	19.50	16[†]

[*]   In these instances, the equation used to calculate the ideal minimum drill-collar size produces an anomalously high value. See Woods and Lubinski (1954) for a complete discussion on how to determine the best collar size for a specific diameter borehole.

[†]   Not API standard-size drill collar.

(Drilco 1979)

Drillpipe is seamless tubing that usually is 20 ft (6.1 m) to 30 ft (9.1 m) long, however other lengths are available. It is manufactured with a tool-joint pin on one end and a tool-joint box on the other (Figure 7.10). To reduce the power required for the pump, drillpipe diameter should hold friction losses in the pipe to acceptable levels. For efficient operation, the outside diameter of the tool-joint should be about two-thirds the size of the borehole diameter; however this ratio might be impractical for boreholes that are larger than 10 in (254 mm).

In table-drive machines, the kelly constitutes the uppermost section of the drill string. It passes through and engages the rotary table, which is driven by hydraulic or mechanical means. A heavy thrust bearing between the two parts of the swivel carries the entire weight of the drill string while allowing the drillpipe to rotate freely. In tophead drive rotary machines the rotational unit moves up and down the mast; energy is obtained from a hydraulic transmission unit powered by a motor-driven pump.

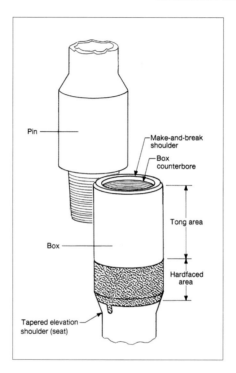

Pin

Make-and-break
shoulder

Box
counterbore

Tong area

Box

Hardfaced
area

Tapered elevation
shoulder (seat)

Figure 7.10. Drillpipe is heavy-walled seamless tubing with tool-joint pin and box-end fittings.

For shallow boreholes—those less than 250 ft (76 m) deep—pull-down pressure can be applied to the bit. In deep direct-rotary drilled boreholes, drilling professionals must hold back (suspend) part of the drill-string weight from the swivel to avoid placing excessive weight on the bit. Drill bit manufacturers can recommend the optimum pressure that an individual bit should receive for ensuring maximum cutting rates.

Drilling fluid (mud) control is essential to efficient rotary drilling. For drilling to proceed efficiently, there must be proper coordination of the borehole size, drillpipe size, bit type, pump capabilities, and drilling-fluid characteristics that all are based on the geologic conditions at the site. In water-well applications, drilling fluids range from air and freshwater to engineered water-based solutions containing special additives for viscosity, density, and solids control. Maintaining optimum uphole velocity is critical for proper borehole cleaning. (See Chapter 8 for a discussion of standard drilling fluids.)

The essential functions of a drilling fluid are to:

* Carry the cuttings from the bottom of the hole to the surface;
* Support and stabilize the borehole wall to prevent caving;
* Seal the borehole wall to reduce fluid loss;
* Cool and clean the drill bit;
* Allow cuttings to separate from the fluid at the surface; and
* Lubricate the bit, bearings, mud pump, and drillpipe.

The hydraulic pressure that typical drilling muds exert against the formation being drilled is greater than the static formation pressure, thus there can be over-balance (invasive) damage to the formation. The overbalanced fluid pressure depends primarily on the density of the drilling mud. Control of drilling-fluid properties during all phases of well construction minimizes both the frequency of occurrence of such damage and the time required to alleviate it. Experience and knowledge of drilling-fluid additives are essential for minimizing formation damage while maintaining borehole control.

Underbalanced Rotary Drilling

In underbalanced drilling programs the objective is to have a lightweight borehole fluid that ideally exerts a hydrostatic pressure equal to or less than the static formation pressure, which eliminates the invasive effects of drilling fluid that cause formation damage. This practice is gaining popularity in locations where it can be applied because it increases penetration rates, reduces lost-circulation problems, minimizes differential sticking, shortens development time, and reduces borehole damage. The use of underbalanced drilling also is popular in the oil industry, where it involves equipment and techniques that are more sophisticated than those required in the water-well industry, because formation pressures can far exceed those normally found in water-well drilling. The rate of return for underbalanced wells, however, typically is greater than for wells drilled using other methods.

Figure 7.11 illustrates the differences between overbalance and under-balanced drilling techniques. Example (A) shows underbalanced drilling, where the fluid pressures are less within the borehole than they are in the aquifer. This situation leads to minimized borehole damage. Example (B) shows a typical drilling situation where fluid pressures in the borehole exceed formation pressures; in this scenario a mudcake develops.

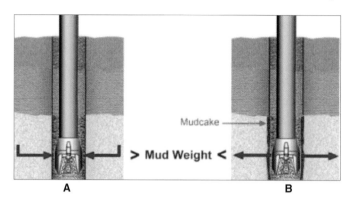

**Figure 7.11. Differences in fluid migration with (A) and without (B)
underbalanced drilling (www.rigzone.com).**

A typical situation is where the static water level is below the land surface.
This situation requires the addition of air or foam to reduce the fluid density
sufficiently and enable drilling in a balanced or underbalanced state unless the
well is flowing. Balanced drilling methods include air rotary and reverse rotary.
Caution should be exercised with air injection and the possibility of increased
corrosion to the drillpipe or tooling. A common example of underbalanced drilling in the water-well industry is air rotary (drilling with air or foam injection).
Underbalanced drilling conditions do not build filter cake (*see* Chapter 8)
because negative differential pressure encourages flow into the borehole and not
out into the formation.

Downhole Hammer Drilling

Another air rotary drilling method is the downhole hammer system. A
pneumatic drill at the end of the drillpipe rapidly strikes the rock while the
drillpipe slowly is rotated. A hammer is constructed from alloy steel and heavy
tungsten-carbide inserts that provide the cutting surfaces. Rotation of the bit
helps to insure even penetration and straighter holes—including when drilling
in extremely abrasive or resistant rock types. The penetration rates for drilling
in hard rock are greater than those obtained by other drilling methods. Hammer
bits in sizes of 5 in (127 mm) and 6 in (152 mm) are most common, with sizes
of up to 24 in (608 mm) also available. Cuttings are removed continuously so

the bit always strikes a clean surface, which makes the air-hammer method highly efficient.

Compressed air must be supplied to the hammer at a pressure of at least 100 psi (690 kPa). The most common pressure on modern rigs used primarily for air drilling is 350 psi (2,415 kPa), with pressures sometimes as great as 500 psi (3,450 kPa). To remove cuttings effectively, the volume of flushing air must be adequate to maintain the upward velocity in the annulus between the drillpipe and the borehole at a minimum of 3,000 ft/min (915 m/min), as determined by the following equation (in U.S. customary units).

$$V_r = \frac{183.34 \cdot cfm}{(D)^2 - (d)^2} \tag{7.1}$$

Where:

V_r = annulus velocity (ft/min);

cfm = cubic ft free air per min;

D = hole diameter (in); and

d = outside drillpipe diameter (m).

A downhole hammer is extremely effective in penetrating dense, resistant formations such as basalt, quartzite, and granite.

When a conventional downhole hammer is used in dual-wall drilling, air is forced down the inside of the hammer and out through the ports. The air passes up around the outside of the hammer shaft into a special crossover sub and then into the inner casing (Figure 7.12). When a reverse circulation downhole hammer is used in dual-wall drilling, cuttings exit the bottom of the borehole through a hole in the face of the bit. The cuttings are carried through the center of the downhole hammer and into the center tube of the dual-wall pipe; from there, compressed air carries the cuttings to the top of the borehole.

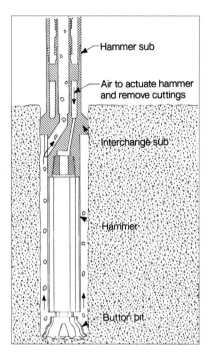

Hammer sub

Air to actuate hammer and remove cuttings

Interchange sub

Hammer

Button bit

Figure 7.12. Diagram of typical downhole hammer configuration (Drilling Services Co.).

Casing Advancement Drilling Methods

Casing advancement drilling methods are used in unconsolidated or difficult conditions when it is desirable to advance the casing as the borehole is created, usually using downhole hammer drilling. Four methods commonly are used for this type of drilling.

Casing Driver

Some manufacturers provide casing drivers that can be fitted to tophead drive, direct air rotary rigs (Figure 7.13). The driver can be suspended in the mast—independent of the rotary drive unit—because of its rather short length. Using a casing driver allows the casing to be advanced during drilling but both drilling and driving can be adjusted independently, based upon the nature of the specific formation. Drivers usually are designed so that they also can drive upward, for example to remove casing or to expose a screen.

Three drilling procedures can be performed when using the casing driver: (1) advancing the drill bit and casing as a unit; (2) driving the casing first (in unconsolidated materials only) and then drilling out the plug in the casing; and (3) advancing the drill bit a few feet beyond the casing, then withdrawing it into the casing, and then driving the casing.

The casing is pulled back to set the screen. It is wise, however, to add a short piece of riser pipe to the top of the screen so that it won't be lost if the casing is pulled back too far.

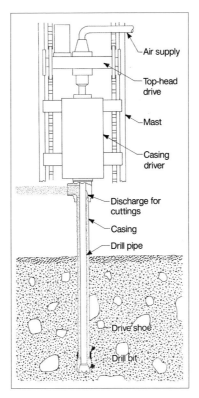

Figure 7.13. Casing drivers can be fitted to tophead drive rotary rigs to simultaneously drill and drive casing (Atlas Manufacturing).

Underreamer

Wings—underreamers—on the drill bit swing out under the casing during drilling allowing the casing to follow the bit into the borehole. When drilling is complete the underreamers are retracted and the entire drill string is removed through the casing (*see* Figure 7.14).

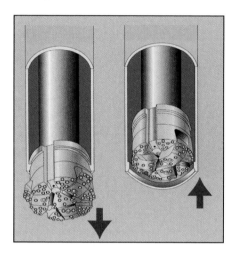

Figure 7.14. Underreaming system (NUMA).

Casing Rotator

The drilling rig is equipped with a device that clamps around the casing to rotate and advance it into the ground (see Figure 7.15). To facilitate drilling, a drive shoe with cutting teeth can be welded onto the end of the casing. The casing can be rotated clockwise or counter-clockwise as required, and the distance from bit face to casing end can be adjusted.

Figure 7.15. Casing rotator rig (Schramm, Inc.).

Casing Float Shoe Engaged by Downhole Hammer

A shoulder on the hammer hits against a mating drive shoe welded to the end of the casing, to drive the casing into the ground as drilling proceeds (*see* Figure 7.16). The casing remains in the borehole after the drillstring is removed.

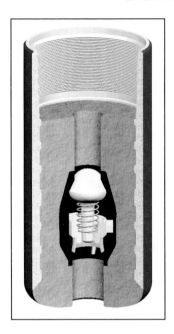

Figure 7.16. Casing float shoe (Weatherford Corp.).

REVERSE CIRCULATION METHODS

In reverse circulation rotary drilling, the flow of the drilling fluid is reversed and the drilling fluid (with cuttings) moves upward inside the drillpipe and discharges at the surface, typically into one or more settling pits. The pump suction is connected to the kelly and drillpipe through the swivel. Centrifugal pumps frequently are used because they handle cuttings without experiencing excessive wear. For large-diameter water-well drilling, uphole velocities of 150 ft/min (45 m/min) or greater are recommended.

Fluid returns to the borehole—via gravity—down the annulus to the bottom of the hole. It reenters the drillpipe, with more cuttings entrained, through ports in the drill bit (Figure 7.17, Figure 7.18). A native drilling mud develops when suspended clay and silt recirculate as drilling proceeds but, when needed, polymer additives are used to reduce friction and to control water loss or the swelling of water-sensitive clays. In deeper wells with deep static water levels, an engineered drilling fluid generally is used.

To prevent caving (from a loss of the hydrostatic pressure that supports the borehole) a positive fluid pressure must be maintained in the borehole at all times—even when drilling is suspended temporarily. Reverse circulation drilling is not commonly practiced where the static water level is less than 10 ft (3 m) below ground surface. A considerable quantity of make-up water must be immediately available at all times when drilling in permeable sand and gravel (at least three times the volume of the material removed during the drilling operation is recommended). The circulation rate during drilling commonly is 500 gpm (2,730 m^3/day) or greater.

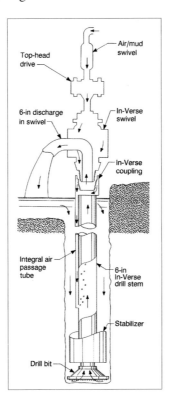

Figure 7.17. Air is injected into a special double-walled drill stem to increase the efficiency of cuttings removal.

Many reverse rigs are equipped with air compressors, and when drilling reaches sufficient depth for air-lift operation (generally 45 ft (13.7 m) to 60 ft (18.3 m)) the mud pump is bypassed and water and cuttings are air-lifted from the borehole. Compressed air is introduced through a 1¼-in (32-mm) to 1½-in (38-mm) air line made of plastic or metal. The air line is suspended inside the drillpipe or through external lines outside of the drillpipe. Most drillpipe used is threaded and coupled pipe that is up to 8 in (203 mm) in diameter, and is operated at depths of 2,000 ft (610 m) or deeper.

It is recommended that a reverse system use at least a 300-cfm (0.1 m³/sec) compressor operating at 125 psi (862 kPa). The reverse-equipped rig operates most satisfactorily with a centrifugal pump or a piston pump.

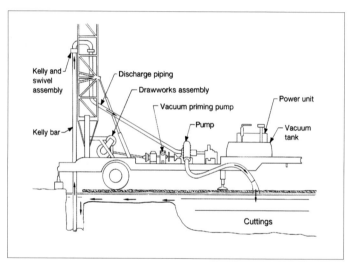

Figure 7.18. Reverse rotary circulation system. Drilling fluid flows from the mud pit down the borehole outside the drill rods, and passes upward through the bit into the drill rods after entraining the cuttings. Fluid flows through the swivel and mud pump and passes into the mud pit where the cuttings settle out.

Reverse circulation drilling is an economical method for drilling large-diameter holes in unconsolidated formations. Most water wells drilled using this method have a diameter of 20 in (508 mm) or larger. Filter packs typically are used in well completions because of the relatively large-diameter borehole.

DUAL-WALL AIR ROTARY DRILLING

Dual-wall drilling was developed in the mining industry to obtain accurate geologic samples from known depths. The method uses flush-jointed, double-wall pipe and the drilling fluid (air or liquid) moves via reverse circulation (Figure 7.19). Unlike in the conventional reverse circulation method, the drilling fluid does not flow downward outside the drillpipe, but rather is contained between the dual walls of the pipe and only contacts the borehole wall near the drill bit. The dual-wall drilling method is applied to water-well construction in all types of geologic formations, and larger rigs are being built for drilling large-diameter boreholes under difficult drilling conditions. Water wells can be drilled to depths of 1,000 ft (305 m) or more using this method.

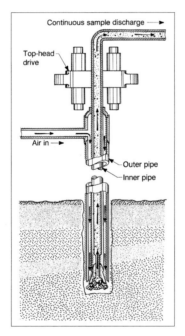

Figure 7.19. Drilling fluid is injected down the outer annulus of dual-walled pipe; cuttings are lifted to the surface through the inner pipe. The pipe is connected directly to either a downhole air hammer or a tricone bit.

A direct rotary, tophead drive machine can be converted into a reverse circulation rig. The equipment is modified by the addition of air assist, using a special 6-in (152-mm) inside diameter, side-discharge swivel assembly, and 5⅞-in (149-mm) drillpipe with built-in air channels. This equipment enables injection of compressed air through a stem into air channels mounted outside the drillpipe. The air then moves into the drilling fluid as it travels up the inside of the drillpipe (Figure 7.20). The drilling fluid and cuttings are assisted to the surface by an air-lift inside the 6-in diameter drillpipe.

Use of the reverse system can increase the capacity of a direct rotary rig to enable the drilling of large-diameter wells. Depending on the rig used, boreholes from 20 in (508 mm) to 30 in (762 mm) routinely can be drilled. If the capabilities of the rig are sufficient, then drilling boreholes of 30 in (762 mm) to 60 in (1,520 mm) is possible in unconsolidated formations.

NONCIRCULATION METHODS

Cable-Tool Drilling

Developed by the Chinese, the cable-tool percussion method has been in continuous use for about 4,000 years. Cable-tool drilling machines, also called percussion or "spudder" rigs, operate by repeatedly lifting and dropping a heavy drill string into the borehole. The reciprocating-tool action mixes the cuttings with water to form a slurry; water is added if little or no formation water present. Slurry accumulates as drilling proceeds, and it eventually reduces the impact of the tools to the point that the cuttings periodically must be extracted by a sand pump or bailer to facilitate optimum penetration rate. Effective action makes the cable-tool rig an ideal machine for well rehabilitation and work-over.

A full string of cable-tool drilling equipment consists of five components: drill bit, drill stem, drilling jars, swivel socket, and a cable (Figure 7.20). The cable-tool bit usually is massive and heavy so that it can crush and mix all types of earth materials. The drill stem gives additional weight to the bit, and its length helps to maintain a straight borehole when used for drilling into hard rock.

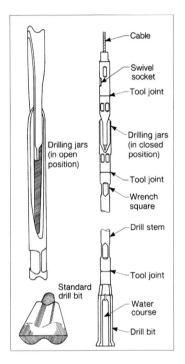

Figure 7.20. A full cable-tool drill string.

Drilling jars consist of a pair of linked, heat-treated steel bars, and their primary function is to free a stuck bit via upward blows of the free-sliding jars. The swivel socket connects the string of tools to the cable, and transmits the rotation of the cable to the tool string and bit so that new rock is cut on each downstroke, thus ensuring a round, straight hole. The cable drill line is a ⅝-in (16-mm) to 1-in (25-mm) left-hand lay cable that twists the tool joints on each upstroke to prevent the joints from unscrewing. A cable-tool rig is shown in Figure 7.21.

Relatively small-diameter holes can be drilled to greater depth, whereas the drilling of large-diameter holes is limited by the weight of the drill string and cable. The depth range for cable-tool rigs ranges from approximately 300 ft (90 m) to 1,500 ft (500 m).

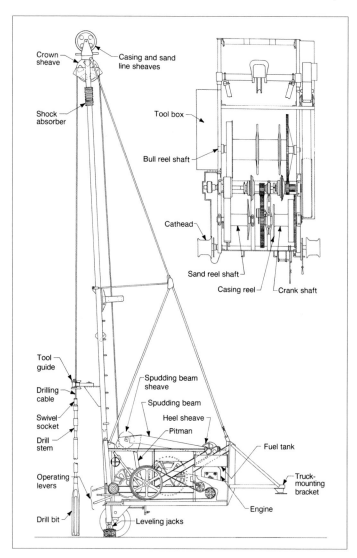

Figure 7.21. Bucyrus-Erie Model 22-W cable-tool rig. The percussion action is imparted to the drill line by the vertical motion of the spudding beam. The shock absorber mounted beneath the crown block helps control the impact of the bit (Bucyrus-Erie Co.).

Most boreholes that are completed in consolidated formations via the cable-tool method are drilled without using casing during part—and sometimes all—of the drilling operation. When drilling in unconsolidated formations, pipe or casing must follow the drill bit closely to prevent caving and to keep the borehole open. To prevent damage, a drive shoe (comprised of hardened and tempered steel) is attached to the bottom of the casing. When wall friction prevents further advancement, a smaller casing is inserted inside the first one and drilling continues. In some circumstances, two or three size reductions are required for the drill to reach the desired depth.

The casing sometimes is jacked (pushed into the ground by hydraulic jacks) as drilling and bailing proceeds. Drilling proceeds at a faster rate because it is not necessary to stop to drive pipe. Constant downward pressure on the casing during drilling minimizes caving and over-excavation. Casing also can be retrieved using jacks.

The cable-tool drilling method survives because it is reliable for use in a wide variety of geologic conditions. It remains a practical method in coarse glacial till; boulder deposits; basalts; or rock strata that are highly disturbed, broken, fissured, or cavernous. In thin and low-yielding aquifers, the cable-tool operation permits identification of zones that might be overlooked when using other drilling methods.

Bucket Auger Drilling

The bucket auger drilling method utilizes a large-diameter bucket auger to excavate materials (Figure 7.22) which then are collected in a cylindrical bucket that has auger-type cutting blades on the bottom. The bucket is attached to the lower end of a kelly bar that passes through—and is rotated by—a large ring gear that serves as a rotary table.

Wells more than 250 ft (76.2 m) deep have been drilled using this method, although attainment of depths of 50 ft (15.2 m) to 150 ft (45.7 m) is more common. Water wells drilled with bucket augers range in diameter from 18 in (457 mm) to 48 in (1,220 mm), but few wells are larger than 36 in (914 mm). Rotary bucket drilling primarily is used in clay formations that can stand without caving. Drilling in sand below the water table is difficult but it is not impossible if the borehole remains filled with water or drilling fluid.

Figure 7.22. Bucket auger drilling rig (Powers et al. 2007).

A major disadvantage of the bucket auger drilling method is that it is limited to use in relatively shallow depths (generally less than 100 ft (30 m)), and in unconsolidated sediments or poorly cemented sedimentary rocks. Table 7.2 summarizes the advantages and disadvantages of each drilling method.

Table 7.2. Advantages and Disadvantages of Drilling Methods

Direct Circulation Methods	
Advantages	**Disadvantages**
Penetration rates are relatively high in all types of materials	Drilling rigs require a high level of maintenance
Minimal casing is required during the drilling operation	Mobility of the rigs can be limited
Rig mobilization and demobilization are rapid	Most rigs must be handled by a crew of at least two people
Well screens can be set easily as part of the casing installation	Collection of accurate samples requires special procedures
	Use of drilling fluids can cause plugging of certain formations
	The drilling method is difficult and less economical in extremely cold temperatures
	Drilling fluid management requires additional knowledge and experience

Air Rotary Drilling	
Advantages	**Disadvantages**
Cuttings removal is extremely rapid	Restricted to use in semi-consolidated and well-consolidated materials
Aquifer is not plugged with drilling fluids	High initial cost and maintenance costs of large air compressors
Mud pumps are not used during air drilling, eliminating that maintenance cost	
Bit life is extended	
Drilling operations are not hampered by extremely cold weather	
Penetration rates are high (especially when using downhole hammers) in highly resistant rocks such as dolomite or basalt	
An estimate of the yield of a particular formation can be made during drilling	

Casing Advancement Methods	
Advantages	**Disadvantages**
Wells can be drilled in unconsolidated geologic materials	Additional cost of equipment
A borehole is fully stabilized during the entire drilling operation	Noise of operation (casing hammers are noisy)
Penetration rate can be rapid even in difficult conditions	Clays or sticky shales can reduce depth capacity
Lost-circulation problems are eliminated.	
Accurate formation and water samples can be obtained	

Reverse Circulation Methods	
Advantages	**Disadvantages**
Porosity and permeability of the formation near the borehole are relatively undisturbed (as compared to other methods)	Large water supply generally is needed during drilling
Large-diameter holes can be drilled quickly and economically	Reverse rotary rigs and components usually are larger and more expensive
Casing is not required during the drilling operation	Large mud pits are required
Well screens can be set easily as part of the casing installation	Some drill sites are inaccessible because of the rig size
Most geologic formations can be drilled (except igneous and metamorphic rocks)	For efficient operation, a larger crew generally is required as compared to that needed for other drilling methods
Little opportunity exists for washouts in the borehole because of the low velocity of the drilling fluid	Extra costs for drillpipe, special swivel, and air compressor (if the rig is not equipped with one)
Large-diameter boreholes can be drilled	Drillpipe handling time can increase for deep holes
Penetration rates are high in unconsolidated sediments	
Less drilling–fluid additive is required to lift the cuttings	
Reduced development time	

Dual-Wall Air Rotary Drilling	
Advantages	**Disadvantages**
Continuous representative formation samples and water samples can be obtained	High initial cost of drilling rig and equipment
Estimates of aquifer yield can be made easily at many depths in the formation	Limited to rather small holes, less than 9 in (229 mm) to 10 in (254 mm)
Fast penetration rates are possible in coarse alluvial or broken fissured rock	Limited to depths of 1,200 ft (366 m) to 1,400 ft (427 m) in alluvial deposits (most effective at depth of 600 ft (183 m)) and at up to 1,900 ft (579 m) in hard rocks
Washout zones are reduced or eliminated	Well-trained drilling crew is needed
Screens and conventional casing can be installed	

Noncirculation Methods	
Cable-Tool Drilling	
Advantages	**Disadvantages**
Rigs are relatively inexpensive, have low energy requirements, and require little sophisticated maintenance	Slow penetration rates
Because of their size, machines can be operated in difficult terrain or areas where space is limited or road conditions do not allow heavy equipment	Casing costs usually are higher (because heavier-walled or larger-diameter casing can be required)
A borehole is stabilized during the entire drilling process, allowing drilling where lost circulation is a problem	Some geologic conditions make it difficult to retract long strings of casing without using special equipment
Wells can be drilled in areas where little make-up water exists	
Recovery of reliable samples is possible from every depth (unless heaving conditions occur)	
Wells can be bailed at any time to determine the approximate water yield at the current depth	
Bucket-Auger Drilling	
Advantages	**Disadvantages**
Used for drilling large-diameter wells	Limited to depths of less than 100 ft (30 m)
	Can drill only in unconsolidated sediments (primarily clayey materials)

SUMMARY

Selection of the best, most efficient, and most effective drilling method requires an understanding of the geologic conditions of the formation and the physical limitations of the drilling rig and drilling method. Many drilling difficulties occur because the drilling professional either is unprepared to handle the wide range of subsurface conditions or has pushed the rig beyond its safe operating limits.

Table 7.3 provides relative performance ratings for the different drilling methods when used in various geologic formations. The relative performance differences between drilling methods, however, also depend on the experience level of the drilling professional, the presence of any geologic anomalies at the site, and the pressure conditions affecting the groundwater. Table 7.4 provides a comparison of drilling methods for various borehole sizes and conditions.

Table 7.3. Relative Performance of Different Drilling Methods in Various Types of Geologic Formations

Formation	Cable Tool	Fluid Rotary	Air Rotary	DTH Air Rotary	Casing Advancing Systems — Hammer	Underreamer	Rotator	DTH Driven	Reverse Fluid	Dual-Wall Reverse DTH	Fluid Rotary
Sand & Gravel	4	5	NR	NR	6	2	5	2	4	6	6
Boulders In Drift	3 to 2	2 to 1	NR	NR	5	4	5	3	2 to 1	4	NR
Clay & Silt	4	5	NR	NR	5	3	5	2	5	5	4
Firm Shale	4	5	4	5	5	5	5	5	5	5	6
Sticky Shale	4	5	3	4	5	5	5	5	5	5	6
Brittle Shale	4	5	3	3	4	5	5	5	4	5	6
Sandstone, Poorly Cemented	4	4	NR	NR	4	6	4	5	4	5	4
Sandstone, Well Cemented	3	4	5	4	NR	5	NR	6	3	5	3
Chert Nodules	3	3	3	5	NR	5	3	5	3	5	5
Limestone	3	3	3	6	NR	6	3	4	5	6	3
Limestone with Chert Nodules	3	5	5	6	NR	5	3	4	3	3	4
Limestone, Broken	3	3	5	6	NR	5	3	4	3	5	5
Limestone, Caverous	3	3 to 1	2	5	NR	4	3	4	1	5	4
Dolomite	3	4	4	6	NR	5	NR	3	5	5	5
Thin Basalt in Sedimentary	3	3	5	6	NR	5	NR	3	3	5	5
Basalts in Thick Layers	3	3	4	5	NR	4	NR	3	3	5	5
Basalt, Fractured	3	1	3	3	NR	3	NR	2	1	4	4
Metamorphic Rocks	3	3	4	5	NR	4	NR	3	3	4	3
Granite	3	3	4	5	NR	4	NR	3	3	4	3

NR - Not Recommended
* Assuming sufficient hydrostatic pressure is available to contain active sand (under high confining pressures)

Rate of Penetration
1 Impossible
2 Difficult
3 Slow
4 Medium
5 Rapid
6 Very Rapid

The following table provides a comparison of drilling methods for various borehole sizes and conditions (in U.S. customary units).

Table 7.4. Comparison of Drilling Methods for Various Borehole Sizes and Conditions

	Drilling Method	Relative Penetration Rate	Typical Borehole Diameter Range (in)	Depth Range (ft)	Borehole Damage	Cuttings Removal	Hole Stability Control
Direct Circulation	Mud Rotary	G	4 to 20	5,000+	H	G	G
	Air Rotary	E	4 to 12	5,000+	M	G	G
	Casing Rotator	E	12 to 30	500 to 1,200	I	E	E
	Casing Hammer	G	4 to 8	200 to 600	L	E	E
	Under-reamer	E	6 to 48	300 to 1,000	L	E	E
	DTH Driven	G	4 to 48	200 to 800	L	E	E
Reverse Circulation	Mud Rotary	G	4 to 36	3,000	M	G	G
	Dual-Wall Air Rotary	E	5 to 12	2,500	L	G	F
Non-Circulation	Cable Tool	P to F	4 to 36	1,500	L	G	E
	Bucket Auger	F	24 to 48	150	M	F to G	F
Key: Excellent (E); Good (G); Fair (F); Poor (P); High (H); Moderate (M); Low (L).							

ACKNOWLEDGMENTS

Various individuals from Schramm, Inc. (West Chester, Pennsylvania (U.S.A.)) provided valuable technical input and review of this chapter, including:

- Mr. Richard E. Schramm, Chairman;
- Mr. Robert V. Edwards, VP-Development;
- Mr. Frank C. Gabriel, VP-Sales; and
- Mr. Brian D. Brookover, Applications Engineer.

Mr. Tom Downey, President, Downey Drilling Inc. (Lexington, Nebraska (U.S.A.)) also provided a review and comments. His experiences as a drilling professional brought valuable insights to this chapter.

CHAPTER 8
Drilling Fluids

Ron Peterson
Baroid Drilling Fluids

Fred Rothauge
Quality Drilling Fluids

Drilling fluids are a combination of a base fluid (e.g., water, air), other additives selected specifically to achieve desired fluid properties, and the solids or other materials generated by the drilling process. In the late nineteenth century, water was the only principal fluid used in rotary drilling, although some entrainment of natural clay particles into the fluid must have occurred much of the time.

The general term "mud" originated when drillers began adding certain types of clays to water to form drilling fluid. Recent industry advances, however, have made the term "mud" somewhat obsolete. There now are numerous types of additives used to impart specific properties to the drilling fluids, therefore modern systems are termed "drilling-fluids systems." Water-well drilling-fluids technology has reached the point where drilling-fluid additives are designed and selected based on their fitness for the intended use and their compatibility with potable aquifers.

Much of the progress in drilling-fluid development initially occurred in the oil industry, and the developments later were applied in the water-well industry. As the water-well industry has advanced so has its drilling fluid technology, and now developments in the water-well industry also are used successfully in the oil industry.

The National Sanitation Foundation (NSF) was founded in 1944 and, in cooperation with the U.S. Environmental Protection Agency, in 1985 began certifying drinking-water additives for use in drilling wells in potable aquifers. Today the NSF, Underwriters Laboratory (UL), American National Standards Institute (ANSI), and similar organizations certify many drilling-fluid additives for use in drilling wells for potable aquifers.

The drilling-fluid system typically represents 10% or less of the total cost of a water well, however the economic success of the drilling operation might be determined primarily by the drilling professional's ability to control the physical characteristics of the drilling fluid.

TYPES OF DRILLING FLUIDS

Quite simply, a fluid is defined as anything that flows and assumes the shape of its container. Drilling fluids used in the water-well industry include water-based and air-based systems (Table 8.1). Oil-based fluids— commonly used in drilling for oil and gas—cannot be used in the water-well industry and are not discussed in this chapter. There basically are three types of drilling fluids used in the water-well industry: water based, natural mud (no treatment), and air based.

Table 8.1. Major Types of Drilling Fluids Used in the Water-Well Industry

Water Based	Air Based
Clean freshwater	Dry air
Water with clay additives	Mist: Droplets of water entrained in the airstream
Water with polymeric additives	Foam: Air bubbles surrounded by a film of water containing a foam-stabilizing surfactant
Water with clay and polymeric additives	Stiff foam: Foam containing film-strengthening materials such as polymers and bentonite

Many special additives, such as flocculants, thinning agents (dispersants), weighting materials, filtrate reducers, lubricants, and lost-circulation materials, are used to further adjust the properties of drilling fluids. Thus, the term "drilling fluid" in the water-well industry refers variously to clean freshwater; dry air; a suspension of solids or a mixture of liquid additives in water and droplets of water dispersed in air; or a mixture of water and surfactant—or water, surfactant, and colloids—dispersed in air.

Water-Based Fluid

Water-based drilling fluids consist of a liquid phase, a suspended-particle (colloidal) phase, and a drill-cuttings phase. The colloidal portion can comprise from less than 1% of the fluid to much more.

A freshwater-based drilling fluid is a mixture of a freshwater continuous phase with clays, polymers, surfactants, and other conditioning additives combined (as necessary) to impart the desired properties to the drilling fluid. Water-based systems provide a positive head (hydrostatic pressure) on the formation, providing borehole stability where unconsolidated formations or highly swelling clays are evident. The fluid density in water-based systems can be increased to control water flows or shallow gas.

Natural Mud (Native Mud)

The term "clear-water drilling" often is used to denote natural (or native) mud; no materials are added to the fluid and the properties are due to the entrainment of drill cuttings into the system. In reality, "clear-water drilling" usually pertains to systems using polymer flocculants and properly designed floc tanks or pits to settle all solids before the fluid is returned to the borehole. A clear-water system, however, seldom exists: Water plus solids equals mud. Natural muds— usually mistaken as "clear-water drilling"—occur when the driller allows native solids to become incorporated into the clear-water system. If not monitored, this system could have solids content that is greater than 10% and weights that are greater than 11 lb/gal (1.3 kg/ℓ). For most drilling situations and drilling fluids, the desirable solids content is less than 6% and the desired weight is less than 9.3 lb/gal (1.1kg/ℓ).

Air-Based Fluid Underbalanced Drilling

Air-based systems are composed of air as the continuous phase. As needed, water (with and without surfactants) can be injected into the airstream and clays or polymers can be added to the injection fluid.

Air-based drilling fluids might consist of only a dry-air phase but, more often, they contain some water to which a surfactant is added to produce a drilling foam. Occasionally, a small amount of clay or polymer is added to stiffen the foam. Thus the primary drilling fluids—water and dry air—can be used alone, but a great variety of additives are available to modify their physical and chemical properties and to significantly enhance their performances.

Aerated-Mud Underbalanced Drilling

Aerated-mud systems are water-based systems that use air to reduce fluid density. These systems are used where underbalanced drilling is preferred, or when lost circulation occurs. Such systems usually require a mud pump and air compressor. Air is added between the mud pump and the drill string. As this aerated fluid turns the corner at the bit, the air starts up the annulus—decompressing and lowering the weight of the fluid column. These systems also are used where highly permeable or fractured formations are under-pressured, and the static fluid level might be below the surface. The use of loss-circulation materials is optional for this type of system.

SELECTING A DRILLING-FLUID SYSTEM

The exact drilling-fluid system selected principally depends on the rock formation or stratigraphy expected and the equipment available. Remoteness of the drilling site, availability of drilling equipment, water supplies, environmental regulations, and the experience of the drilling crew also are important considerations in selecting the fluid system.

Drilling in hard rock, for example, requires procedures different from those used for drilling in sedimentary rock or unconsolidated formations. Water-based drilling-fluid systems using clay or polymeric additives typically are used in unconsolidated and highly bentonitic formations; air is used in well-consolidated or semi-consolidated rocks and sediment; and clear-water systems are used where formation protection is less important, usually above the aquifer and where higher penetration rates are desired. Clear-water systems also can be used in consolidated, semi-consolidated, and nonsensitive (nonswelling) sediments. The success of any drilling-fluid system mainly depends on the chemistry of the mix water, the particular additives selected, and the physical and chemical characteristics of both the cuttings created and the water contained in the formation being drilled.

The best way to control or prevent potential formation problems is to be familiar with the formations anticipated, and to use the proper drilling equipment and a well-designed drilling fluid.

DRILLING FLUID FUNCTIONS

Drilling fluids can perform many functions, depending on the physical and chemical conditions found in the borehole. The primary functions of these fluids are described below.

Clean the Bit and the Borehole Bottom

Cuttings must be prevented from sticking to the face of the bit because they reduce its ability to effectively continue to advance the hole. "Bit balling" can result from incorrect bit design, improper drilling-fluid design, or inadequate circulation.

The drilling-fluid system also must remove the cuttings from the bottom of the borehole during drilling or the cuttings continue to be reground, become entrained in the drilling fluid, and impede the drilling process. The rate at which cuttings can be removed depends on the viscosity, density, and uphole velocity of the drilling fluid, and the size, shape, and density of the cuttings. Table 8.2 provides recommended annular velocities to maintain a clean borehole.

**Table 8.2. Recommended Annular Velocities for Maintaining
Adequate Borehole Cleaning**

Circulating Medium	Recommended Annular Velocities	
	ft/min	m/min
Air-mist	3,500 to 4,500	1,067 to 1,372
Water	120 to 300	37 to 91
Normal mud	100 to 140	30 to 43
Very thick mud	60 to 80	18 to 24
Stiff foam	40 to 60	12 to 18
© 2005 Baroid, a Halliburton PSL		

Ideally, the drilling-fluid should entrain the cuttings at the bit, carry them to the surface, and allow them to drop into a settling pit or tank before the fluid is recirculated. Inefficient removal of cuttings can reduce the penetration rate, adversely affect the physical properties of the drilling fluid, and increase the energy required to recirculate the drilling fluid. Excessive solids in the drilling fluid also results in increased torque on the drill string, excessive wear on the drill string, and wasted energy. The cuttings generated by drilling a 12¾-in (32.4-cm) diameter hole 1,000 ft (305 m) deep, for example, will exceed more than 100,000 lb (45,000 kg).

Stabilize the Borehole

Drilling fluid stabilizes the borehole walls to maintain an open borehole, and prevents the expansion of swelling clays. When using water-based systems, the drilling fluid must provide a pressure greater than that existing in the formations penetrated. The pressure exerted against the borehole wall depends on the height of the fluid column and the weight of the drilling fluid.

If water flows into the wellbore from the penetrated formations then sloughing of the hole can occur, resulting in wasted time, increased drilling costs, and potential loss of the borehole. Occasionally, a portion of the drill string becomes buried by a caving formation and requires an extensive fishing operation; the drill string even could be lost permanently—causing abandonment of the borehole.

Drilling fluids should prevent formation clays from expanding into the borehole during drilling. Some hydrating clays can absorb large volumes of water, thereby increasing the physical dimensions of the clay. To control this problem, the drilling fluid must isolate formation clays from the water in the drilling fluid. This usually is achieved by adding polymeric drilling-fluid additives to water-based drilling fluids that contain clay additives. These polymeric additives tighten the filter cake, coat the formation clays, and minimize swelling caused by hydration. The coating effect easily can be seen when examining clay cuttings brought to the surface in the drilling fluid. Rather than being dispersed into the drilling fluid, the clay cuttings are carried up the borehole intact.

Cool and Lubricate the Drill Bit

Bit cooling is a critical function of the drilling fluid. Fluids circulating through the drill string cool and lubricate the bit, thereby reducing potentially damaging heat buildup, avoiding unnecessary bit wear, and minimizing maintenance needs.

Control Fluid Loss

All water-based drilling-fluid systems must control drilling-fluid loss in highly permeable formations by creating a nearly impermeable clay filter cake or polymeric film on the borehole wall. The quality of the solids in a drilling fluid is critical to the quality of the filter cake. Good-quality sodium bentonite solids, supplemented with properly selected polymers, provide the most effective filter cake. Drilling fluids that have high fluid loss can allow penetration of water-sensitive formations—causing the hole to collapse—and also can permit excessive buildup of filter cake on the borehole, which might result in differentially stuck drillpipe.

Drop Cuttings into a Settling Pit

As drilling fluid is circulated through a settling pit, cuttings should drop out and not be recirculated. The gel strength of the drilling fluid is the primary factor controlling the settling rate of cuttings and is a measure of a fluid's ability to suspend cuttings when the fluid is at rest. Importantly, the shape and size of the settling pit also control a fluid's flow rate.

Excessive solids buildup results in greater drilling-fluid weights and causes increased pressures on the borehole—and this can cause self-induced lost returns. The ability to control the buildup of weight can be supplemented by diluting the drilling fluid with water and also via mechanical solids control.

Provide Information About the Wellbore

Drilling-fluid systems should facilitate the recovery of representative cuttings and also permit accurate geophysical logging of the well.

Suspend Cuttings in the Borehole

When a drilling fluid is not being circulated or is not in motion, cuttings tend to settle in the borehole. If such settling occurs at an excessive rate, then cuttings can accumulate around the drill bit or stabilizer and jam the rotation of the drill string when drilling resumes. The rate of particle settling is controlled by the drilling fluid's ability to develop gel strength.

Control the Formation

Proper drilling-fluid design is essential to control formations with abnormal pressures and to avoid creating artesian fluid flows.

Maximize Productivity

When properly designed, mixed, and used, drilling fluids reduce a well's development time and maximize its productivity; however no single drilling fluid can fulfill all functions perfectly. Usually a specific drilling-fluid and additive system is designed to create the optimum physical and chemical characteristics essential for control of individual downhole conditions. During drilling the principal objectives are to maintain desirable drilling-fluid properties, adapt to changing downhole and surface conditions, and control the buildup of suspended drill cuttings. In most cases, continuous monitoring and maintenance of the drilling fluid is necessary to achieve the best results.

PROPERTIES OF WATER-BASED DRILLING FLUIDS

Although most drilling-fluid systems used in water wells are relatively simple, the drilling-fluid properties listed in Table 8.3 should be understood thoroughly by water-well professionals. Regardless of which drilling-fluid system is used, its effectiveness depends upon the drilling professional's ability to anticipate the chemical and physical changes taking place during drilling and to make system modifications as required.

Table 8.3. Principal Properties of Water-Based Drilling Fluids

Density	Filter cake and fluid loss
Viscosity	pH
Yield point	Calcium content
Gel strength	Sand content

The drilling-fluid tests used in the water-well industry essentially are the same as those used in the oil and gas industry, and most were developed and designed under the sponsorship of the American Petroleum Institute (API).

The physical and chemical behaviors of bentonite and polymers differ significantly. These differences are examined separately in the discussion of each individual drilling-fluid property.

Drilling-Fluid Density

Control of drilling-fluid density is a fundamental factor in successful water-well drilling. Density is defined as the weight per unit volume of fluid; thus, the terms "density" and "weight" can be used interchangeably. Density is expressed in U.S. customary units in pounds per gallon (lb/gal) or pounds per cubic foot (lb/ft^3); in SI units it is expressed in grams per cubic centimeter (g/cm^3) or kilograms per cubic meter (kg/m^3). The densities and specific gravities of several common substances used in drilling fluids are provided in Appendix 8.A (DVD).

The actual pressure exerted at any point in a borehole by a static drilling fluid depends on the fluid density and the height of the fluid column above that specific point. Many drilling contractors automatically associate high-density drilling fluids with extra downhole pressure required to contain pressurized formations. Specific gravity—another way to express the density of a drilling fluid—is the ratio of the weight of a given volume of drilling fluid compared with the weight of an equal volume of water.

Drilling-fluid density is measured easily with a drilling-fluid (mud) balance (Figure 8.1). The procedure for measuring the density of a drilling-fluid sample is given in Appendix 8.B (DVD), and a drilling-fluid weight conversion table is supplied in Appendix 8.C (DVD).

Selection and maintenance of proper drilling-fluid density prevents both the collapse of the borehole and the flow of water into it. To maintain an open borehole, the pressure exerted by the drilling-fluid column must equal or slightly exceed the pore pressure (water and gas) in the aquifer. Typically, a minimum excess pressure of 5 psi (34.5 kPa) is desirable, although this pressure requirement can be greater when pressures from confined formations are encountered, and can be lesser in unconfined or underpressured formations.

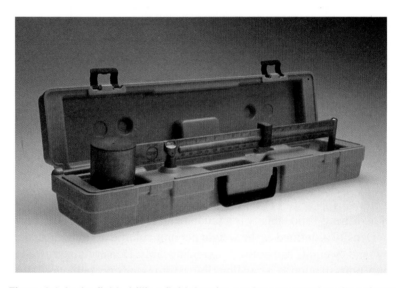

Figure 8.1. In the field, drilling-fluid density can be measured easily using a drilling-mud balance. The specific gravity and direct weight of the fluid also can be determined (Baroid, a Halliburton PSL).

Hydraulic pressure occurs in the pores of both unconfined and confined aquifers. In an unconfined aquifer the pressure at any point is represented by the head of water above that point. Ordinarily, the water pressure within a freshwater aquifer is 0.433 psi per ft (9.8 kPa per m) of depth, unless the total dissolved solids is abnormally high. Thus, at a depth of 10 ft (3.1 m), the pore pressure is 4.33 psi (29.9 kPa).

Under confined conditions, the potentiometric surface is above the top of the aquifer. Thus, pore pressures within the confined aquifer always exceed the normal 0.433 psi/ft (9.8 kPa/m) hydraulic pressure of aquifer thickness. Before the bit penetrates a confined aquifer, the excess pressure partially supports the overlying formations. Typically, the weight of this overlying material exerts a pressure of approximately 1 psi per ft (22.6 kPa per m) of depth. If the overburden was supported entirely by pore pressure, then the pressure in the aquifer should equal the head of water in the aquifer (0.433 psi/ft; 9.8 kPa/m) plus the weight of overlying materials (1 psi/ft; 22.6 kPa). Usually only part of the overburden is supported by confined pressure, and a figure of 0.465 psi/ft (10.5 kPa/m) often is used to estimate pore pressure in confined aquifers.

Drilling professionals should be able to calculate the downhole pressures exerted by the drilling fluid when it is at rest, and determine whether the hydrostatic pressure is sufficient to control the pore pressure in the formation. A simple equation for determining the hydrostatic pressure exerted by the drilling fluid in a borehole is provided in Equation 8.1. Hydrostatic pressure is given in psi, density in lb/gal, and height in ft (U.S. customary units).

$$\text{Hydrostatic pressure (psi)} = \text{fluid density (lb/gal)} \cdot \text{height of fluid column in feet} \cdot 0.052 \tag{8.1}$$

The resulting value is the hydrostatic pressure when the drilling fluid is at rest. The pump exerts additional pressure (called dynamic pressure) in the borehole when the drilling fluid is circulated. The total pressure exerted on the borehole as a result of the fluid density and induced circulating pressures is the equivalent circulating density (ECD). When the drilling fluid is thick or has a high density, the ECD is increased and can induce lost circulation. Lost circulation occurs when the formation absorbs drilling fluid because the borehole's hydrostatic pressure exceeds the formation pressure or fracture gradient. This often occurs in zones of high hydraulic conductivity or in fractured sections, and it can lead to reduced return of drilling fluid and cuttings at the flow line (or no return at all), and could result in a collapsed hole.

For most drilling conditions, the hydrostatic pressure exerted by the weight of the drilling-fluid column above the static water level in the borehole is sufficient to create positive pressures in the borehole. The hydrostatic pressure created by the drilling fluid usually is great enough to keep the borehole open. When static water levels are high, however, the weight of the drilling-fluid column above the static water level might not be sufficient to keep the borehole open. Unstable conditions in the borehole can be prevented by keeping the water level as high as possible and by increasing the density of the drilling fluid. Figure 8.2 is a diagram of the fluid forces in a borehole during drilling. The deeper the borehole becomes, the smaller the increase in the flow pressure (such as those caused by confining pressures) needed to overcome the positive outward pressure. Unstable conditions in the borehole can be prevented by keeping the water level as high as possible and by increasing the density of the drilling fluid.

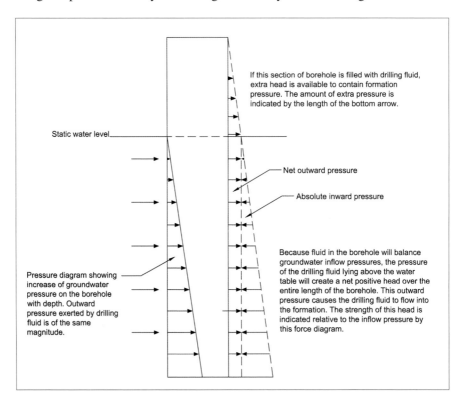

Figure 8.2. Diagram showing fluid forces in a borehole during drilling.

Under ordinary conditions, the maximum density that can occur in a clay system as a result of the entrainment of solids during drilling is approximately 11 lb/gal (1,320 kg/m^3). To increase density any further but maintain a proper solids-fluid ratio, higher-density material must be introduced so that a lesser quantity of solids (by volume) is needed to achieve a specific density.

Barite, which has a specific gravity of 4.2 to 4.35, is a standard weighting material and is much heavier than clay additives and most formation materials (which have specific gravities of 2.6 to 2.7). Barite particles are not active and are sized appropriately so as to remain suspended in the drilling fluid without affecting its flow characteristics. Another heavy mineral, ilmenite (which has specific gravity of 4.7), also can be used for weighting drilling fluids. Polymer drilling fluids lack gel strength and cannot keep heavy minerals in suspension at low uphole velocities or when at rest.

Soluble salts such as sodium chloride (NaCl) and calcium chloride ($CaCl_2$) are useful for weighting some drilling fluids that are made with polymeric additives. To ensure that the potable aquifer is not compromised, exercise extreme care when using salts to increase density.

The density of a fluid made with polymeric additives thus depends less on the amount of suspended solids contained than on the fluid's total dissolved solids. Contact the manufacturer of any additives used to insure that the polymer chosen is designed for use in a water well and is salt tolerant.

Practical drilling-fluid densities range from virtually 0 lb/gal for air to more than 15 lb/gal for bentonite with barite additives. In general, the density of the drilling fluid must be great enough to balance any confined pressure conditions in the borehole. Conversely, excessive drilling-fluid densities can cause high levels of fluid loss, the plugging of the aquifer, unsatisfactory cuttings removal in the mud pit, and pumping costs that are greater than necessary (Hutchinson & Anderson 1974; Tschirley 1978) (Figure 8.3).

To control the flow of water into the borehole, the drilling-fluid density should be increased before it reaches the confined formation. The additional drilling-fluid density required to equalize the confined pressure is determined by using the following formula.

$$\textit{Weight of water} \cdot \frac{\textit{Elevation of water above top of confined aquifer}}{\textit{Elevation of top of confined aquifer}} \qquad (8.2)$$

The calculated drilling fluid density only balances the confined pressure, however, therefore a safety factor of 0.3 lb/gal (36 kg/m^3) usually is recommended. The total added density should be sufficient to control any potential collapse of the formation during circulation of the drilling fluid and withdrawal of the drillpipe.

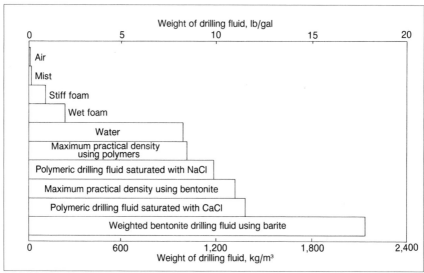

**Figure 8.3. The range of drilling-fluid weights (densities)
(Hutchinson & Anderson 1974; Tschirley 1978).**

During the drilling process, solids tend to accumulate in the drilling fluid causing the density to increase. If silt, clay, or poorly consolidated shale is present, then the density increase can be significant and solids must be removed or water must be added to reduce the solids-fluid ratio. Too great an increase in density can affect the drilling and well-completion processes in the following ways.

- Large volumes of drilling fluid and cuttings can be forced into the aquifer during drilling. Removal of the drilling fluid and cuttings during development can be extremely difficult, especially if clay is present.
- Material costs increase because of high fluid losses, particularly in areas where mix water is expensive or must be transported great distances.
- Rate of penetration is reduced. As cuttings are created by the bit, the hydrostatic pressure on the bottom of the borehole pushes down on them and impedes their removal from the borehole.
- Sample collection is more difficult and less reliable, because cuttings do not drop out of the drilling fluid at the surface and instead intermingle with the samples collected.

- ◆ Mud pump wear is increased because the pump must keep recirculating a high volume of unnecessary solids.
- ◆ Pumping costs increase because solids are continually recirculated and circulation of heavier fluids requires more energy.

Buildup of solids can be controlled through adequate pit design, by using mechanical solids-control equipment, and by adding freshwater.

Rheological Properties

Rheology deals with the deformation and flow of matter. Understanding rheological concepts is vital because successful completion of the borehole depends on creating the correct physical and chemical qualities for the drilling fluids. Drilling fluids behave in predictable ways due to the specific chemical and physical characteristics produced by particular additives when they are combined with the base system.

The flow characteristics (rheology) of a drilling fluid—viscosity, gel strength, and yield point—depend primarily on the size, shape, and molecular structure of the particles in the fluid. Clay particles are less than 0.16 mil (4 microns) in size, silt and barite are 0.16 mil (4 microns) to 2.5 mil (63 microns) in size, and fine to medium sand is 2.5 mil (63 microns) to 19.7 mil (500 microns) in size. The silt and barite, if present, mainly provide density, whereas the clay particles enhance the viscosity and filtration characteristics (as described below). Polymeric particles usually are much smaller than those of clay. Finely ground polymeric particles, such as those made from guar seeds, are about $3.9 \cdot 10^{-6}$ mil (0.0001 microns) in size. Consequently, the addition of even small volumes of polymers to a drilling fluid can have a significant effect on viscosity and filtration control.

Particle shape is important in determining how a fluid flows. Flat, tabular particles have large surface areas for their sizes and can "tie up" relatively large volumes of water. Some small particles, such as clay colloids, possess powerful electrical charges that affect the fluid both when it is in motion and when it is at rest. In contrast, polymeric particles can be anionic, cationic, or nonionic. They usually have a long-chained molecular structure that causes distinctive changes in the flow characteristics of a drilling fluid, depending on the amount of stress applied at various points in the circulation system.

Viscosity

Viscosity is a fluid's resistance to flow or to being pumped. The viscosity and uphole velocity are the primary factors determining the ability of a drilling fluid to remove cuttings from around the bit and move them up the borehole and the rate at which the cuttings settle when the fluid is at rest. The viscosity of any drilling fluid depends on many factors, including: (1) viscosity of the base fluid used; (2) number of particles (solids) per unit volume of drilling fluid; (3) density, size, and shape of particles; and (4) the attracting or repelling forces between the individual solid particles and between the solids and the base fluid (hydration potential).

In general, high-viscosity drilling fluids are required to lift coarse sand or gravel, whereas lower-viscosity drilling fluids are adequate for lifting fine sand and silt. Separation or settling of solids at the surface and effective cleaning of the bit face during drilling are facilitated by drilling fluids having low viscosity and low gel strength. Viscosity of a fluid can be measured using a viscometer or a Marsh funnel. Additional discussion regarding viscosity and measurement techniques is contained in Appendix 8.D (DVD).

Viscosity of Drilling Fluids Made with Clay Additives

The viscous nature of drilling fluids made with clay additives originates from the small size of clay particles (typically 0.16 mil (4 microns) or smaller) and their relatively large surface areas. Most clay particles have a platelike structure and groups of these platelets are common. The edges of clay platelets are positively charged and the flat surfaces are negatively charged. Because clay particles are so small, electrostatic charges govern their activity and they are strongly attracted to—or repulsed by—each other and various other substances.

Clay particles typically swell when exposed to water because the electrically unbalanced water molecules are strongly attracted to the plate surfaces and consequently force the plates apart. This results in the clay particles occupying a larger space, which leads to a more viscous fluid. The viscosity of a drilling fluid with clay additives also is a function of the rate at which the fluid is pumped. At lower velocities the viscosity is higher because it is governed by the charges of the plates; at higher velocities the charges of the plates have less effect. The gelling characteristics of a drilling fluid when at rest also result from these charges. Additional discussion of the viscosity of drilling fluids made with clay additives can be found in Appendix 8.E (DVD).

Viscosity of Drilling Fluids Made with Polymeric Additives

A polymer is a long-chained chemical compound consisting of many small molecular units (monomers or mers) combined together. Polymers can be either natural or synthetic, typically have a high molecular weight, and form chains of monomers that can be several thousand units long. Initially natural polymers were used in drilling fluids, however the understanding of polymers and the use of natural and synthetic polymeric colloids in drilling fluids has increased.

When using any natural polymer in a water well, performing prechlorination ensures that the polymer won't propagate bacteria growth. When the chains become linked they tend to make a strong film. Polymers can be used as the primary additive or to beneficiate bentonitic drilling fluids, and are described as low-solids or clay-free drilling-fluid additives. Polymers also increase drilling rates and drilling-fluid yields, thereby decreasing operational costs. Product information regarding Johnson Screens' Revert® is contained in Appendix 8.F (DVD).

The unique physical and chemical properties of polymers offer several specific advantages.

- Boreholes can be drilled with reduced bottom-hole pressures.
- Fluid loss can be controlled without the buildup of a thick filter cake.
- Torque and friction losses are reduced.
- Cores and other samples are not affected by the drilling-fluid additive.
- Some polymers are compatible with brackish water or brine.
- Cuttings settle rapidly at the surface so it is possible to circulate clean, lightweight, nonabrasive fluids.
- Some polymers also increase the effectiveness of certain well-logging methods because of their high resistivity.

When selecting a polymer for use in a drilling fluid, it is critical to understand the limitations of the polymer and to insure that it is fit for use in drilling a potable water well. When using natural polymers it is essential that all residual polymer is removed from the well and that the well is properly sanitized upon completion, to avoid leaving "food" for any bacteria that might be present.

Natural Polymeric Gum

Natural polymeric colloids (e.g., Johnson Screens' Revert®) consist of long-chained polymers referred to as polysaccharides (Figure 8.4); when hydrated in water, they form a viscous colloidal dispersion. One type of natural organic colloid is obtained from the finely ground seed of the guar plant. The endosperm portion of the seed is ground into colloid-sized particles ($3.9 \cdot 10^{-6}$ mil; 0.0001 micron) and used as food-grade guar gum for building viscosity in many food products. When used as a drilling-fluid additive, these nonionic colloids form a low-solids, biodegradable polymeric drilling fluid that does not introduce non-native clay particles into water-bearing strata.

Guar gums and certain synthetic polymers possess physical qualities that result in unusual hydration, gelling, and viscosity characteristics. Specific recommendations for working with guar additives are provided by the suppliers and should be consulted before using guar as a drilling-fluid additive. Specific properties can be controlled via processing and chemical techniques. Additional discussion on natural polymeric additives can be found in Appendix 8.G (DVD).

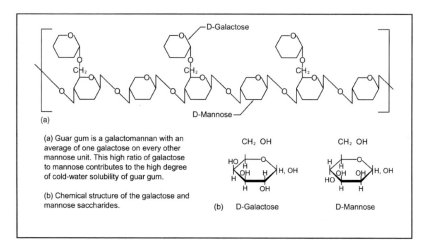

(a) Guar gum is a galactomannan with an average of one galactose on every other mannose unit. This high ratio of galactose to mannose contributes to the high degree of cold-water solubility of guar gum.

(b) Chemical structure of the galactose and mannose saccharides.

Figure 8.4. General chemical structure of the guar-gum molecule.

Synthetic Polymers

Synthetic polymers are of two basic types—natural materials that are produced synthetically, and completely synthetic materials that contain hydroxyl and carboxyl groups similar to natural gums and resins. The latter materials are distinguished by their imperviousness to the biological decomposition and resulting bacterial propagation that affects both natural and synthetically produced natural polymers.

Some synthetic polymers developed for the oil and exploration drilling industries are designed for high-alkaline fluid systems not commonly used in water-well drilling. The most common synthetic polymers used in the drilling industry are sodium polyacrylates (SPA), polyanionic cellulose (PAC), and partially hydrolyzed polyacrylamides (PHPA).

Polyanionic cellulose is a very effective synthetic polymer. It is available in both regular and low viscosity, and in many different grades or qualities. Importantly, the PAC used does not propagate bacterial growth and is designed for use in water wells. This polymer is very effective in controlling water loss in a bentonite-based drilling fluid. Regular PAC can be used when additional viscosity is desired and low-viscosity PAC be used when minimal viscosity is required. It should not be overused, however, because it is difficult to break down. Typical concentration levels are 0.5 lb (0.2 kg) to 4 lb (1.8 kg) per 100 gal (379 ℓ).

Partially hydrolyzed polyacrylamide polymers are very effective in controlling formation shales and clays. They come in numerous forms and each has specific properties. Different PHPAs provide different viscosity characteristics to the drilling fluids, so choosing the best one for the specific drilling application is critical. These polymers can be oxidized easily using an oxidizing agent like sodium hypochlorite. Swimming pool chlorine such as calcium hypochlorite (HTH) also should not be used, because it causes an insoluble precipitate to form. Typical concentrations of PHPA vary due to the individual characteristics of the individual PHPAs.

When using polymers the manufacturer's instructions must be observed, otherwise complexing (formation of solids) can clog water-bearing formations, filter packs, and well screens. Additionally, many of the chemicals used to compound synthetic polymers are not desirable for use in potable water wells. Drilling professionals should consult the manufacturer (in advance) to determine a polymer's acceptability or suitability.

Polymers provide many benefits to a drilling fluid. They can provide viscosity modification (thickening or thinning it), shale encapsulation, filtration control, friction reduction, and improvement of foam qualities. Polymers should be selected to enhance the desired properties of the drilling fluid.

The most notable field problem experienced with synthetic polymers has been a lack of shear stability that leads to reduced viscosity as drilling continues. Thus, the initial cost of synthetic polymer additives does not represent the total cost, because repeated additions of new or fresh polymer are required to maintain the desired viscosity. Polymers generally tend to coat the drill solids and are removed from the drilling fluid as the solids are removed. This requires that drilling-fluid properties be monitored and maintained by adding additional polymers as necessary.

Stress and Yield Point

Substances deform differently under stress, depending on their physical characteristics. A fluid (such as water) that deforms proportionately to an applied stress (or force) is called a Newtonian fluid (Figure 8.5). Drilling fluids with clay additives, however, act more like plastic materials—that is, they do not begin to deform until a certain amount of stress is applied.

The yield point is the pressure at which the pump begins to move the drilling fluid. The yield point is controlled by the strength of the attractive forces between individual particles in the drilling fluid. Drilling fluids become Newtonian when the yield point has been reached. Beyond the yield point, the relationship between stress and strain is more or less constant, indicating that the viscosity does not change significantly with increasing stress. Before the yield point is reached, the viscosity changes continuously in response to increasing stress. The stress required to induce flow is a measure of the viscosity of the drilling fluid.

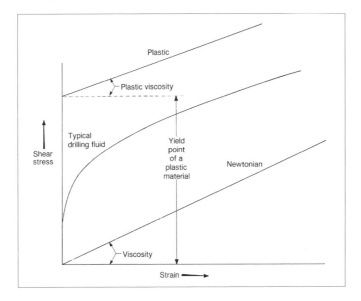

**Figure 8.5. Graph of the deformation (flow) characteristics for
Newtonian and plastic substances.**

Gel Strength of Drilling Fluids Made with Clay Additives

Gel strength is a measure of a drilling fluid's ability to support suspended particles when the fluid is at rest. The gel structure of a drilling fluid made with clay additives is produced when the clay platelets align themselves to join together. The positively charged edge of a plate aligns itself with the negatively charged flat surface of an adjacent plate; this process is called flocculation. This structure gives the liquid a plastic (quasisolid) form with strength properties called gel strength. If enough stress (force) is applied to the drilling fluid by the pump, then the gel breaks down.

The actual strength created by the gelling process is a function of how well the clay particles have been mixed into the water and the extent of their hydration. Dispersion of the platelets occurs when they have been thoroughly separated by pumping or some other form of agitation. If mixing is incomplete, then the clay platelets still might be loosely assembled as stacked groups in an aggregated state (Figure 8.6).

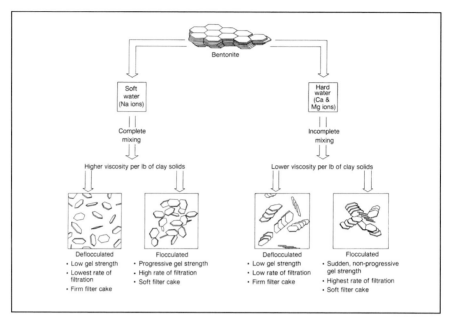

Figure 8.6. When clay particles are mixed into water they either become dispersed evenly throughout the liquid or exist in an aggregated condition.

In both the aggregated and the dispersed condition, groups of platelets or individual platelets tend to repel one another when the fluid is in motion. When a drilling fluid is at rest, however, some of the clay plates orient themselves to balance the electrical charges on the edges and flat surfaces of other plates. Occasionally, the gel strength can become excessive even though the fluid is kept in motion. The addition of an appropriate thinner deflocculates the fluid by reducing the attractive forces and separating the platelets. The highest viscosity occurs when the clays become dispersed and flocculated in the fluid. If the water is hard the clay platelets remain in an aggregated state, thereby limiting the viscosity. Individual particles or groups of particles can become either flocculated or deflocculated in each of these conditions. The hardness of the water and the flow rate determine which conditions exist.

A drilling fluid generally exhibits more than one physical condition. The four common drilling fluid states are: (1) aggregated-flocculated, (2) aggregated-deflocculated, (3) dispersed-flocculated, and (4) dispersed-deflocculated. The greatest gel strength occurs when the drilling fluid is in a dispersed-flocculated state. If the clay additives are mixed thoroughly so that the platelets are dispersed, for example, and the drilling fluid then is allowed to remain at rest, the drilling fluid assumes a dispersed-flocculated state leading to a high gel strength and a uniform solids content.

If a drilling fluid with clay additives is left standing in a borehole or mud pit, over time its gel strength increases as more clay plates align themselves. This quality is called thixotropy. After the drilling fluid has been allowed to remain at rest for some time, excessively high gel strengths might demand so much pump pressure to resume circulation that the drilling fluid could be forced into a fractured or weak formation. Gel strength does not instantly break down after the mud pump is started, and continued agitation is needed. The most effective way to break down the gels, and consequently to minimize the pressure exerted by the pump, is to rotate the drill rods prior to starting the pump. Pump agitation eventually restores the drilling fluid to its original viscosity.

Adding bentonite increases gel strength, but adding too much retards the settlement of cuttings at the surface. As such, adding only enough bentonite needed to lift the cuttings and support any weighting material at the desired pumping rate is most effective.

Water chemistry also affects the gel strength of a drilling fluid made with clay additives. Soft water helps clay additives become well flocculated; however in hard water groups of clay platelets tend to remain together, and gel strengths are somewhat lessened.

Gel Strength of Drilling Fluids Made with Polymeric Additives

Most natural and synthetic polymeric drilling fluids have virtually no gel strength. This lack of gel strength insures that cuttings removal is exceptionally good at the surface, wear on the mud pump by abrasive material is minimized, and pumping pressures are minimized during normal circulation and when circulation resumes. To prevent the cuttings from accumulating around the drill bit, however, drilling professionals should make sure that the borehole is cleared of all cuttings before circulation is stopped.

Many polymeric additives have little gel strength because the colloids are nonionic; that is, they are not held together by electrical charges. A polymeric additive therefore does not produce a thixotropic condition in a drilling fluid. When calculating the yield point of a drilling fluid, it is important to remember that the calculated yield point for bentonite (a true thixotropic drilling fluid) is a direct indication of its gel strength. No similar comparison can be made for a drilling fluid made with polymeric additives; the calculated yield point is meaningless because the drilling fluid has no gel strength.

When a sudden plugging effect is needed in a borehole (for example, in zones of lost circulation), natural polymers such as Revert® can be strongly gelled chemically. If borate is added to Revert® and the pH of the water is more than 7.5, then the borate ion acts as a cross-linking agent with hydrated guar gum to form cohesive three-dimensional gels (Figure 8.7). The gel strength is determined by pH, temperature, and the concentration of reactants (boron and guar colloids). If temperature and concentration are held constant and the pH of the water is raised from 7.5 to 9.2 (the optimum pH), then the gel strength increases. At its optimum condition drilling fluid is similar to a firm, food-grade gelatin. The Revert® gel can be liquefied by dropping the pH to slightly less than 7.0, which changes the hydrated borate ion $(B(OH)_4)$ to boric acid $(B(OH)_3)$. Lowering the pH to less than 7.0 can destroy the viscous characteristics of the drilling fluid.

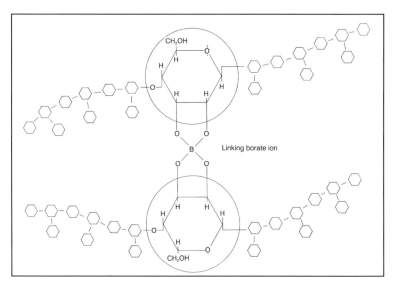

Figure 8.7. When borax is introduced into a natural polymeric drilling fluid made from guar, it cross-links the molecules. In this process, guar molecules become linked together to form a strong gel.

Filtration

Another of the principal requirements for a drilling fluid is that it prevents fluid loss by forming a filter cake or low-permeability film on the porous face of the borehole. The sealing property depends on the amount and nature of the colloidal materials in the drilling fluid. The filter cake produced by clays and the thin film created by polymeric colloids are physically dissimilar—the size and shape of the particles differ and the ability of each material to hydrate is significantly different. Colloidal particles and suspended cuttings entrained during drilling are important components of the total solids that create a filter cake or film. Thus, the filtration properties of all drilling fluids are, in part, supplied by materials derived from the borehole. Thickness of filter cake is measured in thirty-seconds of an inch (only a few mm).

When drilling begins, hydrostatic pressure in the borehole causes the drilling fluid to flow into porous formations. When using drilling fluids made with clay additives, the fluid and some clay particles initially enter the formation unhindered. As the suspended solids and cuttings continue to close off the pores, however, clay particles filter out and form a cake on the borehole wall. The remaining pores around the borehole become clogged with particles, and progressively smaller volumes of water can pass into the formation (Figure 8.8). Over time, a filter cake effectively limits water flow through the borehole wall except in highly permeable zones, where lost circulation is apt to occur. Filter-cake formation must happen as quickly as possible, and its development occurs on porous and permeable formations.

Permeability of the filter cake depends on the type of clay used in the drilling fluid; generally, the greater the number of colloidal particles present, the lower the permeability of the cake. For example, Gray (1972) points out that—for the same duration of filtration and at the same viscosity for both drilling fluids—the thickness of filter cake formed on a sandstone from a native-clay drilling fluid with a density of 10.3 lb/gal (1,230 kg/m^3) is 36 times greater than the thickness of that resulting from a premium bentonite drilling fluid having a density of 8.6 lb/gal (1,030 kg/m^3).

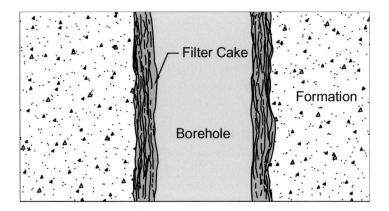

Figure 8.8. Hydrostatic pressure in the borehole forces drilling fluid into the formation, clay particles in the drilling fluid form a filter (mud) cake on the borehole wall, and eventually the fluid loss is reduced significantly.

During drilling, the thickness of the clay filter cake varies according to the rate of erosion caused both by the rotation of the tools and by the uphole velocity of the drilling fluid. In addition, thicker filter cakes build up in formations that have higher hydraulic conductivity. When circulation stops, the filter cake continues to build up on the wall of the borehole.

The nature of a filter cake or film, and the way it forms, are quite different when drilling fluids are prepared with or enhanced with polymers. Guar gum is a polysaccharide that provides natural fluid-loss control. This property is derived from both the soluble guar gum particles (sols) dispersed in the drilling fluid and the insoluble cell-wall residue (insols) of the gum. Each of the insol particles is covered with a relatively thick, viscous film of fluid produced by the dissolved sol particles—and, as insols build up on a borehole wall, fluid is prevented from leaving the borehole. Thus, fluid loss can be controlled with a relatively thin coating on the wall of the borehole (Figure 8.9). A thicker layer of clay particles might be required to achieve the same fluid-loss properties. In general, polymeric films are much thinner than the filter cakes created by clay particles, even though the water-loss characteristics are the same.

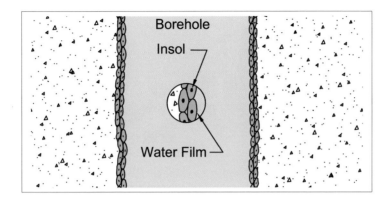

Figure 8.9. When polymers are used as drilling fluid additives, thin polymeric films form on the borehole wall, and insol particles are plastered onto the wall of the formation.

The filtration rate of a drilling fluid can be determined using a filtration test device (Figure 8.10). Such devices can measure the volume of fluid that might be lost to the formation and the resulting thickness of the filter cake deposited on the permeable walls of the borehole. Bentonite filtration testing procedures using API standards are not completely valid for polymers, because the rates of hydration vary for different polymeric materials. Systems that combine bentonite gels and viscosifiers such as polyanionic cellulose powder, carboxymethylcellulose (CMC), and PHPAs, however, can be tested for water-loss characteristics with filtration test equipment. The filter cake from a well-maintained bentonite-based fluid is thin and impermeable (Figure 8.11).

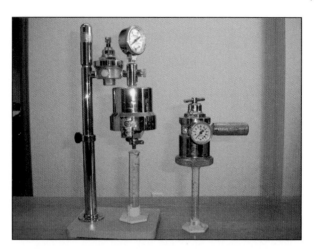

Figure 8.10. A filter press (e.g., full-area press left side, half-area press right side) can be used to measure the flow rate of water through a specific thickness of filter cake (Quality Drilling Fluids).

Figure. 8.11. Examples of filter cake thickness. A well-maintained drilling fluid deposits a thin filter cake on the borehole wall (right side). Inadequately designed or poorly maintained fluid, or a native mud, deposits much thicker cake (left side) (Quality Drilling Fluids).

Failing to adequately maintain the drilling-fluid system, allowing solids to build up, and uncontrolled filtration all can result in a very thick filter cake and can cause a stuck pipe—creating development problems (Figure 8.12).

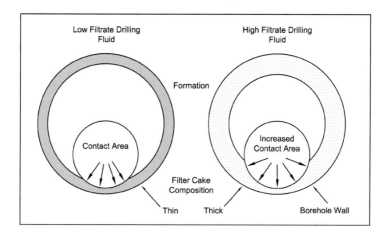

Figure 8.12. A thick filter cake allows more contact with the drillpipe and can result in differentially stuck pipe (© 2005 Baroid, a Halliburton PSL).

Although a filter cake is required during drilling, after the well has been completed any residual clays on the borehole wall and in the aquifer are highly detrimental to the well's productivity. Drilling fluids should be conditioned (thinned) when the well is completed and before the gravel pack is placed. Well-development procedures should be conducted as soon as possible after a well has been drilled, otherwise complete drilling fluid removal can become impossible—especially if clay additives are used. Filter-cake removal during development can be accomplished primarily via mechanical means.

Polymeric films also should be removed or broken down, because some clays become entrained in the film during normal drilling operations. Many polymeric drilling fluids and films can be broken down chemically—within minutes—using chlorine or other strong oxidizing materials. Although these chemical processes are not well understood, Figure 8.13 shows that polymeric drilling fluids can be removed in the initial development episode with the least-powerful development method because of the presence of naturally occurring enzymes, whereas clay filter cake removal can require thinners, mechanical methods, and additional time. In the wells shown in Figure 8.13, the Revert® was allowed to break down naturally before development procedures were initiated. More aggressive development methods are required to remove bentonite drilling fluids (Driscoll et al. 1980).

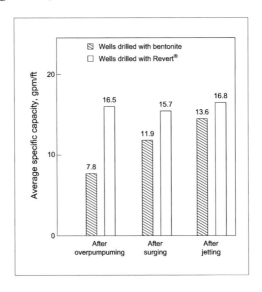

Figure 8.13. Comparison of the average specific capacities after three development episodes on each well. Ten shallow wells were constructed in glacial outwash and drilled with either bentonite (7 wells) or Revert® (3 wells) (Driscoll et al. 1980).

TREATMENT OF MIX WATER FOR DRILLING FLUIDS

For maximum drilling efficiency, the chemical characteristics of the mix water should be adjusted, if necessary, before mixing begins. If the water has a pH of less than 6.5, for example, the performance of a drilling fluid with clay additives might not be satisfactory. Most drilling-fluid additives perform best in water having a pH range of 8.5 to 9. In general, the lower the pH, the more likely it is that the water has high concentrations of ions such as calcium and magnesium in solution (hard water). Drilling-fluid additives typically perform best when the total hardness of the water is kept at less than 200 ppm.

Clay yields can be increased and water losses decreased if hard water is softened before it is used for mixing the drilling fluid. Soda ash (sodium carbonate (Na_2CO_3)) can be added to the mix water to precipitate the calcium (as calcium carbonate ($CaCO_3$)) before the drilling fluid is mixed. Under ordinary conditions, 0.5 lb (0.2 kg) to 2 lb (0.9 kg) of soda ash (Na_2CO_3) per 100 gal (0.4 m^3) of mix water (hardness is given as $CaCO_3$ in mg/ℓ) is sufficient to soften the water. The addition of soda ash also usually raises the pH to 8.5 to 9.0. The pH of the drilling fluid should be checked after the addition of the soda ash to verify that it is 7.5 or greater.

The hydration potentials of colloidal additives are significantly reduced if metallic ions occur at high concentrations. If iron concentrations are 3 ppm (3 mg/ℓ) or greater, for example, then the viscosity buildup in a natural organic system could be retarded. Polyvalent metallic ions can be removed from water by chlorination at a 50 ppm (50-mg/ℓ) concentration.

It is good practice to chlorinate all water used to mix the drilling fluid, as well as any makeup water added to the system. The mix water should be chlorinated to a concentration of from 50 ppm (50 mg/ℓ) to 100 ppm (100 mg/ℓ), depending on the particular additive selected. An easily measurable free-chlorine residual of approximately 10 ppm (10 mg/ℓ) should be maintained during drilling, and this concentration can be checked using chlorine paper. Chlorine treatment kills bacteria introduced into the borehole or aquifer during drilling and minimizes the amount of chlorine required for completion of the well. Mix water never should be taken from surface water near the well site. Not only are pathogenic bacteria likely to be in these water supplies but iron bacteria also commonly are found, and their subsequent growth in the well can cause severe problems. Because chlorine is unstable, its residual concentration should be checked periodically during drilling.

Sand Content

Sand content is a measure of the grit in the drilling fluid. Sand also is a particle size and is not a mineral; particles larger than 200 mesh are considered sand. Sand particles usually are abrasive, increase the weight of the drilling fluid, result in excessive wear on equipment, and waste fuel. It is desirable to keep sand content as low as possible—preferably to less than 2%.

Design of Mud Pits

Drilling fluid usually is mixed adjacent to the drilling rig in either portable or excavated pits. The capacity of portable pits for direct rotary rigs should be 1 to 2 times the borehole volume. When a reserve pit (used to contain spoils or high-solids mud removed from the system) is not used, then excavated pits should be 5 to 7 times the borehole volume. Pits that are 3 to 4 times the borehole volume are suitable for reverse circulation drilling. The size of the mud pit is dictated by the volume of drilling fluid contained in the finished borehole and the need for a reserve volume, which varies according to the particular rotary system used. Usually the volume of the pit is 1.5 to 3 times the volume of the finished hole. Mud pit capacities can be calculated using the information provided (in U.S. customary units) in Table 8.4.

Table 8.4. Mud Pit Capacities and Dimensions

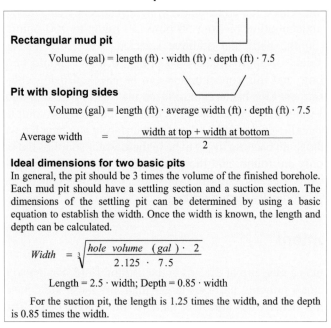

Rectangular mud pit

Volume (gal) = length (ft) · width (ft) · depth (ft) · 7.5

Pit with sloping sides

Volume (gal) = length (ft) · average width (ft) · depth (ft) · 7.5

$$\text{Average width} \quad = \quad \frac{\text{width at top} + \text{width at bottom}}{2}$$

Ideal dimensions for two basic pits

In general, the pit should be 3 times the volume of the finished borehole. Each mud pit should have a settling section and a suction section. The dimensions of the settling pit can be determined by using a basic equation to establish the width. Once the width is known, the length and depth can be calculated.

$$\text{Width} \quad = \sqrt[3]{\frac{hole \;\; volume \;\; (gal) \cdot 2}{2.125 \cdot 7.5}}$$

Length = 2.5 · width; Depth = 0.85 · width

For the suction pit, the length is 1.25 times the width, and the depth is 0.85 times the width.

When designing a mud pit, several factors should be considered (Figure 8.14). The principal objectives for the pit are storage of an adequate volume of drilling fluid and to act as an effective settling basin for suspended cuttings. For efficient removal of the suspended cuttings, the pit should be constructed in two sections—the settlement portion and the suction portion (Figure 8.15). Frequently, however, single-reservoir pits that serve both of these functions are used. The velocity of the drilling fluid as it moves through the mud pit during the storage interval must be as low as possible. This can be achieved by changing the direction of flow as the drilling fluid moves through the pits, as well as by deepening part of the pit or using baffles and overflows. Changing the direction of flow through the mud pit helps prevent gel development and allows the cutting to settle out more effectively. Deeper trenches are more satisfactory in reducing drilling-fluid velocity than are wider trenches, although for large pits the excavation equipment available might limit the configuration somewhat.

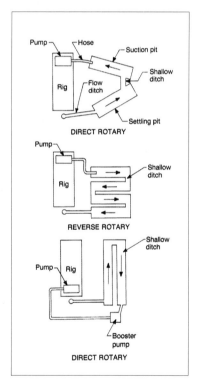

Figure 8.14. Common mud pit designs for rotary systems. The design selected depends on the type of additive used in the drilling fluid, the depth of the borehole, and the type of drilling rig used.

When a single pit is used, sometimes the bottom of the pit is sloped downward toward the pump suction point to slow the velocity and to create a place for the cuttings to settle. The suction hose must be mounted above the bottom of the pit. The bottom of an excavated mud pit should be sealed with a plastic film or a compacted layer of clay.

Figure 8.15. The mud pit often is comprised of two reservoirs, to be more effective in settling cuttings (Clear Creek Associates).

Mixing Additives into Water-Based Systems

Dispersion of the colloids into the drilling fluid and the subsequent rate of hydration are critical and both depend on the mixing method. Mixing essentials require that the makeup water be free of contaminates, that bentonite additives have adequate shear and time to yield, and that polymers have adequate shear and time to yield. Adequate shear breaks up:

- The bentonite from its aggregated state and exposes the surfaces to water;
- The polymer particles in a dry polymer, providing maximum surface area for adequate hydration; and

♦ The emulsion in a liquid polymer so that the individual polymer particles can be exposed to water and hydrate effectively.

Additives should be added through mud mixer (hopper) connected to a high-velocity venturi mixer; an alternative to a venturi mixer is a submersible prop mixer. Advantages of using a mixer include faster fluid mixing speed, greater hydration of the additive particles, and elimination of lumps of clay or polymer (called gum balls or fish eyes). Under ordinary conditions, a good mixer can mix 600 lb (270 kg) to 6,000 lb (2,700 kg) of clay and 50 lb (23 kg) to 500 lb (230 kg) of polymeric additives per hour. It is important to insure that the mixer has adequate time to do its job.

Mechanical mixers proportion the amount of clay or polymer to the proper amount of water (Figure 8.16). Venturi mixers are most effective when operated at a speed of 30 gpm (164 m³/day) at a pressure of 90 psi (621 kPa). After the proper flow rates are established, the dry polymer or clay is poured into the funnel or cone slowly—this tool is a mixing hopper, not a storage hopper. Sometimes a suction hose is used to vacuum the additive directly from the bag. Agitation of the particles in the water stream helps assure rapid hydration without the formation of gum balls. Submersible mixers are most effective if the mud pit is not full.

Figure 8.16. Mud mixers are extremely effective in hydrating the drilling-fluid additive; they also prevent the formation of gum balls or fish eyes that impede the viscosity buildup of the drilling fluid (© 2005 Baroid, a Halliburton PSL).

When an adequate mixer is not available, additives can be poured directly into the suction pit so that they are immediately carried through the pump and sheared. This is much less effective than using a mixing hopper. Liquid polymers are mixed with water mixers or added directly to the pit near the hose. Other liquid additives such as chlorine also should be added to the pit near the suction hose to disperse them as quickly as possible.

When additives are mixed in the mud pit, the additive is sprinkled on the surface of the nearly full pit or tank and a powerful water source is directed at the surface to create turbulence and cause hydration. This method is not recommended because a full pit makes mixing more difficult. It takes more time to mix the product and pick it up via suction than when the pit is not filled. More gel balls and "fish eyes" also are formed in a full pit.

Pouring product directly into the pit also is not recommended. This method usually wastes 30% to 40% of the product used, and poorly mixed product is very difficult to break down and remove during development. Figure 8.17 shows the preferred means to mix additives.

Figure 8.17. The drilling fluid additives are being mixed through a venturi mixer, which is the most effective way to mix drilling-fluid additives and insure proper hydration (© 2005 Baroid, a Halliburton PSL).

When mixing drilling fluids, materials must be added in the following order.

1. Soda ash (treat the makeup water first)
2. Bentonite (allow sufficient time for full yield)
3. Polymers (allow adequate time for yield)
    *   Dry polymers first (PAC before PHPA)
    *   Liquid polymers next

4. Surfactants (surfactants tend to foam therefore, following their addition, agitation of the system should be minimized)
5. Thinners and lost-circulation material are added as necessary

Using a prehydration tank is a very effective way to add bentonite to a system that includes polymers, and it insures that the bentonite is mixed thoroughly. Use extreme care to insure that no raw bentonite or polymers enter the system—especially the aquifer.

Various components of an ideal fluid-circulating system for direct rotary are presented in Figure 8.18 This particular design is for large-diameter, deep holes, but—except for the use of smaller components—most of the same requirements exist for any fluid system.

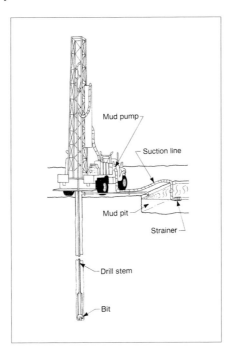

Figure 8.18. Components of a drilling-fluid circulating system for a direct rotary rig.

Solids Control

Solids control is critical in water-well drilling. A 9⅞-in (25-cm) borehole drilled to a depth of 200 ft (61 m) generates about 12,000 lb (5,440 kg) of solids. These solids must be removed from the hole and left at the surface—and must not be entrained in the drilling fluid. The first measure for controlling solids buildup is a properly designed drilling fluid. As discussed above, in a well-designed pit system the fluid has minimal viscosity and allows the solids to settle out. Other tools, such as shakers and desanders, also can be used. If solids-control equipment is limited, then a desilter-desander provides very effective and low-cost solids control. Figures 8.19 and 8.20 show the components of desanders.

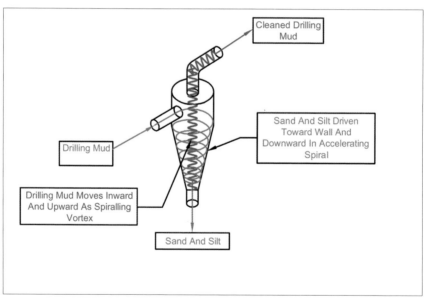

Figure 8.19. A hydrocyclone or desander helps remove solids from drilling fluid and minimize weight buildup (© 2005 Baroid, a Halliburton PSL).

Using a desander cone removes much of the solids (2.75 mil (70 microns) and larger) which helps maintain a minimum weight. Desander cones run most efficiently with an input pressure of 40 psi (275 kPa) and a flow of 40 gpm (218 m³) or greater.

**Figure 8.20. A correctly adjusted desander in a properly maintained system
has a fan-like discharge with minimal entrained solids
(© 2005 Baroid, a Halliburton PSL).**

LOST CIRCULATION

Lost circulation occurs when the weight of the fluid column (hydrostatic pressure) exceeds the formation pressure. These losses generally are a result of drilling into highly porous or fractured formations. Lost circulation also can be the result of incompetent formations and poor drilling practices. If a mud ring (boot) is forming on the drill string, a blockage occurs in the annulus and increases the pressure in the borehole below it. The increased pressure can induce hydraulic fractures, causing lost circulation. Monitoring pump pressure enables a drilling professional to note any significant increases and assume that a mud ring is forming. The pipe can be worked up and down to ream out the mud ring and prevent losses.

When lost circulation occurs, frequently a drilling professional's first reaction is to increase the pump speed to bring returns to the surface; this only aggravates the situation. Instead, the drill string should continue rotating and be pulled up off the borehole's bottom, the pump speed should be reduced, and then the situation should be evaluated.

Sometimes the easiest and most-effective treatment is to increase the viscosity of the drilling fluid. When greater measures are necessary the products used must be chosen carefully. Never introduce anything into a water well that would impair the water quality or propagate bacteria growth—especially when drilling near the aquifer. When lost circulation material is needed, the best choice is mineral fiber. Mineral fiber has two advantages: it does not propagate bacteria growth and, if necessary, it can be removed with acids typically used in water-well remediation. Lost circulation is best treated aggressively.

In areas where lost circulation occurs and fracturing is encountered, losses can be prevented by using fibrous acid-soluble material (e.g., acid wool, magma fiber), often called "lost circulation material." Whenever drilling can be performed without the addition of lost circulation materials, none should be added. In some cases it is very difficult to reach the blockage with acid to remove the materials after the well is completed.

UNDERBALANCED DRILLING

Underbalanced drilling—a situation where pressures in the borehole are less than formation pressures—minimizes formation damage by providing a negative differential pressure between the formation and the wellbore. Lost circulation and differential sticking also are minimized and penetration rates typically are greater in wells drilled using this method.

Techniques for underbalanced drilling include: (1) using lightweight drilling fluids; (2) injecting gas, air, or nitrogen down the drillpipe; (3) injecting gas, air, or nitrogen through a parasite string; and (4) injecting foam.

In the water-well industry, air or foam injection as well as lightweight drilling fluids are used most commonly. Lightweight drilling fluids can include aerated fluid systems. Reverse circulation using a non-flooded suction method also can constitute an underbalanced-drilling practice.

When using a non-flooded suction method, additional air can be required to lift the cuttings, or dual-wall pipe can be used. This method primarily is used when there is an adequate amount of surface pipe, the casing is set in a consolidated formation, and the static fluid level is difficult to maintain due to low formation pressure.

AIR DRILLING

Many water wells now are drilled using air because of the relative simplicity and effectiveness of air systems and the increasing number of rotary rigs that are equipped with air compressors. The earliest attempts to use air as a circulating medium—performed in the 1950s—showed that significant increases in penetration rates and bit life could be obtained (Cooper et al. 1977). Air drilling now is recognized as a primary means to reduce both drilling time and the cost of a well. Air drilling is discussed in Chapter 7. The mechanics of air drilling are more difficult to understand than those of typical water-based systems, because the drilling fluid is compressible and often contains water, an incompressible fluid, and other special additives.

To drill using air, the drilling rig must be equipped with an adequate compressor and a water pump that can inject up to 10 gal/min (37.9 ℓ/min) of water and chemicals into the airstream. On some rigs a special chemical pump is used to inject surfactants and chemicals into water before the water goes into the drill rods. Although using a chemical pump is not necessary, it allows the driller to add chemicals more accurately and enables greater control of the air system. The compressor usually is the key component in successful air drilling—mainly because insufficient air volume and pressure are the principal problems encountered when using this method.

The two types of compressors typically used on water-well rigs are piston (reciprocating) or helical-screw. Piston-type compressors are efficient for compressions up to 30:1 and possess high-pressure capacity. Screw-type compressors typically have somewhat lower pressure capacity than that of piston compressors, but they use positive displacement and consequently produce a constant air volume. In general, screw-type compressors operate at about 220°F (104°C), which is 40°F (2.2°C) to 50°F (10°C) cooler than the operating temperature of piston-type compressors. In screw-type compressors, the rotors operate in an oil bath and do not come into contact with one another or with the casing (Figure 8.21).

Figure 8.21. Screw-type air compressors are very efficient. This figure shows a single-stage screw-type compressor (Atlas Copco Company).

Compressors are rated to deliver a given air volume at a certain operating pressure (*see* Table 8.5). A two-stage compressor can deliver 600 cfm (0.3 m³/sec) to 750 cfm (0.4 m³/sec) at 250 psi (1,720 kPa). In practice, air delivery at a rated pressure means that a specific quantity of air (ft³ or m³) at atmospheric pressure can be compressed and delivered to the rig at that pressure in a specific amount of time (ft³/min; m³/sec). Once the air has been compressed to the delivery pressure, it no longer has the original free-air volume.

Table 8.5. Typical Pressure and Volume Capacities for Compressors Mounted on Water-Well Rigs

Number of Stages	Pressure		Volume	
	psi	kPa	ft³/min	m³/sec
1	125	862	600–900	0.28–0.42
1	150	1,030	750–1,150	0.35–0.54
2	275	1,900	750–900	0.35–0.42
2	350	2,410	900–1,050	0.42–0.5
2	500	3,450	1,050	0.5

For example, 750 ft³ (21.2 m³) of air compressed to 250 psi (1,720 kPa) has a compressed volume of only 42 ft³ (1.2 m³). The compressor rating is valid at sea level (maximum air density) at an air temperature of 60°F (15.5°C). The rating usually is designated at a compressor speed of 1,800 to 2,100 revolutions per minute (rpm). Correction factors must be used if the air temperature or elevation of the rig varies significantly from standard conditions (Table 8.6).

For instance the rated volume for an air compressor is reduced about 17% if it is operated at 60°F (15.5°C) in Denver, Colorado (U.S.A.) (at elevation of more than 5,000 ft (1,500 m)).

Table 8.6. Temperature and Pressure Correction Factors for Elevations above Sea Level

Elevation Above Sea Level		Atmo-spheric Pressure		Temperature									
				-17.8° C	-6.7° C	4.4° C	15.5° C	21.1° C	26.7° C	32.2° C	37.8° C	48.9° C	60° C
ft	m	psi	kPa	0°F	20°F	40°F	60°F	70°F	80°F	90°F	100°F	120°F	140° F
0	0	14.70	101.3	1.13	1.08	1.04	1.00	0.98	0.96	0.94	0.92	0.89	0.85
1,000	305	14.18	97.7	1.08	1.04	1.00	0.96	0.94	0.92	0.91	0.89	0.86	0.83
2,000	610	13.66	94.2	1.05	1.00	0.96	0.93	0.91	0.89	0.87	0.86	0.83	0.80
3,000	914	13.17	90.8	1.01	0.97	0.93	0.89	0.87	0.86	0.84	0.83	0.80	0.77
4,000	1,219	12.69	87.5	0.97	0.93	0.89	0.86	0.84	0.83	0.81	0.80	0.77	0.74
5,000	1,524	12.22	84.3	0.94	0.90	0.86	0.83	0.81	0.80	0.78	0.77	0.74	0.72
6,000	1,829	11.78	81.2	0.90	0.86	0.83	0.80	0.78	0.77	0.75	0.74	0.71	0.69
7,000	2,133	11.34	78.2	0.87	0.83	0.80	0.77	0.75	0.74	0.73	0.71	0.69	0.66
8,000	2,438	10.91	75.3	0.84	0.80	0.77	0.74	0.72	0.71	0.70	0.69	0.66	0.64
9,000	2,743	10.50	72.4	0.80	0.77	0.74	0.71	0.70	0.68	0.67	0.66	0.64	0.62
10,000	3,048	10.11	69.7	0.77	0.74	0.71	0.68	0.67	0.66	0.65	0.63	0.61	0.59

Similarly, if the temperature rises to a point significantly greater than 60°F (15.5°C), then air density decreases and—although the same volume of air is taken into the compressor—the mass of the air is lessened. Thus, as atmospheric pressure decreases or temperature increases past 60°F (15.5°C), less standard air volume is compressed at a given rpm. Some temporary factors also affect the ability of a compressor to produce its rated air volume, including: significant changes in atmospheric pressure caused by storm systems, large diurnal changes in air temperature, and placement of the air intake (avoiding the pulling in of hot air from the engine).

Both piston compressors and screw-type compressors can have one or more stages (compression units). Air volume or pressure demands often require that more than one compressor be used. Compressors connected in a series increase the pressure in an air system, whereas a parallel arrangement increases the volume. Although the output pressure can be regulated on a screw compressor, it should never be reduced when a downhole air hammer is being used in air drilling. The pressure can be adjusted downward for well-development work, however, so that the screen is not damaged. This is especially important if the pressure is greater than 300 psi (2,070 kPa).

The standard compressors used on water-well rigs have increased in air-volume capacity and pressure capability to drill deep, large-diameter holes, achieve high penetration rates, and maximize drilling rates with downhole hammers. In general, drillers rarely have too much air available. A good method for verifying that sufficient air is available to remove the cuttings efficiently in dry-air drilling is to check the time needed for the air to clean up after drilling ceases. The time required to clean the cuttings should not greatly exceed 6 sec to 7 sec per 100 ft (30.5 m) of borehole (Cooper et al. 1977). More air is needed as boreholes deepen; and 30% to 40% more air is required when drilling with air-mist systems (Magcobar 1979). For downhole air hammers, higher pressures translate into increased penetration rates when drilling with dry air because the hammer action is faster. Higher available pressure also can be used to overcome static heads following a temporary cessation of drilling.

Several drilling system options exist when air is used as the drilling fluid.

* Air only (dry air)
* Air-mist
* Air and a small volume of water
* Air, a small volume of water, and a small amount of surfactant
* Air-foam
* Stable foam—air and surfactant
* Stiff foam—air, surfactant, and high-molecular-weight polymer or bentonite
* Aerated drilling fluid—water-based drilling fluid and air

Factors to consider when deciding which of these systems to use include the volume of water entering the borehole, the penetration rate, the volume of air available, the nature of the formations being drilled, and environmental conditions affecting the drilling process.

Dry-Air Systems

The simplest air-drilling system involves using only dry air as the drilling fluid. Optimum drilling rates are achieved by using dry air because the column of air puts minimum pressure on the bottom of the borehole. As removal of the rock overburden proceeds, the cuttings become progressively easier to chip off because the overlying weight of the rock is reduced. Figure 8.22 shows how the penetration rate is affected adversely by downhole pressure. Water-well drillers ordinarily begin drilling using only dry air, but dust and influx water usually create the need to alter the dry-air system.

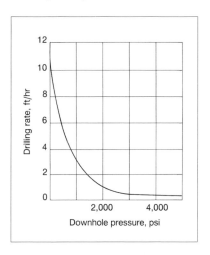

Figure 8.22. Effect of downhole pressure on drilling rate. This test was conducted in Indiana limestone using a 1,000 lb 2-cone rock bit operating at 50 rpm (Cunningham & Eenink 1958).

Compared with water-based drilling fluids, dry-air systems offer the following advantages.

- High penetration rates in dense, consolidated rock
- High solids-carrying capacity
- Reduced bit wear
- Reduced formation damage
- Reduced self-induced fluid loss
- Low water requirements
- Reduced chance of swelling problems associated with water-sensitive clays

Air drilling is extremely effective in hard, stable formations such as igneous and metamorphic rocks, and tough, dense sedimentary rocks such as dolomite, where penetration rates often are exceptional. Air has the lowest density of any drilling fluid and therefore places minimum downward pressure on the formation being drilled, and cuttings chip off readily when using either a roller or a downhole air-hammer bit. Boreholes are kept clean by the high annular velocity, which ranges from 3,000 ft/min ((915 m/min) to 5,000 ft/min (1,520 m/min) for dry air. Uphole velocities of up to 7,000 ft/min (2,130 m/min) can be desirable for deep holes drilled at high penetration rates. In the range of 3,000 ft/min (915 m/min) to 5,000 ft/min (1,520 m/min), cuttings lift easily despite air's low density and viscosity.

Note, however, that cuttings do not rise up the borehole at the same velocity as that of the drilling fluid. If the dry air has a velocity of 5,000 ft/min (1,520 m/min), for example, then fine (dust) cuttings move up the borehole at about 3,000 ft/min (915 m/min), and the large cuttings might rise at only 1,000 ft/min (305 m/min) to 2,000 ft/min (610 m/min). In general, the lifting capacity of air is proportional to its density and to the square of its annular velocity. Thus, to maintain the required annular velocity, the drilling professional adjusts air volume and pressure at the surface to compensate for the weight of the cuttings and for increases in density with depth. See Appendix 8.H (DVD) for uphole velocities based on borehole diameter, drill-pipe size, and air volume.

Advantages

Air drilling is particularly advantageous where drill and drive techniques are used for unconsolidated formations such as bouldery tills. In this type of drilling, borehole instability is not a major problem and the many benefits of drilling with air make the technique attractive. Air also is helpful in overcoming lost-circulation problems in highly fractured igneous and metamorphic rock and in highly porous formations. If large crevices or cavities are encountered, many drillers using water-based drilling-fluid systems change immediately to an air or air-foam system. Lost-circulation problems, however, can occur when air systems are used to drill permeable sandstone. In this type of formation, so much air is lost that uphole velocities can be insufficient to lift the cuttings. To overcome this problem polymers and water sometimes are added to the air. The thin polymeric film seals the formation pores and minimizes air loss.

Obstacles

Obstacles encountered when using air drilling (especially dry-air drilling) usually involve an insufficient air supply that results in an annular velocity that is inadequate for carrying the cuttings to the surface. For a given borehole diameter, hole depth is a primary factor affecting cuttings removal because it directly relates to air-volume requirements.

Erosion of the borehole walls also can create an increase in the demand for air that exceeds the compressor's capacity. Conversely, too much air also can be a problem because soft formations in a borehole wall can be eroded, resulting in blowouts (borehole enlargement). This, in turn, can lead to even greater air-volume demands. Table 8.7 (rendered in U.S. customary units) shows the minimum dry-air volume requirements (in standard cubic feet per minute (SCFM)) for various borehole and drill-pipe sizes for a use at a drilling rate of approximately 60 ft (18.3 m) per hr.

Table 8.7. Minimum Air-Volume Requirements for Dry-Air Drilling

Hole Size (in)	Drillpipe (in)	Depth & Volume Required (SCFM)*					
		500 ft	1,000 ft	1,500 ft	2,000 ft	3,000 ft	4,000 ft
4¾	2	253	278	303	328	377	427
	2⅜	293	315	338	360	405	450
6¼	3½	461	493	524	557	620	684
	2⅞	522	551	579	608	665	723
6¾	3½	568	601	634	667	733	799
7⅜	3	710	745	780	815	885	955
7⅞	4½	711	752	794	836	918	1,000
	3½	834	870	906	943	1,015	1,088
8¾	5	873	920	966	1,013	1,106	1,199
	4½	946	990	1,033	1,077	1,164	1,252
	3½	1,070	1,109	1,147	1,186	1,263	1,341
9	5	945	992	1,039	1,086	1,181	1,273
	4½	1,019	1,063	1,107	1,152	1,240	1,329
	3½	1,142	1,182	1,221	1,261	1,340	1,419

Hole Size (in)	Drillpipe (in)	Depth & Volume Required (SCFM)*					
		500 ft	1,000 ft	1,500 ft	2,000 ft	3,000 ft	4,000 ft
9⅞	5½	1,131	1,183	1,235	1,287	1,391	1,495
	5	1,212	1,261	1,311	1,360	1,459	1,557
	4½	1,286	1,333	1,379	1,426	1,519	1,613
11	6⅝	1,299	1,361	1,423	1,485	1,609	1,733
	5½	1,511	1,566	1,621	1,676	1,786	1,896
	4½	1,666	1,717	1,767	1,818	1,919	2,020
12¼	6⅝	1,765	1,830	1,895	1,960	2,090	2,220
	5½	1,977	2,037	2,096	2,156	2,275	2,394
	4½	2,134	2,190	2,245	2,301	2,412	2,523
15	6⅝	2,980	3,056	3,131	3,207	3,358	3,509
	5½	3,195	3,267	3,338	3,410	3,553	3,696
	4½	3,353	3,422	3,490	3,559	3,696	3,833
17½	6⅝	4,297	4,386	4,474	4,563	4,740	4,917
	5½	4,513	4,599	4,684	4,770	4,941	5,112
	4½	4,671	4,754	4,837	4,920	5,086	5,252

* The volume required is based on an estimated penetration rate of 60 ft/hr (18.3 m/hr) and an annular velocity of 3,000 ft/min (915 m/min). Air volumes are given at standard pressure (sea level) and temperature 60°F (15.6°C)) (Magcobar 1979).

Implosion can become a problem when air is forced into the formation during drilling and then, when the air is turned off, the borehole unloads. Another drilling problem occurs when small amounts of water enter the borehole during dry-air drilling. Water mixes with the smallest rock cuttings to produce mud that can plug the formation and limit the potential yield of the well. If enough mud is present to form rings (or collars) on the drill string or borehole wall, air flow is restricted and the drill rods can stick in the borehole. When mud collars form, restriction of the annulus causes excessive pressure buildup below the collar, and the formation materials can fracture. Fracturing and blowouts can be minimized if the drill rig is equipped with compressors that can be controlled by a relief valve at the operator's station. This equipment enables the operator to take immediate action if the pressure rises suddenly, and thus reduces the chances for blowouts and fracturing in loose formations.

Air-Mist Systems

Adding small amounts of water to air creates an air-mist system, which helps to control dust and to break down any mud collars forming on the drill rods. To increase the wetting action of the injected water, small amounts of surfactant also can be added to the airstream. Air-volume requirements usually increase substantially when switching from dry air to air misting, because greater downhole pressure prevents the immediate expansion of the air as it leaves the drill bit. Air-mist techniques can be used satisfactorily if only a small volume of influx water (15 gpm (81.8 m³/day) to 25 gpm (136 m³/day)) enters the borehole from the aquifer; if this volume increases, however, then an air-foam system must replace the air-mist system.

Air-Foam Systems

Ordinarily, foam is defined as a dispersion of air in water. In an air-foam drilling system, however, air is the continuous phase and water is the dispersed or discontinuous phase. Thus, drilling foam is created when water and surfactant are injected into an airstream.

Although some foam forms naturally when water enters an airstream, the amount and stability of the foam is enhanced significantly when a surfactant is added. "Foam drilling" is a process where a surfactant-water mixture is introduced into the air system for drilling. Surfactants include anionic soaps, alkyl polyoxethylene nonionic compounds, and cationic amine derivatives. All of these are available commercially, but it is important to insure that the surfactant chosen is designed for use in drilling potable water wells.

The addition of a surfactant to an air-based drilling fluid in essence thickens the air. It has several advantages over the use of air alone, including:

- ✦ Higher solids-carrying capacity;
- ✦ Ability to lift large volumes of water;
- ✦ Reduced air-volume requirements;
- ✦ Reduced erosion of poorly consolidated formations;
- ✦ Effective dust suppression; and
- ✦ Increased borehole stability.

The air is thicker, therefore the required air volume is lower and the amount of air must be reduced to compensate. An air-foam system is not effective when a confined formation is intercepted, however. In such situations the downhole pressure could be so low that the borehole becomes unstable, or so much water enters the borehole that the air-foam system cannot remove it.

Foams primarily are used to enhance the rate of cuttings removal by preventing cuttings from aggregating, which enables them to be lifted to the surface more easily. Foaming agents also are added to air when the airstream no longer can lift the water entering the borehole. A surfactant injected into the airstream helps break up the water mass by reducing the surface tension of the water droplets. Once a water droplet is broken up it can be lifted easily. Upon reaching the surface, the foam breaks down rather quickly, depending on the particular foaming agent used and the prevailing environmental conditions.

Foams reduce the uphole velocity requirements to 50 ft/min to 1,000 ft/min (15.2 m/min to 305 m/min), which is considerably less than the rate required for drilling with air alone. The lowest uphole velocities are possible when using high concentrations of surfactant together with clay or polymeric additives. Lower uphole velocities reduce the amount of air required (Table 8.8). Lower air-volume requirements, in turn, also can reduce the pressures needed. As a result, the loss of air into the formation is minimized. Foam is recommended for use in weakly consolidated formations where the higher uphole velocities required for dry air would cause excessive erosion of the borehole.

Often, surfactants are mixed with water in a large container (mist tank) placed adjacent to the rig, and then are injected slowly into the airstream at a rate sufficient to lift the cuttings. They also can be injected directly into a water stream through a metered chemical pump. The volume of surfactant required usually ranges from 1 qt/hr to 3 gal/hr (1 ℓ/hr to 11 ℓ/hr), depending on the type of surfactant used, the volume of water entering the borehole, the diameter and depth of the borehole, and the quantity and size of the cuttings. The surfactant concentration commonly varies from 0.25% to 2% of the injected water, but significantly more can be required for deep, large-diameter boreholes having large quantities of influx water.

Table 8.8. Air Requirements for Uphole Velocities of 100 ft/min (30.5 m/min) to 300 ft/min (91.4 m/min)

Hole Diameter		Air Volume	
in	mm	cfm	m³/sec
6	152	30–60	0.01–0.03
10	254	75–150	0.04–0.07
15	381	200–300	0.09–0.14
26	660	400–600	0.19–0.28

Surfactants used in water wells must be both biodegradable and nontoxic. When using foam in urban areas, however, some drillers might encounter complaints from local residents and other parties if foams build up on the ground around the drilling machine (as do some long-lived foams). It is the drilling professional's responsibility to control the foam, and under no circumstances should surfactants ever be allowed to enter any waterway. If a strong wind is blowing, large masses of dry foam could travel hundreds of feet before dissipating. Uninformed onlookers could perceive the foam as dangerous to the environment and alert local health officials or law enforcement authorities. Foam can be dissipated by using a spray nozzle and injecting acceptable defoamers into the flow at the end of the discharge line. Oilfield-type defoamers should be used in water-well drilling only if they are approved for such use. In some instances, water can be sprayed onto the foam to help break its surface tension and dissipate it.

Foams are classified into several different types based on their resistance to slumping. A foam's initial resistance to slumping depends on the concentration of the surfactant, the volume of injected water, and whether other additives such as polymers or bentonite are added to the airstream (Table 8.9). Bentonite cannot be added to an air-foam system if a downhole air hammer is being used, however, because the clay particles rapidly can cause the hammer to malfunction.

Table 8.9. Types of Foam as Determined by Water Content

Type of Foam	Liquid-Volume Fraction
Dry foam	< 2%
Stable foam	2% to 10%
Wet foam	10% to 25%

The addition of high-molecular-weight polymers or bentonite increases the viscous qualities of foam, reduces uphole velocity requirements for effective penetration and adequate cleaning, helps stabilize borehole walls, and can reduce friction in the borehole. Polymers also are biodegradable and therefore do not plug the formation after breakdown. If bentonite is used to stiffen the foam, then any filter cake forming on the borehole walls must be removed during development. Typically, 5 lb (2.27 kg) to 10 lb (4.54 kg) of bentonite is mixed with 100 gal (0.4 m^3) of water. Bentonite concentrations to 50 lb (22.7 kg) per 100 gal (0.4 m^3) of water sometimes are needed in larger boreholes with lost circulation or large influxes of water. To provide shale inhibition and desired viscosity, small amounts of bentonite (2 lb to 10 lb per 100 gal of water) and polymers can be added. Lesser amounts of polymers are required to create similar viscous qualities in the foam.

Surfactant is added to the mixture in a concentration of 0.25% to 2%. The surfactant always should be added after any clay, polymer, or other chemicals are mixed. The resulting mixture is injected into the airstream, ideally at a rate of 2% of the free-air volume (rated capacity of the compressor). The addition of either a polymer or bentonite generally raises foam density to between 2 lb/ft^3 (32 kg/m^3) and 6 lb/ft^3 (96.1 kg/m^3).

Aerated Drilling Fluids

Air sometimes is injected into water-based drilling fluids to reduce the weight of the drilling-fluid column. This procedure is used commonly in inverse systems and for air-assist reverse-circulation rotary drilling. The introduction of air increases the penetration rates from 10% to 50% more than that of conventional mud drilling (Kuetzing 1981). Additionally, fluid loss to highly permeable zones often is reduced or eliminated. One disadvantage of aerated water-based drilling fluids is that they cause higher rates of drill-pipe corrosion. See Chapter 7 for a description of air rotary drilling methods. A description of the physics associated with drilling is contained in Appendix 8.I (DVD). The appendix discusses the pressure and temperature relationships associated with air drilling.

Physical Conditions and Liquid-Volume Fraction

Two changing physical conditions affect the liquid-volume fraction (LVF) of the foam as it rises to the surface (LVF is defined in Appendix 8.J (DVD)). The LVF—based on the initial volume of water and surfactant added by the drilling professional—decreases to 2% by the time the foam reaches the discharge point. This occurs because the air expands gradually as it flows up the borehole and regains its original (free-air) volume by the time it reaches the surface. This decrease in LVF is only theoretical, however, because—at the same time— water entering the borehole increases the LVF by breaking down some of the foam. The foam becomes less stiff and by the time it leaves the blooey (flow) line it can appear quite "runny."

A blooey line is a flow line which has an inner diameter of 6 in (152 mm) to 10 in (254 mm), and it is used to conduct cuttings away from the rig. In dry-air drilling a blooey line reduces dust problems around the rig and, if foam is being used, reduces the accumulation of thick layers of foam in the area around the wellbore. In dry-air drilling it is important that the blooey line have no bends because dust particles will cut the line. Although blooey lines in oil fields might be 150 ft (45.7 m) to 200 ft (61 m) long, the lines used for water wells generally are from 20 ft (6.1 m) to 50 ft (15.2 m) long.

When a high percentage of the bubbles produced by the surfactant has been dissipated by the influx water, this indicates that the LVF has risen to 20% to 25%. To avoid an overly runny, inefficient foam, and instead create a foam stiff enough to remove the influx water effectively from the borehole, increase the concentration of the surfactant.

Typical Calculations Used for Air-Foam Systems

Pressure and temperature changes affecting an air-foam system are predictable in their impacts on the percent LVF, air-volume requirements, and annular velocity. Although most of these relationships can be calculated using equation 8.I.2 (*see* Appendix 8.I (DVD)), they also can be illustrated using graphs such as those shown in Figure 8.23 and Figure 8.24. These graphs (rendered in U.S. customary units) can help drilling professionals visualize what changes are occurring in the drilling-fluid system and whether the physical conditions are facilitating or slowing the drilling process.

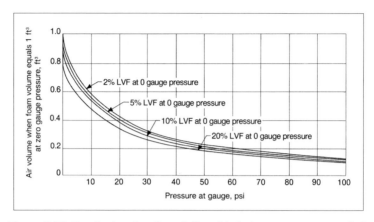

Figure 8.23. Graph showing the relationship between pressure and air volume for several liquid-volume fractions at atmospheric pressure (14.5 psi)). The higher the initial LVF, the lower the relative air volume at a particular pressure.

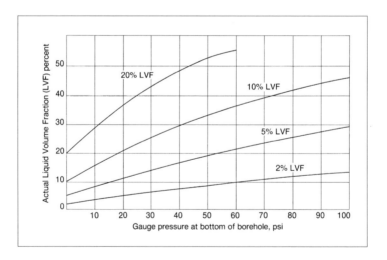

Figure 8.24. Graph showing the effect of increasing pressure on several liquid-volume fractions. Generally, the higher the percent LVF at low-pressure points in the system the greater the likelihood of the drilling fluid being inefficient at high-pressure points.

Calculating an Injection Rate

To calculate (in U.S. customary units) the volume of water needed to produce a specific LVF (e.g., a 2% LVF), multiply the desired LVF by the annular volume of 1 ft of the borehole. Assume, for example, that an uphole velocity of 100 ft/min is sufficient to lift the cuttings from an 8-in borehole. The drill rod has a 4-in outside diameter; a 250-psi, 450-cfm compressor is mounted on the rig; and static water level at the drill site is at a depth of 120 ft.

The annular volume between the rods and the borehole wall can be calculated by using the equation for the volume of a cylinder.

$$v = \pi r^2 h \tag{8.3}$$

The volume of water required per foot of borehole for a 2% LVF is $0.262 \cdot 0.02 = 0.005$ ft^3. Thus, in this example, injection of the surfactant and water should start at a rate of $0.005 \cdot 100$ (annular velocity) $= 0.5$ cfm $= 3.8$ gpm. An initial surfactant concentration of 0.5 gal per 100 gal of injection water is selected. As drilling proceeds, the injection rates of both water and surfactant are adjusted as required.

Determining Air-Volume Requirements

Most air-foam drilling situations require 50 cfm (0.02 m^3/sec) to 500 cfm (0.2 m^3/sec) of air at pressures ranging from 100 psi to (690 kPa) 350 psi (2,410 kPa). The compressor should be able to maintain an uphole velocity of 50 ft/min to 1,000 ft/min (15.2 m/min to 305 m/min).

$$v_a = \frac{100 \cdot v_w}{LVF} - v_w \tag{8.4}$$

In the example provided above, the water volume required to achieve a 2% LVF is 3.8 gpm (0.5 cfm). Thus, using equation 8.4, the air-volume requirements are as follows.

$$v_a = \frac{100 \cdot 0.5}{2} - 0.5 = 24.5 \ cfm \tag{8.5}$$

The calculated air-volume requirement normally should be increased by 25% so that losses into the formation do not reduce the annular velocity below the desired rate. The total minimum air volume then is about 30 cfm (0.01 m^3/sec), delivered at an assumed pressure of 125 psi (862 kPa) (the compressor is adjusted to deliver air at the lower pressure to conserve fuel). This volume is much less than the available compressor capacity of 450 cfm (0.21 m^3/sec). Therefore, in this example, the air-volume requirements can be met easily.

Air volume also determines annular velocity. Annular velocities change due to air expansion or, to a lesser extent, because of compression as the drilling fluid circulates down the inside of the drillpipe and up the annulus. The relationship of air-volume, velocity, and cross-sectional area is shown in equation 8.6.

$$v_a = VA \qquad\qquad (8.6)$$

Where v_a is the air volume, V is velocity, and A is the cross-sectional annulus area. Because v_a and V are directly proportional, a change in one caused by pressure variations causes a corresponding change in the other.

Determining Pressure Requirements

Ordinarily, the pressure requirements for foam systems during drilling are rather low because the fluid column contains so much air. Calculation of the maximum pressure required to operate the drilling-fluid system depends on the total weight of the foam; cuttings; water entering the borehole; and the presence of any clay or polymeric additives. If drilling ceases, however, then the pressure delivered by the compressor when drilling resumes must be sufficient to overcome any head of fluid that has accumulated in the borehole. The question then is whether the original operating pressure and air volume are adequate to restart the drilling process. In the example provided above, if drilling ceases for a few hours after reaching a depth of 480 ft (360 ft beneath the water table), and assuming that the borehole is completely filled with water to the static water level and there are no friction losses in the drillpipe, the minimum pressure (in U.S. customary units) required to restart the air-foam system is 156 psi (360 divided by 2.31). This is higher than the initial operating pressure of 125 psi, but still is well within the capability of the compressor (250 psi).

Regulating an Air-Foam Drilling System

In air-foam drilling operations, some drilling professionals have an intuitive perception of whether the drilling-fluid system is functioning properly—based mainly on the penetration rate. Similar to water-based drilling-fluid systems, for maximum drilling efficiency to be maintained, adjustments to the physical characteristics of the drilling fluid must be based on more than just intuition. Conditions change as the drilling fluid circulates in the system, therefore the required pressure, air volume, and LVF normally should be established for the most critical point—the annulus just above the bit. At this point, the LVF should be 2% to 5%; in no case should it be more than 15%.

Observations and Measurements

It rarely is possible to actually measure pressure or temperature conditions at many points in the circulation system. The various physical characteristics of the air-foam system therefore must be observed when possible (usually at the discharge point) and professionals must learn to relate these characteristics to drilling efficiency.

The important visual observations or measurements that indicate when adjustments should be made include the following.

- Water volume, air volume, and pressure
- Foam pressure at the standpipe
- Percentage of surfactant and other foam stabilizers being injected
- Foam consistency at the surface (based on visual assessment of consistency, density, percent LVF, percent and size of solids, volume)
- Regularity of returns at the surface
- Drill-string torque requirements

Some of these factors can be measured directly using gauges. Other factors, such as percent solids, density, and volume, however, must be estimated visually. An experienced drilling professional often can estimate the LVF by evaluating the foam; high-LVF foam tends to form streams and low-LVF foam tends to billow up around the rig (Figure 8.25).

As a general operating principle for an air-foam system, once the rates of penetration and water removal are satisfactory, foam consistency should be maintained. A drilling professional's ability to make the correct adjustments to the system by using visual observations and actual measurements is a learned skill that improves over time and with experience.

A

B

Figure 8.25. The LVF determines the foam appearance as it leaves the borehole. When the foam is relatively dry it collects around the top of the borehole (photo A); if the LVF is high then the foam tends to run away on the surface of the water brought up the borehole (photo B) (Gefco).

General Guidance

When initiating drilling using an air-foam system, the following actions and conditions generally are observed (Magcobar 1979).

- Before the foam has become stable downhole, a steady rush of air leaves the blooey line. If foam does not form, then either fluid (injection) volume should be increased or air volume should be decreased for a few minutes.
- When the proper foaming action begins downhole, a gentle puffing of air can be felt at the blooey line.
- When foam returns begin, the foam should extrude steadily and have good stiffness.
- Good foam-carrying capacity usually occurs when a gentle surging action is observed at the blooey line. If the foam is too stiff, this surging action does not occur. If the foam surges violently, then too much air is being pumped into the borehole.
- As conditions change, the proper foam concentration, water injection rate, and air volume must be maintained to achieve good penetration (Figure 8.27).

Common problems with foam drilling fluids are indicated by the physical condition of the foam at the surface and by pressure buildup in the borehole (Figure 8.26). These foam or pressure conditions and suggested adjustments are listed in Table 8.10. Additional practical information on air-drilling problems and procedures is presented later in this chapter.

Figure 8.26. A properly run foam exits the blooey line in a uniform steady flow, and has a consistency similar to shaving cream (© 2005 Baroid, a Halliburton PSL).

Table 8.10. Common Air-Foam System Problems

Problem	Cause	Corrective Adjustment
Air blowing free at the blooey line with a fine mist of foam	Air has broken through foam mix preventing stable foam formation	Increase liquid injection rate or decrease air injection rate
Foam is thin and watery	Formation water entry, with possible salts contamination	Increase liquid and air injection rates; possibly increase percent of foaming agent
Quick pressure drop	Air has broken through foam mix preventing stable foam formation	Increase liquid injection rate or decrease air injection rate
Slow, gradual pressure increase	Increase in amount of cuttings or formation fluid being lifted to surface	Increase air injection rate slightly
Quick pressure increase	Bit is plugged or formation is packed off around drill pipe	Stop drilling and move pipe to attempt to regain circulation

Steps in air drilling (shown in Figure 8.27, a through d) are listed below.

- **Drilling above the water table (a).** Start with dry air and add a small volume of water to the air to control dust. Increase the air volume with depth.
- **Drilling below the water table (b).** Add surfactant to injection water to remove water and cuttings. The LVF should be maintained at between 2% and 10% at the bit.
- **Drilling has stopped and must be restarted (c).** Air pressure must be sufficient to overcome head of water in the borehole. Increase air volume as the hole deepens and keep the LVF at 2% at the bit.
- **Drilling continues (d).** If uphole velocity cannot be maintained by air-volume increase alone, then the foam can be stiffened by adding clay or polymers and increasing the concentration of surfactant. Increased concentrations of surfactant help maintain the lifting capability.

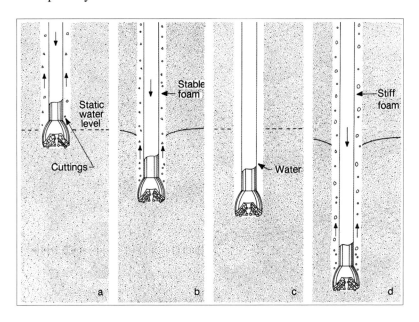

Figure 8.27. Diagram of steps in air drilling.

Recommendations

Specific suggestions for successful air-foam drilling include the following.

Lifting Capacity

The greatest lifting capacity for foam occurs when the LVF is about 2%; at the bottom of the borehole the LVF therefore should be as close as possible to 2%. If the LVF exceeds 25% then the lifting capacity of the foam will be unsatisfactory.

From a practical standpoint, drilling professionals generally do not increase the injected water volume in direct proportion to any increase in air volume requirements. For example, if 3.8 gpm (20.7 m³/day) is required to produce an LVF of 2% at 30 cfm (0.85 m³/min), a drilling professional ordinarily does not pump 15.2 gpm (82.9 m³/day) if the air-volume requirements rise to 120 cfm (3.4 m³/min). Limited injection-pump capacity and the natural entry of water into the borehole either prevents—or renders unnecessary—a proportional increase in the injection rate.

Annular Velocity

The annular velocity at the bottom of the borehole should be at least 50 ft/min (15.2 m/min).

Injection Rate

To calculate the correct volume of water to be injected to achieve an LVF of 2% and an uphole velocity of 100 ft/min (30.5 m/min), multiply the annular volume for 1 ft of borehole by 2.

For example, if the volume of 1 ft of borehole is 0.262 ft³ (0.0074 m³), then the injection rate is 0.524 ft³/min (2 · 0.262) or 3.9 gpm (0.0148 m³/min (2 · 0.0074) or 21.3 m³/day), at an uphole velocity of 100 ft/min (30.5 m/min). For other annular velocities, multiply the figure for 100 ft/min by the appropriate number. Another good "rule of thumb" is to inject at a rate of 0.5 gpm (2.7 m³/day) to 1 gpm (5.5 m³/day) per 1 in (25.4 mm) of borehole diameter.

Air Volume

The air-volume requirements for any borehole can be calculated using equation 8.4 for a specific LVF. For most shallow water wells, 50 cfm (0.02 m³/sec) to 500 cfm (0.2 m³/sec) of air is needed at a pressure of 100 psi (690 kPa) to 350 psi (2,410 kPa). A safety factor for calculated air volume usually is 25%. A temperature correction for air-volume changes might be necessary but, for most drilling operations, the temperature change is not sufficient to necessitate a correction.

Borehole Conditions

Certain chemical and physical conditions in the borehole can have an adverse effect on the efficiency of air-foam systems. Typical problems include lost circulation, contaminants, abnormally high borehole pressures, and swelling clays.

Contaminants such as salt, cement, natural gases, gypsum, and anhydrite reduce the drilling foam's capacity to lift cuttings. Occasionally, to correct a contaminant problem, chemical treatment of the fluid is required before its injection. High borehole or high surface temperatures also can cause drastic fluctuations in air volume if the drilling fluid becomes cooled at other points in the circulation system.

Appropriate adjustments to the physical characteristics of an air-foam system require a thorough understanding of what is occurring within the entire circulation system. Although measurement of physical conditions in the borehole normally is impossible, a skilled drilling professional can relate visual observations at the surface to what is happening in the borehole.

DRILLING-FLUID ADDITIVES

When selecting the appropriate drilling-fluid additives, state and local regulations and environmental concerns all must be considered carefully. Many regulatory agencies require that any products used be certified by the NSF, UL, ANSI, or similar agencies. Only products that have been specifically designed and selected for use in the water-well industry should be used. Drilling-fluid additives have proliferated since 1940, and a discussion of the factors determining when and how to use these additives is beyond the scope of this chapter. To determine which drilling-fluid additives are best for an application, consult local regulations and contact individual suppliers and manufacturers.

For most water-well drilling operations certain standard procedures are followed, and these depend on the particular type of drilling fluid used. Specific ranges for viscosities, uphole velocities, and additive concentrations are well established and represent the starting point for mixing most drilling fluids (see Table 8.11, rendered in U.S. customary units). Unusual borehole structure or groundwater chemistry, however, could dictate a change from these initial drilling-fluid conditions. Examples of solving typical drilling problems are discussed in Appendix 8.K (DVD). Another typical drilling problem is discussed in Appendix 8.L (DVD).

Table 8.11. Typical Additive Concentrations, Resulting Viscosities, and Required Uphole Velocities for Major Types of Drilling Fluids Used in Various Aquifer Materials

Base Fluid	Additive/ Concentration	Marsh Funnel Viscosity (sec)	Annular Uphole Velocity (ft/min)	Observations & Uses
Water	None	26 ± 0.5	100–120	For normal drilling (sand, silt, and clay)
Water	Clay (high-grade bentonite)*	—	—	Increases viscosity (lifting capacity) of water significantly
	15–25 lb/100 gal	35–55	80–120	For normal drilling conditions (sand, silt, and clay)
	25–40 lb/100 gal	55–70	80–120	For gravel and other coarse-grained, poorly consolidated formations
	35–45 lb/100 gal	65–75	80–120	For excessive fluid losses
Water	Polymer	—	—	Increases viscosity (lifting capacity) of water significantly
	4.0 lb/100 gal	35–55	80–120	For normal drilling conditions (sand, silt, and clay)
	6.1 lb/100 gal	65–75	80–120	For gravel and other coarse-grained, poorly consolidated formations
	6.5 lb/100 gal	75–85	80–120	For excessive fluid losses; cuttings should be removed from the annulus before the pumping stops, because polymeric drilling fluids have very poor gel strength

Base Fluid	Additive/ Concentration	Marsh Funnel Viscosity (sec)	Annular Uphole Velocity (ft/min)	Observations & Uses
Air	None	—	3,000– 5,000	Fast drilling and adequate cleaning of medium to fine cuttings; but can cause dust problems at the surface
	None	—	4,500– 6,000	Range of annular uphole velocities required for dual-wall drilling method
Air	Water (air-mist)	—	3,000– 5,000	Controls dust at the surface; is suitable for formations that have limited entry of water
Air	Surfactant/water (air-foam)	—	50– 1,000	Extends the lifting capacity of the compressor
	1–2 qt/100 gal (0.25% to 0.5% surfactant)	—	—	For light drilling; small water inflow; sticky clay, wet sand, fine gravel, hard rock; few drilling problems
	2–3 qt/100 gal (0.5% to 0.75% surfactant)	—	—	For average drilling conditions; larger diameter, deeper holes; large cuttings; increasing volumes of water inflow; excellent hole cleaning
	3–4 qt/100 gal (0.75% to 1% surfactant)	—	—	For difficult drilling; deep, large-diameter holes; large, heavy cuttings; sticky and incompetent formations; large water inflows
	N/A	—	—	Injection rates of surfactant/water mixture Unconsolidated formations: 3–10 gpm Fractured rock: 3–7 gpm Solid rock: 3–5 gpm

Base Fluid	Additive/ Concentration	Marsh Funnel Viscosity (sec)	Annular Uphole Velocity (ft/min)	Observations & Uses
Air	Surfactant/ colloids/water (stiff foam)	—	50–100	Greatly extends lifting capacity of the compressor
	3–4 qt/100 gal (0.75% to 1% surfactant) plus 3–6 lb polymer / 100 gal or 30–50 lb bentonite /100 gal	—	—	For difficult drilling; deep, large-diameter holes; large, heavy cuttings; sticky and incompetent formations; large water inflows
	4–8 qt/100 gal (1% to 2% surfactant) plus 3–6 lb polymer / 100 gal or 30–50 lb bentonite /100 gal	—	—	For extremely difficult drilling; large deep holes; lost circulation; incompetent formations; excessive water inflows

* When polymers are added to address specific borehole situations, the bentonite can be reduced to avoid to high a viscosity.

(compiled in part from Imco Services 1975; Magcobar 1977; Baroid 1980)

SUMMARY

This chapter examines common drilling-fluid systems and some typical problems that occur in different geologic materials. Many specific problems associated with drilling can be resolved with the help of drilling-fluid products suppliers. Often suppliers can provide onsite help in the field, and suppliers sponsor training classes covering drilling-fluid systems. Drilling professionals always should remember one point: Whatever drilling-fluid system is chosen, be sure to understand it thoroughly.

CHAPTER 9
Production Water-Well Design

Mike Mehmert
Johnson Screens

INTRODUCTION

Water-well design is the process of specifying the physical parameters for a well. The design must meet the requirements for the well's intended purpose and must incorporate adequate features to assure future groundwater protection, as economically as is practical. The principal objectives of good design should insure the following.

- Desired yield consistent with aquifer capability
- Minimum drawdown
- Good water quality
- Aquifer protection
- Sediment-free yield
- Reasonable longevity
- Practical capital cost
- Minimal maintenance cost

The well site should be chosen with an awareness of potential contamination sources, and the well should be constructed in a manner that insures that surface contaminants do not adversely impact water quality in the aquifer. The design guidelines presented in this chapter focus on municipal, industrial, and irrigation wells. Design of these wells typically aims for high yield, efficiency,

353

and production of sediment-free water—all of which directly influence operating costs. Other design factors related to domestic, farm, and small commercial wells also are discussed in this chapter; the design of monitoring wells is covered in Chapter 14.

Important hydrogeologic information required for the design of efficient high-capacity wells includes:

- Stratigraphic information concerning the aquifer and overlying sediments, derived from samples and geophysical logs;
- Hydraulic conductivity, thickness, and storage coefficient values for the aquifer, determined from aquifer tests;
- Current and long-term water-level conditions in the aquifer;
- Grain-size analyses of unconsolidated aquifer materials and identification of rock or mineral types (if necessary); and
- Water quality information determined from laboratory analysis of water samples.

GENERAL CONSIDERATIONS IN CASING AND SCREEN DESIGN

This chapter approaches the design of a production well as having two components: the cased section and the screen. Well designers carefully must determine dimensional factors, strength requirements, construction method, and material selection for both the casing and well screen to provide the best utilization of the aquifer. Design procedures involve choosing the casing diameter and material; determining well depth; selecting the length, diameter, screen slot size; choosing material for the screen; and selecting the construction method. The design criteria presented in this chapter were developed for typical hydrogeologic conditions, but these vary regionally due to local conditions.

The design issues and considerations that are common to both the casing and screen are discussed in this section, including corrosion, incrustation, and bacteria. This chapter provides an overview of how these issues impact the overall design of a well. Chapter 13 presents a more in-depth discussion of incrustation, corrosion, and bacteria growth.

Chemical- , Electrochemical- , and Microbial-Induced Corrosion

Corrosion results from chemical and electrochemical processes. Chemical corrosion in a water well occurs when a particular constituent is present in groundwater in a concentration sufficient to cause rapid removal of casing or screen materials over broad sections. The more common constituents of groundwater that can be corrosive are carbon dioxide (CO_2), hydrogen sulfide (H_2S), dissolved oxygen (O_2), and the chloride ion (Cl^-) in excess of 200 ppm (200 mg/ℓ). Other constituents seen in mining operations or remediation sites, such as the acid salts of ferric, cupric, and ammonium compounds, can be very corrosive chemically and also can increase electrolytic conductivity.

Chemical Corrosion

The corrosive nature of groundwater is determined using a water-chemistry analysis. A proper analysis shows whether the groundwater is corrosive, incrusting, or both. Steel casing and screen corrosion can add to accumulation of iron oxides (Schnieders 2003). The accumulation of incrustation (mineral and organic deposits) over time affects well performance.

Characteristics Indicative of Corrosive Water

Water that has some of the following characteristics should be considered corrosive.

- A pH level that produces a negative saturation index (see Chapter 5 for a complete definition)
- Dissolved oxygen concentration greater than 2 ppm (2 mg/ℓ) (often found in shallow unconfined aquifers)
- Hydrogen sulfide concentration greater than 1 ppm (1 mg/ℓ) (indicated by rotten-egg odor)
- Total dissolved solids concentration (TDS) greater than 1,000 ppm (1,000 mg/ℓ) (supports electrolytic corrosion)
- Carbon dioxide concentration greater than 50 ppm (50 mg/ℓ)
- Chloride concentration greater than 200 ppm (200 mg/ℓ)

The presence of 2 or more corrosive agents intensifies the corrosive attack on metals, as compared to the effect caused by individual agents. In most potable water wells, Type 304 stainless steel performs satisfactorily for many years.

Under anoxic conditions, or when used where there are high concentrations of chlorides or halides, it can fail quickly. Alternate materials that are more corrosion-resistant under varying conditions include: the 316 and 316L stainless steels; the nickel-chromium alloy, Inconel®; the nickel-copper alloy, Monel®; and the nickel-molybdenium alloy, Hastelloy® A, B, and C. Other materials, such as 400 Carpenter®, 20Cb-3, and Incoloy®, have characteristics that are useful in specific corrosive environments. Thermoplastic screens are corrosion resistant, but might not have sufficient strength for some applications and development techniques. Well designers should contact the well-screen manufacturer for specific recommendations on screen materials for corrosive conditions. Importantly, prior to material selection (and when it is practical), obtaining a laboratory analysis of at least one water sample from each hydrostratigraphic unit encountered by the casing or screen is recommended.

Characteristics Indicative of Incrusting Water

Incrusting water deposits minerals on the screen surface and in the formation and filter-pack pores adjacent to the screen, plugging both. Indicators of incrusting groundwater are described below.

- High pH, exceeding 7.5
- Carbonate hardness exceeding 300 ppm (300 mg/ℓ) (calcium carbonate likely is present)
- Iron exceeding 0.5 ppm (0.5 mg/ℓ) (some precipitation might begin at 0.25 ppm (0.25 mg/ℓ))
- Manganese exceeding 0.2 ppm (0.2 mg/ℓ) (and high pH if oxygen is present)

W. F. Langelier (1936) derived the saturation index, a measure of a solution's ability to dissolve or deposit calcium carbonate (Schnieders 2003). The equation Langelier developed makes it possible to predict the tendency of water either to precipitate or to dissolve calcium carbonate. A more thorough discussion of the Langelier Saturation Index and incrustation issues is contained in Chapter 5. Water that deposits a carbonate layer tends to protect the metal surface from the effects of the corroding ions.

Mineral deposits often are removed with acids. Corrosion-resistant casing and screen materials should be selected for use where frequent acid treatments are anticipated; otherwise, less-corrosive acids should be selected (*see* Chapter 13). Generally, stainless-steel well casings and screens are more resistant to acid attack (with the exception of hydrochloric (muriatic) or other halide acids) than are materials composed of carbon steel, however it is prudent to limit the exposure of any metal to an acid. Thermoplastic and fiberglass casings and screens are highly resistant to many forms of corrosion, but generally are as susceptible to incrustation as metal screens, and screen slot openings can become narrowed due to incrustation.

Electrochemical Corrosion

In electrochemical corrosion, flow of an electric current facilitates the corrosive attack on a metal. Two conditions are necessary: a difference in electrical potential on metal surfaces, and water containing sufficient dissolved solids to be a conductive fluid (electrolyte). A potential (electrical) difference might develop between two different kinds of metals, or between nearby but separate areas on the surface of the same metal.

Differences in potential on the same metal surface, such as steel pipe, can occur at:

- Heat-affected areas around welded joints;
- Heated areas around torch-cut slots;
- Work-hardened areas around machine-cut slots (e.g., louvers, bridge slots, punch screens);
- Surfaces of exposed threads at pipe joints;
- Breaks in surface coatings such as paint and mill scale; and
- Areas under a biological or mineral deposit.

In these cases both a cathode and an anode develop; metal is removed from the anode. Bimetallic (galvanic) corrosion results when two different metals are in contact and immersed in an electrolyte. A galvanic cell is created and corrosion occurs at the anode as the electrochemical action proceeds. A well casing or screen made of two different metals such as low-carbon steel and stainless steel, for example, will be damaged because the mild-steel (less noble) forms the anode and is the area that sacrifices the metal.

The relative potential between different metals can be estimated from the galvanic series shown in Table 9.1. The farther apart the position of any two metals in this series, the greater the voltage that will develop in a galvanic cell. When two dissimilar metals are coupled in a conductive fluid, the metal nearer the bottom of the galvanic series (less noble) becomes the anode and therefore suffers corrosion. The metal nearer the top becomes the cathode.

Groundwater and Wells, Third Edition

Table 9.1. Galvanic Series of Metals and Alloys

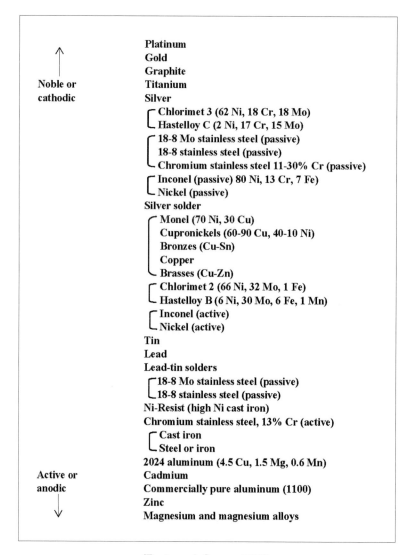

Noble or
cathodic

Platinum
Gold
Graphite
Titanium
Silver
⌐ Chlorimet 3 (62 Ni, 18 Cr, 18 Mo)
⌐ Hastelloy C (2 Ni, 17 Cr, 15 Mo)
⌐ 18-8 Mo stainless steel (passive)
| 18-8 stainless steel (passive)
⌐ Chromium stainless steel 11-30% Cr (passive)
⌐ Inconel (passive) 80 Ni, 13 Cr, 7 Fe)
⌐ Nickel (passive)
Silver solder
⌐ Monel (70 Ni, 30 Cu)
| Cupronickels (60-90 Cu, 40-10 Ni)
| Bronzes (Cu-Sn)
| Copper
⌐ Brasses (Cu-Zn)
⌐ Chlorimet 2 (66 Ni, 32 Mo, 1 Fe)
⌐ Hastelloy B (6 Ni, 30 Mo, 6 Fe, 1 Mn)
⌐ Inconel (active)
⌐ Nickel (active)
Tin
Lead
Lead-tin solders
⌐18-8 Mo stainless steel (passive)
⌐18-8 stainless steel (passive)
Ni-Resist (high Ni cast iron)
Chromium stainless steel, 13% Cr (active)
⌐ Cast iron
⌐ Steel or iron
2024 aluminum (4.5 Cu, 1.5 Mg, 0.6 Mn)

Active or
anodic

Cadmium
Commercially pure aluminum (1100)
Zinc
Magnesium and magnesium alloys

(Fontana & Greene 1978)

   When electrochemical corrosion takes place, corrosion products can be deposited at the cathode (Figure 9.1, Figure 9.2), and these deposits usually can be voluminous. If iron or steel is corroded, then the corrosion products are iron combined with other elements, typically ferric hydroxide or ferric oxide.

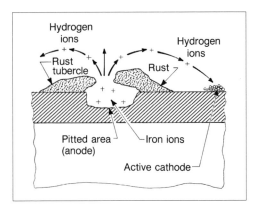

Figure 9.1. Anodes and cathodes can develop in nearby areas on the same metal surface, resulting in corrosion.

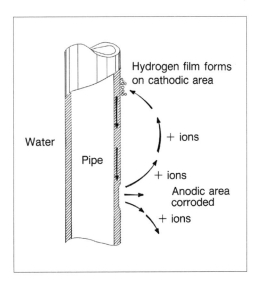

Figure 9.2. Corrosion of iron at anodic areas leads to the depositing of iron hydroxide and oxide at cathodic areas.

Prevention and Treatment of Corrosion

The following observations concerning corrosion apply to many situations in the groundwater industry.

- Work-hardened steel (such as louvers or bridge slots) corrodes more if not stress released than does the same metal that is in an annealed (heat-treated) condition.
- Stressed metal parts are more likely to corrode than are unstressed parts.
- Higher groundwater temperatures increase corrosion rates. The rate of corrosion accelerates with increasing temperature, generally doubling for each additional 50°F (10°C).
- Higher groundwater velocities usually increase corrosion rates. Efforts should be made to reduce groundwater velocities near the well screen.
- Dissolved gases such as oxygen, carbon dioxide, hydrogen sulfide, and methane—when present in water—increase corrosion rates.
- Generally, electrochemical corrosion can cause loss of material on sections of well screens and casings, with some of these corrosion products being deposited elsewhere in the well or water-distribution system. This usually occurs in water that is slightly acidic. Corrosion can result in the structural failure of a casing or screen. Corrosion also can result in a reduction in yield by plugging of the screen openings with corrosion products.
- When using stainless-steel screens and low-carbon steel casing in water that has TDS greater than 500 ppm (500 mg/ℓ), a dielectric coupling should be considered for use between the stainless steel and the low-carbon steel.

Stainless steels resist corrosion caused by many types of constituents of groundwater and, although they are resistant to the low concentration of chlorides usually present, they are susceptible to increased concentrations of the ion such as when found in incidents of contamination or where hypochlorite or hydrochloric acid are used. Chromium is the element that, through oxidation, forms the passive or protective layer. Chlorides are ions that easily can penetrate this layer and initiate corrosion.

Microbial-Induced Corrosion

Iron bacteria for years were thought to be the principal biological nemesis found in a water well. Much has been learned about bacterial organisms and wells since the publication of the second edition of *Groundwater and Wells* in 1986, and the present edition contains much of the new information. A discussion of the chemical and biological issues associated with wells and how to treat them is presented in Chapter 13 of this book. Additionally, a detailed discussion of bacteria in water wells can be found in Schnieders (2003).

There basically are three types of bacteria: aerobic, anaerobic, and facultative. Aerobic bacteria require oxygen to live, anaerobic bacteria require an oxygen-free environment, and facultative bacteria can live in environments with or without oxygen. Further, there are three main groups of bacteria that cause most problems in water wells and water systems: slime formers, iron oxidizers, and anaerobes (Figure 9.3).

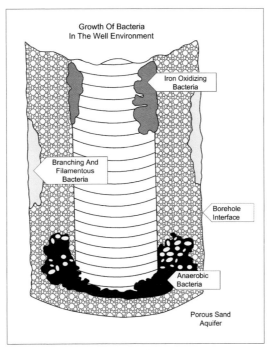

Figure 9.3. Bacteria populations in a well environment (Schneiders 2003).

Slime Formers

Slime formers comprise the largest group and are prolific producers of exo-polymer (slime). This type of bacteria can be found in practically all areas of a well system.

Iron Oxidizers

Iron oxidizers include many slime formers. Particularly problematic are stalked sheath-forming bacteria that oxidize iron (or manganese), and which can leave dense deposits in screen intakes and gravel packs.

Anaerobes

The most common anaerobes are sulfate-reducing bacteria (SRB) which can produce corrosive hydrogen sulfide gas (giving off the familiar rotten-egg odor), that accumulate in dead zones of well systems. Dead zones are areas that receive little or no water movement on a regular basis. The most common is the sump (blank casing at total depth), which is part of many well designs.

Well Design and Bacteria Management

Design consideration begins with an understanding that bacteria exist, potentially can cause problems, and require future periodic control measures. Key areas of design consideration to better manage well bacteria include the following.

Nature of Aquifer

The chemical nature of an aquifer provides nutrients for bacteria, therefore the composition and features of individual aquifers should be understood and aquifers that provide rich food sources should be blanked off and not be allowed access to the well. Geologic zones of high hydraulic conductivity often are responsible for carrying large amounts of dissolved oxygen to the well, encouraging bacterial growth. Well design should not encourage the introduction of vadose water (which often is rich in oxygen) via cascading water or another means of entry.

Well Head Design

Consideration should be given to future maintenance and rehabilitation, access, clearances, diameters, and chemical feed for cleaning.

Annular Thickness

Annular thickness has a direct bearing on the ability to clean the borehole wall during development and future redevelopment—thinner is better.

Screen Geometry

Open area directly impacts well development (even more so well redevelopment); high open-area, continuous-slot screens allow for consideration of more development tool options. Popular jetting methods, for example, are not effective when used with louver, bridge-slot, or mill-slot screen designs.

Sump

The occurrence of little or no water movement is ideal for the accumulation of anaerobic bacteria over time. When possible the sump should be eliminated. If a sump is needed, then using a short sump (5 ft (1.5 m) to 10 ft (3.1 m)) is a more practical approach than use of the typical 20-ft (6.1-m) length. Even better would be to make provisions to fill the sump area once development is complete and before the permanent pump is placed in the well.

Development

Chemicals such as NuWell® 220 Clay Dispersant—and not polyphosphates—should be used to remove natural clays and bentonite-based muds. Phosphates are food sources for bacteria, and their use can result in an increase in biofouling. Development methods should be selected to transfer energy through the screen and filter pack to remove fines (see Chapter 11 for well-development techniques).

Pump Placement

Many studies have been conducted regarding inlet flow and pump placement. Strategic pump placement (and strategic screen placement) that minimizes low-flow zones can prevent or minimize the development of bacterial growth.

THE WELL CASING

Every well consists of a cased section and the intake section (Figure 9.4). The cased section usually houses the pump, draws water from the source aquifer to the pump, and seals the aquifer from contamination from adjacent zones. In practice, the cased portion often consists of a surface casing or conductor casing and a production casing (a single string of casing commonly the same diameter as the screen) or an intermediate casing of smaller diameter. The aboveground termination of the surface casing depends on the type of pump used and whether the discharge is above or below the ground, and also possibly on aesthetic or application purposes. Elements to be considered are sources of contamination, stresses, and the corrosiveness of the local water. In certain applications, such as for monitoring or extraction wells, injection wells, and aquifer storage and recovery (ASR) wells, special requirements or conditions might have to be satisfied.

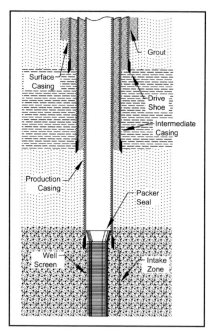

Figure 9.4. A water well constructed using successively smaller-diameter casings, with depth.

Pipe-Size Nomenclature

The term "nominal" is used in designating the inside diameter because the actual size (outer diameter (OD) and inner diameter (ID)) varies with pipe diameter and wall thickness. For example, 6-in (152-mm) nominal pipe has an outside diameter of 6.625 in (168 mm); for standard wall thickness the inside diameter is 6.065 in (154 mm). Pipe larger than 12 in (305 mm) is designated by its outside diameter. The actual inside diameter is controlled by the wall thickness and is significantly smaller than the indicated outside diameter. A diagram and description of the pipe manufacturing process is provided in Appendix 9.A (DVD).

To meet certain pressure requirements, pipe is manufactured in three general weight classes: standard, extra heavy, and double–extra heavy. The American National Standards Institute (ANSI) has assigned schedule numbers to classify wall thicknesses for different pressure applications.

- ANSI Schedule 40 is the same as standard pipe (Table 9.2) in nominal sizes ⅛ in (3.2 mm) through 10 in (254 mm).
- ANSI Schedule 80 is the same as extra-heavy pipe in nominal sizes ⅛ in (3.2 mm) through 8 in (203 mm).

For larger sizes of pipe, Schedules 40 and 80 can vary greatly from the specifications for standard and extra-heavy pipe. Additionally, there is no schedule number that correlates with double-extra-heavy pipe. Table 9.2 illustrates that no direct correlation exists between schedule numbers and the weight classes (standard, extra-heavy, double-extra-heavy).

Pipe used for constructing water wells is built to the standards developed for two major pipe markets: (1) water, chemical, and gas transmission (American Society for Testing and Materials (ASTM) standards); and (2) oil and gas industries (American Petroleum Institute (API) standards). Most wells constructed in North America use pipe conforming to either ASTM or API standards (Appendix 9.B (DVD)).

Various ASTM standards for steel pipe cover such properties as:

- Type of steel;
- Chemical composition;
- Tensile and bending requirements for the pipe dimensions;
- Pipe weights;
- End finish;

- ◆ Galvanizing; and
- ◆ Quality control (quality-control standards define permissible variations in weight, dimensions, metal composition, and performance testing (*Handbook for Steel Pipe* 1979)).

Appendix 9.C (book for U.S. customary units; DVD for SI units) contains additional data on all sizes of standard and line pipe. In general, ASTM-standard steel pipe is recommended for most drilling situations and typical water-quality conditions. Heavier wall thickness or alternative metals should be considered for use in exceptionally corrosive water, deep wells, or unusually demanding drilling conditions. The wall thickness must be sufficient to withstand full hydraulic loading if the casing is pumped dry (Table 9.2, in U.S. customary units). The collapse strength must exceed 1 psi (6.9 kPa) for every 2.31 ft (0.7 m) of depth beneath the top of the water level as measured in the well.

Table 9.2. Physical Dimensions of Common Steel Pipe Sizes

Schedule	Outside Diameter (in)	Inside Diameter (in)	Wall (in)	Wt / ft lbs	Collapse* (psi)
5	4.500	4.334	0.083	3.92	261
10	4.500	4.260	0.120	5.61	627
40 (STD)	4.500	4.026	0.237	10.79	2,316
5	5.563	5.345	0.109	6.35	304
10	5.563	5.295	0.134	7.77	498
40 (STD)	5.563	5.047	0.258	14.62	1,869
5	6.625	6.407	0.109	7.59	195
10	6.625	6.357	0.134	9.29	328
40 (STD)	6.625	6.065	0.280	18.97	1,585
5	8.625	8.407	0.109	9.91	97
10	8.625	8.329	0.148	13.40	218
40 (STD)	8.625	7.981	0.322	28.55	1,259
10	10.750	10.420	0.165	18.65	163
40 (STD)	10.750	10.020	0.365	40.48	1,045

Schedule	Outside Diameter (in)	Inside Diameter (in)	Wall (in)	Wt / ft lbs	Collapse* (psi)
10	12.750	12.390	0.180	24.16	131
(STD)	12.750	12.000	0.375	49.56	776
20	14.000	13.375	0.313	45.68	416
30 (STD)	14.000	13.250	0.375	54.57	633
20	16.000	15.375	0.313	52.36	301
30 (STD)	16.000	15.250	0.375	62.58	467
	18.000	17.625	0.188	35.67	58
20	18.000	17.375	0.313	59.03	224
(STD)	18.000	17.250	0.375	70.59	353
	20.000	19.625	0.188	39.67	43
	20.000	19.375	0.313	65.71	171
(STD)	20.000	19.250	0.375	78.60	272
10	22.000	21.500	0.250	58.07	73
	22.000	21.375	0.313	72.38	133
20 (STD)	22.000	21.250	0.375	86.61	214
10	24.000	23.500	0.250	63.41	58
	24.000	23.375	0.313	79.06	106
20 (STD)	24.000	23.250	0.375	94.62	171
	26.000	25.500	0.250	68.75	46
10	26.000	25.375	0.313	85.73	85
(STD)	26.000	25.250	0.375	102.63	139
	28.000	27.500	0.250	74.09	38
10	28.000	27.375	0.313	92.41	70
(STD)	28.000	27.250	0.375	110.64	114
10	30.000	29.375	0.313	99.08	58
(STD)	30.000	29.250	0.375	118.65	95
10	36.000	35.375	0.313	119.11	35
(STD)	36.000	35.250	0.375	142.68	58

* Calculated using Timoshenko formula: yield = 35,000 psi; tensile = 70,000; modulus = 30,000,000; poissons = 0.28; ecc = 1%.

See Appendix 9.C (DVD) for an expanded sizes table.

Casing Diameter

Choosing the proper casing diameter for the well is important, and it can affect the well's cost significantly. The diameter should satisfy two requirements, it should be large enough to provide adequate installation and safe operation of the pump, and it should be sufficient to assure that uphole velocity is 5 ft/sec (1.5 m/sec) or less, to minimize friction loss.

The size of the pump is the controlling factor in choosing the size of the casing. Ideally, the casing diameter should be two pipe sizes larger than the nominal diameter of the pump. In all cases, however, the casing must be at least one nominal size larger than the pump bowls. Table 9.3 lists recommended casing sizes for various pumping rates.

Table 9.3. Recommended Well Diameters for Various Pumping Rates*

Anticipated Well Yield		Nominal Size of Pump Bowls		Optimum Size of Well Casing[†]		Smallest Size of Well Casing[†]	
m³/day	GPM	mm	in	mm	in	mm	in
< 545	< 100	102	4	152 ID	6 ID	127 ID	5 ID
409 to 954	75 to 175	127	5	203 ID	8 ID	152 ID	6 ID
818 to 1,910	150 to 350	152	6	254 ID	10 ID	203 ID	8 ID
1,640 to 3,820	300 to 700	203	8	305 ID	12 ID	254 ID	10 ID
2,730 to 5,450	500 to 1,000	254	10	356 OD	14 OD	305 ID	12 ID
4,360 to 9,810	800 to 1,800	305	12	406 OD	16 OD	356 OD	14 OD
6,540 to 16,400	1,200 to 3,000	356	14	508 OD	20 OD	406 OD	16 OD
10,900 to 20,700	2,000 to 3,800	406	16	610 OD	24 OD	508 OD	20 OD
16,400 to 32,700	3,000 to 6,000	508	20	762 OD	30 OD	610 OD	24 OD

[*] For specific pump information, the well-designer should contact a pump supplier, and provide the anticipated yield, the head conditions, and the required pump efficiency.

[†] The size of the well casing is based on the greater outside diameter (OD) of the pump bowls or, for submersible pumps, the pump and motor. Although done, it is not good practice to place the pump bowls (or submersible) in the screen area, particularly in high-capacity wells.

Adequate pump-bowl clearance can be expected if the recommendations in Table 9.3 are used and if well-plumbness standards are met. Heat build-up can be a problem for a submersible pump set (in a sump) beneath the screen, because the pump intake is above the motor. This completion occurs where there is not adequate flow from the shallow water-bearing zone. The pump manufacturer should be consulted for motor cooling flow-rate recommendations. Increasing the casing diameter might be necessary to accommodate a pump and motor shroud (if required).

Telescope Casings and Well Depth

Conductor pipe or surface casing typically are large-diameter casings (sometimes temporary steel casings are used) set to sufficient depth to stabilize the ground surface for equipment and for drilling operations (Figure 9.4). Intermediate or production casing is installed next and is cemented to assure that surface contaminates cannot penetrate into the well annulus. It is important to note that most regional and local regulatory agencies have mandatory minimum surface, intermediate, or production casing guidelines or specifications. The intermediate or production casings can be single or multiple diameters set independently or continuously. Reducers are used for single string, multiple-diameter installations. More than one inner casing can be telescoped, depending on the well depth. In stable formations, the overlap could be as little as 20 ft (6 m), whereas in unconsolidated formations an overlap of 50 ft (15.2 m) or more is not uncommon.

In deep wells that have both high static water levels and high pumping water levels, the production casing diameter might be reduced to a depth below the lowest anticipated pump setting to decrease material costs. Uphole velocity in any smaller-diameter casing beneath the pump bowls should be 5 ft/sec (1.5 m/sec) or less. Table 9.4 lists maximum discharge rates for various casing sizes that produce only moderate friction losses.

Table 9.4. Maximum Discharge Rates for Certain Diameters of Standard-Weight Casing Based on an Uphole Velocity of 5 ft/sec (1.5 m/sec)

Nominal Casing Size		Maximum Discharge	
in	mm	gpm	ℓ/sec
4	102	200	12.6
5	127	310	19.6
6	152	450	28.4
8	203	780	49.2
10	254	1,230	77.5
12	305	1,760	111
14	356	2,150	135
16	406	2,850	179
18	457	3,640	229
20	508	4,540	286
24	609	6,620	418

Selection of Casing Materials

The casing material properties should be appropriate for the application loads and additional stresses expected during installation. Materials should have the right physical properties for the depth intended and should include an adequate margin of safety (generally 1.5 to 2).

Selection of casing material is based on water quality, planned depth, well diameter, drilling method, materials cost, and compliance with appropriate regulations. Common casing materials are low-carbon steel, stainless steel, and thermoplastic (PVC) pipe. Although low-carbon steel still is the most common well casing material, PVC, stainless steel, fiberglass, and steel alloys also are used. Table 9.5 lists some common physical characteristics of casing materials.

Table 9.5. Approximate Comparison of Well-Casing Material Properties

		Carbon Steel	Stainless Steel	PVC	Fiberglass
Specific Gravity		7.8	8	1.4	1.9
Yield Strength	psi	35,000	30,000	7,000	12,000
	Mpa	240	210	50	80
Axial Modulus	psi	30,000,000	28,000,000	400,000	2,000,000
	Mpa	206,900	193,100	2,800	13,800
Poissons Ratio		0.28	0.3	0.4	0.6
Service Temperature	°F	< 1,000	< 1,000	< 140	< 300
	°C	< 538	< 538	< 60	< 149
Coefficient of Thermal Expansion	in/in °F	6.60E-05	1.01E-04	2.95E-05	1.00E-05
	cm/m °C	1.19E-04	1.82E-04	5.40E-05	1.80E-05
Water Absorption	wt % per 24 hr	Nil	Nil	0.05	0.2
(PVC data from Harvel Plastics Engineering Manual. Fiberglass data from Centron Fiberglass Pipe Products literature.)					

In corrosive water—or to extend service life—using PVC or stainless steel can be preferable if strength requirements are satisfied. The use of PVC casing has expanded greatly for shallow, small-diameter wells because of its corrosion resistance, ease of handling, and low cost. Its use for irrigation wells also has increased.

Steel casing always must be used whenever casing is driven and pulled back using the cable tool method, or when casing is installed in open boreholes that are subject to caving. It is important to note that steel casing manufacturing tolerances for weight, wall thickness, and length are published by most suppliers. Weight tolerance for standard line pipe is plus or minus 5%, and wall thickness is less than 12.5%. These variations must be taken into account when estimating strengths.

Low-Carbon Steel

Low-carbon steel is the most commonly used casing material. When installing steel casing in corrosive soil or water conditions, longer life is achieved by using greater wall thickness. Although considerably more expensive than low-carbon steel, extremely corrosive conditions and a need for assured longevity typically call for stainless-steel casing because it delivers longer service life. In recent years, many municipal and industrial well designs specify the use of stainless steel, various types of carbon steel, or PVC casing.

Standard water-well steel casing conforms to ASTM Designation A53/A53B, or API Standard Specification 5CT or 5L. The ASTM specification A53/A53B for welded and seamless steel pipe covers black and hot-dipped zinc-coated (galvanized), welded, and seamless steel pipe in sizes of from ⅛ in (3.2 mm) to 26 in (660 mm).

API Standard Specification 5L includes threaded and coupled line pipe of ⅛-in (3.2-mm) to 20-in (508-mm) OD and plain-end line pipe of from ⅛-in (3.2-mm) to 48-in (1,220-mm) OD. API Standard Specification 5A covers threaded and coupled casing of from 4.5-in (114-mm) to 20-in (508-mm) OD, and tubing that is from 1.05-in (26.7-mm) to 4.5-in (114-mm) OD. Many countries manufacture products that conform with API Standard 5L or 5A. Western European manufacturers produce pipe that is similar—but not identical—to that created using API standards, and which often is made using Standard International units of measurement rather than U.S. customary units.

Stainless Steel

Stainless-steel casing (ASTM A312/A312M or A409/A409M) sometimes is specified for municipal and industrial wells to increase well life. The addition of chromium (more than 11.5%) to regular steel produces a stainless steel capable of resisting corrosion. The presence of nickel and molybdenum in 304 and 316 also helps prevent certain forms of corrosion. The 300 series austenitic stainless steels are used widely for well screens and casings. The steels typically contain from 16% to 20% chromium and from 8% to 14% nickel, and generally are resistant to corrosion. The initial cost of stainless steel is more than that of low-carbon steel but—in most environments—it also lasts longer which, in the long term, can offset the cost. Three types of 304 are available, helping make it the most common stainless steel used in water wells. Also, note that the higher the carbon content the greater the yield strength (Table 9.6). The composition of several alloy metals is given in Table 9.7.

Table 9.6. Carbon Content of Common 304 Series Stainless Steels

Grade	Carbon Content	
304 L	Low carbon	0.03% max
304	Medium carbon	0.08% max
304H	High carbon	up to 0.1%

Table 9.7. Basic Composition and Suggested Applications of Various Metals for Water-Well Casing and Screens

Metal	Composition		Suggested Applications
Low-Carbon Steel	Carbon	0.8% max	Not corrosion resistant. Satisfactory life in noncorrosive, nonincrusting waters.
	Iron	Balance	
200 Series Stainless Steel	Chromium	16.5% max	Corrosion resistance similar to Type 304. Non-magnetic, greater tensile than Type 304.
	Manganese	9% max	
	Nickel	4% max	
	Carbon	0.15% max	
	Iron	Balance	
Type 304 Stainless Steel	Chromium	18% min	Excellent corrosion resistance. Type of stainless steel widely used in water-well construction.
	Nickel	8% min	
	Manganese	2% max	
	Carbon	0.08% max	
	Iron	Balance	
Type 316L Stainless Steel	Chromium	16% min	Used in moderate saline groundwater. Molybdenum resists pitting/crevice corrosion in moderate saline water. Better resistance to stress-corrosion cracking than Type 304.
	Nickel	10% min	
	Molybdenum	2% min	
	Carbon	0.03% max	
	Iron	Balance	
Carpenter® 20Cb-3	Nickel	32% min	Strong resistance to stress-corrosion cracking, pitting, and crevice corrosion. Satisfactory in high-saline water and at temperatures greater than 100°F (38°C).
	Chromium	19% min	
	Copper	3% min	
	Molybdenum	2% max	
	Carbon	0.03% max	
	Iron	Balance	

Metal	Composition		Suggested Applications
Monel® 400	Nickel (plus Cobalt)	63% min	Satisfactory in sea water (high sodium chloride with dissolved oxygen). Is sensitive to hydrogen sulfide.
	Copper	28% min	
	Iron	2.5% max	
	Manganese	2% max	
Incoloy® 825	Nickel (plus cobalt)	38% min	Low corrosion potential in high-chloride water, resists cracking, pitting, and crevice corrosion. Used for geo-thermal, oil, and gas-injection wells.
	Iron	22% min	
	Chromium	19.5% min	
	Molybdenum	2.5% min	
	Copper	1.5% min	
Inconel® 600	Nickel (plus cobalt)	72% min	For use in geothermal, oil and gas, and injection-well applications. Strong resistance to stress-corrosion cracking.
	Chromium	14% min	
	Iron	6–10%	
Hastelloy® C	Nickel	51% min	Extremely corrosion-resistant alloy. Used in aggressive environments (brine, corrosive gases), and where temperatures exceed 200°F (93°C). For use in geothermal, oil and gas, and injection wells.
	Molybdenum	15% min	
	Chromium	14.5% min	
	Iron	4% min	
	Tungsten	3% min	
	Cobalt	2.5% max	
	Vanadium	0.35% max	

Plastic

Polyvinyl chloride (PVC) commonly is used in small-diameter wells, such as residential wells and those used for environmental monitoring. The use of plastic well casing has grown significantly since the 1960s. Stronger materials and advances in extrusion technology have broadened the range of diameters and wall thicknesses available. Corrosion resistance, lightweight, low cost, easy installation, and resistance to acid treatment make PVC casing desirable for use where its strength is adequate. PVC is almost completely resistant to biological attack and cannot serve as a nutrient to microorganisms.

Standardization of thermoplastic well casing is covered under the ASTM Standard F480 entitled, "Standard Specification for Thermoplastic Water Well

Casing, Pipe and Couplings Made in Standard Dimension Ratios (SDR), SCH40 and SCH80." This document specifies the minimum physical and chemical characteristics of PVC materials, and defines the standard dimension ratio (SDR) as the outside diameter divided by the minimum wall thickness (equation 9.1).

$$SDR = \frac{Outside\ Diameter}{Wall\ Thickness} \qquad\qquad (9.1)$$

As the diameter increases, the wall thickness also increases. In this way the collapse resistance remains the same for all sizes of pipe built to a given strength standard. The exceptions to the standard dimension ratios occur in schedules such as Schedule 40 or Schedule 80, where the wall thickness and diameter have no distinct relationship and are built using the standards for steel.

ASTM Standard D1784, "Standard Specification for Rigid Polyvinyl Chloride (PVC) Compounds and Chlorinated Polyvinyl Chloride (CPVC) Compounds," specifies the minimum physical property requirements for the materials used in the production of PVC pipe and fittings. Table 9.8 gives physical characteristics of a commonly used size of PVC casing. Because regulations vary concerning the use of plastic casing, the appropriate regulatory agency should be consulted for current laws and regulations.

Table 9.8. Typical Physical Properties of PVC Well Casing Compared to CPVC at 73.4°F (23°C)

Property	ASTM Test Method	PVC Cell Class 12454 (ASTM D1784)	CPVC Cell Class 23447 (ASTM D1784)
Specific Gravity	D-792	1.40 +/- 0.02	1.52 +/- 0.02
Tensile strength (psi)	D-638	7,450	7,320
Tensile Modulus of Elasticity (psi)	D-638	420,000	360,000
Poisson's Ratio		0.410	0.386
Compressive Strength (psi)	D-695	9,600	10,000
Impact Strength, Izod Method, Notched (ft-lb/in)	D-256	0.75	2.0
Deflection Temperature (°F) Under Load (264 psi)	D-648	170	226
Coefficient of Linear Expansion (in/in °F)	D-696	2.9×10^{-5}	3.4×10^{-5}
(Harvel Plastics, Inc.)			

Chlorinated polyvinyl chloride (CPVC) is used in higher-temperature applications—up to 180°F (82°C). The CPVC cell classification 23447 is CPVC Type IV, Grade I, rigid un-plasticized CPVC. See Appendix 9.D (DVD) for the resin types and numerical values for these variables and the methodology for the cell classification scheme.

Plastic casing deforms at relatively low temperatures (Table 9.8), and temperatures greater than ambient temperature reduce its working strength. When grouting, it is important to minimize the effects of the heat of hydration (Table 9.9). Restricting the annular grout thickness to no more than 2 in (51 mm) thick or filling the casing with water can minimize temperature effects.

Table 9.9. The Effect of Temperature on PVC Pipe Strength

Temperature of Liquid in or Around Pipe		Maximum Design Value of Work Strength
°F	°C	
73.4	23	100%
80	27	88%
90	32	75%
100	38	62%
110	43	50%
120	49	40%
130	54	30%
140	60	22%

PVC pipe is more flexible than steel, and it should be centered in the borehole before any backfilling or filter packing is completed. Any voids in the backfill or filter-pack material could lead to a collapse of formation materials against the casing, and also cause it to break. The collapse strength of plastic casing is much less than that of steel casing. Design hydraulic collapse pressures for thermoplastic casings manufactured under ASTM F-480 are given in Figure 9.5. See Appendix 9.E (book) for collapse strengths of PVC casing.

Under ideal conditions, where well-compacted materials fully support the casing, the values for collapse resistance given in ASTM F-480 are reliable. The actual strength needed for any situation depends on the standard dimension ratio, wall thickness uniformity, roundness of the casing, rate of loading, and temperature of the casing when the loading is applied. Although plastic casing can be set to depths of 1,000 ft (305 m), industry professionals should follow good design practices for drilling wells that are deeper than 300 ft (91.5 m).

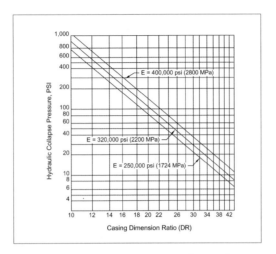

Figure 9.5. Hydraulic collapse pressure at 73°F (22.8°C) versus casing dimension ration (DR) for thermoplastic well casing. The DR is the ratio of average casing outside diameter to minimum wall thickness; E is the modulus of elasticity (NWWA 1981).

Other strengths applicable to plastic materials include impact resistance, toughness, and pipe stiffness. Long-term exposure to the sun's ultraviolet rays can significantly reduce the impact strength of the material. There also are several issues unique to PVC that should be considered. When casing protrudes above ground level it must be protected—PVC is not as strong as steel. When handling the material in cold weather, care must be used to prevent shattering the material—especially when the temperature is below 32°F (0°C). Tensile strength usually is less important for PVC, because PVC generally is used in shallow wells. The weight of PVC is about one-fifth the weight of steel, so it occasionally floats during installation and creates special handling problems.

Fiberglass-Reinforced Plastic

Casing for water wells also is constructed from various types of fiberglass-reinforced plastic materials, which usually are called fiberglass casing. Fiberglass casing is resistant to most forms of corrosion, it is not conductive, and—for its weight—its strength is equivalent to that of steel. This type of casing has been used successfully for injection of highly corrosive waters to recharge oil reservoirs. It also is used for water-supply wells and, in some areas of the world, for irrigation purposes. Heat can significantly reduce the collapse strength of fiberglass pipe, but for most water wells this reduction in collapse resistance is minimal due to the fact that the temperature of most groundwater is not elevated.

Fiberglass casing is somewhat permeable and, in formations where poor-quality water is cased off above potable water, some contamination of the water supply could occur. Well fittings such as centralizers, couplings, and surface fittings constructed of fiberglass are available for use with this type of casing. Table 9.10 lists the standard properties of fiberglass well casing that has a wall thickness of 0.375 in (0.925 cm). Standard properties for other wall thicknesses can be obtained from casing manufacturers. A table containing the SI conversion of this information is found in Appendix 9.F (DVD).

Table 9.10. Properties of Polyester Resin–Based Fiberglass Well Casing*

Pipe Size (in)	Nom OD (in)	Wall (in)	Internal Pressure (psi)	Collapse (psi)	Tensile (lb)	Wt/Ft (lb)	Coupling Diameter (in)
4.5	5.25	0.375	575	3,380	21,750	4.4	7.5
6.5	7.25	0.375	400	1,280	30,975	6.3	9.5
8.5	9.25	0.375	300	615	39,975	8.3	11.5
10.5	11.25	0.375	250	340	49,000	10.2	13.5
12	12.75	0.375	225	230	55,750	11.6	15.0
14	14.75	0.375	200	150	64,750	13.5	17.0
16	16.75	0.375	175	115	73,750	15.4	19.25
All values are approximate (Burgess Well Co.).							

Casing Strength Requirements

Collapse Strength

Radial casing collapses result from both fixed and dynamic forces. The overlying formation weight and water column generally are considered to be fixed; caving, filter pack movement, subsidence, and earthquakes are dynamic stresses.

It is very difficult to establish and plan for the impacts of dynamic forces. Collapse resistance of pipe is a function of the material's physical properties and the ratio of diameter to wall thickness. It also is important to consider acceptable tolerances in manufacturing of the pipe, as these variations can affect the overall strength of the pipe. For example, acceptable steel-pipe manufacturing tolerances allow up to 12.5% wall thickness reductions. The consequences of such an allowance are indicated in Figure 9.6. This figure (rendered in U.S. customary units) is a plot of collapse pressure (psi) versus the ratio of pipe diameter (D) versus wall thickness (t). A 12.5% reduction in wall thickness increases the D/t ratio, thus reducing collapse resistance for a given pipe diameter.

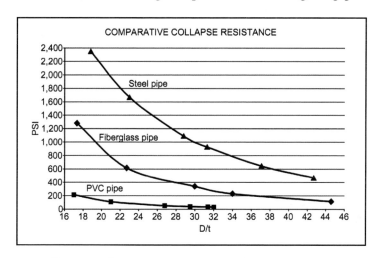

Figure 9.6. Common collapse ratings (psi) of steel pipe versus *D/t* ratios.

The most widely accepted methods for calculating steel casing collapse pressure are the equations derived by Stephen P. Timoshenko and those established by the API (the API equations are supplied in Appendix 9.G (DVD)). Timoshenko's theoretical collapse pressure for perfectly round steel casing is shown in equation 9.2.

$$Pcr = \frac{2E}{(1-u^2)\cdot\left(\dfrac{D}{t}-1\right)^3}$$

(9.2)

Where:

Pcr = perfect cylinder collapse pressure (psi);

E = Young's modulus ($2.1 \cdot 10^8$ kPa or $3.0 \cdot 10^7$ psi for steel; $1.9 \cdot 10^8$ kPa or $2.8 \cdot 10^7$ for stainless steel);

u = Poisson's ratio (0.28 for steel, 0.3 for stainless steel);

D = outside diameter of casing (in or cm); and

t = wall thickness (in or cm).

Timoshenko (1976) derived the formula below to take into consideration the effect of eccentricity. Eccentricity is defined as the distance between the centers of the outside and inside diameters in a cross section. It can be stated in percent of the nominal wall thickness.

$$Pd^2 - \left\{ \frac{2Yp}{D/t - 1} + \left[1 + 3\left(\frac{D}{t} - 1 \right)e \right]Pcr \right\}Pd + \frac{2YpPcr}{\left(D/t - 1 \right)} = 0 \qquad \textbf{(9.3)}$$

Where:

Pd = design collapse (psi or kPa);

Pcr = perfect cylinder collapse (psi or kPa) (equation 9.2);

Yp = material yield strength (35,000 psi or 244,000 kPa for steel, 30,000 psi or 207,000 kPa for stainless steel); and

e = eccentricity constant (typically 1%).

As noted above, manufacturing tolerances allow up to 12.5% reduction in pipe wall thickness. Table 9.11 shows the effect of wall-thickness reduction for three common diameters using equation 9.3. Pressure differentials and manufacturing tolerances should be examined carefully.

Safety factors for collapse resistance should be about 1.5, depending on how the collapse load is determined and due to possible manufacturing tolerances. If excess differential for mud (or cement) density is part of the load calculation, then the chance of a collapse occurring could be lessened, because the inside of the casing rarely is completely dry. Disregarding minimum wall-thickness tolerances—unless otherwise directed by the manufacturer—can result in problems.

Table 9.11. Steel Pipe Collapse Reduction Due to Wall-Thickness Tolerance Variance

Pipe OD		Standard Wall				Change
in	cm	Thickness (in)	Thickness (cm)	Collapse (psi)	Collapse (kPa)	Reduction in Collapse
8.625	21.9	0.25	0.64	752	5,184	-26%
12.75	32.4	0.3125	0.79	518	3,571	-27%
16	40.6	0.375	0.95	467	3,219	-27%

Pipe OD		Standard Wall Minus 12.5%				Change
in	cm	Thickness (in)	Thickness (cm)	Collapse (psi)	Collapse (kPa)	Reduction in Collapse
8.625	21.9	0.2188	0.56	560	3,861	-26%
12.75	32.4	0.2734	0.69	378	2,606	-27%
16	40.6	0.3281	0.833	339	2,337	-27%

Most often, the overlying formation weight is self-supporting but, where such an assumption is suspect, estimating this pressure at 1.0 psi/ft (23 kPa/m) of depth is an accepted approach. Note that occurrences such as sudden earth movement, caving, subsidence, or careless development practices can result in much greater collapse forces. Hydrostatic pressure exerted by freshwater is 0.433 psi/ft (9.8 kPa/m). In a given well this pressure at total depth can be calculated by using equation 9.4.

$$P = h \cdot 0.433 \; psi \,/\, ft \qquad \text{(U.S. customary units)}$$

$$P = h \cdot 9.77 \; kPa \,/\, m \qquad \text{(SI units)} \qquad \textbf{(9.4)}$$

Where:

P = fluid pressure at depth (psi or kPa);

h = height of static fluid from bottom of well (ft or m); and

0.433 ft (3 kPa/m) = pressure gradient for freshwater (psi/ft or kPa/m).

If the water levels inside and outside of the casing are equal, then the hydrostatic pressures are offset. During cementing or development, the fluid levels typically are not equal and the annulus contains cement or drilling fluid. The unequal levels and greater density of the annular fluids creates a pressure differential. Drilling mud density commonly is 9 lb/gal (1 kg/ℓ) to 10 lb/gal

(1.2 kg/ℓ) and cement density can be up to 15 lb/gal (1.8 kg/ℓ). Equation 9.5 adjusts for fluid density.

$$\Delta P = (H - h) \cdot 0.433 \, psi \, / \, ft \cdot \left(\frac{\rho_o}{\rho_w} \right)$$ (U.S. customary units)

$$\Delta P = (H - h) \cdot 9.77 kPa \, / \, m \cdot \left(\frac{\rho_o}{\rho_w} \right)$$ (SI units)   **(9.5)**

Where:

ΔP = pressure differential exerted on the casing (psi or kPa);

H = height of fluid outside the casing from total depth (ft or m);

ρ_o = fluid density outside the casing (lb/gal or kPa); and

ρ_w = 8.33 lb/gal (1.0 kg/ℓ) = density of freshwater (lb/gal or kPa/m).

Consider, for example, a well requiring 16-in (406-mm) casing cemented from 1,200 ft (366 m) to the surface, a static water level of 600 ft (183 m), and cement density of 13.5 lb/gal (1.6 kg/ℓ). The pressure differential at the bottom of the casing is calculated using equation 9.5, as shown below.

H = (1,200 − 600) = 600 ft

ΔP = (1,200 ft − 600 ft) · 0.433 psi · (13.5/8.33)

ΔP = 600 ft · 0.433 · 1.62

ΔP = 421 psi   (U.S. customary units)

H = (366 − 183) = 183 m

ΔP = (366 m − 183 m) · 9.8 kPa/m (1.6 kg/ℓ)

ΔP = 183 m · 9.8 kPa/m · 1.6 kg/ℓ

ΔP = 2,869 kPa   (SI units)

The collapse resistance of a standard ⅜-in (9.5-mm) wall 16-in (406-mm) OD steel casing is 467 psi (3,200 kPa). Considering the allowable tolerances for steel pipe, the actual pressure that could cause collapse could be as low as 339 psi (2,340 kPa) (Table 9.11). In this instance, the casing could collapse during cementing operations if cementing is not performed in intervals.

Table 9.11 shows that a 25% safety factor is necessary when calculating design collapse strength for carbon-steel casing if allowing for common manufacturing tolerances.

The American Water Works Association (AWWA) has published guidelines recommending the minimum wall thickness for carbon-steel casing (Appendix 9.H (book)), and these guidelines have been utilized in the well industry for many years. Table 9.12 shows the data from Appendix 9.H presented as psi/ft (kPa/m).

Table 9.12. Minimum psi/ft (kPa/m) for Carbon-Steel Casing

Depth ft (m)	8 in (203 mm)	10 in (254 mm)	12 in (305 mm)	14 in (356 mm)	16 in (406 mm)	18 in (457 mm)	20 in (508 mm)	24 in (610 mm)
0–100 (0–30)	7.6 (25.2)	4.6 (14.9)	3.1 (10.2)	2.4 (8.1)	1.7 (5.7)	1.3 (4.2)	1.0 (3.2)	1.1 (3.6)
100–200 (30–61)	3.8 (12.4)	2.3 (7.6)	1.5 (5.0)	1.2 (4.0)	0.9 (2.8)	0.6 (2.1)	0.5 (1.6)	0.5 (1.8)
200–300 (61–91)	2.5 (8.3)	1.5 (5.1)	1.0 (3.4)	0.8 (2.7)	0.6 (1.9)	0.8 (2.5)	0.6 (1.9)	0.4 (1.2)
300–400 (91–122)	1.9 (6.2)	1.2 (3.8)	0.8 (2.5)	0.6 (2.0)	0.8 (2.5)	0.6 (1.9)	0.4 (1.4)	0.4 (1.4)
400–600 (122–183)	1.3 (4.1)	0.8 (2.5)	0.5 (1.7)	0.4 (1.3)	0.5 (1.7)	0.4 (1.2)	0.3 (0.9)	0.3 (0.9)
600–800 (183–244)	0.9 (3.1)	0.6 (1.9)	0.4 (1.3)	0.5 (1.7)	0.4 (1.2)	0.28 (0.9)	0.3 (1.1)	0.21 (0.7)
800–1,000 (244–305)	0.8 (2.5)	0.5 (1.5)	0.3 (1.0)	0.4 (1.4)	0.3 (1.0)	0.23 (0.7)	0.27 (0.9)	0.25 (0.8)
1,000– 1,500 (305–457)	0.5 (1.7)	0.5 (1.7)	0.3 (1.1)	0.28 (0.9)	0.3 (1.0)	0.24 (0.8)	0.18 (0.6)	NA
1,500– 2,000 (457–610)	0.4 (1.2)	0.4 (1.2)	0.26 (0.9)	0.21 (0.7)	0.24 (0.8)	0.18 (0.6)	0.20 (0.7)	NA

The data presented illustrate that wells that deviate considerably from strict adherence to design that is based on 1.0 psi/ft (23 kPa/m) or 0.433 psi/ft (3 kPa/m) guidelines (Figure 9.7) have been installed successfully (particularly large-diameter and deep wells). The important consideration is to allow an adequate safety factor for the design.

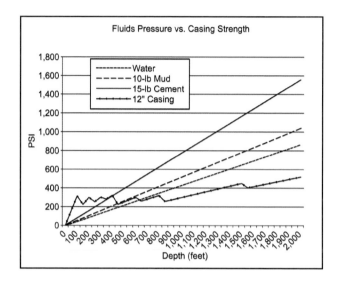

Figure 9.7. Comparative collapse resistance.

Tensile Strength

The axial tension loads imparted to the casing string during installation come primarily from the weight of the suspended pipe and screen, and also from additional drag forces that could be transferred to the string assembly during gravel packing. The weight of a single-diameter casing assembly is easily calculated using equation 9.6.

$$Wt = \left[k \cdot t \cdot (D - t)\right] \cdot L \qquad\qquad (9.6)$$

Where:

Wt = total weight casing (lb or kg);

t = wall thickness of pipe (in or cm);

D = outside diameter of pipe (in or cm); and

L = total length of pipe (ft or m).

	LCS	SS	PVC	Fiberglass	
$k =$	10.68	10.78	2.1	2.7	U.S. customary
	0.229	0.231	0.15	0.62	SI

An equation commonly used for determining casing tensile strength is shown in equation 9.7 (AWWA Standard for Water Wells, ANSI/AWWA A100-97, Appendix K, § K.3).

$$Cts = \frac{\pi \cdot t \cdot S_t (D_o - t)}{2000} \qquad\qquad (9.7)$$

Where:

Cts = casing tensile strength (tons or kg);

D_o = casing outside diameter (in or mm);

S_t = ultimate tensile strength of material (LCS = 70,000 psi or 413.7 MPa); and

t = casing wall thickness (in or mm).

During installation, casing assemblies are subject to buoyancy effects from the fluids in the borehole. The buoyancy factor applies only to the portion of the casing assembly that is totally immersed in fluid, and can be calculated using equation 9.8.

$$B = \frac{(Dm - Df)}{Dm} \qquad\qquad (9.8)$$

Where:

B = buoyancy factor (dimensionless);

Dm = density of casing material (lb/ft^3 or kg/m^3); and

Df = density of fluid (lb/ft^3 or kg/m^3).

Example
The formula below can be used to determine the expected hook-load of 1,000 ft (305 m) of 12.75-in (32.39-cm) OD steel casing, weighing 49.6 lb/ft (73.8 kg/m) set into a borehole filled with freshwater that has a static water level 400 ft (122 m) below ground surface. Hook-load is defined as the combination of screen and casing weight that must be carried by the drill-rig lifting hook during the setting of the well material into the well. The following equation is rendered in U.S. customary units.

$$\begin{aligned}
\text{Dry String Wt} &= 49.6 \text{ lb/ft} \cdot 1{,}000 \text{ ft} = 49{,}600 \text{ lb} \\
B &= (490 \text{ lb/ft}^3 - 62.4 \text{ lb/ft}^3)/490 \text{ lb/ft}^3 = 0.873 \\
\text{Hook Load} &= (400 \text{ ft} \cdot 49.6 \text{ lb/ft}) + [600 \text{ ft} \cdot (49.6 \cdot 0.873)] \\
\text{Hook Load} &= 45{,}820 \text{ lb} \ (8\% \text{ less than dry string weight})
\end{aligned}$$

As shown, buoyancy has a relatively small effect on tensile loads and typically is ignored in tensile load calculations. Typical safety factors for tensile-strength calculations range from 1.5 to 2.0. If design loads are based on full air-weight of the casing, then the actual weight (most often) is less—due to a buoyancy effect as the string is set into fluid—and the true weight can be less than the weight calculated using nominal wall thickness values. Tensile strength also usually is greater than the calculated value, due to the difference between actual and specified (or published) minimum values of yield and tensile strength used in calculations. The final safety factor should be determined by the engineer—and be based on experience.

Column Strength

If the downward compressive force on a laterally unsupported casing assembly exceeds the yield strength of the material, then the casing will buckle. The axial compressive (column) strength of steel casing can be calculated using equation 9.9 (which also is published in the AWWA Standard for Water Wells, ANSI/AWWA A100-97, Appendix K, § K.3).

$$Cas = \frac{\pi \cdot t \cdot S_{yp} (D_o - t)}{2000} \tag{9.9}$$

Where:

Cas = casing axial compressive strength (tons or kg);

S_{yp} = material yield strength (LCS = 35,000 psi or 241.3 MPa);

D_o = casing outside diameter (in or mm); and

t = casing wall thickness (in or mm).

Correct field procedure is to suspend the casing and screen assembly from the surface until properly filter packed and cemented as required. Most screens are not designed to withstand the full total-depth weight of the assembly. Drilling professionals thus never should allow a full assembly to touch the bottom of the borehole. Oftentimes, the borehole is partially filled with material sloughed from the wall or cuttings settled from drill fluid.

Joining Casing

Field assembly of well casing is accomplished by welding or by using mechanical joints. Mechanical joints typically are threads; some are a groove and spline assembly or a snap-together locking joint. Each type has benefits and features that facilitate speed, strength, or flexibility, or which address special application needs. Welding is a common practice but requires cutting if the casing must be removed. Threaded pipe typically is more costly, however joints using such pipe can be disassembled if necessary (which might save time as compared with the cutting of a welded joint and the subsequent welding). The following sections describe methods for joining common casing materials.

Welding Steel Casing

Steel casing usually is prepared for welding by the beveling of the pipe ends approximately 30 degrees. The welding should follow standardized procedures (American Welding Society 1981).

The three typical casing welds are fillet, butt, and V-groove. Fillet welds are used to secure lap joints, corner joints, and T-joints (common with a slip collar). Weld metal is deposited in a corner formed by the fit-up of the collar shoulder to the pipe wall. Butt welds are circumferential welds around squared pipe ends in the same plane. The degree of penetration is important in determining the quality of a fillet or butt weld.

V-groove welds are used when two squared, beveled pipe ends butt together. The entire groove should be filled, and this type of weld typically requires multiple passes to completely fill the groove. Care should be taken to avoid burn-through, so that metal is not deposited inside the casing (which can hinder or prevent tool movement or screen installation).

The proper selection of electrodes is critical to joining dissimilar metals. Either E 312-16 or E 309-16 (AWS-ASTM classification) electrodes are recommended for joining low-carbon steel to stainless steel. Type E 309 electrodes are readily available and cost less than E 312-16 material. Type E 308-15 or E 308-16 electrodes are used to weld stainless steel to stainless steel. If mild steel electrodes are used to join stainless steel to stainless steel then chromium precipitates. This creates areas of low corrosion resistance that eventually lead to structural weakness or failure. See Appendix 9.I (DVD) for details on field-welding procedures and electrode recommendations.

Steel Casing Threads

Standards for general-purpose pipe-thread applications are described in the ANSI Standard "Pipe Threads, General Purpose (INCH) ANSI/ASME B1.20.1." Line pipe threads are covered by the API Standard "API Specification 5B." There are specially adapted couplings available for casing and pump column pipe (*see* Figure 9.8). Individual manufacturers should be consulted for proper application.

Figure 9.8. Johnson ZSM Tubexor™ connection. The exterior coupling part is shown in the figure on the left; the portion of the coupling that is fitted into the coupling shown in the figure on the right, along with the cable lock system which is installed after the coupling is joined.

Typically, non-recessed taper tapped (NPT) couplings are used with standard-weight pipe (sizes 2½ in (64 mm) to 6 in (152 mm)) and recessed taper tapped (RTT) couplings are for extra-strong and double-extra-strong pipe (8 in (203 mm) and larger). Taper tapped recessed couplings are the same type as those used with line pipe, and are covered by "API Specification 5L." Line pipe couplings are recessed to help center the pipe in the coupling and guide it into the threads. Recessing also covers incomplete threads created by the taper, and minimizes corrosion at that point. Common API casing threads are the buttress and round threads, varying from square to rounded thread patterns and having tapers of ¾ in/ft (0.625 mm/cm) and 5 to 8 threads/in (2 to 3 threads/cm). Thread strength is determined by examining the remaining cross-sectional pipe-wall area after cutting the thread pattern removes material.

The following equations provide reasonable estimates of round-thread joint strength, and apply to both short and long threads and couplings. Equation 9.10 expresses failure by fracture and equation 9.11 shows failure by pullout. The lesser of the two calculated results is considered to be the joint strength. These equations are provided in U.S. customary units. Table 9.13 provides minimum joint strengths for standard threaded pipe.

Fracture Strength

$$P_f = 0.95 \cdot A \cdot U \qquad\qquad (9.10)$$

Pullout Strength

$$P = 0.95 \cdot A \cdot L \cdot \left[\frac{0.74 \cdot D^{-0.59} \cdot U}{0.5L + 0.14D} + \frac{Y}{L + 0.14D} \right] \qquad (9.11)$$

Where:

P_f = fracture strength (lb);

P = pullout strength (lb);

A = cross-section area of pipe wall under last perfect thread (in²)
   = $0.7854[(D–0.1425)^2 – d^2]$;

L = engaged thread length (in);

d = inside diameter of pipe (in);

D = outside diameter of pipe (in);

U = minimum pipe tensile strength (psi); and

Y = minimum pipe yield strength (psi).

Table 9.13. Minimum Joint Strength of Standard Threaded Line Pipe

Nom Size (in)	OD (in)	Wall (in)	Threads (per in)	Engaged Thread (in)	Joint Strength Grade (lb) A	B
4	4.500	0.237	8	1.094	61,900	74,500
5	5.563	0.280	8	1.187	79,200	95,100
6	6.625	0.280	8	1.208	95,800	115,000
8	8.625	0.277	8	1.313	107,000	128,000
8	8.625	0.322	8	1.313	133,000	159,000
10	10.750	0.279	8	1.460	122,000	146,000
10	10.750	0.307	8	1.460	141,000	168,000
10	10.750	0.365	8	1.460	178,000	213,000
12	12.750	0.330	8	1.610	173,000	206,000
12	12.750	0.375	8	1.610	205,000	244,000
14	14.000	0.375	8	1.812	226,000	283,000
16	16.000	0.375	8	2.062	253,000	301,000
18	18.000	0.375	8	2.250	376,000	328,000
20	20.000	0.375	8	2.375	294,000	349,000
Strength basis is pullout (ARMCO Tubulars Division).						

Plastic Casing

Plastic casing can be joined by using either solvent welding (using a solvent cement to join casing segments) or mechanical means. For solvent welding, primer is used to clean and etch the surface of both ends of the pipe and coupling before the solvent cement is applied. After the solvent has been uniformly applied to the casing and the pieces are joined, sufficient time must be allowed for curing. Two major problems that affect the integrity of a joint are low temperatures (less than 40°F (4.4°C)) and poor fit caused by joint inter-ferences. The drilling professional must be sure to use the correct solvent cement for a particular casing type. In temperatures colder than 40°F (4.4°C), plastic components should be joined with a low-temperature solvent cement. A special solvent must be used when joining PVC and ABS casing because the materials have different chemical compositions (*see* ASTM D-3138).

Two types of solvent-welded joints commonly are used. One type uses a coupling (collar) to join casing lengths of equal or unequal diameter. The ends of the casing fit tightly into the molded plastic coupling. In the second type, a "bell-end" socket is molded at one end of each casing length to receive the straight (spigot) end of the next casing length. It is important that the bell or coupling be manufactured to close tolerances so that the fit around the pipe is uniformly snug. See Appendix 9.J (DVD) for solvent-welding procedures. When working in higher temperatures, solvent-cemented joints should be considered under the rating of strength effects for threaded joints. When solvent-welded joints are made properly, the strength of the joint is equal to or greater than the strength of the pipe itself.

Plastic casing also can be joined mechanically by threaded couplings, spline lock, or special slip-and-lock joints.

Threaded connections most frequently are used on small-diameter plastic casing (e.g., pump column pipe) and on monitoring wells, when joints must be watertight and the use of solvents is not allowed. For applications where temperatures exceed 110°F (43°C), standard threaded connections should not be used and instead special reinforced adapters or optional joint designs should be evaluated and the manufacturer be consulted. Special thread lubricants and sealants must be used. Avoid using solvent cement on threads, because the cement might set faster than the threads can be tightened.

Mechanical connections allow disassembly and reuse if necessary, require no solvents, and save installation time. Stainless-steel screens can be attached to PVC casings using either a threaded connector or a PVC-to-stainless-steel adaptor.

Fiberglass Casing

Typically, fiberglass casing is joined using threaded joints because of the long setting time that is required when using epoxy or polyester-resin cement. In some cases, fiberglass casing is joined by slip joints or by using a flexible key that locks the pin and box ends of the casing together. Metallic screens can be attached to fiberglass casing by the use of threaded adaptors. Coupling diameters (Table 9.10) are large as compared to steel. Steel couplings typically add about 1 in (25 mm) to the outside diameter of the pipe and fiberglass couplings add 2 in (51 mm) or more.

Cementing

The annulus from the surface to the aquifer typically is filled with grout or some acceptable sealing media. Mechanical seals or grout should be considered for use in the annulus between overlapping casings if the material can heave or if the two casings are set in materials with different static-water levels. If the casings are set in clay, then use of grout might be unnecessary (unless required by local agencies). Cementing is covered thoroughly in Chapter 10.

Cementing techniques also are employed in the well-abandonment process; again, with the objective being aquifer protection. Most states (U.S.A.) have strict guidelines regarding well abandonment and generally require permits and sometimes mandate inspections.

THE WELL INTAKE

The intake section is where groundwater enters the well. The well screen is a structurally supporting filter device that allows inflow, retains select material, and is the access for aquifer development and future aquifer maintenance. Immediately outside the screen are the borehole annulus, the borehole wall, and the drilling-affected zone (Figure 9.9). Depending on the aquifer type and the drilling method used, screen design affects how each of these "zones" impacts the well's performance in varying ways.

Well screens are manufactured in a variety of materials and configurations. The value of a screen is best determined by how it effectively contributes to the success of a well—not by what it costs per unit length. Important screen-design features and how they impact well performance are listed in Table 9.14.

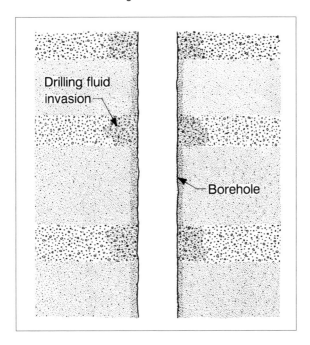

Figure 9.9. Diagram showing a borehole and some drilling-fluid invasion.

Table 9.14. Key Screen-Design Features

Feature	Impacts	Objective
Open area	Development Entrance velocity Bacteriological growth	High efficiency and production Low operating cost
Slot geometry	Development	Particle evacuation Low operating cost
Material	Corrosion resistance	Long service life
Strength	Installation	Satisfy load requirements

Maximizing each of these criteria is not always possible, depending on the type of screen required. Open areas of more than 30% are common for continuous-slot screens, with no loss of column strength. In highly corrosive waters PVC is desirable, but the low strength of PVC could make it impractical for use in deep wells.

The physical nature and chemistry of aquifer waters range widely, and screen design should accommodate the varying characteristics. Extensive experience shows that screens having the features described below provide the best service in most geologic conditions.

- Continuous slot openings around the screen circumference permit maximum accessibility to the aquifer for more efficient development.
- Slot openings that provide maximum open area consistent with strength requirements take advantage of the aquifer hydraulic conductivity.
- V-shaped slot openings reduce clogging and optimize sand control.
- Construction methods that permit use of a wide variety of materials can minimize the occurrence of corrosion and incrustation.
- Metal screens utilizing single-metal construction minimize galvanic corrosion.
- Screens must withstand stresses normally encountered during and after installation.
- Screens that accommodate a wide variety of fittings and attachments facilitate installation and completion operations.
- Using a wide variety of slot openings (from 0.006 in (0.15 mm) to 0.25 in (6.4 mm)) can be very effective.

Types of Well Screens

Screen Materials

The most common well-screen materials are stainless steel, low-carbon steel, galvanized steel, plastic, and fiberglass. As with casing, strength and corrosion-resistance requirements must be satisfactory for the well's depth and water chemistry. The material selected should enable the screen to have the desired flow properties. Various types of screens are discussed below.

Continuous-Slot Wire-Wrap Screen

The continuous-slot wire-wrap screen is used throughout the world for water, oil, and gas wells, and for environmental well completions. It is the dominant screen type used in the water-well industry. This type of screen is constructed by winding cold-rolled triangular-shaped wire around a circular array of longitudinal rods (Figure 9.10). The wire is welded to the rods and produces a rigid unit that has high strength and minimum weight.

Figure 9.10. Continuous-slot screens are constructed by winding cold-rolled, triangular-shaped wire around a circular array of longitudinal rods.

Slot openings result from the spacing of successive wraps of the outer layers of wire. Slot sizes typically range from 0.006 in (0.15 mm) to 0.250 in (6.35 mm), and manufacturers can keep the sizes to close tolerance (which is important for sand control) by utilizing the all-welded manufacturing method. All slots should be clean and free of burrs and cuttings. The slot openings number designates the corresponding width of the openings in thousandths of an inch (a 10 slot, for example, is an opening of 0.010 in or 0.25 mm).

For continuous-slot screens, the spacing of individual slots can be varied during fabrication. In fact, a single section of screen can be made with many different slot sizes if geologic conditions require these variations in a screen's construction (Figure 9.11). Such screens enable the maximum use of the hydraulic conductivity of each stratum.

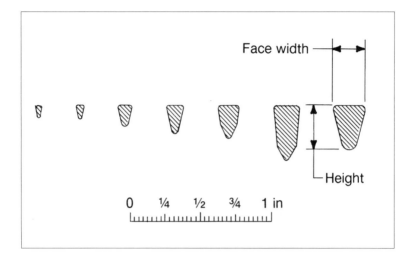

**Figure 9.11. Representative wire profiles used in construction of
continuous-slot wire-wrap screens.
Shapes are described by face width and height.**

Each slot opening between adjacent wires is V-shaped. The V-shaped wires
are manufactured in different heights and widths to address various strength
applications. This is a result of the special shape of the wire that is used to form
the screen surface (Figure 9.12). The V-shaped openings—designed to be non-
clogging—are narrowest at the outer face and widen inwardly. Thus, oversized
particles are retained outside the screen and sand grains that pass through the
opening enter the screen without becoming wedged in the slot. In screens with
cut slots, the entering particles can turn or twist and become lodged in the
slots—which can reduce the available intake area considerably and cause either
lower yield or greater drawdown (Figure 9.13).

Continuous-slot screens provide the highest intake area per unit of surface
area of any screen type. Table 9.15 provides representative open areas for different screens. Increasing face width decreases open area; however larger wires
increase the collapse strength for any given diameter. Some typical wire profiles
are shown in Figure 9.11.

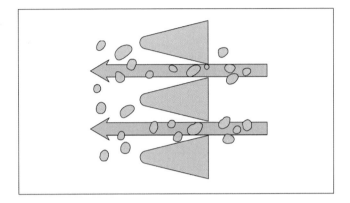

Figure 9.12. Continuous-slot screens have V-shaped openings, and the slots are non-clogging because their openings widen inwardly. Particles that can pass through the narrow outside opening can enter the screen.

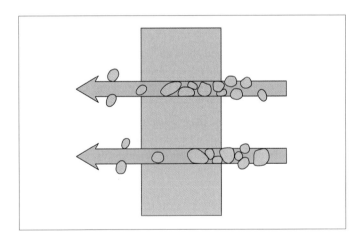

Figure 9.13. Elongated or slightly oversized particles can clog straight-cut, punched pipe, or gauze-type openings.

Table 9.15. Open Areas of Screens

Screen Diameter ID			Continuous Slot % Open Area	Louvered (max. open area) % Open Area	Bridge Slot % Open Area	Mill Spotted Vertical % Open Area	Plastic Continuous Slot % Open Area	Slotted Plastic % Open Area
in	cm	Slot Size						
4	10.16	20	25	—	—	—	13	—
		60	52	—	12	5	30	11
8	20.3	30	25	—	—	—	18	8
		60	41	3	6	5	29	14
		95	51	5	—	7	—	—
12	30.48	30	16	—	3	—	—	—
		60	28	4	7	5	—	11
		95	38	7	—	7	—	—
		125	45	9	14	9	—	—
16	40.64	30	16	—	3	—	—	9
		60	28	4	6	5	—	—
		95	38	6	—	7	—	—
		125	45	8	13	9	—	—

Water flows more freely through high open area than through low open area, because entrance velocity is reduced and head loss is minimized. This reduces drawdown for a given pumping rate, lowering chemical precipitation tendencies by creating a reduced pressure differential around the screen intake.

One of the biggest benefits of continuous slot openings is improved development. All development methods extract particles through the screen openings, so the closely spaced V-shape non-clogging feature saves time and facilitates development effectiveness. Development methods are described in Chapter 11.

Well operational cost is directly related to drawdown, and continuous-slot screens have the least drawdown during pumping. Low open area screens might be less expensive per foot, but the long-term operational costs usually exceed the difference in price between this type of well and a continuous slot well. Over the life of a typical high-capacity well, the operational savings can amount to 50% of the total operating cost—or more. Additional information on screens manufactured by Johnson Screens is contained in Appendix 9.K (DVD).

Prepack Screens (Muni-Pak™)

A prepack screen assembly consists of one screen telescoped inside another, with an annulus filled with filter pack at the factory before shipment. The Johnson Screens' Muni-Pak™ screen (Figure 9.14) is a custom prepack screen designed especially for high-capacity wells. These screens offer unique advantages over conventional rod-based screens with respect to strength. Table 9.16 (in U.S. customary units) provides a comparison of the strength of rod-based and Muni-Pak™ screens. The Muni-Pak™ screen features include: collapse strength equal to pipe; double the tensile strength of standard rod-based screen; a bioresistant, hydraulically superior (to silica sand) pack; all stainless-steel construction; and a greater percentage of open area (for deep applications) than that of a conventional screen, due to the dual-support construction. (For special applications, Johnson Screens makes a PVC prepack screen—the VeePack™).

Prepack screens are ideal for horizontal boreholes and boreholes that deviate from vertical. The Muni-Pak™ also is well-suited for situations where placing a conventional gravel pack is difficult. The Muni-Pak™ screen assemblies save time and reduce logistical planning, because no handling and no installation of bulk pack material is needed. Additional information on Muni-Pak™ screens is contained in Appendix 9.L (DVD).

Figure 9.14. Johnson Screens Muni-Pak™ screen.

Table 9.16. Strength of Muni-Pak™
Compared to Wire-Wrapped Screens

Standard Rod Base vs. Muni-Pak™					
Nominal Size		Collapse Strength (psi)		Tensile Strength (lb)	
Rod Based	Muni-Pak™	Rod Based	Muni-Pak™	Rod Based	Muni-Pak™
2	2 x 4	3,830	16,500	4,000	18,800
3	3 x 5	1,350	5,650	4,800	21,400
4	4 x 6	660	2,830	5,800	25,700
5	5 x 7	420	1,550	6,600	28,300
6	6 x 8	180	990	17,600	33,200
8	8 x 10	320	1,160	24,200	67,500
10	10 x 12	170	630	30,800	81,600
12	12 x 15	150	880	35,200	127,900
14	14 x 16	220	1,110	34,000	127,900
16	16 x 18	150	760	38,400	135,400
18	18 x 20	110	540	39,600	143,000
Typical constructions for 600 ft to 1,000 ft					

Pipe-Based Screen

Pipe-based screens are used in water wells in many parts of the world and are common in oil-field work because of their strength and durability in non-vertical (deviated) borehole applications. The assembly for this screen is made by perforating a base pipe and then mounting a continuous-slot screen over it via one of three methods: (1) winding trapezoid-shaped wire directly onto a pipe (wrap-on pipe); (2) winding wire over longitudinal rods mounted around a pipe's circumference (pipe base); or (3) slipping a separate continuous-slot well screen jacket over a pipe (screen jacket). Winding wire over longitudinal rods is superior to the wrap-on pipe design because the rods hold the wire away from the pipe surface, blocking fewer of the base-pipe openings (Figure 9.15).

Figure 9.15. A pipe-based screen is exceptionally strong and often is specified for oil wells and deep-water wells. Both steel and plastic materials are used in this screen's construction.

The pipe-based screen has two sets of openings, the outer continuous slot and the holes drilled in the pipe base. The open area of the pipe base generally is less than that of the outer screen open area, and the inner pipe has a maximum open area of 10%. Hydraulic performance of the assembly depends on the open area in the pipe base, which usually is made of steel and has an outer screen made of stainless steel. This bimetal contact typically supports some electrolytic (galvanic) action and causes corrosion of the steel pipe. One way to prevent corrosion is to use pipe and screen made of the same metal—the cost might be somewhat higher, but the product is more durable.

Louvered Screen

Louvered screens have slots that are perpendicular to the pipe axis and are arranged in rows (Figure 9.16). The slots are mechanically punched in the wall of the pipe. The punching process could harden the metal around the perforations, making it more susceptible to stress-corrosion cracking. The slotting process (a hydraulic-punch against a die) limits the number of slot sizes that can be made without a wide number of die sets. In practice, slots finer than 0.040 in (1 mm) are not practical.

Figure 9.16. Louvered screens.

The difficulty of producing a consistent fine-slot configuration (except for very coarse material) limits the use of louvers in naturally developed wells. The application of louver screens primarily is in filter-packed wells. During development, the openings can be blocked easily and are not conducive to highly effective jetting procedures. Louvers, like pipe-base or mill-slot designs, offer high tensile and collapse strength as compared to wire-wrap screens.

The percentage of open area in louvered screens is limited because considerable blank space must be left between openings. Open areas typically are less than 8%. Screens commonly are made in 20-ft (6.1-m) to 40-ft (12.1-m) lengths and threaded or welding collar connections are common. Louvered screens are available in low-carbon, stainless, and alloy steels.

Bridge-Slot Screen

Bridge-slot screen openings are arranged in rows running parallel to the screen axis (Figure 9.17). Like louvers, slots are punched in the pipe wall (or in a flat sheet which then is rolled into a pipe). The limits of the punch and die equipment determine the size and width of the openings created. The shape of the bridge-slot screen limits its use in naturally developed wells if the aquifer material contains appreciable amounts of sand and other fine-grained materials. During well development the bridge-slot openings block easily; they also are not well-suited for jetting procedures. The application of bridge-slot screens primarily is in filter-packed wells.

Open areas of bridge-slot screens typically range from less than 5% to 10%. The open areas are limited because adequate blank spaces must be left between slot openings of the screens. Most bridge-slot screens are composed of mild steel and stainless steel, and commonly are made in 5-ft (1.5-m) to 20-ft (6.1-m) lengths that are welded together, but threaded connections also are available.

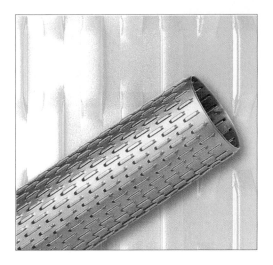

Figure 9.17. Bridge-slot screen.

Mill-Slot Screen

Slotted-steel pipe is produced using saws (Figure 9.18) or cutting torches. Mill-slot pipe has poor corrosion resistance and the perforation methods tend to hasten corrosive attack on the metal when used in poor-quality water. Jagged edges and slot surfaces also are susceptible to selective corrosion. In general, using slotted-steel pipe limits effective development, increases maintenance costs, and can significantly reduce the life of the well. The open area of mill-slot screens typically ranges from 2% to 4%.

Figure 9.18. Mill-slot screen.

Slotted PVC Screen

Slotted PVC often is used in environmental sampling, remediation, observation wells, and small-diameter domestic wells, where low yield and well efficiency are not primary objectives. Continuously slotted PVC screen is made by extruding pipe with molded nodes as rods and then slotting it using a cutting wheel on a lathe. A continuous slot is cut into the pipe as the pipe rotates past the cutting wheel. The critical internal open area is limited due to the shallow depth of penetration into the pipe (Figure 9.19). For continuously slotted PVC screen, clogging is similar to that of regular slotted pipe due to the manufacturing method used.

In contrast, continuously wrapped PVC screen is made by wrapping triangular-shaped wire around a circular array of PVC rods which are attached by sonically welding each rod to each wire, forming a high open-area PVC rod–based well screen. The V-shaped pattern opens inward from the slot entrance to the inside of the well screen, and any sand entering the screen cannot plug the slot opening (Figure 9.20).

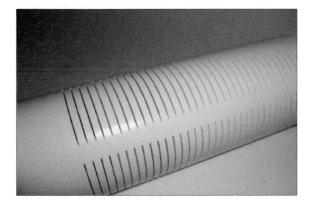

Figure 9.19. Slotted PVC screen.

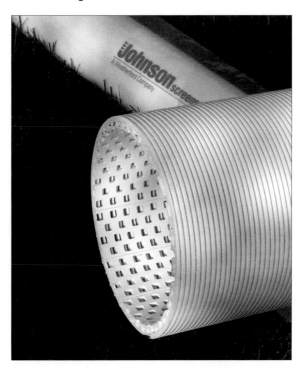

Figure 9.20. Slotted wire-wrapped PVC screen.

CONTINUOUS-SLOT SCREEN DESIGN

Sediment-Size Analysis

The first step in selection of slot sizes for naturally developed and filter-packed wells is conducting a grain-size analysis. A description of the collection of appropriate samples is provided in Chapter 3. Selection of slot size is a critical step in assuring maximum well performance. Both the slot size of the screen and the particle sizes of the filter pack are based on results of a size analysis conducted on sediment samples collected from the aquifer. Grain-size distribution curves are made from the sieve analysis, and several methods can be used to obtain information on the grain-size distribution. A description of sieve analysis is contained in Chapter 2.

Screen Slot Size

One of the most important purposes of a screen is to retain native sands and filter pack while stabilizing the aquifer. This is either natural formation, artificial filter pack, or a stabilizing pack material. Following is a discussion of each situation for completion.

Naturally Developed Wells

In a naturally developed well, a portion of the finer formation material near the borehole is removed through the screen during development. This results in a zone of graded formation materials extending outward from the screen. The increased hydraulic conductivity reduces near-well drawdown during pumping.

For non-homogeneous sediments, when the groundwater is not particularly corrosive and aquifer sample reliability is good, the typical approach is to select a slot which passes 60% of the material and retains 40%. More-corrosive water or poor sample quality requires retaining 50%. Using an even smaller slot size is a wiser choice in corrosive water and with low-carbon steel screens, because slot enlargement of only a few thousandths of an inch (or centimeter) could allow the well to pump sand. Slot enlargement from corrosion generally is not a problem for stainless-steel or PVC screens.

Other situations dictating a conservative slot opening (retaining 40% to 50%) are where screens are used in calcareous formations which dissolve readily with acid treatments; if the aquifer is thin and overlaid by fine-grained loose material; if development time is at a premium; and if the formation is well sorted.

Coarse sand and gravel allow greater latitude in selecting the slot openings (Figure 9.21). The slot size might retain between 30% and 50% of the aquifer material. A slot-size increase of a few thousandths of an inch results in the allowing of only a small amount of additional material to pass through the well screen during development. Retaining only 30% means that more material is removed and development time thus increases.

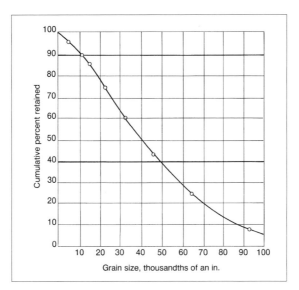

Figure 9.21. Slot openings of from 0.040-in (1.0-mm) to 0.060-in (1.5-mm) are selected from this grain-size distribution curve for a naturally developed well. For the larger slot sizes, development time is greater.

Extra development work is offset by gaining increased screen open area. In incrusting water, for example, longer service life results before plugging reduces the well's yield. Larger slot size permits extending the permeable zone around the screen, which generally increases specific capacity and efficiency, thereby lowering operating costs.

Slot openings for different sections of the well screen can be chosen according to different material gradation, if the layers are at least 4 ft (1.2 m) thick and their depths are accurately known.

First, carefully determine whether fine material overlies coarse material; then

- extend 3 ft (0.9 m) or more of screen designed for the fine material into the coarse layer below; and
- size the slot opening, for the screen section installed in the coarse layer, to no more than double the slot size for the overlying finer material.

Figure 9.22 shows how screen openings affect the boundary between the two layers. As material is removed from the coarser zone, slumping of the overlying fine-sand layer might occur.

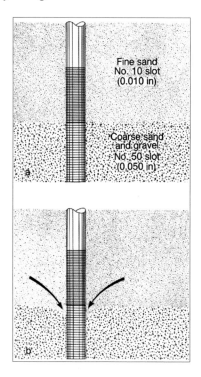

Figure 9.22. Diagram showing that (a) larger slot size screen in the lower part of the stratified aquifer should be shorter than the total thickness of the coarser sand; and (b) potential consequences of not extending the screen designed for the fine material 3 ft (0.9 m) or more into the coarse layer below it.

Artificial Filter Pack

Artificial filter-pack wells initially were used because of their low cost and the need to reduce sand pumping by using wide-slot screen devices made from torch-cut perforations, louvers, mill slots, and punched openings. In filter-packed wells, the zone immediately around the well screen is replaced with specially graded material. A specific filter-pack size is chosen to retain most of the formation. A screen slot size then is selected to retain 90% or more of the filter pack (after development). Filter-pack materials should be well sorted to assure good porosity and hydraulic conductivity. Most commercial filter packs have uniformity coefficients of approximately 2.5. The uniformity coefficient is defined as the 40% retained size of the sediment divided by the 90% retained size. The lower the value, the more uniform the grading of the sample between these limits.

Filter packing can be advantageous in situations where:

+ Sediments are highly uniform and fine grained;
+ Sediments are highly laminated, making it difficult to determine precise layer locations (the grading of the filter pack should be based on the grain size of the finest layer to be screened);
+ Materials to be used in construction must be on site before drilling begins;
+ Small slot size required for natural development limits the transmitting capacity of the screen so the desired yield could not be obtained;
+ The water is extremely incrusting; or
+ Poorly cemented sandstone aquifers require lateral support for the screen.

It is important, however, to recognize that the installation of a filter pack and screen can reduce the specific capacity of a well that previously was an open-hole type. Nevertheless, a reduction in yield is preferable to maintenance problems created by sand pumping.

Figure 9.23 shows the construction details of a filter-packed well finished in semiconsolidated sandstone. The larger space around the screen is created by underreaming that increases the borehole diameter where required. The oversize borehole provides sufficient annular area for a filter pack.

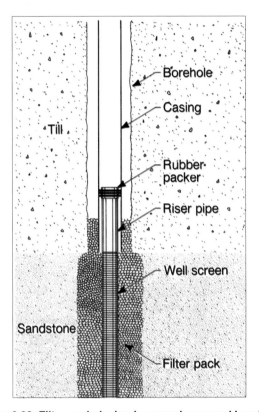

Figure 9.23. Filter pack design in an underreamed borehole.

The hydraulic conductivity of a filter pack generally is several times greater than that of even a coarse-grained geological unit, because the pack has a more uniform distribution of sediments. Filter-pack material should consist of clean, well-rounded grains of a uniform size, composed mostly of siliceous particles. An allowable limit of calcareous material is up to 5% (by weight). Table 9.17 lists the desirable physical and chemical characteristics for a filter pack and the advantages of using these materials. All filter-pack material that is delivered to the well site should be protected from contamination at the well site prior to installation.

**Table 9.17. Desirable Filter-Pack Characteristics and
Derived Advantages**

Characteristic	Advantages
Clean	Little loss of material during development Less development time
Well-rounded grains	Greater hydraulic conductivity and porosity Reduced drawdown Higher yield More-effective development
90% to 95% quartz grains	No loss of volume caused by dissolution of minerals
Uniformity coefficient of 2.5 or less	Less separation during installation Lower head loss through filter pack

Steps in Designing a Filter Pack

1. Choose the layers to be screened and construct sieve-analysis curves for these formations.
2. Base the filter pack grading on an analysis of the layer composed of the finest material. (Figure 9.24 shows the grading of two samples, the finest material lies between 75 ft (22.9 m) and 90 ft (27.4 m).)
3. Multiply the 70% retained size of the sediment by a factor of between 3 and 8 (see the selection criteria below). Place the result of the multiplication on the graph as the 70% size of the filter material.
   a. As a general rule, for unconsolidated sand use a 4 to 6 multiplier.
   b. Use a 3 to 6 multiplier if the formation is uniform and the 40% retained size is 0.010 in (0.25 mm) or smaller.
   c. Use a 6 to 8 multiplier for semiconsolidated or unconsolidated aquifers when formation sediment is highly non-uniform and includes silt or thin clay stringers to aid in complete development.
   d. Using multipliers greater than 8 could result in creating a sand-pumping well.
4. In Figure 9.24, 0.005 in (0.127 mm) is the 70% size of the sand between 75ft (22.8 m) and 90 ft (27.4 m). Multiplying by 5 produces a 70% size of the filter material as 0.025 in (5 · 0.005) (0.65 mm). This is the first point on the curve that represents the grading for the filter-pack material.

5. Through this initial point, draw a smooth curve representing material with a uniformity coefficient of approximately 2.5 or less. (In Figure 9.24, the solid-line curve has a uniformity coefficient of 1.8, the dashed-line curve a coefficient of 2.5.) Always draw the filter-pack curve as uniform as practical, thus in this example the material indicated by the solid-line curve is more desirable.

6. Select a commercial filter pack that fulfills the dimensional and chemical requirements listed in Table 9.17.

7. As a final step, select a screen slot size that will retain 90% or more of the filter pack material. In the present example, the correct slot size is 0.018 in (0.46 mm).

8. Calculate the volume of filter pack required using data from Table 9.18. The pack should extend well above the screen to compensate for any settling occurring during development. Using a caliper log could reveal the presence of washouts in the borehole, necessitating additional filter pack. It is good practice to have extra filter pack on the site, especially if the size and stability of the borehole is questionable.

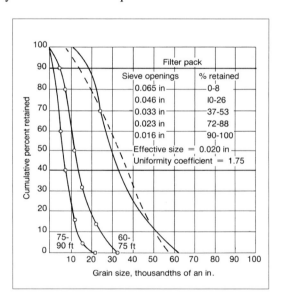

Figure 9.24. Grain-size curves for aquifer sand and corresponding curve for properly selected filter-pack material.

Table 9.18. Volume of Filter Pack Required*

ID of Pipe or Borehole		Outside Diameter of Well Screen															
in	mm	4 in ft³/ft	102 mm m³/m	6 in ft³/ft	152 mm m³/m	8 in ft³/ft	203 mm m³/m	10 in ft³/ft	254 mm m³/m	12 in ft³/ft	305 mm m³/m	16 in ft³/ft	406 mm m³/m	18 in ft³/ft	457 mm m³/m	20 in ft³/ft	508 mm ms³/m
8	203	0.27	0.03	0.15	0.01	—	—	—	—	—	—	—	—	—	—	—	—
10	254	0.47	0.04	0.36	0.03	0.2	0.02	—	—	—	—	—	—	—	—	—	—
12	305	0.7	0.07	0.6	0.06	0.45	0.04	0.24	0.02	—	—	—	—	—	—	—	—
16	406	1.3	0.12	1.2	0.11	1.05	0.1	0.86	0.08	0.62	0.06	—	—	—	—	—	—
20	508	2.1	0.2	2	0.19	1.9	0.18	1.65	0.15	1.4	0.13	0.8	0.07	0.42	0.04	—	—
24	610	3.05	0.28	2.95	0.27	2.8	0.26	2.6	0.24	2.35	0.22	1.75	0.16	1.4	0.13	1	0.09
30	762	4.85	0.45	4.7	0.44	4.6	0.43	4.4	0.41	4.15	0.39	3.5	0.33	3.15	0.29	2.75	0.26

* Slightly more filter pack is required for telescope-size screens, and slightly less for pipe-size screens.

There are two common errors made by water-well professionals in designing and constructing filter-packed wells. The first mistake is using the same stock (size) pack in all wells, regardless of the characteristics of a particular formation—a practice that can lead to low yields or wells that pump sand. A second error is using a screen which has slot sizes that are too small. In this case, again, low yields are likely because of the reduced hydraulic efficiency and a tendency for greater incrustation.

Wells that pump sand can be avoided by carefully following the steps listed above. The filter-pack provides mechanical retention of the formation material and minimizes the movement of sediment into the well.

Changes in sediment gradational consistency occurring in the materials of sources used by filter-pack suppliers can result in changes in filter packs. Water-well professionals should contact their filter-pack suppliers for current material information.

Thickness of Filter Pack

Theoretically, a filter-pack need be only two or three grains thick to retain and control a formation. Laboratory tests conducted by Johnson Screens have demonstrated that a thickness of less than 0.5 in (13 mm) of properly sized material successfully retains formation particles, regardless of the velocity of the water passing through the filter pack.

In practice, it is impossible to place filter pack that is only 0.5 in (13 mm) thick and expect to completely surround the well screen. To insure that filter material surrounds the entire screen, the minimum design annulus should be at least 3 in (76 mm).

Filter-pack thickness does little to reduce the pumping of sand, because the controlling factor is the grain-size ratio of the pack material to the formation material. Ideally, filter packs should not exceed a thickness of 5 in (127 mm), because a pack that is too thick makes development very difficult. The filter pack should be 2-in (50.8-mm) to 5-in (127-mm) thick; 3 in (76.2 mm) is optimal. The use of centering guides (centralizers) is very important to insure complete and even distribution of filter pack along the screen length. Fine-grained filter packs also tend to be more difficult to place around well screens than are coarser-grained materials, which settle more readily.

A filter pack might allow water from an overlying aquifer to percolate downward into the screen; however calculations show that this contribution is insignificant relative to total yield. Under the conditions shown in Figure 9.25, 90% of a confined aquifer is screened, and the overlying sediments are water bearing and connected hydraulically to the screen portion of the well by the 6-in (152-mm) filter pack. The volume of water that (theoretically) can move downward from the upper aquifer to the well screen can be calculated by using the Darcy Equation, provided in equation 9.12.

$$Q = KIA \qquad\qquad\qquad (9.12)$$

Where:

Q = vertical flow through the pack material (gpd or ℓ/sec);

K = hydraulic conductivity of filter pack (gpd/ft^2 or cm/sec);

I = hydraulic gradient causing vertical flow in the filter pack; and

A = cross-sectional area of the filter pack (ft^2 or cm^2).

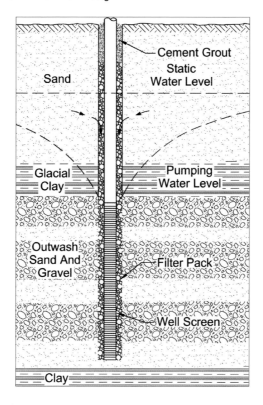

**Figure 9.25. Under the conditions shown, the filter pack contribution
is minimal.**

Example

In the well shown in Figure 9.25, the available head is 30 ft (9.1 m), which is
the difference between the pumping level in the well and the static-water level
in the upper aquifer. The average distance through which the upper water must
move is about 28 ft (8.5 m), which is the distance from the midpoint of the
upper aquifer to the top portion of the screen.

Where:

I = 30 ft/28 ft (9.1 m/8.5 m) = 1.1; and

A = 2.25 ft² (0.209 m²).

The hydraulic conductivity (K) of the filter pack must be estimated. A reasonable upper limit for pack materials is 17,000 gpd/ft^2 (8 · 10^{-3} m/sec). The amount of water transmitted vertically in this example, therefore, is as shown below.

$$Q = 17{,}000 \text{ gpd/ft}^2 \cdot 1.1 \cdot 2.25 \text{ ft}^2 = 42{,}075 \text{ gpd} = 29.2 \text{ gpm}$$

(U.S. customary units)

$$Q = 8 \cdot 10^{-3} \text{ m/sec} \cdot 1.1 \cdot 0.209 \text{ m}^2 = 1.8 \cdot 10^{-3} \text{ m}^3/\text{sec}$$

(SI units)

The contribution of 29.2 gpm (1.7 · 10^{-3} m^3/sec) is a relatively small proportion of the total amount of water that can be pumped from the well in this example. If the lower aquifer has a hydraulic conductivity of 1,000 gpd/ft^2 (4.72 · 10^{-4} m/sec), then its transmissivity is approximately 50,000 gpd/ft (7.2 · 10^{-3} m^2/sec). An efficient well in this aquifer should develop a specific capacity of about 25 gpm/ft (0.005 m^3/sec/m) of drawdown. A drawdown of 30 ft (9.1 m) means that the yield of the lower formation (alone) is about 750 gpm (0.047 m^3/sec). Theoretically, the yield from vertical flow in the filter pack is 29.2 gpm (1.8 · 10^{-3} m^3/sec), or about 4% of the total for the well.

The actual contribution to the yield through the filter pack depends upon how the pack is placed, how much drilling fluid remains in the borehole, and the physical and chemical changes that take place in the filter pack over time.

When the filter pack material is tremied into the well, uneven settling of the material can create zones of finer particles interspersed with coarser material. This layering effect can reduce the vertical hydraulic conductivity of the pack significantly. Poorly conditioned drilling fluid with clay and solids left from the drilling fluid decreases the porosity and hydraulic conductivity of the pack. Development methods are effective only around the screen (*see* Chapter 11). Even more important than these two factors, however, are the physical and chemical changes that occur in the upper part of the filter pack over time.

Formation Stabilizer

The primary purpose of a formation stabilizer is to keep the borehole open and to prevent caving of overlying clays or other fine material into the screen portion of the well (Figure 9.26). In unstable formations, use of a stabilizer should be considered if the borehole is more than 2 in (51 mm) larger than the casing or screen. In South Dakota (U.S.A.), for example, screened siltstone formations often are packed with stabilizer materials to prevent the pumping of silty water.

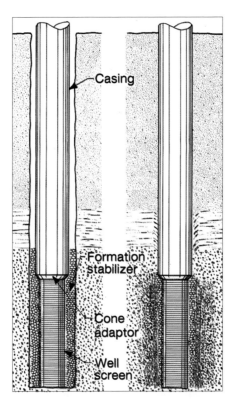

Figure 9.26. Formation stabilizer placed next to a well screen.

Stabilizers also are used to prevent premature caving of formation material prior to development. Formation caving can be a major problem in oversized boreholes or where confining pressures are present, because the caving of highly stratified materials can cause significant reduction in the porosity and permeability of aquifer material. A second function of the stabilizer material is to maintain or augment the hydraulic conductivity of the natural formation.

The type of stabilizer used depends on the physical characteristics of the formation materials. For unconsolidated formations such as alluvial sands and silts, or glacial sands and gravels, the stabilizer should be chosen with care.

Because the well is to be naturally developed, the 40% retained size dictates the screen slot size. The stabilizer then is chosen so that its graded sizes are similar to—or slightly larger than—the natural formation. In practice, the 50%-retained size of the formation is used as the basis for selecting the stabilizer. During development, 50% to 60% of the stabilizer material is removed.

In some cases, the physical characteristics of a stabilizer used in an unconsolidated formation are more important than the actual grain sizes of the formation. The particles, which should be well rounded, also should have a low calcareous content and be free of contaminating material. The stabilizer should be well sorted so that its presence enhances the natural porosity and hydraulic conductivity of the materials immediately outside the well screen. The use of a stabilizer never should reduce the potential hydraulic efficiency of a well.

Local experience plays a large role in determining when the use of a stabilizer is more advantageous than using a filter pack. In formations consisting mainly of shell fragments, for example, the installation of a filter pack as a stabilizer might significantly reduce the potential yield because of the filter pack's relatively small grain-size distribution. In this situation wells are quite successful when a stabilizer material that is much coarser than the recommended filter pack is used. Although some calcareous material might be taken into solution or particles might migrate through the stabilizer, installing a coarser-grained stabilizer does not result in freeing a significant number of sand grains. Conversely, using a coarse stabilizer is used in a formation that consists mainly of sand or silt-sized grains held together by calcareous cement, could result in a well that pumps sediment. Guidelines for the selection of a formation stabilizer are given in Table 9.19. In fractured rock aquifers, the stabilizer (gravel) helps support the screen and casing in the borehole, reducing the column loads while preventing catastrophic failure of the borehole (as compared to an open-hole completion) that could occur as the well ages.

Table 9.19. Selecting Formation Stabilizers for Unconsolidated and Semiconsolidated Aquifers

	Type of Aquifer		
	Unconsolidated Aquifers	Semiconsolidated Aquifers	Consolidated Aquifers
Composition	Alluvial and glaciofluvial sands, gravels, and beach deposits	Dirty sandstones and siltstones and sandy formations not containing shells	Fractured rock aquifers
Purpose	Provide temporary support for the borehole walls next to the screen	Permanently hold back the formation and provide mechanical retention of small particles	Stabilize the borehole and remove column loads and tension from the completion string
Characteristics of Stabilizer	Grain-size distribution should be equal to or slightly larger than the formation	Grain-size distribution usually is greater than 12 to 13 times the 70% retained size	Gravel-sized materials used with slots > 0.08 in (22 mm)
Development	Approximately 50% to 60% of the stabilizer is removed during natural development of the formation	None of the stabilizer passes through the screen during development	None of the stabilizer passes through the screen during development
Result	The part of the formation stabilizer that remains next to the screen has hydraulic conductivity similar to the natural formation so that flow is unimpeded; stabilizer also plays a major role in preventing the migration of fine particles into the screen	The formation cannot slump against the screen even if it becomes weakened over time; the porosity and hydraulic conductivity of the stabilizer are high, reducing drawdown in the immediate vicinity of the screen	Enhances probability of laminar flow to the screen and less stress on the borehole and well structure

Most stabilizer materials are placed by hand, but placement through a tremie pipe is preferable. To prevent excessive bridging, the use of centralizers is recommended for screens more than 30 ft (9.1 m) long. The final thickness of the stabilizer in longer boreholes varies according to the amount of material removed during development, approximately 30 ft (9.14 m) to 50 ft (15.2 m) of stabilizer should extend above the top of the screen before development begins.

Screen Strength

The choice of well-screen material might be dictated by strength requirements. The three forces imposed on a screen are column (vertical compression), tensile (vertical tension), and collapse (lateral compression) (Figure 9.27). An example of column loading is when all (or a portion) of the string assembly weight is placed on the screen during installation. Higher tensile loads can occur when long sections of screen having intermittent blank sections are installed. Collapse forces occur when borehole materials collapse around the screen, gravel packs settle during development, and when differential hydraulic pressures are exerted against the screen during pumping.

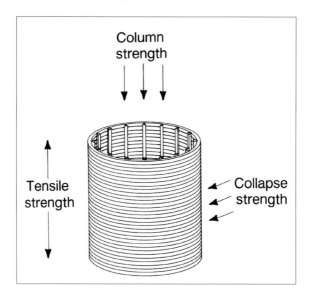

Figure 9.27. Forces acting on a screen.

Failure to properly analyze these forces can result in lost time, the need for materials replacement, or, occasionally, the loss of the well—at considerable expense. Most structural failures occur during installation, filter packing, and development, when the influences of dynamic forces are greatest.

A screen's tensile, column, and collapse strengths depend on the material used for construction (e.g., plastic, steel); the screen's dimensions; and the slot configuration (e.g., continuous slot, bridge slot, mill slot). Long-term service life is obtained by selecting material that is compatible with the existing water-quality conditions. Additionally, it is poor practice to "overdesign" a screen (e.g., incorporating unnecessary excess strength), because typically this both reduces the open area and increases the cost.

A manufacturer's general information usually describes standard construction specifications. Johnson Screens, for example, publishes a list of recommended well-screen designs, based on setting depths of 100 ft (30.5 m) 250 ft (76 m), 600 ft (183 m), and 1,000 ft (300 m). Whenever possible, design recommendations should be verified with the screen manufacturer, especially for installation depths exceeding 1,000 ft (300 m).

Screen Tensile Strength

Minimum tensile strength must accommodate the material loads presented by the screen interval. For economic reasons, blank pipe or tightwind (screen with a 0 slot size) sometimes is placed between screens or interspaced throughout a long screen interval. Load estimates must include the weight of all screen and blank pipe in the screen interval, and make allowances for external loads and a margin of safety. Often the design of a well does not include consideration of the forces exerted when filter-packing a well or screen. The following is an assessment of these loads.

Filter-pack exerts lateral (collapse) and axial (drag) forces on a tubular assembly. Field reports indicate that additional load factors—equal to 10% to 25% of the total casing and screen assembly weight—commonly are measured by weight indicators on the rig floor during filter-pack placement. The loads result from the weight of the pack being distributed by gravity and frictional resistance—among the pack grains—between the borehole wall and the casing or screen surface. These additional loads decline when well development is completed and the filter pack is consolidated against the formation and well screen.

Unlike hydrostatic pressure (which increases proportionately with depth) the lateral grain-column stresses are not isotropic, and pressure is almost independent of grain-column length—it is influenced more by the hole-to-pipe ratio. A general force balance for a coaxial column of pack is represented in the expression below (Kim 2005). See Appendix 9.M (DVD) for additional discussion of loading.

$$\frac{n}{4}\pi\left(D^2 - d^2\right)\rho\, g\, dz - \frac{1}{4}\pi\left(D^2 - d^2\right)dP - \left(\pi\, D\, \tau_D - \pi\, d\, \tau_d\right)dz = 0 \quad \textbf{(9.13)}$$

Where:

ρ = pack grain density;

n = volume porosity;

D = borehole diameter;

d = casing/screen diameter;

g = gravitational attraction;

dz = depth increment;

P = average downward static pressure; and

τ = wall friction (function of grain geometry, borehole condition, tubular surface).

Numerous static and dynamic variables interact, such as: size and shape of the grains; thickness of the filter pack; friction coefficients (between pack and borehole, and between pack and screen); length of gravel-pack interval; smoothness of the screen surface; rate and degree of compaction during development; and buoyancy effects. To date, no precise method to accurately predict these forces has been developed.

Generally, observations indicate that a finer-grained and angular pack material imparts a higher drag effect than does a more coarse-grained pack. An excessively long pack interval doesn't necessarily increase the gravel-loading effect over a short interval. If more research is conducted on this phenomenon, results could help avoid unnecessary expenses.

Rod-based screen tensile strength is determined by using the cross-sectional area of the longitudinal rods. Design tensile strength for wire-wrapped screen is calculated using equation 9.14.

$$Ts = (0.7854 \cdot d_r^{\,2}) \cdot N_r \cdot Y \cdot Ew \qquad\qquad \textbf{(9.14)}$$

Where:

Ts = tensile strength of screen (lb or kg);

d_r = diameter of support rod (in or mm);

N_r = number of support rods;

Y = material yield strength (LCS = 35,000 psi; SS = 30,000 psi or LCS = 21.1 kg/mm², SS = 24.6 kg/mm²); and

Ew = attachment weld efficiency safety factor (85%).

Screen manufacturers often use the term "safe hanging weight," which is the recommended weight to be suspended below the top (shallowest) screen in a vertical well. Safe hanging weight is determined by dividing the calculated screen tensile strength (equation 9.14) by an additional safety factor of 2.

Occasionally it is important to know the exact amount of upward pull that can be applied to a screen without its being damaged. This measurement would be helpful, for example, when a borehole collapses (during installation) before the screen reaches the correct depth, or when it is necessary to remove a screen to abandon a well. To determine a reasonable estimate of the force required to pull a screen to failure (rupture due to tensile strength failure), use equation 9.14 and substitute the material's ultimate tensile strength value in place of the yield strength.

Tensile strength of screens primarily is a function of the cross-sectional area. Tensile strength of louver and bridge-slot screens is a function of the non-perforated cross-sectional area of the pipe wall. This can be calculated using the following equations.

$$Ys = \left(\frac{\pi \cdot (D-t) - (l \cdot n)}{\pi \cdot (D-t)} \right) \tag{9.15}$$

$$T = \left(\frac{\pi \cdot (D-t) - (l \cdot n \cdot r)}{\pi \cdot (D-t)} \right) \cdot t \cdot Y \cdot \pi (D-t) \tag{9.16}$$

Where:

T = screen tensile strength (lb or kg);

D = outside diameter (in or cm);

t = wall thickness (in or cm);

   l = length of slot (in or cm); and

   n = number of slots per row.

Typically, perforating reduces a cross-section area by about 50%; thus, the tensile strength of a perforated pipe is about 50% less than that of blank pipe, and this should be factored into design calculations.

Screen Column Strength

A screen's resistance to column loading is directly proportional to the yield strength of the material used to fabricate the screen. Column strength, like tensile strength, is supplied by the cross-sectional area of the screen wall. For louvered, bridge-slot, or mill-slot screens, the cross-sectional area of the non-slotted portion of the pipe supplies the column support. For continuous-slot screen the cross-sectional area of the vertical rods supports the load.

If the screen is not aligned with the casing above it, a severe reduction in column strength occurs. This problem easily can occur where an oversized borehole is drilled to accommodate a filter pack. To avoid this situation the use of centralizers is recommended (if the screen is more than 20-ft (6.1-m) long), and guides should be installed at least every 40 ft (12.2 m). Column strength is important only until the well is developed or gravel packed; thereafter the surrounding packing stabilizes the screen.

Screen Collapse Strength

The collapse resistance of continuous-slot screen is determined by the material's modulus of elasticity, the moment of inertia of the wrapping wire, the screen's diameter, and the slot size. The moment of inertia of the wrap wire is related to wire height. A segment of thin wall cylinder has a moment of inertia which is shown in equation 9.17.

$$I = \frac{W \cdot T^3}{12}$$

(9.17)

Where:

   T = cylinder wall thickness (in or mm) (Figure 9.28(A)) and

   W = cylinder wall segment length (ft or cm).

Wrap-wire moment of inertia (*I*) is related to the equivalent thickness (Te) of width (w + s) (Figure 9.28(B)). This thickness yields a moment of inertia value the same as that of a cylinder of wall thickness (T) as shown in Figure 9.28(A).

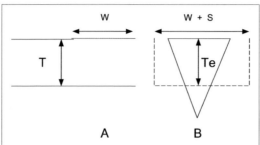

Figure 9.28. Equivalent thickness and moment of inertia.

Equivalent thickness and moment of inertia are related as shown by equation 9.18.

$$Te = \sqrt[3]{\frac{12 \cdot I}{w + s}}$$ **(9.18)**

The design collapse resistance (*Clp*) of wire-wrap screen then is calculated using equation 9.19.

$$Clp = \frac{(24 \cdot E \cdot I)}{(1 - u^2) \cdot (w + s) \cdot D^3}$$ **(9.19)**

Where:

Clp = design screen collapse resistance (psi or kPa);

E = Young's modulus of elasticity
(LCS = 30 x 10^6; SS = 29 x 10^6) psi;
(LCS = 1.96 x 10^6; SS = 2 x 10^{12}) dynes/cm^2;

I = moment of inertia of wrap wire (in^4 or mm^4);

u = Poissions ratio (SS = 0.30, LCS = 0.28);

w = wrap-wire face width (in or mm);

s = slot width (in or mm); and

D = screen outside diameter (in or mm).

As the equation demonstrates, collapse strength decreases as the diameter or slot size increases for a given wire shape.

Collapse resistance for drilled pipe (pipe-base screen) can be calculated by using a variation of equation 9.19 as shown in equation 9.20 below (in U.S. customary units).

$$Pcr = \frac{24 \cdot E \cdot I}{(1 - u^3) \cdot HS \cdot D^3}$$ (9.20)

Where:

$$I = \frac{b \cdot h^3}{12};$$

$b = HS - HD$;

Pcr = design collapse of base pipe (psi);

HD = hole diameter (in);

HS = hole center spacing (in); and

h = wall thickness of pipe (in).

The overwhelming utilization of continuous-slot screens proves their acceptance as the preferred intake device for high-capacity water-well completion. Screens are open and theoretically are not susceptible to collapse from fluids, therefore the collapse strength must be greater than formation loads, filter pack, and pressures placed on the screen during construction and development.

Safe Depth

The safe depth concept is based in part on a drilling professional's past experience. Some estimating approaches are listed below.

- ½ psi/m = 0.15 psi/ft (0.03 bar/m)
- 2 psi/10-ft depth = 0.20 psi/ft (0.05 bar/m)
- 1 psi/m = 0.31 psi/ft (0.07 bar/m)

The hydrostatic pressure exerted by freshwater is 0.433 psi/ft (0.1 bar/m), which shows that successful well completions need not necessarily be based on full hydraulic loading. Furthermore, the information presented in Table 9.12 and Figure 9.6 demonstrates that installations based on less than full hydrostatic gradient still have continued to function for years.

Johnson Screens many years ago developed an empirical approach to establish a depth rating for a given screen design (wire size, diameter, slot). The approach is illustrated by the following equation.

$$SD = (A^{1.4} \cdot B^{3/4} \cdot C)^{1.5} \qquad\qquad (9.21)$$

Where:

  SD = safe depth (ft or m);

$$A = \left(\frac{Te}{D}\right)^3 \cdot \frac{2E}{1-u^2} \qquad B = \frac{Te^2}{D} \cdot Y \cdot \frac{\pi}{3} \qquad C = \frac{w}{w+s} \;;$$

  Te = equivalent thickness (in or mm);

  D = screen outside diameter (in or mm);

  E = Young's modulus of elasticity (psi or dynes/cm^2);

  w = wrap-wire face width (in or mm);

  u = Poissons ratio;

  s = slot width (in or mm); and

  t = wall thickness (in or mm).

The expression is considered applicable for D/t values greater than 35, which includes most large-diameter designs for high-capacity wells. Based on several thousand screen applications occurring over the past 15 years, a guide-line table of minimum collapse values was developed (Table 9.20, Table 9.21). The values represented in the table provide a quick means to perform a practical estimation of minimum collapse to be considered for a given situation, and further evaluation of a final collapse design and costs can be simplified.

Table 9.20. Estimating Collapse Criteria (psi/ft) for Wire-Wrap Screen

Minimum Collapse Criteria (psi/ft)					
		Casing Diameter			
Class	Depth	≤ 6"	8" > 12"	14" > 18"	20" >
Shallow	≤150 ft	0.40	0.30	0.25	0.20
Intermediate	150–650 ft	0.30	0.25	0.20	0.15
Deep	650–1,000 ft	0.25	0.20	0.15	0.10
	> 1,000 ft	add 7 psi/100 ft			
Note: If slot < 40, then multiply the values listed above by 1.20.					

**Table 9.21. Estimating Collapse Criteria (psi/m) for
Wire-Wrap Screen**

Minimum Collapse Criteria (psi/m)					
		Casing Diameter			
Class	Depth	≤ 6"	8" > 12"	14" > 18"	20" >
Shallow	≤ 50 m	1.30	0.99	0.82	0.66
Intermediate	50–200 m	0.99	0.82	0.66	0.49
Deep	200–300 m	0.82	0.66	0.49	0.33
	> 300 m	add 7 psi/30 m			
Note: If slot < 1 mm, then multiply the values listed above by 1.20.					

Screen Length

The determination of the optimum length of a well screen is based on aquifer thickness, available drawdown, and the stratification of the aquifer. Placing screens opposite layers of highest hydraulic conductivity is a typical practice for production-well design. These layers are identified from driller's logs, lost circulation, penetration rate, and geophysical-log analysis. Recommended criteria for determining screen lengths in various hydrogeological situations are given below.

An economical alternative to stainless-steel pipe—when leakage to the well is acceptable—is a tightwind screen. A tightwind screen commonly is used to make short sumps and casing extensions that attach to K-packers (Figure 9.29).

Unconfined Aquifers

- Experience demonstrates that screening the lower third to the lower half of an aquifer provides the optimum design.
- If the aquifer is non-homogenous, selectively placing screens in the most permeable layers of the lower portions of the aquifer maximizes available drawdown and yield.

Figure 9.29. Tightwind screens with K-packers.

Selecting a screen length involves a compromise between (1) obtaining higher specific capacity with the longest screen possible, and (2) utilizing more available drawdown with the shortest screen possible. An efficient screen addresses both issues by minimizing head losses a s drawdown increases. Figure 9.30 shows that, from a theoretical (hydraulic) standpoint, it is impractical to pump a well in an unconfined aquifer at a drawdown that exceeds two-thirds of the thickness of the water-bearing sediment.

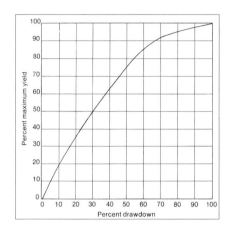 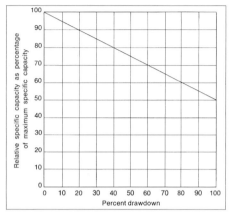

Figure 9.30. Relationships between percent drawdown and yield, and between percent drawdown and specific capacity for a water-table well located in a homogeneous unconfined aquifer.

Confined Aquifers

- Where a material is homogenous, 80% to 90% of the aquifer thickness should be screened (assuming that the pumping water level remains above the aquifer).
- Where a material is non-homogenous, 80% to 90% of the most-permeable thickness should be screened.
- Optimum results are obtained by centering the screen section in the aquifer.
- Maximum available drawdown should be the distance from the potentiometric surface to the top of the aquifer. If available drawdown is limited, then drawing the pumping level below the bottom of the upper confining layer could be necessary. When this occurs the aquifer responds like an unconfined aquifer during pumping.

Using these rules for screening enables the obtaining of from 90% to 95% of the specific capacity that would be obtained by screening the entire aquifer.

Screen Diameter

Unless dictated by a well's casing size and completion (single string), a screen diameter is selected to provide ample open area so that the entrance velocity generally does not exceed the design standard of 0.1 ft/sec (0.03 m/sec). To minimize friction losses the uphole velocity should be 5 ft/sec (1.5 m/sec) or less. The diameter can be adjusted within narrow limits after the length and slot size are selected. Well yields are affected by screen diameter, but the impact is far less than that of screen length. The theoretical increase gained by enlarging the diameter can be calculated using the relationship given in equation 9.22. Chapter 2 and Chapter 6 discuss hydraulic conductivity.

$$Q = \frac{K(H^2 - h^2)}{1055 \cdot \log R/r} \tag{9.22}$$

This equation can be stated as follows.

$$Q \approx \frac{C}{\log R/r}$$

Where:

$$K = \text{hydraulic conductivity } (L/T);$$

H and h = heads (L);

R and r = radii edge of drawdown and of well (respectively) (in L); and

$$C = \text{all the constant terms.}$$

Table 9.22 lists the figures obtained when the radius (R) is 400 ft (122 m), which is a typical radius of influence for unconfined conditions. The table shows that—with other factors remaining constant—doubling the diameter of a 6-in well creates an approximate 10% increase in yield (tripling size increases yield by about 17%). In confined aquifers the yield increase is less (about 7%), because the radius is much larger. These comparisons indicate that there is no substantial enhancement of specific capacity or yield gained by increasing a well's diameter. In some cases, however, it might be worthwhile to increase a well's diameter for even a 15% to 25% yield increase, depending on need and cost factors.

Table 9.22. Well Diameter Versus Yield Ratio (in %)

6 in (152 mm)	12 in (305 mm)	18 in (457 mm)	24 in (610 mm)	30 in (762 mm)	36 in (914 mm)	48 in (1219 mm)
0%	10%	17%	22%	27%	31%	37%
—	0%	6%	11%	16%	19%	25%
—	—	0%	4%	8%	12%	17%
—	—	—	0%	4%	7%	12%
—	—	—	—	0%	3%	8%
—	—	—	—	—	0%	5%

These ratios also apply to specific capacity. Thus, an 18-in (457-mm) well has about 7% more specific capacity than does a 12-in (305-mm) well; and a 24-in (610-mm) well has about 12% more.

Screen Open Area

Screen manufacturers provide tables that show the open area (OA) per ft of screen for each size of screen and for various widths of slot openings. The open area for different slot configurations varies significantly. Table 9.15 shows that continuous-slot screens have much larger open areas than do bridge-slot, louvered, or mill-slotted screens. Open area of wire-wrapped screen is determined using equation 9.23.

$$OA\% = \left(\frac{s}{(s+w)} \right) \cdot 100 \qquad\qquad (9.23)$$

Where:

s = slot size (in or mm); and

w = wrap-wire face width (in or mm).

The open area of louver, bridge-slot, or mill-slot screen is determined using equation 9.24.

$$OA\% = \frac{sl \cdot w \cdot n}{k \cdot D} \cdot 100 \qquad\qquad\qquad (9.24)$$

Where:

    sl = slot length (in or mm);

    w = slot size (in or mm);

    n = number of slots/ft screen;

    D = screen outside diameter (in or mm); and

    k = constant (37.7 U.S. customary units; 957.5 SI units).

If a well screen has a maximum open area, then development can be more complete by removing viscous and plastic-type drilling muds and debris. In the areas where debris has been removed, there are more open-voids so that if mineral is deposited in the future, premature plugging won't occur (Schnieders 2003).

A study of wells completed in the same aquifer near Camarillo, California (U.S.A.), shows that wells completed with wire-wrap screens have 2.5 times the specific capacity as those completed with louvered screens (Schafer 1982). A copy of this study is contained in Appendix 9.N (DVD). Limited open area and slot geometry affect well development, often resulting in increased drawdown and higher pumping costs. Figure 9.31 shows how different screen designs affect the direction of development energy. Chapter 11 provides more details on well-development techniques. In the last ten years, the importance of open area has become more apparent for the rehabilitation and disinfection of existing wells.

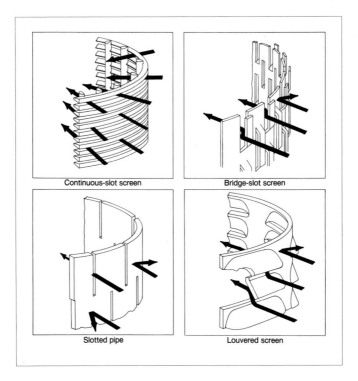

Figure 9.31. The open area of the screen and the configuration of the slot openings are important factors controlling the effectiveness of development procedures using water jetting.

Entrance Velocity

Field experience and laboratory tests have demonstrated that the average entrance velocity of water moving into the screen should not exceed 0.1 ft/sec (3 cm/sec). At this velocity, laminar flow conditions near the screen are probable, with negligible occurrence of friction losses through the screen itself. Higher entrance velocities induce turbulent flow, resulting in a less-efficient well operation. An experiment which studied aspects of well development (e.g., particle movement, gradients, time, hydraulic properties, slot size) was conducted. The data collected confirmed that a maximum entrance velocity of 0.1 ft/sec (3 cm/sec) to 0.2 ft/sec (6 cm/sec) is required to maintain laminar flow in a well (Wendling, Chapuis & Gill 1997).

The average entrance velocity is calculated by dividing the well's yield by the total area of the screen openings. If the velocity is greater than 0.1 ft/sec (3 cm/sec), the screen length—and possibly the diameter—should be increased to provide enough open area so that the entrance velocity is 0.1 ft/sec (3 cm/sec) or slower. Lengthening a screen in an unconfined aquifer might decrease the available drawdown thereby reducing the yield. Conversely, a screen that is fully penetrating a confined aquifer enhances yields, as long as the aquifer is not dewatered. Occasionally it can be possible to vary the construction character-istics of a screen to increase the open area. For example, the wire width could be decreased in a continuous-slot screen if strength requirements are met. An example of a well design and the variations that can be made is contained in Appendix 9.O (DVD).

Transmitting Capacity

Well-screen transmitting capacity, expressed as gpm/ft (cm^3/min/m or ℓ/min/m) of screen, is calculated from open area. Multiplying the square inches (square centimeters) of open area, 0.31 gpm $\cdot$ in^2 (0.18 ℓ/min $\cdot$ cm^2), gives the transmit-ting capacity at the recommended velocity of 0.1 ft/sec (3 cm/sec).

$$0.31 \text{ gpm} = 0.1 \text{ ft/sec} \cdot 60 \text{ sec/m} \cdot 7.5 \text{ gal/ft}^3/144 \text{ in}^2/\text{ft}^2 \qquad \textbf{(9.25)}$$

An 8-in (20.32-cm), 60-slot wire-wrap screen with 135 in^2/ft open area (Table 9.15), for example, has a transmitting capacity of 42 gpm/ft (522 ℓ/min/m) at an entrance velocity of 0.1 ft/sec (3 cm/sec).

When aquifer characteristics are available and well yields are anticipated, well-screen transmitting capacity can be used to select a proper screen length. The transmitting capacity of a well screen is not an indicator of the formation's ability to yield water. In non-homogeneous aquifers, some sediment layers have greater hydraulic conductivity than that of other layers, and water from such zones can enter the screen at a velocity greater than the average calculated. Similarly, entrance velocities from finer-grained layers will be lower than average. Experience shows that these velocity differences along the screen are not of significant concern if the overall screen is designed to insure the recom-mended average entrance velocity of 0.1 ft/sec (3 cm/sec).

SPECIAL CONSIDERATIONS

Pump Placement

Whether to place a pump intake within the well screen long has been a much-debated topic—sometimes creating significantly divergent viewpoints among drilling professionals. Most prevailing specifications and practices to date cautioned against installing the pump intake in the well screen. This was based on a belief that such installation results in increased velocity and, thus, decreased well efficiency.

A study utilizing a physical model tested the effect on efficiency with pump placement within the screen (Korom, Bekker & Helweg 2003). The conclusions of this study indicate that strategically placing the pump intake into the screen does not have a negative effect on well efficiency. This deviation from conventional practice must be considered carefully along with other design considerations. The study also indicates that further research could reveal additional design opportunities.

Pressure-Relief Screens

In some well installations, the drawdown outside the well might be significantly above the pumping level inside the casing. In these circumstances high-pressure differentials could cause a powerful upward flow of water in the filter pack. Occasionally, the difference between the pressure in the casing and the pressure in the borehole is significant enough to lift off K-packers, or to lift filter pack material up to the pump intake (if no packer is used). Low-permeability or highly stratified formations are the most likely to experience high differential pressures. To relieve pressure in the filter pack, a short pressure-relief screen should be installed in the riser pipe, placed just inside the bottom of the casing (Figure 9.32).

During pumping, pressure differentials are relieved through the screen rather than up through the filter pack. It is good design practice to install a pressure-relief screen between the top of the production screen and the top of the riser pipe to eliminate the build-up of differential pressures during pumping.

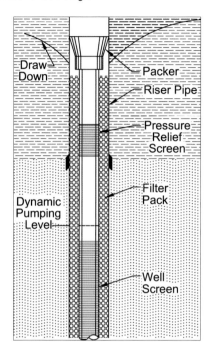

Figure 9.32. To relieve large differential pressures, a pressure-relief screen should be installed inside the bottom of the casing.

SUMMARY

The information presented in this chapter illustrates that practical considerations should be balanced with technical logic and good information. A successful well-design process should allow a variety of input; consider material and construction options; encompass flexibility to prepare for unforeseen circumstances; and include appropriate safety factors. Although engineering and physics determine much regarding well design, the *art* of well design never should be disregarded totally. There always will be a "human factor" needed in the well-building process, so seek the advice of local experts whenever possible.

Protecting our vital groundwater resources from contamination always should influence decision making throughout the process. The Well-Design Program (Appendix 9.P (DVD)) is a useful practical tool for reviewing well-design options. Detailed material evaluations and specifications easily are generated for making comparisons. The program utilizes standard industry engineering methods and calculations for strength evaluations. Wire-wrap screen recommendations are based on the existing guidelines and practices of Johnson Screens North America. Appendix 9.Q (DVD) is a flow chart (from Clear Creek Associates) that provides the various steps in the design and construction of a successful well.

ACKNOWLEDGMENTS

Mr. Ray Schreurs, Johnson Screens, retired, and John H. Schneiders, PhD, President, Water Systems Engineering Inc., provided comments and additions to this chapter. Their insights are appreciated.

CHAPTER 10
Water-Well Construction and Abandonment

Mike Mehmert
Johnson Screens

OVERVIEW OF WELL CONSTRUCTION

A well's construction should be planned so as to utilize every available natural sanitary protection, and should be executed in a manner that avoids any man-made contamination. Key phases of well construction are:

- Maintenance of borehole integrity during drilling;
- Installation of casing and screen;
- Confirmation of screen's exact location;
- Installation of filter pack (if used);
- Placement of cement, accurately and effectively;
- Development; and
- Disinfection.

Adequate depth and the installation of a surface-grout seal are important to insuring that the well remains free from any contamination caused by surface or near-surface sources. Virtually all high-capacity municipal and industrial wells have surface-grout seals, as do many domestic wells—especially those constructed in rock. Grouting procedures vary depending on the well-drilling and screen-installation methods, as well as by regulatory requirements. They are discussed in detail in this chapter.

Generally, location requirements for high-capacity wells are more restrictive than those for private wells, due to the size of drilling equipment and surface equipment used. Casing depth and grouting criteria usually are established for each individual well prior to installation. If there is any doubt about which well-completion method provides the best protection, then local regulatory agencies should be consulted.

Proper installation of casing and screen is followed by well development and disinfection. Well development—discussed in Chapter 11—is one of the most important parts of well construction. Well disinfection is the final operation completed before placing a well into service. Local regulations often specify minimum mandatory procedures for disinfection. Drilling professionals always should select the construction method that is most compatible with available equipment and local geologic conditions.

INSTALLING CASING

The surface casing is set so that an annulus exists around the permanent casing, which is centered and then is advanced into the formation. As the operation proceeds, the annular space around the permanent casing—in the upper borehole—should be kept about two-thirds full of clay slurry. Some of this slurry is carried downward as the casing advances, and it seals the formation around the pipe. The clay slurry remains viscous as long as it is saturated and a seal is maintained between the advancing casing and the formation, even after the casing is pulled back to expose a screen. The slurry remaining in the annulus between the surface and permanent casing is displaced by grout and the surface casing is removed.

In the southwestern portion of the United States—an area that is dominated by alluvial basins—large-diameter bucket augers are used to drill a borehole for the surface casing for large production wells. For smaller-diameter wells, surface casing can be installed using mud rotary or air rotary drilling methods. These methods can involve borehole stabilization with drilling fluids rather than a casing pull-back.

Casing and Joint Types

When using the direct rotary drilling method, the borehole is filled with fluid during the entire drilling operation. In such overbalanced conditions either multiple (telescope) casing or single-string casing and screen installations are employed.

Using the telescope method, the permanent casing is set and grouted in place using adequate centralizers. After the cement has set, a smaller (or expandable underream) bit drills the borehole below the casing to the appropriate completion depth. In a single-string installation, the screen and casing are fitted with centralizers and placed in the open hole; a filter pack then is installed around the screen. Prior to grouting, fine sand (or fine sand followed by bentonite pellets) or a layer of bentonite is placed on top of the filter pack to prevent the grout from seeping downward. Grout then is installed in the annulus to the surface.

In the field, casing is picked up with special clamps called elevators. Elevators typically slip around the outside diameter of the casing and are closed with a latch or bolt. A pair of elevators is used—while one hoists a single joint into connecting position, the second is resting on the rotary table (or surface casing) supporting the preassembled joints in the borehole. For small-diameter threaded casings, a male-thread hoisting plug combined with a landing-slip receptacle can be used in place of a pair of elevators. The elevator engages the outside diameter upset of a coupling, welded collar, or lifting lugs (*see* Figure 10.1). Well-casing joints are assembled using either welding or mechanical joints. Mechanical joints typically are threads; groove and spline slip-collars, or snap-together locking joints. Each type has benefits and features that facilitate speed, strength, or flexibility, or which address special application needs. Welding (including using solvents to join PVC) is common practice, but the joint then is difficult to disassemble if that need arises. Threaded pipe is more costly, but disassembly—if required—is quicker.

Figure 10.1. Elevator clamp.

More frequently, flush-thread PVC is used along with mechanical joints. If the outside diameter of the pipe remains constant across joints, then pipe typically is raised with a male plug threaded to engage the female-thread end of the casing. The assembly is held vertically in the rig table either by using slips or with a simple tongue-and-groove landing plate (Figure 10.2). An elevator clamp is the recommended means to hold PVC pipe.

Figure 10.2. Landing plate.

Joining Steel Casing

Steel-casing pipe ends that are to be welded should be beveled approximately 30 degrees. The welding should follow standardized procedures (American Welding Society 1981). Casing welds used are fillet, butt, or V-groove. Fillet welds are used to secure lap, corner, and T-joints (common with a slip collar). Weld metal is deposited in a corner formed by the fit-up of the collar shoulder to the pipe wall. Butt welds are circumferential welds around squared pipe ends in the same plane. The degree of penetration is important in determining the quality of a fillet or butt weld.

V-groove welds are used when two squared, beveled pipe ends butt together. The groove should be filled entirely, and this type of weld typically requires multiple passes to complete. Burn-through should be avoided so that metal is not deposited inside the casing—which can hinder or prevent tool movement or screen installation.

Proper selection of electrodes is critical to joining dissimilar metals. Either E 312-16 or E 309-16 (AWS-ASTM classification) electrodes are recommended for joining low-carbon steel to stainless steel. Type E 309 electrodes are readily available and cost less than E 312-16 material. Type E 308-15 or E 308-16 electrodes are used to weld stainless steel to stainless steel. If mild steel electrodes are used to join stainless steel to stainless steel then chromium precipitates, creating areas of low corrosion resistance that eventually leads to structural weakness or failure.

Joining Plastic Casing

Plastic casing can be joined by using either solvent welding or mechanical means. In solvent welding, primer is used to clean and etch the surface before the solvent cement is applied. The solvent is applied uniformly to the casing and the pieces are joined; curing time then is required. Due to flammable vapors emitted by some primers and solvent cements, no welding or other open flames should be allowed near the well head immediately after the PVC joints have been connected.

Low temperatures (less than 40°F (4.4°C)) and poor fit caused by joint inter-ferences are two major problems that affect the integrity of the joint. Drilling professionals must be sure to use the correct solvent cement for each particular casing type and for the specific temperature encountered. In temperatures colder than 40°F (4.4°C), plastic components should be joined with a low-temperature solvent cement. Additionally, a special solvent must be used when joining PVC and ABS casing due to the different chemical composition of these materials (*see* ASTM D-3138).

Two types of solvent-welded joints commonly are used. One type uses a coupling (collar) to join casing lengths of equal or unequal diameter, and the ends of the casing fit tightly into the molded plastic coupling. A second type uses a "bell-end" socket that is molded at one end of each casing length to receive the straight (spigot) end of the next casing length. It is important that the bell or coupling be manufactured to close tolerances, so that the fit around the pipe is uniformly snug. See Chapter 9 for solvent-welding procedures. When working at higher temperatures, solvent-cemented joints should be considered under the rating of strength effects for threaded joints.

Plastic casing also can be joined mechanically using threaded couplings or special slip and lock joints (e.g., Johnson Screens Shur-A-Lock™ joint, Figure 10.3). Threaded connections most frequently are used on small-diameter plastic casing (e.g., pump column pipe) and on monitoring wells when joints must be watertight and the use of solvents is not permitted.

For applications performed in conditions where temperatures exceed 110°F (43°C), standard threaded connections should not be used and, instead, special reinforced adapters or optional joint designs should be evaluated for use (and the manufacturers consulted). Special thread lubricants and sealants must be used. Avoid using solvent cement on threads because the cement might set more quickly than the threads can be tightened. Larger-diameter PVC casing is joined by special slip and lock joints, using gaskets to create a seal. Mechanical connections enable disassembly and reuse (if necessary), require no solvents, and save installation time.

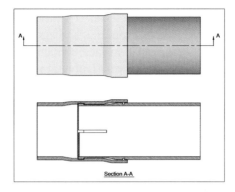

Figure 10.3. Shur-A-Loc™ joint.

Joining Fiberglass Casing

Typically, fiberglass casing is joined using threaded joints because of the extended setting time required when using epoxy or polyester resin cement. In some cases, fiberglass casing is joined by slip joints or by using a flexible key that locks the male and female ends of the casing together. Metallic screens can be adapted for fiberglass casing by the use of threaded adaptors. Coupling diameters (*see* Chapter 9) are large as compared to those of steel couplings. Steel couplings typically add about 1 in (25 mm) to the outside diameter of the pipe and fiberglass couplings add 2 in (51 mm) or more.

GROUTING AND SEALING A WELL CASING

The annulus from the surface to the aquifer typically is filled with grout or some acceptable sealing media. Mechanical seals or grout should be considered for use in the annulus between overlapping casings if the sediments might heave or if the two casings are set in sediments with different static water levels. If the casings are set in clay, then grout use could be unnecessary (unless it is required by local agencies).

Grouting (cementing) a casing involves filling the annular space between the casing and the drilled hole with suitable slurry of cement or bentonite. The length of the borehole section to be grouted varies according to local regulatory codes, the aquifer structure, and water quality. Typically, all public water-supply wells must be grouted from the land surface to a depth of at least 50 ft (15.2 m), to prevent leakage of surface contaminants. Water wells constructed in rock that is overlain by relatively thin, loosely unconsolidated sediment usually are grouted from the land surface to the rock interface. In some formations where aquifers with poor water quality are interspersed with high-quality water zones, the poor-water-quality aquifers are cemented off. Grouting also is standard practice in monitoring-well construction. It is important to avoid blistering the PVC casing when using a cement grout seal, which can occur due to the heat of hydration while the cement is curing.

The grouting procedures presented below focus primarily on the use of cement and water (neat cement), although in certain uses the slurry can contain sand, bentonite, pozzolan (fly ash), calcium chloride (as an accelerator), or hydrated lime. A slurry made with a high-solids bentonite (granular or chips) also can serve as a grouting seal, provided that it is used at a depth where dehydrating and shrinking of the grout will not occur, and where water movement will not wash away the clay particles. In unique situations (low-pH environments), synthetic polymers can be used as grouting materials.

Various types of portland cement are manufactured to accommodate different chemical and physical conditions. Table 10.1 lists five API cement classes used in water-well construction, although Classes A, B, and C commonly are used. (Cement classifications that are used outside of the United States are provided in Appendix 10.A (DVD). The constituents of these cements are given in API Standard 10A.)

The compressive strengths of portland cement (types A and B) and high–early strength cements (type C) are shown in Table 10.2 for setting times of 24 hr and 72 hr at various temperatures. For most drilling operations, the cement should reach a compressive strength of 500 psi (3,450 kPa) before drilling is resumed. The temperature in the borehole, chemistry of the formation water, dilution of the cement, and downhole pressure affect the rate at which the cement cures. Generally, the 500 psi (3,450 kPa) compressive strength is reached between 12 hr and 24 hr after placement. Equipment for mixing and placing cement grout does not need to be elaborate, however, because the chemical reaction causing hardening begins as soon as cement and water are mixed. The equipment therefore only must be adequate to complete the installation while the grout is fluid.

Table 10.1. Classifications of Cements Used in Water Wells

API Classification	Special Properties	Recommended Range for Well Depth	
		ft	m
A (similar to ASTM C150, Type I)	None	0 to 6,000	0 to 1,830
B (similar to ASTM C150, Type II)	Moderate to high sulfate resistance	0 to 6,000	0 to 1,830
C (similar to ASTM C150, Type III)	High early strength	0 to 6,000	0 to 1,830
G	Can be used with accelerators and retarders	0 to 8,000	0 to 2,440
H	Can be used with accelerators and retarders	0 to 8,000	0 to 2,440

Typically, to achieve the desired result of a uniform sheath of cement around the casing for the vertical distance to be grouted, the borehole diameter should be (at minimum) 4 in (102 mm) larger than the casing. Tight places and "dead spots" result where casing that is not properly centered touches the wall of the hole, and causes channeling of the slurry. Local laws usually dictate the minimum length of grout required for certain types of wells, and drilling professionals should be familiar with these regulations.

Table 10.2. Compressive Strengths of Portland and High Early Cement

Tempera-ture		Borehole Pressure		Typical Compressive Strength*							
				24 hr				72 hr			
				Portland		High Early		Portland		High Early	
°F	°C	psi	kPa	psi	kPa	psi	kPa	psi	kPa	psi	kPa
60	15.6	0	0	615	4,240	780	5,380	2,870	19,790	2,535	17,480
80	26.7	0	0	1,470	10,140	1,870	12,890	4,130	28,480	3,935	27,130
95	35	800	5,520	2,085	14,380	2,015	13,890	4,670	32,200	4,105	28,300
110	43.3	1,600	11,030	2,925	20,170	2,705	18,650	5,840	40,270	4,780	32,960
* Strengths are based on the criteria shown in Table 10.3.											

Table 10.3. Compressive Strength Criteria

	Portland		High Early	
Water	5.19 gal/sack	19.6 ℓ/sack	6.32 gal/sack	23.9 ℓ/sack
Slurry weight	15.6 lb/gal	1,870 kg/m^3	14.8 lb/gal	1,770 kg/m^3
Slurry volume	1.18 ft^3/sack	0.03 m^3/sack	1.33 ft^3/sack	0.04 m^3/sack
(Halliburton 1968; Smith 1976)				

Cement grouts exert greater collapse pressure on casing than that exerted by water or drilling fluid. Table 10.4 (below) shows the increase in pressure exerted on casing by cement slurry compared with that exerted by a typical drilling fluid.

Table 10.4. Hydrostatic Loads on Casing

	Slurry		Weight		Pressure Gradient	
	lb/gal	**kg/ℓ**	**lb/ft³**	**kg/m³**	**psi/ft**	**kPa/m**
Freshwater	8.33	1.0	62.4	1,000	0.433	1.42
Typical Drill Fluid	9.5	1.14	71.2	1,141	0.494	1.62
Neat Cement Slurry	16.0	1.9	120	1,922	0.833	2.73

The potential pressure usually is greatest at the bottom of the casing. For example, the maximum pressure exerted by the cement grout at the bottom of a 500-ft (152-m) casing is 500 multiplied by 0.833, which equals 416 psi (2,868 kPa). A safety factor of 50% is recommended for use when selecting the wall thickness for the casing. Fluid inside the casing reduces the cement column pressure, depending on the relative heights of the fluid and cement columns. If the inside of the casing is dry, then the casing must be strong enough to support the entire grout column.

Cementing Tools and Products

Sometimes referred to as "casing jewelry," cementing tools and products are the mechanical attachments and devices that are incorporated within or onto the casing string to facilitate installation, centering, cementing, and development of the well. Some of the most common devices are described below (*see* Figure 10.4 through Figure 10.7).

Centralizers

A centralizer (Figure 10.4) is a device that keeps the casing centered in the borehole and away from the borehole walls to facilitate proper cementing. Many types of centralizers are available—from crude shop-made "fins" to specially made commercial varieties. Centralizer devices primarily should not impede installation (hang-up) and should have sufficient centering power (spring steel resistance) to keep the pipe away from the borehole walls. Centralizers also are available with welded and non-welded, high-quality spring steel bows. To prevent galvanic corrosion, centralizers must be composed of the same type of steel that is used for the well casing or screen.

Figure 10.4. Centralizer.

Cement Baskets

Cement baskets (Figure 10.5) are designed to protect weak formations from any excessive hydrostatic pressure exerted by the weight of a cement column. These attachments typically are installed on the casing string above the zone to be protected and are used in stage cementing or in cementing the annulus from the surface. The overlapping metal fins provide maximum flexibility and fluid passage while maintaining optimum support characteristics. They should be installed over stop collars to facilitate pipe reciprocation.

Figure 10.5. Cement basket.

Scratchers or Scrappers

Scratchers or scrappers (Figure 10.6) are attached to the casing, and remove excessive wall cake to improve the bond between cement and porous formations. Typically, a series of scratchers is mounted on the casing string.

Figure 10.6. Scrapper.

Float Shoes

Float shoes (Figure 10.7) are special end-fittings and contain a drillable check valve. They are attached to the bottom of the casing assembly to provide buoyancy during installation and to facilitate pumping of the cement from the bottom of the casing assembly (Halliburton method).

Figure 10.7. Float shoes.

Proportioning Cement Grout

Laboratory tests indicate that 5.2 gal (19.7 ℓ) of water are needed to hydrolyze 94 lb or one sack (42.6 kg) of portland cement and produce a slurry weight of 15.6 lb/gal (1,870 kg/m³). The proper water-cement ratio facilitates more effective bridging of cement particles in the pores of permeable formations, preventing excessive penetration. Water is squeezed out of thinner mixtures by pressure against permeable formations—therefore more water means more shrinkage. Cement settles out of the slurry if the amount of water is greater than 10 gal (38 ℓ) per sack, and fluid-loss agents can be used to control such water loss. Water for grouting should be potable and free of oil and other organic material, and its total dissolved solids (TDS) content should be less than 2,000 mg/ℓ (high sulfate content is particularly undesirable).

Bentonite holds cement particles in suspension, reduces shrinkage, and improves the fluidity of the mixture. Approximately 3 lb (1.4 kg) to 5 lb (2.3 kg) of bentonite should be mixed with 6.5 gal (25 ℓ) of water per 94 lb (42.64 kg) of cement. If the amount of bentonite exceeds 6%, excessive shrinkage occurs. It is best to mix the bentonite and water first and then add cement to the clay-water suspension.

Adding sand or other bulky material helps control fluid-loss conditions but increases the difficulty of handling and placing grout. Additives might be necessary to reduce the cost of the well materials if large openings must be filled. It is important to know the chemical composition of any additives used in grout seals (e.g., fly ash contains trace metals). The physical effect of additives commonly added to the cement is given in Table 10.5.

Table 10.5. Effects of Additives on the Physical Properties of Cement

		Bentonite	Diatomaceous Earth	Pozzolan	Sand	Heavy Minerals	Accelerator	Sodium Chloride	Retarder
Density	Decreased	●	●	●					
	Increased				●	●		○	
Water Required	Less								
	More	●	●	○	○				
Viscosity	Decreased						○	○	●
	Increased	○	○	○	○	○			
Thickening Time Required	Accelerated						●	●	
	Retarded	○	○						●
Early Strength	Decreased	○	○	○					●
	Increased						●	●	
Final Strength	Decreased	●	●	○		○			
	Increased								○
Durability	Decreased	○	○						
	Increased			●					
Water Loss	Decreased	●							○
	Increased		○						

○　Denotes minor effects
●　Denotes major effects or principal purpose for which used

(American Petroleum Institute 1959; Smith 1976)

Mixing Grout

Grout should be mixed thoroughly and be free of lumps. If it is purchased from a ready-mix concrete plant, the correct proportions must be insured by the vendor, and the delivery trucks must be cleaned thoroughly before transporting materials to the well site to avoid retaining stones and lumps of concrete. As a final precaution, there should be a protective strainer on the tank from which the grout is pumped.

Portable grouting machines effectively combine both the mixing and pumping operations (Figure 10.8). Most grouting machines are equipped with a positive displacement pump, because effective operation with a centrifugal pump is limited under high-head conditions. Avoid use of the drilling rig's mud pump because cement has abrasive qualities and is difficult to remove completely. Irregularities of the borehole size and losses into fractured rock make it difficult to accurately estimate the volume of grout required, therefore approximately 20% to 30% more than what is calculated always should be included as part of the original mix.

Figure 10.8. Portable grouting machines are capable of performing both the mixing and pumping operations (ChemGrout, Inc.).

Heat is produced and released during hydration (Figure 10.9). The amount of heat released during hydration depends on the volume of cement grout surrounding the casing, the ambient temperature of the formation, and the drilling-fluid pressure in the borehole. The amount of heat is a function of the cement volume (more cement means more heat). If the formation temperature

is high or accelerator additives are used, then the hydration process is acceler-
ated and heat is released more quickly. Cement filling a 2-in (51-mm) annulus
produces a maximum temperature rise of 35°F (1.7°C) to 45°F (7.22°C) during
hydration (Smith 1976). Heat of hydration is critical in PVC and permafrost
installations.

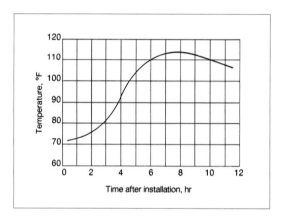

Figure 10.9. Graph showing the temperature change over time at a depth of
550 ft (168 m), where the formation temperature was 65°F (18.3°C), the
mixing-water temperature was 74°F (23.3°C), and the slurry weighed
15.4 lb/gal (1,850 kg/m³) (Canadian Institute of Mining and Metallurgy 1965).

Slurry Placement Methods

Successful cement placement depends on the method, the borehole temperature
and pressure, and how well the casing is centered. Temperature affects how fast
the slurry hydrates (how fast cement strength develops), and pressure (drilling-
fluid weight) can reduce the slurry pumping rate. In deep water wells (which
have higher temperatures and pressures) the hardening time can be substantially
reduced. The use of centralizers every 40 ft (12.19 m) is important to assure a
uniform thickness of cement around the casing. The lower end of the casing
should be closed with a drillable plug or be driven into clay. If necessary, the
buoyant effect of the slurry is overcome by filling the casing with water, drilling
mud, or other fluids, or by holding it down with the weight of the drill rig.
Using the drill rig can be dangerous if excessive pressures are built up in the

borehole. Several satisfactory placement methods are described below, but it is critical to always insure that channeling does not occur.

To assure a satisfactory seal, grout typically is placed in one continuous operation. When designing the well, hydrostatic loads should be evaluated carefully to prevent structural or formation damage. Regardless of the method used, to minimize contamination or dilution of the slurry or bridging of the mixture, the grout first should be introduced at the bottom. Suitable pumps should be used to force grout into the annular space under turbulent flow conditions, which enhances both drilling fluids removal and the more complete filling of voids. Diaphragm and positive-displacement pumps are used most often to pump cement grout. A positive-displacement pump with an effective output pressure of 250 psi (1,720 kPa) is recommended, but it should not be permitted to pump sand or other abrasives. Diaphragm pumps have lower output pressures (110 psi (758 kPa)), however they can handle particles of up to ¼ in (6.5 mm) to ⅜ in (9.5 mm) in diameter. Both pump types are used for batch mixing.

For larger grouting jobs, use of either positive-displacement pumps or (less frequently) centrifugal pumps is favored. Positive-displacement pumps (2 x 3, 3 x 4, or 5 x 6) can build pressures to 250 psi (1,720 kPa), and have been used successfully to place grout to 3,000 ft (914 m) or deeper via a 2-in (51-mm) tremie pipe. Because they develop less pressure, centrifugal pumps can be arranged so that a hopper feeds the pump under pressure, thereby increasing pump output.

If an open borehole is drilled below the casing depth, the hole must be back-filled or a bridge (cement basket or formation packer shoe) be set to retain the slurry at the desired depth. Backfilling with clean fine sand is a common procedure used to prevent cement from penetrating downward more than a few inches. If the borehole cannot be backfilled, then external packers with float shoes are used to support the cement column. Cement baskets are clamped on the outside of the casing (Figure 10.10). External packers are installed in the casing string (Figure 10.11) and then expanded before cementing begins.

Figure 10.10. Cement basket.

**Figure 10.11. An external packer equipped with a float shoe can be installed
in the casing string to facilitate placing cement grout.**

Cement always should be allowed to adequately harden (typically for 24 hr) before drilling resumes, therefore "waiting on cement" (W.O.C.) time should be included in the well-construction procedures and schedules. It is unwise to risk damaging a good grouting job by drilling the plug too soon.

Tremie Pipe Located Outside Casing

A string of small-diameter pipe, called tremie pipe or grout pipe, is placed outside of the casing (Figure 10.12). The casing is lowered with centering guides attached. If the tremie is set separately, the centering guides must be aligned along the entire length of casing that is to be grouted. Grout can be placed using gravity, but pumping is preferred because the required volume can be introduced rapidly and with less chance of voids occurring within the grout. The bottom of the tremie always should be submerged a few feet beneath the grout level. Pump pressure must equal or exceed the hydrostatic pressure of the grout plus the fluid friction in the grout pipe and annular space.

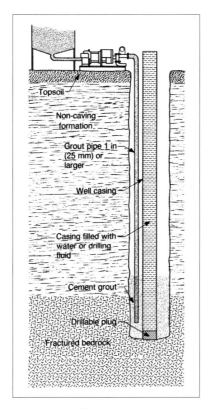

Figure 10.12. Illustration of grouting using a tremie pipe suspended in the annulus outside the casing.

In shallow holes, the cementing operation is completed in a single step (if a positive-displacement pump with adequate pressure is used) and the tremie pipe is not moved as the annulus fills. If a centrifugal pump is used, or if the hole is deep, the tremie must be raised periodically to keep the hydraulic head below the working pressure of the pump. Usually the tremie is withdrawn (one or more joints at a time), but the bottom always should remain beneath the surface of the cement. The depth to the top of the grout can be detected by using a weighted line or a weight indicator, or by estimating the volume of material that the hopper contains before grouting begins as compared to unit volume in the annulus.

The grout pipe must be large enough for grout to be placed before hardening begins. A ¾-in (19-mm) or 1-in (25-mm) pipe can be used, although 2-in (51-mm) pipe is used for deeper holes. To accommodate the pipe, the borehole should be 4 in (102 mm) to 8 in (203 mm) larger than the casing. If the tremie pipe becomes plugged, then it should be raised above the grout level and not be lowered back into the slurry until all of the air and water inside the pipe have been displaced by grout.

When multiple filter-pack screens are separated by grouted casing sections, a larger-diameter hole is drilled and slurry usually is placed using a tremie that is outside of the casing. The top of the filter pack is at least several feet above the top of the screen, and the grout is run up slightly higher than the formation to be isolated. Low-permeability sand is placed on top of the filter pack to contain the grout until it hardens (Figure 10.13).

An alternative is to use a layer of coated bentonite pellets. Once the lower grout has set, additional filter-pack material is introduced for the next screen, followed by another layer of low-permeability sand, and then another grouted section (if necessary).

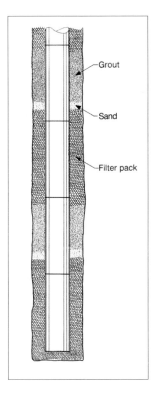

Figure 10.13. Sand sometimes is placed on top of the filter pack to prevent grout from penetrating the pack.

Tremie Pipe Located Inside Casing (Inner-String Method)

If using a grout pipe outside the casing is impractical, then pipe temporarily is installed inside the casing (Figure 10.14). This often is referred to as the inner-string method. Before the casing is placed in the borehole, a float shoe is attached to the bottom of the casing. A tremie pipe then is suspended inside the casing and lowered until it engages the shoe. The float shoe permits the grout to pass into the annular space but prevents backflow into the casing (Figure 10.15). All the internal parts (e.g., valve, spring) can be drilled out easily upon completion of the cementing.

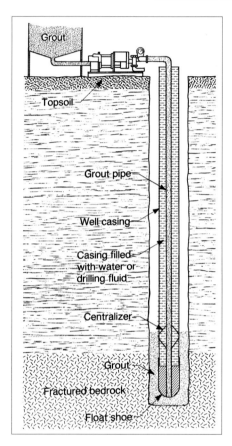

Figure 10.14. Illustration of the inner-string method for placing grout.

The casing is filled with water and suspended just off the borehole's bottom. Grout is pumped through the grout pipe and float shoe, and moves upward around the outside of the casing. When cement appears at the surface, but before the grout pipe is pulled out to displace any remaining slurry, the pipe is disconnected from the float shoe and flushed with water. After completing the cementing operation, the casing is completely flushed with clean water to prevent drilling-fluid contamination. A braden head also can be used for the prevention of casing collapse during cementing.

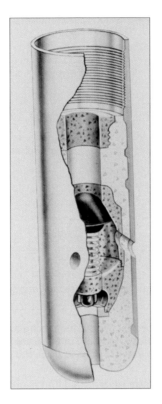

Figure 10.15. A cementing shoe has a ball-type check valve that prevents the grout from reentering the casing when the tremie pipe is withdrawn.

Casing Method

Adopted from oilfield well-completion methods, the casing grouting method involves pumping grout down the well casing, out the base of the casing or float shoe, and into the annular space. Two spacer-plugs (wiper plugs) are used, the first separates the cement slurry from the drilling fluid in the casing, and the second separates the slurry from the water pumped behind to wash the slurry from the casing (originally called the Halliburton method, Figure 10.16). Spacer-plugs should be made of drillable materials; wood and rubber often are used.

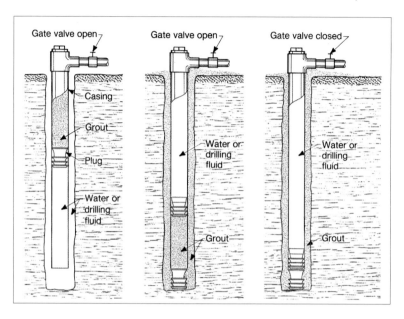

Figure 10.16. Grout can be placed into the casing and then forced out of the bottom and up the annulus. Plugs are used to separate the grout from the drilling fluid and water is used to drive the grout into place.

In the casing method, water or drilling fluid is circulated through the annular space to clear obstructions, the first plug is inserted, the casing is closed with a head manifold, and then a measured volume of grout is pumped. A second wiper plug is released from inside the manifold and a measured volume of water is pumped, pushing the second plug to the bottom and forcing most of the cement slurry from the casing into the annular space. The manifold is closed, holding the water in the casing under pressure to prevent backflow. After the cement has hardened, the plugs and any remaining cement in the casing are drilled out. Drilling can continue into the formation, or the drilling fluid can be conditioned or replaced (if contaminated by residual cement). It occasionally is necessary to remove residual cement scale from casing walls using brushes or scrapers.

An optional single-plug procedure includes pumping a predetermined quantity of grout directly into the drilling fluid–filled casing. A plug then is inserted and enough water is pumped into the casing to force all but 10 ft (3 m) to 15 ft (4.6 m) of grout from the casing. To achieve an uncontaminated, uniform seal, the initial slurry—now diluted by the drilling fluid—must be expelled to the surface as waste. The plug insures that slurry and water remain separate, for creation of a proper seal at the bottom of the casing.

To eliminate over-displacement or under-displacement of the cement, a landing collar is set 10 ft (3 m) to 20 ft (6.1 m) above the bottom of the casing, and this stops the drillable plug at the appropriate depth. To avoid damaging the bottom of the casing by exerting excessive pump pressure after the plugs have come together, a wire line sometimes is attached to the upper plug so that depth can be measured accurately.

Sometimes the borehole must be grouted after installation of the casing and screen. A single string of screen and casing that must have grout above the screen requires cement baskets for isolating the screen from the annulus. The cement baskets (the use of two or more is preferable) are attached above the screen during installation and a drillable bridge plug is placed in the casing above the screen. Holes are cut into the casing above this plug by a mills knife or other kind of perforator, and cement slurry is pumped into the casing and forced into the annular space above the cement basket (Figure 10.17). Grout usually is extended 5 ft (1.5 m) above and below the formation to be sealed. This method should not be used where zones containing poor-quality water must be sealed off in multiple-screen installations.

Installing Bentonite Grout

Bentonite grout has several advantages over cement grout: It has a faster setting time, does not experience the heat of hydration, has lower hydrostatic pressure (specific gravity is 9.2 for the grout given in Table 10.6), and costs much less than cement. Bentonite also adheres to both walls of the annulus; cement adheres firmly only to the soil. It swells rather than shrinks over time, and bentonite essentially is chemically inert.

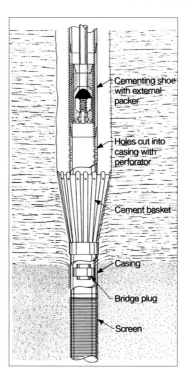

Figure 10.17. A cementing shoe directs the grout out into the annulus above cement baskets mounted in the casing string.

Table 10.6. Amounts of Bentonite, Water, and Polymer Required to Grout 100 ft (305 m) of Three Common Borehole Diameters

Pipe Size/Borehole Diameter	Bentonite		Water		Polymer*	
	lb	kg	gal	ℓ	qt	ℓ
2-in (51-mm) pipe / 4-in (102-mm) hole	75	34	50	189	0.5	0.5
4-in (102-mm) pipe / 6-in (152-mm) hole	112	51	75	284	0.75	0.7
5-in (127-mm) pipe / 8-in (203-mm) hole	225	102	150	568	1.5	1.4
* Concentration of polymer recommended for EZ mud.						

Bentonite is widely used as a grouting material. Due to its low cost and ease of placement, it is especially applicable for monitoring wells and water wells where surface contamination could occur. Commercial bentonite that is used for grouting is available in either pellet, granular, or chip form. When mixed with water bentonite begins to hydrate immediately, thus making it difficult to place the granular form by dropping the particles into the annulus. Even pellets begin to stick together or adhere to the walls of the annulus within only a few feet of the surface—bridging high above the intended depth. Freezing the pellets allows them to settle a greater distance before they begin sticking. It is recommended that the pellets be tamped into place to eliminate any bridging; however this might not be possible given the depth of placement.

A much better practice when grouting with bentonite is to use a tremie pipe to pump a prepared bentonite slurry that is limited to 20% to 30% solids. A mixture of only 1 lb (0.5 kg) of bentonite granules per 1 gal (3.8 ℓ) of water results in viscosity near the limit of pumping capacity. Even though the ground around the grout usually remains somewhat moist, grout with this concentration of bentonite eventually might shrink up to 25%—an unsatisfactory shrinkage rate. Virtually no shrinkage occurs when mixing 1.5 lb (0.7 kg) bentonite per 1 gal (3.8 ℓ) of water, but this concentration can be pumped only if the water is pretreated with 1 qt (0.9 ℓ) of polymer per 100 gal (380 ℓ) of water. The polymer prevents clays from hydrating immediately, and once properly mixed the viscosity remains low enough to pump for about 20 min. Mixing should be done using a paddle and not a mixer—which breaks up the particles causing the viscosity to increase prematurely. Bentonite grouts therefore are best mixed in batches.

The diameter of the suction hose on the grout pump should be as large as possible and, to make the pump operate more efficiently, the slurry reservoir should be above the pump intake. The pump and all piping should be flushed with clean water after each batch of grout is pumped into place. The volumes of bentonite, polymer, and water for various annulus sizes (per 100 ft (30.5 m) of depth) are given in Table 10.6 (above). Other bentonite grout limitations are listed below.

- ◆ Bentonite should not be used above underreamed boreholes because the "set" might not be sufficient to withstand the vertical pressures.
- ◆ Bentonite should not extend so close to ground surface that it dries out and shrinks due to low soil moisture.

◆   Saltwater causes bentonite grout to flocculate and lose viscosity.
◆   Acids (organic and inorganic) can destroy the impervious character
    of the grout seal.

Grouting Failures

Several factors can contribute to grouting failures, including premature setting, partial setting, insufficient grout-column length, voids or gaps in the grout, excessive shrinkage, and casing collapse. Premature setting can be a serious problem and usually is caused by incorrect assumptions concerning borehole temperature, use of hot mixing water, improper water-to-cement ratios, contaminated mixing water, mechanical failures, and interruption of the pumping operation. Voids within the grouted annulus usually are caused by the casing coming into contact with the borehole wall or by the presence of washouts. Careful planning of any grouting job is important.

TESTING THE GROUT SEAL

Prior to drilling the grout plug the effectiveness of the seal can be checked using three methods: measuring the water-level change inside the casing over time; pressure testing; and analysis of an acoustic (sonic) cement-bond log (*see* Chapter 4). In areas where there is a low static-water level relative to the depth of the well, the casing can be filled with water or drilling fluid and later checked for fluid loss. A loss is indicative of leakage in the grout seal. If the static-water level is high outside of the casing, then the fluid level in the casing can be lowered and any influx of water can be measured. This procedure, however, should not be used with thin-walled casing. When using pressure testing the grout must be able to contain pressures of 7 psi (48.3 kPa) to 10 psi (69 kPa) after curing for at least 1 hr. If acoustic logging is used, then it must show that no voids or gaps exist in the grouted annular space.

Abandoned and improperly constructed wells provide vertical openings or channels through which contaminated water can enter usable freshwater aquifers. Regardless of the grouting technique, a more complete seal is attained if the grout slurry is placed in a turbulent manner.

INSTALLING WELL SCREEN

Many different screen installation methods exist. Certain procedures are more practical or more economical, and the choice of installation method depends on the nature and hydraulic conditions of the aquifer, the drilling method used, the borehole dimensions, and the selection of casing and screen materials. The most common and most successful installation methods are described below.

Setting Screen in Rotary-Drilled Wells

The pull-back method is used in cases of extreme caving or lost circulation, when the drilling fluid is unable to control borehole problems adequately. The exceptions are:

+ When drilling in relatively shallow, unconsolidated sediments where natural compaction is not great;
+ When drilling in confined aquifers where the material is close to a condition where any suction or other disturbance in the borehole causes the sediment to "run" toward low-pressure;
+ If a delay is anticipated between drilling and screen installation; or
+ If a casing-advance drilling method, such as cable tool or dual rotary, is used in an unconsolidated or unstable formation.

Air-rotary tools equipped with casing drivers typically sink the casing to the top of a clay layer under the aquifer, insert the screen, and then pull back the casing. If no clay exists and heaving is a problem, then it might be necessary to change from air-based to water-based drilling fluids to control pressures in the formation so that the screen can be set. Occasionally stiff foam is sufficient to control the formation.

Double-String Installation

A typical procedure for installing screens in high-capacity wells includes the following steps.

+ Drill a small-diameter test hole, keep a detailed geologic drill log, and collect geologic samples.

- Log the test hole using geophysical methods (typically including SP, resistivity, natural gamma, and caliper measurements). Including side-wall or standard cores is optional.
- Collect water samples from a temporary well or drill-stem test (if water-quality data is required).
- Analyze test-hole data and make final design decisions.
- The test hole often is used as a pilot hole and is enlarged (reamed) for the installation of the production screen. The test hole also can be completed as an observation well, temporarily providing make-up water for drilling the production well.
- The borehole is drilled to the top of the aquifer (Figure 10.18).

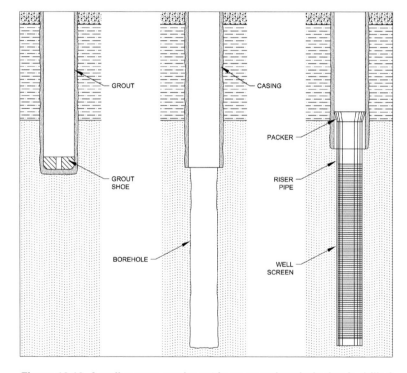

Figure 10.18. A well screen can be set in an open borehole that is drilled below the well casing after the casing has been grouted.

- ◆ The casing generally is set with a drillable or "stab-in" grout (float) shoe (made of cast aluminum or cement) on the bottom, which allows grout to be pumped through the bottom of the casing (the best way to insure proper centering).
- ◆ The casing is grouted and allowed to set for at least 24 hr.
- ◆ The grout shoe and excess grout are drilled out and the drilling fluid is replaced before beginning any drilling into the aquifer. These steps keep grout from entering the aquifer and prevent drilling fluid contamination.
- ◆ The aquifer is drilled (or underreamed) according to the design diameter for either a natural or filter-pack completion.
- ◆ A suitable length of riser pipe is attached to the top of the screen. If there will be blank pipe between the top of the screen and the bottom of the casing and the well is filter packed, then include a 5-ft (1.5-m) length of pressure-relief screen in the riser pipe string and set it at the bottom of the casing (pressure-relief screens are discussed in Chapter 9).
- ◆ The screen assembly is attached to the top of the riser pipe and telescoped into the open borehole connected to the bottom of the drill-pipe assembly. In deep holes, a longer drill-pipe assembly can exert high loads on back-off threads, and should be held in tension while disengaging. If the well is to be filter packed, then at least one centralizer is attached near the bottom of the screen and another attached near the top (Figure 10.19). Centralizers for screen lengths of less than 200 ft (61 m) are spaced every 20 ft (6.1 m); or (for economic reasons) every at 40 ft (12.2 m) on screen intervals of more than 200 ft (61 m).
- ◆ If borehole sloughing or fill requires washing the screen into place, then mount a self-closing wash plug with internal left-hand threads in the screen bottom. A wash pipe attached to this fitting can be used either to set the screen or to displace drilling fluid from the borehole, thus aiding development.

Figure 10.19. Centralizer on a screen (Clear Creek Associates).

♦   For a naturally developed well completion, the formation around
    the screen is induced to collapse by lowering the hydrostatic
    pressure in the well, or by thinning the drilling fluid or lowering its
    level in the borehole. The setting tool is removed and development
    begins. Shale catchers (traps) and formation packers sometimes are
    used to prevent sloughing of overlying materials (especially clays)
    when a well is naturally developed. If the well is gravel packed,
    then the setting tools remain in place during packing and are
    removed when development is started. Once the well is developed,
    a packer or grout seal can be installed to provide a seal between the
    riser pipe and casing. Normally no packer is required if the riser
    pipe is extends 50 ft (15m) or more into the casing.

Single-String Installation

In most deep wells the screens are attached directly to the bottom of the casing.
A long assembly of casing and screen is flexible with a high ratio of length relative to its diameter, and little column strength. A string that is 200 ft (61 m) long
and 12 in (305 mm) in diameter has a length to diameter ratio of 200 to 1 (similar

to 12 in (305 mm) of 1/16-in (1.5-mm) wire). It always is best to suspend the string from the surface during installation without resting the column on the well bottom. Once lateral support is attained—either by gravel packing or collapsing the formation in a naturally developed well—the column safely can be released. Failure to observe this precaution, however, might result in a collapsed or crooked well. Centralizers are extremely effective in maintaining proper alignment and are recommended for all screens that are more than 20 ft (6.1 m) long.

If the screen diameter is smaller than the casing, then a cone adaptor is used (Figure 10.20). The casing and screen are set and the drilling fluid is thinned. Drilling-fluid not properly thinned can remain outside of the screen, creating differential pressures between the screen and the formation—pressures potentially sufficient to collapse the screen or casing. One way to prevent this situation is to fill the casing and screen with drilling fluid or water. The drilling fluid must be in proper condition (e.g., thinned).

For naturally developed wells, the formation is induced to cave around the screen interval immediately after the screen is set. For gravel-packed completions the filter-pack material is placed before formation caving is induced. To prevent silts and clays that are above the aquifer from sloughing during natural development, sometimes a formation stabilizer is installed (Figure 10.20) to hold these materials in place until the formation caves against the stabilizer. (The size gradation of a stabilizer is discussed in Chapter 9). In most cases, a formation stabilizer is not needed if the borehole is only slightly larger than the screen and the top of the screen is placed 3 ft (0.9 m) or more below any clay zone. To prevent sloughing, shale catchers (or cement baskets) also can be mounted on the casing in place of a stabilizer.

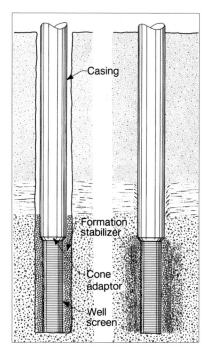

Figure 10.20. Illustration of how a formation stabilizer prevents sloughing against the well screen from formations above.

Packer Use in Screen Installation

A packer could be required to prevent sediment from entering the space between the two overlapping assemblies. Two types of packers can be attached to the top of the screen: a static packer or a mechanical packer. A simple static packer (also called a K-packer) typically is a ring made of neoprene rubber that is attached to a long weld-ring above the screen. A mechanical packer expands once in place. Both types are attached directly to the top of the well screen or the riser pipe.

K-Packer

A flexible neoprene K-packer is attached to a steel ring or coupling and fits tightly in the casing, sealing the casing to the screen (Figure 10.21). This type of packer is popular because no expansion is required. It is recommended that two or more K-packers be used in series to compensate for small deviations in well-casing dimensions, weld-slag protruding inside the casing, damage from improper handling, or for screens set to depths exceeding 300 ft (91.5 m).

Figure 10.21. Self-sealing neoprene rubber packers (K-packers) form an effective seal between the casing and upper end of the screen or riser pipe.

Liner Hanger

Liner hangers (Figure 10.22) often are used in deep wells and are more expensive than K-packers. One type of expandable packer uses a sliding mandrel to expand a hollow rubber cylinder. The packer ordinarily is attached to a riser pipe and is expanded in the casing. The top of the packer is fitted with a left-hand thread and enables the drillpipe to be disengaged. A sliding-end packer has a smaller expansion ratio than does an inflatable packer.

Figure 10.22. Liner hanger.

Inflatable packers (Figure 10.23) generally have larger expansion ratios than do casing hangers. The packer is inflated by injecting gas, water, or a solidifying liquid. Inflatable packers can be used for a short time and then retrieved or can be installed permanently. Some fixed-end packers can be inflated to two times the uninflated diameter or more, but they generally are designed for lower-pressure applications than are sliding-end packers. Sliding-end packers are used where the differential pressures range from 200 psi (1,380 kPa) to 2,000 psi (13,800 kPa) or more, or where high expansions are required.

Figure 10.23. Inflatable packers are used as permanent or temporary sealing devices to isolate portions of the wellbore (Baski Inc.).

Installing Prepack Screens—Muni-Pak™

When a filter pack is desired, the many practical and economic advantages offered by prepack screens should be considered. Prepack screens are ideally suited for horizontal wells, deviated wells, and wells having conventional vertical orientations. Borehole diameter requirements typically are less than what is needed for conventional filter packing and equipment, and the logistics necessary to receive, handle, and place filter pack onsite are eliminated—saving additional time and costs. Typically the recommended borehole diameter for a Muni-Pak™ screen is 2 in (50 mm) to 4 in (102 mm) larger than the Muni-Pak™ outside diameter.

The outside diameter of the Muni-Pak™ screen assembly is larger than the connections, thus extended connections are standard. Individual screen lengths of up to 40 ft (12 m) are available. Muni-Pak™ screens have 4 to 6 times the design collapse strength and approximately 3 times the design tensile strength of conventional rod-based screens. Procedures for setting Muni-Pak™ screens are the same as for conventional screens.

Collapsing the formation around Muni-Pak™ is the ideal first step in development. When a Muni-Pak™ screen is installed as a single string with the casing, shale traps or cement baskets should be attached above the screen zone to prevent premature sloughing of shallow, unstable fine-grained lenses, particularly if the borehole drilled is "oversized" to allow for cementing through a tremie or grout pipe.

Muni-Pak™ uses hydraulically efficient carbolite™ with a filter thickness approximately one-half that of a conventional gravel pack, therefore it is easier to develop. Placing a formation stabilizer outside the Muni-Pak™ is not recommended. As with other screen installations, before aggressive development is initiated, flow through the screen should be established. Muni-Pak™ screens are suited for both telescoping and single-string completions.

Installing Polyvinyl Chloride Screens

Polyvinyl chloride (PVC) materials have predictable physical limitations but—when properly selected and handled—they provide wells with adequate strength, good hydraulic characteristics, and long life. For depth settings exceeding 300 ft (91.5 m), contact the screen manufacturer for recommendations.

Installation of screens made from PVC is similar to installation of steel screens but, because a PVC screen's strength is much less than that of steel, PVC screens require different handling. Johnson Screens custom collared elevator and grooved pipe greatly facilitate handling large-diameter PVC (Figure 10.24). Figure 10.25 is a photograph of a PVC joint in an elevator. Additionally, PVC casing can be buoyant when placed in the borehole, so setting procedures might require modification. Today, more hybrid wells (which have plastic casing and stainless steel screens) are installed using both the telescope and the direct-attached well-completion methods.

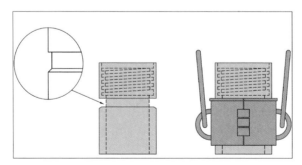

Figure 10.24. Collared elevator and grooved pipe.

Figure 10.25. Elevator holding PVC pipe.

The most common PVC casing used in wells is made to meet Schedule 40, 80, or SDR-21 specifications. A wide variety of end fittings is available to fit any size PVC screen on the market, and includes male adaptors, female adaptors, reducers, and slip couplings.

Plastic screens are attached directly to casing using solvent-weld couplings or mechanical connections (e.g., flush or standard threads, spline couplings on slip-lock fittings such as the Shur-A-Lock™ design). After placement the screen can be filter packed and the annular space sealed, commonly with bentonite grouts. Placement of the pack and backfill material should be completed carefully, because the collapse resistance of PVC is less than that of steel casing. If no filter pack is used, then a rubber shale trap often is fastened to the casing above the top of the screen and backfilled with a small amount of clean clay material. Bentonite can be placed in the annulus above the fill material. PVC can be grouted in place with neat cement, however the curing temperature of the cement must not be so high that the casing deforms. For this reason, exercise caution when using cement grout to seal the annulus of a PVC-cased well in formations that might be prone to borehole washouts.

Stainless steel and PVC vee wire screens often are telescoped through steel and PVC casing via a K-packer. The varying inside diameter (depending on schedule or SDR number) can cause problems with packer fit, therefore consulting the manufacturer can prevent the potential for sand problems.

During development, differential hydrostatic pressures exerted on both the casing and the screen must be minimized. Development should be done gently, until all drilling fluid is removed from the annulus around the screen and water is flowing freely into the screen. The casing and screen never should be "blown dry" with an air compressor. If compressed air is used for development, then start the development process well above the screen and at first remove only small quantities of water. Additional details regarding development are provided in Chapter 11.

Wash-Down Installation Methods

There are two common wash-down installation procedures. One method is used for installing well screens through casing. The wash-down bottom tool with a spring-loaded (or float ball) valve permits the washing of a screen into place, and space around the packer allows return flow outside the well screen (Figure 10.26).

The casing first is set and grouted, and then the cement plug is drilled out. A string of pipe (usually drillpipe) is used as the wash line; this is threaded into the self-closing bottom with a left-hand thread. Water or lightweight drill fluid then is pumped through the line with adequate volume and pressure to produce a jetting action to loosen and remove sediment, thus allowing the screen to sink with no rotation. The sediment washes up around the screen and inside the casing. As velocity decreases above the packer, some larger particles drop inside the screen. Excessive sediment buildup in the screen could sand lock the wash line which makes it difficult to disconnect and remove.

When the screen reaches bottom, clean water should be circulated to remove fines and collapse the formation around the screen. In general, the same wash-down procedure is used in an open hole. Sloughing might occur and grip the screen, or the casing and screen can be placed just above the aquifer and washed into place. This method commonly is used in the United States for completing coal-bed methane wells, where a pilot hole is drilled before the screen is washed into place.

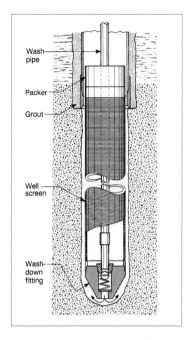

Figure 10.26. A wash-down bottom tool with spring-loaded valve.

A second wash-down method for installing small-diameter screens (usually 2 in (51 mm)) is to use a temporary wash pipe inside of the well screen before the screen is attached to the bottom joint of the casing. The wash pipe (commonly ¾ in (19 mm)) extends 1 ft (0.3 m) to 2 ft (0.6 m) into the casing (Figure 10.27), or to the surface if the well depth is not great. A coupling screwed to the lower end of the wash pipe rests in a conical seat in the self-closing wash-down fitting (equipped with a plastic-ball closure). A semi-rigid plastic ring seal (doughnut) is slipped over the upper end of the wash pipe and pushed into the top of the well screen, closing the space around the wash pipe directing the jetting water into the pipe. If the wash pipe extends to the surface, the ring seal prevents return flow of jetting water to the space between the wash pipe and the screen. All return flow takes place outside of the screen and casing.

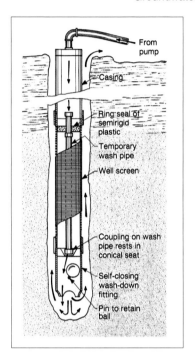

Figure 10.27. Illustration of a temporary wash pipe inside the well screen, used to wash small-diameter screens into place.

When jetting with water, screens can be installed efficiently to depths of approximately 50 ft (15 m) or less, due to fluid loss and caving when a casing is added. To achieve greater depths, a drilling-fluid additive must be mixed with the jetting water. About 5% of the jetting water leaks from around the bottom wash pipe and out through the screen, which helps prevent fine sand from entering during the jetting operation and reduces the possibility of sand locking the wash pipe inside of the screen.

When the well screen has been set at the proper depth, the wash pipe is removed and the well is developed. In some cases, screens can be set without the wash pipe and seal, however significantly larger volumes of water are required because some water escapes through the sides of the screen and does not aid the jetting action occurring at the bottom of the screen.

Installing Well Points

Well points typically are installed using some of the same methods described above, as well as via the pull-back method or by driving beyond the end of casing. Figure 10.28 illustrates a well-point installation completed by pulling back the casing and causing weight to be placed on the well point. Many 2-in (51-mm) stainless-steel well points are installed in 4-in (102-mm) wells by use of this method. Small 2-in (51-mm) well points are set easily through hollow-stem augers, where the string is lowered inside the auger to the bottom of the borehole and the auger flight then is retrieved. This method is particularly suitable for use in shallow, unconsolidated, or caving formations, and for installing monitoring wells. See Chapter 3 for additional information on the auger method.

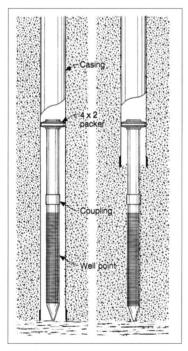

Figure 10.28. Two-inch (51-mm) well points can be set in 4-in (102-mm) diameter wells via the pull-back method.

Before driving a well point, all the sediment in the casing is removed to prevent sand locking. If there is a chance that the sediments might heave, the casing should be kept full of water while the point is set. A K-packer is attached to the top of the well point and is placed through the casing. A driving bar, drill stem, or other tool is raised and lowered to drive the well point through the bottom of the casing. To minimize potential damage to the screen, using a weight that is less than 250 lb (113 kg) together with a 2-ft (0.6-m) stroke is recommended. Careful measurements must be made so that the drilling professional knows when the screen has been driven the correct distance. Use of a 3-ft (1-m) to 5-ft (1.5-m) riser pipe also is advised.

Some well points are manufactured to include a drive plate (Figure 10.29) so that the driving force is directed at the point; however not all drive points are created to withstand driving from the bottom, so it is important to confirm the specifications when ordering the points from the manufacturer. Driving a point from inside a casing is recommended for points longer than 5 ft (1.5 m); but attempting this procedure without having a drive plate in place can cause severe damage to the bottom of the screen.

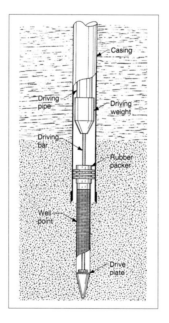

Figure 10.29. A driving bar can be used to drive well points inside the casing.

Pull-Back Installation Method

The pull-back installation method reduces problems such as setting the screen at the wrong depth, the heaving of sediment, and the sloughing of borehole walls caused by swelling clays or low hydrostatic pressure within the borehole. The pull-back procedure enables screen removal and replacement without disturbing the casing seal, and the cost (of pulling, cleaning, or replacing) usually is small as compared to the cost of drilling a new well.

The pull-back installation procedure is particularly suited for rotary rigs that can drill and drive casing, and for cable tool drilling rigs. This method involves installing casing to the total depth, telescoping the screen inside to full depth, and then extracting (pulling back) the casing far enough to expose the screen to the water-bearing formation (Figure 10.30). The casing must be strong enough to be set to full depth and then be pulled back the entire length of the screen.

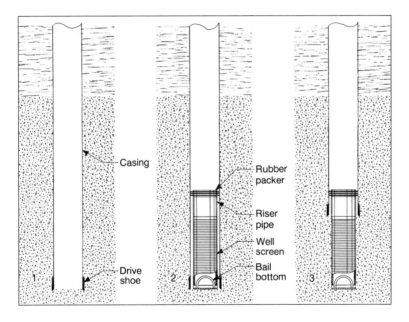

Figure 10.30. Basic operations in setting a well screen using the pull-back method: (1) driving, bailing, or lowering the casing to the full depth of the well; (2) lowering the screen inside the casing; and (3) pulling the casing back to expose the screen to the aquifer.

Telescope-size screens are available to be set using this method, and their dimensions allow them to be slipped inside standard pipes of the same diameter. Telescope sizes enable installation of the largest-diameter screen possible for a given casing diameter. Pipe-size screens (one or more diameters smaller than the casing) also are telescoped through larger-diameter casing.

It is good practice to attach riser pipe to the top of the screen. The riser pipe prevents screen damage during placement, and allows open screen area to be used opposite the formation—not up inside the casing. Recommended riser lengths are listed below.

- ◆   Domestic wells: 2 ft (0.6 m) to 5 ft (1.5 m)
- ◆   Larger-diameter deeper wells: 10 ft (3 m) to 20 ft (6.1 m)
- ◆   Small-diameter wells: 5 ft (1.5 m) to 10 ft (3 m) (helps prevent the casing from unintentionally being pulled back so quickly that the screen is disconnected beneath it)

Controlling sediment movement into the bottom of the casing is important, particularly if the screen has several slot sizes corresponding to individual sediment layers, or has blank sections between screen zones. If sediment heaving is a problem, keep the casing filled with water or a prepared drilling fluid to control fluid loss. If necessary, confining pressure can be controlled by weighting the drilling fluid. Sudden vertical movement of tools—especially bailers—increases the likelihood of heaving problems by reducing the bottom-hole pressure.

After sediment carefully is removed from the casing, the drilling professional must determine whether the casing can be withdrawn. If it cannot, then the drive shoe is removed (using an inside casing cutter) to reduce resistance, and the casing is pulled back a few inches. The screen then is lowered to the bottom of the well. Several means can be used to lower the screen, including: bail and hook, eccentric clevis (offset latch), casing lugs, J-hook, backoff sub, and wash-down bottoms (Figure 10.31).

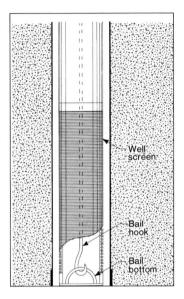

Figure 10.31. Screen is lowered by attaching the sand line to the bail bottom using a bail hook.

The drill string or a weight on the sand line is set on the plate-bottom of the screen, providing sufficient resistance to hold the screen during pull-back. The weight's line tension verifies the position of the screen while pulling. Without weighting, any heaving that occurs forces the screen upward at about the same rate that the casing is pulled. Alternatively, the screen can be placed in the bottom of the well, with the drill string set on top of the screen and the casing jacked back.

The casing can be pulled directly with the casing line by jarring it with the drilling string and bumper block (a timber wrapped with wire mesh or other retaining medium located below the crown that acts as a cushion in the event that the block is raised too far); by hydraulically jacking the string with a pull-ring gripping the casing; or (for long casing strings) by using a vibratory hammer to overcome skin friction between the casing and the formation.

As the screen is exposed, depth measurements to the screen should be taken. If no riser is attached to the screen, then the casing should be pulled back so that the packer is about 12 in (30.5 cm) above the bottom of the casing. The screen can be fully exposed beneath the casing if a riser pipe is attached.

FILTER PACKING WELLS

Many wells are designed to use an artificial filter pack. A filter-packed well has a predetermined thickness, whereas a naturally developed well has a graded permeable zone that is produced by the development process. Both types, when properly constructed, are efficient and stable. Filter-pack thickness has a direct impact on effective development at the formation-pack interface. The optimal thickness for a pack is 3 in (76 mm), and packs thicker than 5 in (127 mm) are not recommended because the effectiveness of the development procedures is impaired severely. Installing a filter pack that is less than 2 in (50 mm) thick is preferred, but is not practical.

All filter-pack materials and equipment should be treated with bactericide—usually sodium or calcium hypochlorite—and all water used in the filter-pack operation should be treated with 50 mg/ℓ free-chlorine solution before use. When possible, the drilling fluid should be thinned and be relatively free of solids before placement.

The grain sizes within filter-pack material should not segregate during placement. Dissimilar-sized particles fall though water at different velocities, thus well-sorted material (limited size distributions) is less apt to segregate during placement.

Tremie Pipe

Using a tremie pipe minimizes the tendency for particle separation and bridging when installing packs with high uniformity coefficients. Pipe that is 2 in (51 mm) or larger works in shallow to moderately deep wells (1,000 ft (305 m) to 1,500 ft (457 m)) when gravity-fed at approximately 1 ft^3 (0.03 m^3) of pack material per 5 gal (19 ℓ) to 10 gal (38 ℓ) of water. In deeper wells, filter pack should be pumped through a tremie pipe, which typically is placed before the screen and casing. The tremie pipe is raised periodically as the filter material builds up around the well screen, and also can be used to feel the top of the filter pack (or a weighted line can be inserted through the tremie).

Telltale Screen

Another filter-pack placement method incorporates use of a short telltale screen that is installed above the production screen (*see* Figure 10.32). Filter pack material is pumped into the annulus, and water flows into the screen and back to the surface through the drillpipe. The top of the casing must be sealed to the drillpipe so that the steadily increasing pressure can be monitored as the screen is covered. Surface pumping stops when an abrupt pressure spike occurs, which indicates that the telltale screen is covered. Suspended filter pack still falls, however the depth to the top of the pack can be calculated using the filter-pack volume in suspension and the water volume in the annular space.

Reverse Circulation

Packing large-diameter wells by using reverse circulation often is performed in a manner similar to packing a telltale screen. The borehole is kept full of fluid and pack material is carried downward outside the inner casing and screen. Sometimes a stinger pipe and dual-swab tool (with a perforated pipe between two rubber swabs) that forces water to the bottom of the screen before returning to the surface is used (this is particularly advantageous for use with long strings or unstable boreholes where use of a tremie pipe is not practical) (Figure 10.32).

Direct Circulation

Direct circulation of clean water can reduce bridging problems, and is an option to consider if pack material is contaminated by organic material (e.g., leaves, grass) or contains too many fines. The low uphole velocity allows gravity settlement, but still is ample to float organic material or fine sediment to the surface and thereby reduce development time. During circulation, make sure to avoid removing the filter cake and causing the borehole to become unstable.

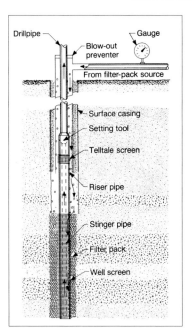

Figure 10.32. When filter packing a long screen, a stinger pipe is installed to force water to flow to the bottom of the screen.

A more complicated direct-circulation method used in small-diameter deep wells is pumping through a crossover tool. The crossover tool generally is used for a deep water well that has a small annulus. Figure 10.33 shows the basic features and flow paths during placement of the filter pack. The crossover tool is connected between the drillpipe and the top of the riser pipe. The top of the riser pipe can be sealed to the casing with a suitable packer (e.g., K-packer) after the filter pack is placed.

The stinger pipe extends to within 3 ft (0.9 m) of the bottom of the screen. The pumping pressure will increase suddenly when the filter pack material reaches the top of the screen. The upper portion of the sand injection pipe (above the crossover sub) is equipped with a left-threaded backoff sub, so it can be removed after sand installation. Careful observation is necessary and the procedure requires elaborate equipment and considerable skill. The operation must be coordinated to insure continuous flow at a rate that will not plug the drillpipe or cause a bridge to form in the borehole.

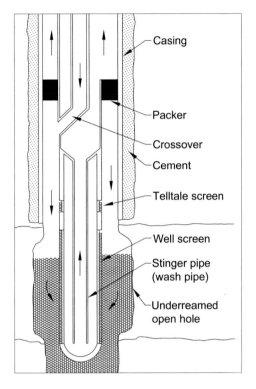

Figure 10.33. Diagram of essential features of crossover tool (Suman et al. 1983).

Filter-Pack Procedure for Telescoping Well Completion

Filter packing a telescoping well completion typically requires that an outer casing first be set to full depth. The inner casing and screen then are installed using centering guides, and the filter pack is placed (usually in stages) in the annular space around the screen—extending high enough above the screen to accommodate settlement as the outer casing is pulled back (Figure 10.34). The filter pack should extend above the top of the screen about one-fourth of the total screen length.

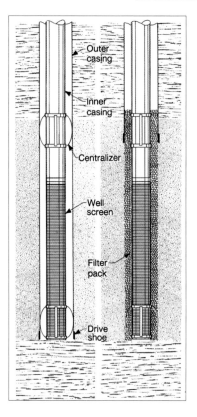

Figure 10.34. Illustration of inner-casing method. Screen assembly is centered in a cased borehole, and the outer casing is pulled back as filter pack is placed.

The depth to the top of the filter pack is monitored carefully so that it never drops below the bottom of the outer casing. A pack height of 5 ft (1.5 m) should be maintained above the screen during withdrawal. To prevent bridging, screen sections often are developed as casing is withdrawn. Overfilling the annulus during withdrawal can lead to sand locking of the outer casing to the screen.

As development proceeds, settlement occurs and more filter pack must be added to keep the top of the filter pack above the screen. Permanent filter-pack tubes sometimes are installed to allow gravel pack to be added to a well after completion if settling occurs (e.g., subsidence, pack quality, acid treatments). These tubes are not necessary if the filter pack is sealed using bentonite pellets or cement grout. The outer (surface) casing can be either removed or left in place.

Filter-Pack Procedure for Single-String Well Completion

In most rotary-drilled wells the screen and casing are placed as a single string (Figure 10.35). Centralizers generally are attached every 20 ft (6.1 m) on the screen body and every 40 ft (12.2 m) on the casing. The drilling rig holds the assembly in tension at the surface while the drilling-fluid viscosity is reduced as much as possible without allowing collapse of the wellbore. Breaking down the drilling fluid reduces development time, minimizes flotation effects, and increases the settlement rate for pack materials.

Downward drag forces on the screen and casing assembly during filter packing are noticeable, especially in larger-diameter deep wells. Finer pack materials exert more drag than do coarser materials, in part due to larger surface-area contact. Forces in excess of 20,000 lb (9,072 kg) have been recorded during filter packing. These dynamic loads should be factored into any deep-string assembly calculations to prevent casing or screen failure.

Filter-pack materials usually extend some distance above the top of the screen, and pack material should be added as required during development. After development and backfilling of the borehole, tension forces on the casing and screen are released.

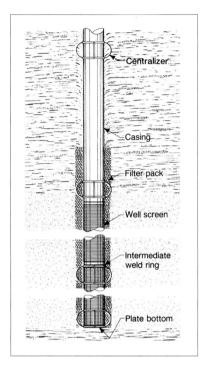

Figure 10.35. A screen and casing can be placed into the borehole as a unit.

REMOVING WELL SCREEN

Screens generally are not removed. Some reasons for removing a screen assembly include incorrect placement; deepening (after some years of use); corrosion damage; well abandonment; and reuse of the recovered screen in another well. Telescoped screens typically are considerably easier to remove than are those placed by other methods. Screens that have been in place for a long time usually are fixed firmly in the formation.

Regardless of the type of screen, to remove it safely the pulling force should be distributed over a considerable portion of the screen length. Light acid treatment helps loosen the screen by dissolving some of the surface incrustation, thus reducing the force needed to pull the screen (see Chapter 13 for discussion of acid-treatment procedures). Injecting NuWell® 400, a surfactant, flocculates sediments around the screen, helping to minimize the force required to remove a screen.

Certain mechanical procedures, such as a washover pipe (see the Glossary for a definition) in underreamed holes, can be used to loosen the surrounding filter pack if the necessary clearance is available. In conventional filter-packed wells, the plate bottom is milled out and bailing or air-lifting is used to remove as much of the pack as possible. A loosened screen can be removed by using an overshot tool (see the Glossary for a definition) or various types of spears (see the Glossary for a definition), however spears can damage screen. Importantly, never attempt to pull on a bail bottom unless the screen has just been set and is held only loosely by the sediment.

Screens that are 4 in (102 mm) in diameter (and larger) are best removed using a pipe of smaller diameter that is sand locked inside the screen and which transmits the pulling force to the well screen. Angular sand placed between the pulling pipe and screen becomes locked when lift is applied to the pulling pipe (Figure 10.36).

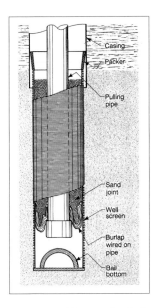

Figure 10.36. Diagram of sand-locking method of removing well screens.

Two or three slots can be cut in the pulling pipe just above the burlap (Figure 10.36), so that the sand joint can be loosened from inside if the below-ground connection must be broken. Slots also can be cut in the pulling pipe, level to the upper part of the screen, so that excess sand runs into the pipe and to prevent overfilling the screen (which could sand lock the drill string). If sand locking occurs then, to disengage the drill string, install right- and left-hand couplings between the bottom of the drillpipe and the pulling pipe. The screen and part of the pulling pipe then remain in the ground. Sometimes attaching weld rings at two or three different levels on the pulling pipe helps evenly distribute sand friction. A series of pipe nipples joined by pipe couplings is especially practical for pulling 6-in (152-mm) diameter (and smaller) screens.

Alternately, if the screen is equipped with a sump pipe then the pulling force can be concentrated there. An elliptical plate that has been cut in half and hinged together folds when lowered and, when lifted, unfolds and locks in the sump pipe. The folding plate should not be so large that it causes bulging of the sump pipe, which could lead to interlocking of the sump-pipe casing.

Table 10.7. Sizes of Pulling Pipe

Size of Telescope Screen		Inside Diameter of Screen		Size of Pulling Pipe		Quantity of Sand	
in	mm	in	mm	in	mm	ft³/ft	m³/m
4	102	3	76	1½	38	0.031	0.003
5	127	4	102	2	51	0.056	0.005
6	152	4⅞	124	3	76	0.070	0.006
8	203	6⅝	168	4	102	0.134	0.012
10	254	8⅝	219	5	127	0.254	0.024
10	254	8⅝	219	6	152	0.187	0.017
12	305	10⅜	264	6	152	0.361	0.034
16	406	13⅛	333	8	203	0.535	0.050
16	406	13⅛	333	10	254	0.308	0.029
18	457	15	381	10	254	0.602	0.056
20	508	17	432	12	305	0.695	0.065
24	610	21	533	12	305	1.52	0.142

WELL PLUMBNESS AND ALIGNMENT

Water wells should be both straight and plumb, although—in practice—any borehole of substantial depth is not perfectly straight or perfectly plumb. A well is straight when each casing section connects while maintaining perfect alignment. A borehole is plumb when its center does not deviate from the (theoretical) vertical line that runs from the earth's surface to its center (Figure 10.37). A wellbore sometimes can be straight but not plumb; but if it is plumb then it must be straight.

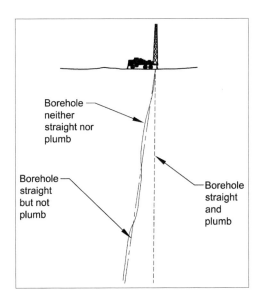

Figure 10.37. A borehole should be both straight and plumb.

Some tolerance in straightness (alignment) and plumbness normally is allowable. Typically, a deviation from plumb of two-thirds the inside diameter per 100 ft (30.5 m) of anticipated pump setting is allowed and is reasonable (American Water Works Association 2006). The AWWA Standard A100 is reasonable for casing diameters larger than 12 in (30.5 cm), but for smaller casing diameters this standard might be too stringent. Table 10.8 shows the allowable limits of deviation for various depths.

Table 10.8. Well-Deflection Limits for
Drift-Indicator Survey

Depth		Allowable Deviation	
ft	m	ft	m
50	15.2	0.4	0.1
100	30.5	0.9	0.3
150	45.7	1.3	0.4
200	61	1.7	0.5
250	76.2	2.2	0.7
300	91.5	2.6	0.8
107	350	3.1	0.9
400	122	3.5	1.1
450	137	3.9	1.2
500	152	4.4	1.3
600	183	5.2	1.6
700	213	6.1	1.9
800	244	7	2.1
900	274	7.8	2.4
1,000	305	8.7	2.7
1,100	335	9.6	2.9
1,200	366	10.5	3.2
1,300	396	11.3	3.4
1,400	427	12.2	3.7
1,500	457	13.1	4
1,600	488	14	4.3
1,700	518	14.8	4.5
1,800	549	15.7	4.8
1,900	579	16.6	5.1
2,000	610	17.4	5.3
2,100	640	18.3	5.6
2,200	671	19.2	5.9
2,300	701	20.1	6.1
2,400	732	20.9	6.4
2,500	762	21.8	6.6

Straightness of the wellbore is most important when a vertical turbine pump is being considered for use. If alignment deviates beyond a certain limit, then the pump cannot be set. A pump can be installed in a well that is straight but which is not plumb; however too much vertical deviation affects the operation and life of some pumps. In general, turbine pumps require a reasonably straight wellbore, whereas submersible pumps can be set in wellbores that are somewhat misaligned.

Conditions that can cause a borehole to be misaligned and out of plumb include the following.

- Character of the subsurface material (faults, boulders in the borehole, dipping strata)
- Placement of too much or too little weight on the drill bit when drilling
- Trueness of the casing and drillpipe
- Pull-down force applied to the top of the drillpipe during rotary drilling (as opposed to weight on the bit that is derived strictly from drill-collar weight)

Gravity tends to make a drill bit cut a vertical hole, but varying hardness of formations encountered deflects a bit from following a truly vertical course. The edge of a boulder can deflect a cable tool, rotary bit, or even a well casing that is being driven, thus causing drift. Too much force applied atop a rotating drill stem bends the slender column of drillpipe causing an off-center cut. Heavy drill collars (located just above the bit) concentrate weight at the bit, tending to overcome drift from true vertical. Collars are more rigid than ordinary drillpipe and stiffen the lower part of the drill string. Large stabilizers also are used to help drill straight holes.

Sections of casing can be slightly bowed, for example, or a joint's center line might not coincide exactly with the casing's center line. Commercial tolerances permit some deviation in straightness and the accuracy of threads, and these must be considered when specifying the allowable deviation of a completed well.

Borehole alignment should be checked several times when drilling a deep well, especially when using the cable-tool drilling method. Immediately correcting any misalignment that is discovered saves both time and money. The alignment often is checked at predetermined intervals with an inclinometer survey tool during rotary drilling (e.g., 100 ft (30.5 m), 500 ft (152 m), 1,000 ft (305 m)). In many cases, however, the alignment is checked only after the well has been completed.

Special deviation instruments are available to measure misalignment. A magnetic or gyroscopic deviation survey commonly is recorded along with standard geophysical logs. Special centralizers keep the instrument centered, and readings (given directly as displacement) are transmitted to the surface. Chapter 4 contains additional information on alignment loss.

UNDERGROUND "PITLESS" DISCHARGE

A sanitary, practical underground discharge is accomplished using either a pitless unit or a pitless adaptor. This device is connected to the well casing below ground level through a hole cut into the side of the well casing (Figure 10.38, Figure 10.39). A pitless unit is installed by first cutting off the casing below ground and then welding the spool-unit directly to the casing. The unit extends above ground level and provides a watertight subsurface connection for buried pump discharge or suction lines. To prevent freezing, the pipes must be buried below the frost line. Additional information on pitless adapters is contained in Appendix 10.B (DVD).

In some cases, the entire water system is located in or near the well. A buried pressure tank provides cooler water, eliminates moisture condensation, and does not take up space in the house (Figure 10.39).

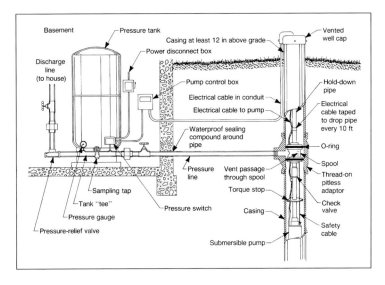

Figure 10.38. Diagram of a typical domestic-well pitless installation equipped with a submersible pump.

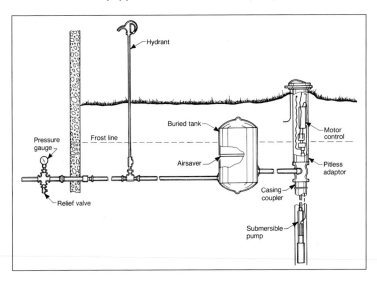

Figure 10.39. Diagram of a pitless adaptor connected to underground pressure tank.

SUMMARY

It is as critical to properly plan and execute the phases of well construction as it is to consider and accomplish all the elements of design. There always are unforeseen circumstances that can arise to complicate construction—which is why reliance on an experienced drilling professional always is a good investment. A properly constructed well delivers years of dependable service and safe, quality water.

ACKNOWLEDGMENTS

Mr. Marvin F. Glotfelty, RG, Principal Hydrogeologist with Clear Creek Associates, and Mr. Tom Downey, President, Downey Drilling Inc., provided valuable review and comments on this chapter. Their work is greatly appreciated.

CHAPTER 11
Development of Water Wells

Thomas M. Hanna, PG
Johnson Screens

Well development includes procedures that are designed to maximize well specific capacity, and has two broad objectives: (1) to repair aquifer damage near the borehole that was caused by the drilling operation, so that the natural hydraulic properties are restored; and (2) to alter the basic physical characteristics of the aquifer near the borehole so that water flows more freely to a well. These objectives are accomplished by applying some form of energy to the aquifer.

Every new well should be developed—before being put into production—to achieve the goal of producing sediment-free water at the highest possible specific capacity. Older wells often require periodic redevelopment to maintain—or even improve—the original specific capacity of the well.

Aquifer stimulation is another type of "development" that is performed when the aquifer does not yield sufficient water, even after the application of typical well-development procedures. This type of development usually is limited to use in semi-consolidated or consolidated aquifers.

This chapter discusses well-development techniques before it addresses aquifer-stimulation procedures, because development applies to every well regardless of the geologic materials present.

AQUIFER DAMAGE AND DEVELOPMENT OBJECTIVES

Aquifer Damage

All drilling operations alter the geologic characteristics of the aquifer materials in the vicinity of the borehole. Such alterations often result in a significant reduction of the aquifer's hydraulic conductivity near the wellbore—even that of a well drilled without using drilling fluids (Hanna et al. 2003) (Figure 11.1).

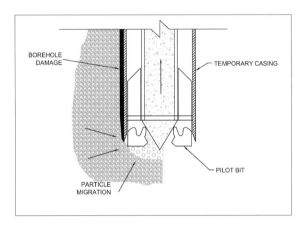

Figure 11.1. A significant reduction in hydraulic conductivity of the sediments surrounding a borehole can occur due to drilling.

Some common causes of borehole and aquifer damage include the following.

- A casing driven through clay or very fine-grained sediments can entrain some of the sediments and carry them down the borehole, coating the borehole in the area adjacent to the aquifer.
- In wells drilled using drilling fluids (especially bentonite), the aquifer can become sealed due to the invasion of fine-grained particles. Such invasion minimizes water movement from the aquifer (Figure 11.2).
- In consolidated or crystalline aquifers, fine-grained cuttings can plug interstices or fracture openings.

- In wells drilled with freshwater, naturally occurring clays can become incorporated into the drilling fluid and plug the pore space of aquifers. Permeable geologic materials are more susceptible to drilling-fluid penetration.

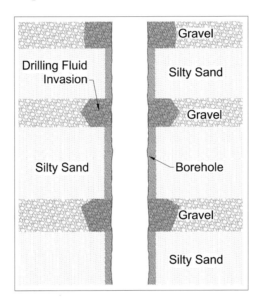

Figure 11.2. When using drilling fluids, some of the fluid flows into the most pervious parts of the aquifer.

Aquifer damage to some degree is unavoidable regardless of which drilling method is used.

Development Objectives

The objectives of development procedures are to:

- Reduce the compaction and intermixing of grain sizes produced during drilling by removing fine sediment from pore spaces adjacent to the borehole;
- Increase the hydraulic conductivity of the previously undisturbed aquifer near the borehole by selectively removing the finer fraction of aquifer material;

- Remove the filter cake or drilling fluid that coats the borehole;
- Remove the drilling fluid and solids that have invaded the aquifer;
- Form a graded zone of sediment around the screen in a naturally developed well, thereby stabilizing the aquifer so that the well yields water attaining a suspended sediment load criterion;
- Create an environment that reduces the potential for bacteria growth thereby increasing the life of the well; and
- Remove fine-grained cuttings from the borehole wall and fracture openings.

Studies conducted by the State of Michigan (U.S.A.) concluded that wells that were properly developed had fewer problems with positive coliform tests (Schneiders 2003). Further work by Schneiders (2003) confirmed the findings of the Michigan study, and showed that no-flow areas (e.g., zones clogged with drilling fluids) that are near the screen are locations for enhanced bacterial growth. Thus, wells that are not properly developed tend to have biofouling problems more frequently than do properly developed wells.

Proper well development insures the production of water of acceptable sediment concentration, maximizes well efficiency, reduces a well's maintenance costs, and increases the service life of a well.

FACTORS THAT AFFECT DEVELOPMENT

Well-Completion Methods

The most common well completion methods used after the casing and screen are installed are natural development, filter packing, use of prepacked screens (e.g., Muni-Pak™), and open borehole (no screen is used). The particular completion method is selected based on the geologic character of the aquifer. To some degree, the completion method determines the effectiveness of specific development methods.

Natural Development

The goal of natural development is to create a more-permeable zone around the screen in the aquifers. This process is best understood by examining what happens throughout a series of concentric cylindrical zones in a sand aquifer surrounding a screen. In the zone just outside the well screen, development removes most particles smaller than the screen openings, leaving only the coarsest sediment in place. Farther out from the screen, some medium-sized grains remain mixed with the coarse sediment; beyond that zone, the material gradually grades back to the original character of the aquifer (Figure 11.3). Finer particles brought into the screen during natural development are removed by bailing or pumping, and development continues until there is negligible movement of fine sediments from the aquifer into the well.

Figure 11.3. Natural development removes most particles near the well screen that are smaller than the screen's slot openings.

Filter Packing

In the filter-packing process, a specially graded sand or gravel—having high porosity and hydraulic conductivity—is placed in the annulus between the screen and the aquifer. The selection of a filter pack is described in Chapter 9.

During the development of a filter-packed well, mechanical energy is directed through the screen and filter pack. The energy impinges on the walls of the borehole and removes the fine sediments from the aquifer and from the finer fraction (5% to 10%) of the filter pack. As the sediments migrate into the well the filter pack settles and bridges are removed, leaving material that grades from fine to coarser from the aquifer to the screen. It is important to note that development of the disturbed aquifer outside the pack still is required to achieve maximum specific capacity.

Wells completed using a prepacked screen (e.g., Muni-Pak™) have the benefit of a properly sized filter pack and have the advantage derived from having the aquifer collapse around the screen (Figure 11.4). This type of completion and subsequent development rectifies the borehole-related damage as the aquifer collapses, creating an efficient well.

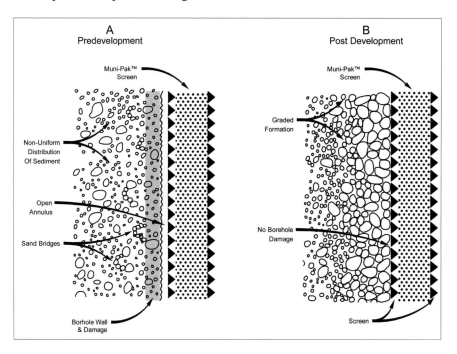

Figure 11.4. Aquifer collapsed around a prepacked (Muni-Pak™) screen after development.

Open Area and Slot Configuration

All development methods work best in wells equipped with screens having both maximum open area and a slot (opening) configuration that permits the greatest hydraulic forces exerted inside the well screen to be directed into the aquifer. Screen open area typically varies from 1% (for perforated pipe) to more than 40% (for continuous-slot, wire-wrap screens). Screens with maximum open area can be developed more effectively because more of the development energy can reach the aquifer (see Chapter 9 for descriptions of various screen types).

Selection of the correct slot size for well screens also is essential for successful well development. Slot openings are chosen to permit maximum removal of the fine material from the aquifer. For naturally developed wells, it is common practice to select a slot width that retains approximately 40% of the sediment in the aquifer adjacent to the screen. For filter-packed wells, the slot openings are selected to retain approximately 90% of the filter-pack material. Chapter 9 provides a detailed discussion of screen slot selection.

It is important to note that removal of too much sediment can cause the overlying geologic materials to settle. This can have undesirable effects on the well and can create dangerous conditions (e.g., land subsidence) for the drilling rig. Conversely, when well screen openings are too small, adequate development might not be possible and the well yield will be below the potential of the aquifer. Greater entrance flow velocities caused by inadequate development or slot size (open area) and the corresponding pressure drop near the wellbore can lead to the formation of mineral precipitates in the screen, filter pack, or adjacent aquifer (*see* Chapter 13).

Slot configuration also controls both how much development energy reaches the aquifer and the area of the aquifer that the energy can affect. More fine-grained material can be removed faster if the available energy can be directed at most or all of the surrounding aquifer. Larger slot sizes and greater open area create wells that both minimize head losses through the screen for a given pumping rate and ultimately are more efficient. For a given pumping rate, large open areas help to maintain entrance velocities at the optimal 0.1 ft/sec (3 cm/sec), thus sustaining laminar flow to the well. If larger slot sizes are used, then—in the attempt to achieve maximum specific capacity and well efficiency—longer development time should be anticipated (Wendling et al. 1997).

Bridge-slotted and louvered screens require significantly more time to develop because of their low percentages of open area, and because the shape of their openings causes dissipation of more of the development energy before the energy can reach the filter pack and aquifer. A study of well development and screen design (Schafer 1982) shows that, in the same well field, wells completed using wire-wrap screens are more efficient than those completed with louvered screens. One of the reasons for this result is that a wire-wrap screen allows for better well development through V-shaped openings of a continuous-slot screen. The slot configuration of a louvered pipe impedes transfer of energy from the well to the aquifer (Figure 11.5).

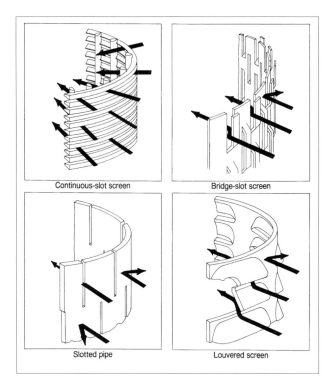

Figure 11.5. Development energy is most effective when the screen open area is maximized and the energy is directed into the filter pack or aquifer.

Drilling Fluid Type

Bentonite and polymers are the two primary drilling-fluid additives used. After a well is drilled, all drilling fluid should be removed from both the borehole walls and the aquifer via either physical or chemical means. Although some polymeric drilling-fluid additives are designed to break down naturally over time, it is recommended that they be broken down chemically and removed from the well at the time that the well is completed.

The rate and effectiveness of drilling-fluid removal depends not only on the type of additive used but also on the physical character of the aquifer, the depth of the well, the length of time the drilling fluid has been in the borehole, and the weight and viscosity of the drilling fluid. Results from an experimental well field show that a large amount of development energy is required to remove drilling fluid containing clay additives (Driscoll et al. 1980). Significantly less development energy is required to achieve maximum specific capacities for wells drilled using polymeric drilling-fluid additives that have been broken down.

Filter-Pack Thickness

The thickness of the filter pack has considerable effect on development efficiency, and the filter pack reduces the amount of energy reaching the aquifer. The thinner the filter pack, the greater the amount of energy transferred to the aquifer to remove undesirable sediment during development. As such, a filter pack generally is designed to be more permeable than the aquifer materials. If the development energy is not properly focused through the filter pack to the borehole wall, then the energy might flow vertically in the filter pack rather than moving into or out of the aquifer. To facilitate the maximum transfer of development energy to the aquifer, filter packs normally should be about 2-in (5-cm) to 5-in (13-cm) thick, with 3 in being optimal. To a large degree, the annulus size is determined by the minimum borehole size needed to properly complete the well, centralize the casing and screen, and install the filter pack.

WELL-DEVELOPMENT PROCESS

Different well-development procedures have evolved in various geographic regions to address the physical characteristics of aquifers present and the types of drilling rigs used. Unfortunately, some development techniques still are used in situations where other more recently developed procedures would produce better results. Effective development procedures should involve the initial break-down of drilling fluids followed by the movement of fluids into and out of the screen and aquifer, for the purpose of removing drilling fluids and fine sediment.

The drilling fluids should be broken down when the screen is placed in the well—as part of the filter-packing procedure if a filter pack is used. Agitation of the filter pack and aquifer results in the removal of the finer fraction of sedi-ment and rearrangement of the remaining aquifer particles (Figure 11.6). Bridges result when the fluid flows only in one direction, and reversing the direction of fluid flow results in the destruction of bridges formed across the screen openings. The outflow portion of the development cycle breaks down bridging, and the inflow portion then moves the fine material toward the screen and into the well so that it can be removed.

It is important to note that using multiple development techniques can greatly enhance development. One of the development methods should move energy alternatively into and out of the aquifer (e.g., surging), and the second should be a method that removes fine-grained sediment from the well (e.g., air-lift pumping, bailing, pumping).

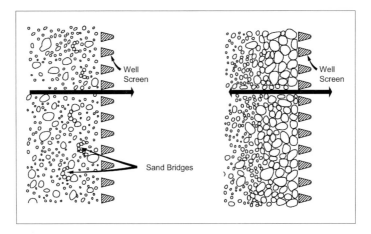

Figure 11.6. Effective development requires movement of fluid in both directions through screen openings (see right side of figure). Movement in only one direction (see left side of figure) does not produce the proper development effect.

A comprehensive development program consists of the following steps (these are discussed in more detail in subsequent sections).

- Break down and remove drilling fluids that are in the aquifer, filter pack, and well.
- Mechanically surge or jet the aquifer and filter pack to rearrange the filter pack and aquifer grains so that fines are brought into the well.
- Pump the well—preferably with air—to remove fine sediment and establish high rates of water flow into the well.

Break Down and Remove Drilling Fluids

The initial step in the well-development process is the breaking down and removal of drilling fluids and natural fines from the aquifer, filter pack, and well. If development is initiated by removal of the drilling fluids very quickly, and without thinning the drilling fluids, there is the potential for collapsing the casing and screen. If the fluids in the annulus are not properly broken down, then they cannot enter the well as fast as fluids are pumped from the well. This can result in a fluid pressure in the aquifer that is significantly higher than that inside the well (differential pressure). If the differential pressure exceeds the collapse resistance of the casing and well, the well can collapse.

Removing bentonite-based drilling fluids first requires breaking down the polymers that manufacturers add to bentonitic muds, which usually is accomplished by using chlorine. In the past, polyphosphates (e.g., sodium acid pyrophosphate (SAPP), sodium tripolyphosphate (STP)) were used to help remove bentonite and clays because the phosphates act as clay dispersants. Phosphates, however, are a potential nutrient source for bacteria. Certain types of polyphosphates can precipitate, and are difficult to remove from wells; they therefore serve as an ongoing source of nutrients. A polyphosphate precipitate also forms a glassy coating that can be very difficult to remove. To eliminate the problems associated with polyphosphates, Johnson Screens developed NuWell® 220 Dispersant Polymer (NW-220), a non-ionic polymer dispersant used for removing silts and clays without introducing a food source for bacteria. The NW-220 dispersant also is more effective than polyphosphates in dispersing clays.

A small amount of NW-220 added either before or during development helps considerably in removing clays that occur naturally in the aquifer or which are part of the drilling fluid. It is critical that sufficient time be allowed between the introduction of NW-220 and the beginning of the well's development, so the clay masses can become completely disaggregated. After the NW-220 is jetted or surged into the screen, clean water should be added to the well to drive the solution farther into the aquifer. Its unique polymer formula allows NW-220 to disperse and to hold fines in suspension until the fluids can be removed from the well.

Typical bentonite drilling fluids can be broken down using the following procedures (provided in U.S. customary units).

- Add sodium hypochlorite (10% concentration) to the drilling fluids at a concentration of about 15 gal per 1,000 gal of drilling fluid to achieve a 1,500-mg/ℓ chlorine concentration in the well.
- Add NW-220 to the drilling fluid at a concentration of 1 gal for every 500 gal of drilling fluid in the well.
- Keep the solution in the well for 12 hr to 24 hr before agitating the solution.
- Agitate the solution vigorously for several hours using mechanical means (approximately one half hour per 20 linear ft (6.1 m) of well screen), until the viscosity of the solution–drilling fluid mixture is reduced to 27-sec funnel viscosity.
- Agitate and remove the remainder of the drilling fluids from the well.

Mechanical Surging

Mechanical surging forces water to flow into and out of a screen by moving a plunger up and down in the casing and screen (similar to the movement of a piston in a cylinder). The tools normally used are called a surge block (Figure 11.7), surge plunger, or swab. Surge blocks are constructed so that the outside diameter of the rubber edges is equal to the inside diameter of the screen. The solid part of the block is 1 in (25.4 mm) smaller in diameter than the screen.

A heavy bailer can be used to produce the surging action, but is not as effective as the close-fitting surge block. As is the case in all mechanical development processes, fine-grained material should be removed from the well as frequently as possible. Best results are obtained when this method is used in conjunction with pumping to remove fines from the well.

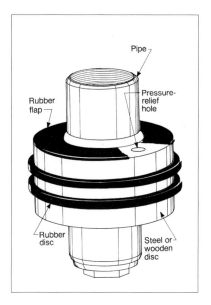

Figure 11.7. Typical surge block made of 2 rubber discs sandwiched between 3 steel or wooden discs.

Before beginning a surge, drilling fluids should be removed from the well and water should be flowing into it. The surge block is lowered into the well until it is 10 ft (3 m) to 15 ft (5 m) beneath the static water level, but still is above the screen (Figure 11.8). The water column effectively can transmit the action of the block to the screen section. The initial surging motion should be relatively gentle, so that any material blocking the screen can break up, be suspended, and then be moved into the well. The surge block (or bailer) should be operated with care—particularly if the aquifer above the screen consists mainly of fine sand, silt, or soft clay that could slump into the screen if a filter pack is not used. Surging also should be started slowly and relatively gently to avoid differential pressures that can cause collapse of the casing or well screen.

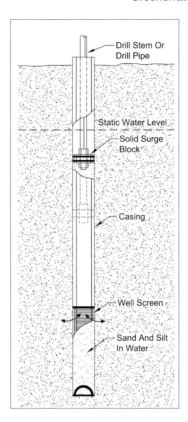

Figure 11.8. A surge block can be an effective tool for well development.

When water begins to move easily both into and out of the screen, the surging tool usually is lowered (in steps) and positioned just above the screen. As the block is lowered the force of the surging movement increases. In a well that is equipped with a long screen, it can be more effective to operate the surge block in the screen to concentrate its action at various levels. Development should begin above the screen and move progressively downward to prevent the tool from becoming sand locked. The force exerted on the aquifer depends on the length of the stroke and the vertical velocity of the surge block. The speed of retraction and length of pull are governed by the physical characteristics of the rig.

Surging should be continued for several minutes, and then the block should be pulled from the well. Air can be used to lift the sediment out of the well if development is done with a rotary rig or if an air compressor is available. Sediment can be removed by a bailer or sand pump when a cable tool rig is used. The surging action is concentrated at the top of the screen, and this effect is accentuated if the lower part of the screen is continually blocked by the sand brought in by the surging process. Occasionally, if the washing action disrupts the seal around the casing formed by the overlying sediments, surging can cause upward movement of water outside the well casing. When this occurs, use of the surge block must be discontinued or sediment from the overlying materials can invade the screened zone.

When used in certain aquifers, surge blocks sometimes produce unsatisfactory results—especially when the aquifer contains many clay lenses—because the action of the block can cause clay to plug the aquifer, resulting in a reduction in yield rather than an increase. Surge blocks also are less useful when the particles comprising the aquifer are angular, because such particles do not sort themselves as readily as do rounded grains. Additionally, if large amounts of mica are present in the aquifer, the flat or tabular mica flakes can align themselves perpendicular to the direction of flow and clog the outer surface of the screen and the aquifer zone adjacent to the screen. Clogging by mica can be minimized when surging procedures are performed gently.

Another type of surging tool is a swab. The simplest type of swab—a rubber-flanged mud scow or bailer—is lowered into the casing to any selected point below the water level and then is pulled upward at about 3 ft/sec (1 m/sec), and no attempt is made to reverse the flow and cause a surging effect (Figure 11.9). The length of the swabbing stroke usually is much greater than that of surging. As the bailer is raised a pressure differential is created near the top of the bailer; this differential allows water to flow from the well into the aquifer. Water, sand, and silt are drawn back into the well beneath the swab because the pressure is lower in the bottom of the well. The bailer usually has a valve at the bottom that opens to increase the fall rate in the borehole. This method of swabbing, called line swabbing, often is used to clean fine material from deep wells that are drilled in consolidated rock aquifers.

Care must be taken when swabbing wells that have plastic casing or screens. In particular, screens that have screen-slot sizes about 0.010 in (0.25 mm) or smaller can become blocked. These wells and associated screens can be particularly troublesome because differential fluid pressures created by the swab by removing fluids from inside the well can collapse PVC casings.

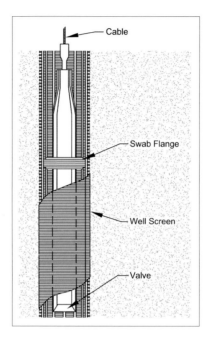

Figure 11.9. Line swabbing primarily is used in consolidated aquifers.

Jetting with Water

The process of jetting with water consists of operating a horizontal jet inside the well screen so that jetting energy is directed out through the screen openings. The equipment required includes a jetting tool with two or more equally spaced nozzles, high-pressure pump or compressor, hoses and connections, pipe, and a clean, potable water supply for jetting. The jets force water through the screen openings, agitating and rearranging the particles of the aquifer surrounding the screen. Filter cake deposited during drilling is effectively broken down by fluid forces. Jetting is particularly successful in developing highly stratified, unconsolidated aquifers.

Figure 11.10 shows a jetting tool with 5 nozzle jets (4 are diametrically opposed and 1 is on the bottom of the tool). Nozzles should be spaced equally around the circumference of the jetting tool to hydraulically balance the tool during operation. Horizontal holes drilled in a plugged pipe or coupling are reasonably effective; however the best results are obtained if the nozzles are designed for maximum hydraulic impact. The jetting tool should be constructed so that the nozzle outlets or holes are as close to the inside diameter of the screen as is practical (generally less than 1 in (25.4 mm) away).

Figure 11.10. The Baski BJT-8, 8-in (200-mm) jetting tool (made for 10-in (250-mm) wells) has 4 jets that are diametrically opposed and 1 bottom jet (Baski, Inc.).

Water used for jetting never should contain sediment. Sediment circulated through the jetting tool can cause erosion of the nozzle bores, resulting in a pronounced pressure reduction at the nozzle face. To minimize erosion of the jets, nozzles should be constructed from abrasion-resistant material. High concentrations of circulated sediment can damage screens and also can cause erosion of screens if the jets are directed at one area for long periods, thus sediment-ladened water periodically should be removed from the well. When jetting, the tool continuously should be rotated and moved vertically in the well.

The lowest nozzle velocity for effective jetting is considered to be approximately 100 ft/sec (30.5 m/sec). Better results are achieved with nozzle velocities of 150 ft/sec (45.7 m/sec) to 300 ft/sec (91.5 m/sec). Much higher velocities have been used successfully (see High-Velocity Water Jetting, below) but care must be exercised. Jetting pressures in screens constructed of PVC or other less abrasion–resistant materials (e.g., fiberglass) should not exceed 100 psi (690 kPa). Table 11.1 provides data for nozzles of several sizes at different operating pressures.

Table 11.1. Approximate Jet Velocity and Discharge per Nozzle

Size of Nozzle Orifice		Nozzle Pressure* 100 psi (690 kPa)				Nozzle Pressure* 150 psi (1,030 kPa)				Nozzle Pressure* 200 psi (1,380 kPa)				Nozzle Pressure* 250 psi (1,720 kPa)				Nozzle Pressure* 300 psi (2,070 kPa)			
		Velocity		Discharge		Velocity		Discharge		Velocity		Discharge		Velocity		Discharge		Velocity		Discharge	
in	mm	fps	m/sec	gpm	m³/day	fps	m/sec	gpm	m³/day	fps	m/sec	gpm	m³/day	fps	m/sec	gpm	m³/day	fps	m/sec	gpm	m³/day
3/16	5	100	31	8	44	120	37	10	55	140	43	12	65	155	47	13	71	170	52	15	82
1/4	6	100	31	15	82	120	37	18	98	140	43	21	114	155	47	24	131	170	52	26	142
3/8	10	100	31	34	185	120	37	41	223	140	43	48	262	155	47	53	289	170	52	58	316
1/2	13	100	31	60	327	120	37	73	398	140	43	84	458	155	47	94	512	170	52	103	516

* To obtain these nozzle pressures, gauge pressure must be somewhat higher to overcome friction losses in the water line. Note that laboratory experiments show that the coefficient of discharge through the nozzle is 0.8.

The pipe that attaches to the jetting tool should have a diameter sufficient to minimize friction losses as water flows through it, so that energy at the nozzle is as great as possible. Some standard pipe sizes are given in Table 11.2.

Table 11.2. Minimum Pipe Diameters Required to Hold Friction Losses to a Total of Approximately 20 ft (6.1 m) of Head

Pumping Rate		Pipe Length							
		100 ft (30.5 m)		200 ft (61 m)		400 ft (122 m)		600 ft (183 m)	
gpm	m³/day	in	mm	in	mm	in	mm	in	mm
35	191	1½	38	1½	38	2	51	2	51
50	273	1½	38	2	51	2	51	2½	64
75	409	2	51	2	51	2½	64	3	76
100	545	2	51	2½	64	3	76	3	76
150	818	2½	64	3	76	4	102	4	102
200	1,090	3	76	3	76	4	102	4	102
250	1,360	3	76	4	102	4	102	5	127
300	1,640	3	76	4	102	4	102	5	127
350	1,910	4	102	4	102	5	127	5	127
400	2,180	4	102	4	102	5	127	5	127

Jetting-tool rotation is controlled by the rig. The tool is placed near the bottom of the screen and rotated slowly while pulling upward at rate of 5 min/ft (15 min/m) to 15 min/ft (45 min/m), depending on the nature of the aquifer. Loosened material accumulates at the bottom of the screen as the jetting tool is raised. This material is removed either simultaneously or later by air-lift pumping or bailing. Slow rotation and upward movement assures treatment of the entire surface of the screen. Jetting should be continued until the amount of additional material removed is negligible. To avoid screen erosion and to expedite development, the jetting tool never should be operated while it is in a stationary position.

Optimal removal of sediment by jetting depends on the time allotted to complete the process. The jetting energy only can focus on a small part of the aquifer at a given moment, therefore more time might be necessary than is needed for other development methods that affect a larger portion of the aquifer. Less-satisfactory results from jetting occur almost inevitably when insufficient time is allowed for completion of a thorough job. To help disperse clays and enhance the development process, a dispersant (e.g., NW-220) often is added to the jetting water.

High-Velocity Water Jetting

At the time of this writing, high-velocity water jetting is a relatively new well-development technique. Pressures as great as 10,000 psi (69,000 kPa) and velo-cities of up to 1,000 ft/sec (300 m/sec) have been utilized successfully for well development. It is important to note that a 10,000 psi (69,000 kPa) pressure is the gauge pressure, and represents the pressure inside the jetting tool and piping. The screen and casing are not subjected to this pressure because the hydrostatic head and frictional losses tend to decrease the pressure at the face of the screen.

It is critical that the high-pressure jetting package be designed specifically for the particular screen-slot size, well diameter, screen material, and aquifer type. The pump and nozzle configuration should maximize the downhole pres-sure and focus the energy appropriately. It also is imperative that jetting tools be rotated and moved vertically to eliminate screen damage caused by abrasion.

The high-velocity jetting technique is an effective way to break up incrusta-tion and remove fine sand material. Jetting the well casing as the tool is removed also can be an effective way of revealing any weaknesses in the casing (A.C. Schultes Inc. 2006).

Water Jetting Combined with Simultaneous Pumping

Although water-jetting procedures are effective in dislodging material from aquifers, optimal development efficiency is achieved when water-jetting procedures are combined with simultaneous air-lift pumping or another pumping method. This combination is especially effective for wells completed with wire-wrap screens. Typically, the well is pumped using either air-lifting techniques or a small submersible pump (the following section describes air surging and pumping). The volume of water extracted always should exceed the volume injected during jetting (the recommended rate is 2 to 3 times the jetting rate). As development proceeds, the water level in the well should be kept below static level to maintain continuous flow of water from the aquifer into the well. The steady inward movement removes suspended material loosened by the jetting operation before the material can settle.

When operating air-lift pumping systems in combination with jetting, best results are obtained when the bottom of the air line is located just above the jetting tool (Figure 11.11). More suspended sediment is removed when using this location and there is no obstruction of the jetting action. When using high-velocity jetting combined with simultaneous pumping, development should start at the bottom of the screen and move upward.

If air-lift pumping is impractical, then a submersible pump can be used instead. Typically, the pump is placed rather far above the jetting tool to minimize sand movement through the pump; this placement allows more sediment to fall to the bottom of the well. Sediment must be removed periodically during the jetting operation.

Jetting with Air

Jetting with air is a very practical procedure and produces acceptable results in both consolidated and unconsolidated aquifers. If the well is drilled with air, then less setup time is required to begin air-jetting procedures. Air jetting also initiates air-lift pumping, which helps remove sediment from the well. Casing size and air line submergence affect the efficiency of air-lift pumping. Note that the jets should be positioned as close to the screen as possible to avoid the loss of development energy.

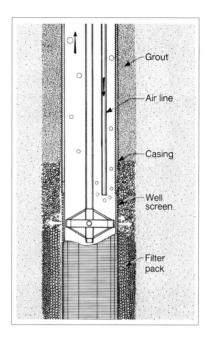

Figure 11.11. The jetting tool and pipe are separate from the air line, therefore jetting and air-lift pumping can be performed simultaneously.

The main disadvantage of air jetting is that drilling rigs often are equipped with compressors that have limited pressure and volume capabilities. A 125-psi (862-kPa) compressor, for example, is effective only at initial heads of less than about 285 ft (87 m). Also, bottom borehole pressure can be so great that—even if the compressor can pump air—the actual compressed air volume is so small that the amount of turbulence generated might not be sufficient to develop the well effectively. If the air compressor on the drilling rig is not adequate, then additional high-pressure, high-volume air compressors should be used to assist in the air-jetting development process.

The methodology used for both air jetting and water jetting is the same. The actual (compressed) volume of air emitted from the jetting tool is controlled by the head of water in the casing. Ordinarily, the compressor capacity of typical rotary rigs is sufficient to create enough air to jet effectively in wells 150 ft (45 m) to 300 ft (90 m) deep. For water-well work, the nozzle sizes for an air-jetting tool are approximately the same size as those supplied in Table 11.1.

Developing by Surging and Pumping with Air

The practice of alternately surging and pumping with air is a common development technique. Surging occurs when air is injected into the well to lift water toward the surface. The air source is shut off as water reaches the top of the casing, which allows the aerated water column to fall back into the well. This creates an outward surge of hydraulic energy through the well screen that aids development. Installing an air line inside an eductor pipe enables air-lift pumping to be used periodically during development to remove sediment from the screen. Eductors generally are required for large-diameter wells when limited volumes of air are available or when the static water level is low in relation to the well depth. Most rotary rigs, however, have sufficient air capacity to use the casing as the eductor for 6-in (15-mm) to 12-in (300-mm) diameter wells. Figure 11.12 shows the basic layout of an air-lift system.

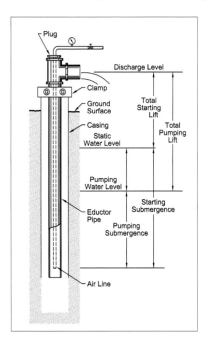

Figure 11.12. Basic air-lift pumping system (Ingersoll-Rand 1971).

The proper placement of eductor pipe and air line in the well also is shown in Figure 11.12. A tee at the top of the eductor pipe is fitted with a 90-degree-angled discharge pipe. A bushing that has an inside opening large enough to clear the couplings of the air line is connected to the top of the tee. A seal made of rubber or similar material is wrapped around the air line just above the tee and is held by slips. This reduces spraying around the top of the well and enables more accurate yield measurements to be taken during pumping (Figure 11.13). The basics of designing an air-lift pumping operation are can be found in Appendix 11.A (DVD).

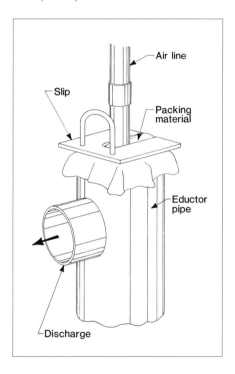

Figure 11.13. Diagram of installation where the top of the well is plugged with rubber packing material during the air-lift procedure, and slips direct the water to the outlet pipe.

Uphole velocities in the range of 1,000 ft/min (300 m/min) to 2,500 ft/min (760 m/min) are required to achieve reasonable discharge rates and sand removal. Generally, predicting actual uphole-velocity requirements is difficult due to submergence factors, total pumping lift requirements, and the unpredictable way that water enters a borehole. If the air volume needed to lift the water adequately is achieved, however, then the uphole velocities are not an issue.

The type of discharge produced from a well during air development depends on the air volume available, total lift, submergence, and annular area. These factors result in the existence of various types of flow regimes of multi-phase flow (Taitel & Dukler 1980; Hestroni 1982; Griffith 1984).

Figure 11.14 presents four common flow regimes that occur when air-lift pumping is performed. The percent submergence, total lift, and capacity of the compressor all control the relative proportion of air and water for a particular well.

Some of the difficulties faced when making a rigorous analysis of systems include the following (which uses Figure 11.14 as the basis for the example).

- ◆ Introduction of a small volume of air under a high head causes little change in the water level in the well. In the present case, the air pressure available is sufficient to overcome the initial head exerted by the water column (Figure 11.14(A)).

- ◆ As air volume increases, the water column becomes partly aerated. Displacement of the water by the air causes the water column to rise in the casing. Drawdown does not change because no pumping is occurring (Figure 11.14(B)).

- ◆ Further increases in air volume cause aerated slugs of water to be lifted irregularly out the top of the casing. Between surges, the water level in the casing falls to near the static level (Figure 11.14(C)).

- ◆ If sufficient air is available, then aerated water continually flows out the top of the well. With average submergence and total lift, the volume of air versus water is about 10 to 1. Higher air volumes can increase the pumping rate somewhat, but additional increases actually can reduce the flow rate because flow into the well is impeded by excessive air volume (Figure 11.14(D)).

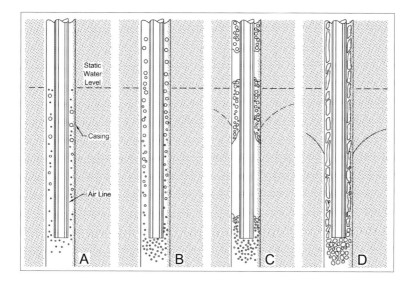

Figure 11.14. Qualitative illustration of how multiphase flow (water and air) occurs in a casing during air development.

Air pressure and volume both are important in initiating and maintaining an air-surging or air-lift pumping operation. For typical head conditions found in wells 300 ft (90 m) to 400 ft (120 m) deep, the compressor used for the air supply should be capable of developing a minimum pressure of 125 psi (860 kPa). This is sufficient to overcome the initial head created by the submergence of the air line and is called the starting submergence. After the pressure initiates flow, the air capacity (volume) becomes the most important factor in successful air-lift pumping. Figure 11.14 illustrates how the addition of different volumes of air affects the water in the borehole. A useful general guideline for determining the proper compressor capacity for air-lift pumping is to provide about 0.75 cfm (0.0004 m³/sec) of air for each 1 gpm (5.5 m³/day) of water at the anticipated pumping rate. In practice, with proper pumping submergence of the air line, a 375-cfm (0.2-m³/sec) compressor usually can pump 400 gpm (2,180 m³/day) to 500 gpm (2,730 m³/day).

The volume of air required to operate an air-lift efficiently depends on the total pumping lift, the pumping submergence, and the area of the annulus between the eductor and casing. Acceptable results can be obtained with a pumping submergence as low as 30%. In select cases, acceptable results have been obtained with a pumping submergence as low as 10%. The air line should not be placed at the bottom of the well when pumping begins unless this is required for proper submergence (see the procedures described below).

The volume of air needed to lift water also depends on whether an intermittent flow or a steady flow is required. For development work, it is not necessary to maintain a steady discharge and, in fact, some surging of the air is beneficial. If steady flow must be maintained (e.g., in pumping tests), then the air-volume requirements are the minimum of those given in Table 11.3 (U.S. customary units).

Table 11.3 lists the recommended sizes of eductor pipe and air line for air-lift pumping. Some variation from these sizes might be necessary for practical reasons, but the combinations shown generally provide acceptable results.

Table 11.3. Approximate Air-Lift Capacities for Air-Lift Pumping

Borehole or Well Pipe Nominal Size (in)	Air Pipe Tube Actual OD (in)	Pumping Submergence %					Air Compressor Delivery CFM
		10% (gpm)	20% (gpm)	40% (gpm)	60% (gpm)	80% (gpm)	
¾	¼		0.4	1.4	2.4	3.4	20
1	⅜		1	3	5	7	31
1½	½		3	8	13	18	77
2	½	0.5	5	15	25	35	120
3	¾	2.5	15	40	65	90	270
4	1	5	28	75	125	175	470
5	1¼	7.5	50	140	230	320	740
6	1½	12	80	225	370	520	1,100
8	2	25	150	450	720	1,000	1,900
10	2½	50	300	800	1,300	1,800	3,000
12	4	75	450	1,200	1,950	2,700	4,000
14	4	90	600	1,700	2,900	4,000	5,100
16	5	100	800	2,400	3,900	5,500	6,600

(Baski, Inc. Catalog 6)

Air development procedures should begin with the establishing of water flowing freely into the screen. When the aquifer is clogged, the application of too much air volume can result in a collapsed screen due to significant fluid pressure differentials between the aquifer and inside the well. To prevent accidental overload, the air line and the eductor (if used) can be placed at a rather shallow submergence (approximately one half of the available drawdown, or less). If this setting is used, then even the introduction of large air volumes initially produces only moderate differential pressures on the well screen. Introduction of small air volumes at greater submergence also produces low yields.

Due to the uneven nature of compressed-air development—and the potential danger of personnel standing too close to an air-discharge pipe—the air-water discharge should be directed into a mud pit or cuttings pit that has a discharge channel or pipe installed. This enables estimation of the discharge rate and sediment content.

When flow has been established the eductor pipe is lowered to within 5 ft (1.5 m) of the bottom of the screen or, if preferred, development can start near the top of the screen. Air is released and the well is pumped until the water produced is relatively free of sand. The air-outlet valve then is closed and, while tank pressure builds, the air line is lowered to 1 ft (0.3 m) or so below the eductor pipe. (Actual pressure depends on the starting submergence; 43 psi (296 kPa) is needed for each 100 ft (30 m) of submergence). Quickly opening the valve drives water outward through the screen openings, and occasionally water blows from the casing and eductor pipe at the surface. Retracting the air line into the eductor pipe resumes air-lift pumping, completing the surging cycle. Cycles are repeated until sand-free water is produced.

Double Surge Block with Air Lift

Some drillers use a double surge block or isolation tool to remove sediment from the aquifer in conjunction with air-lift pumping. Flanged gaskets are mounted on the top and bottom of the isolation tool (Figure 11.15). The gaskets should be sized so that they touch the sides of the screen but allow some sediment to move around them, so that sand locking does not occur. After the screen's initial cleaning, the double surge block is lowered to the top of the screen and the air line is set at the proper depth. After each zone is developed by surging and air-lift pumping, the tool is lowered to the next section. The double surge-block assembly that is attached to the drillpipe is raised and lowered in a screen section to produce turbulence (Figure 11.16). Thus, the aquifer is developed in separate stages. This tool also can be used to introduce dispersant (e.g., NW-220) into the aquifer and surge the dispersant into the appropriate interval (Figure 11.16).

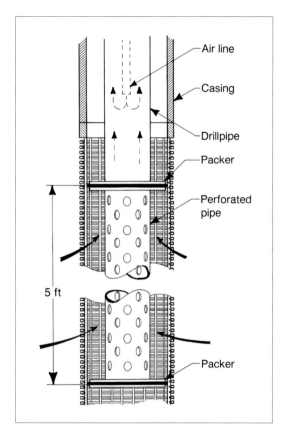

Figure 11.15. Double surge blocks are used to focus the energy of air bursts on a specific part of the aquifer and to remove sediment by air lifting.

The double surge block with air-lift method is especially effective in long screens because it can concentrate the development energy on short sections of the aquifer. It is important to start the procedure at the top of the screen to avoid sand locking the assembly. The double surge block is a cost-effective tool for use in deeper wells, because multiple development techniques can be employed without removing the tools from the well.

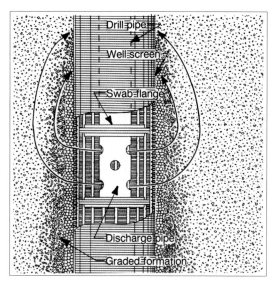

Figure 11.16. When surging or injecting using the double surge block, water moves into the filter pack and aquifer.

Double Surge Block with High-Pressure Jetting

Combination tools—such as a double surge block with high-pressure jetting tool—are used in deeper wells because the time to install and remove tooling for development can be significant (Figure 11.17). Using this tool, wells are developed by alternating high-pressure jetting and air-lift pumping. During high-pressure jetting, the check-valve in the tool remains closed, forcing all of the water through the nozzles. After jetting approximately 20 ft (6 m) to 30 ft (8 m) of screen, the same interval is swabbed and pumped by air-lifting without changing tooling. When air-lifting, the check-valve opens, allowing water and sediment to move through the screens and up the drillpipe. The packers on the tool isolate a 6-ft (2 m) to 10-ft (3 m) section of the screen so that the full force of airlifting is focused on a smaller section to remove any sediment.

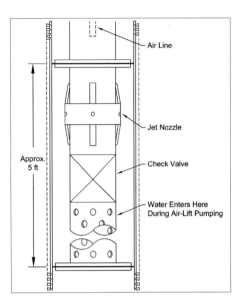

Figure 11.17. Double surge block with high-pressure jetting used in deep wells.

Overpumping

Overpumping is pumping a well at a rate greater than the rate planned for the well when it is put into service. This is an appropriate final step in well development to insure sand-free pumping and to confirm the proper sizing of the permanent pumping equipment.

Overpumping alone seldom produces an appropriately developed well, full stabilization of the aquifer, or acceptable development throughout the screened zones, particularly in unconsolidated aquifers. Most of the development action from overpumping takes place in the most permeable zones of the aquifer closest to the pump intake (which often is near the top of the screen). The longer the screen, the less effective the development in the lower portion of the screen at a given pumping rate. After fine sediments are removed from the upper permeable zones water enters the screen, moving preferentially through the developed zones. The rest of the well is developed insufficiently, contributing only small volumes of water to the well's total yield.

In some cases, overpumping can compact finer sediments around the bore-hole and restrict flow into the screen. If more powerful agitation is not per-formed, then an inefficient well can result. Overpumping might be effective in filter-packed wells in competent, relatively non-stratified sandstone aquifers because flow toward the wellbore is somewhat uniform.

A drawback to using only overpumping is that water flows in only one direction—into the screen—and some sand grains could be left in a bridged condition, resulting in a partially stabilized aquifer (Figure 11.18). After the well is operational the aquifer is agitated during normal pump cycles, and if sand bridges become unstable and collapse then sediment can enter the well.

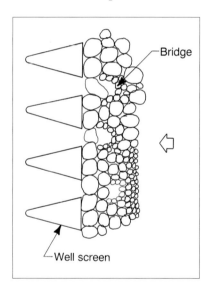

Figure 11.18. During development by overpumping, sand grains can bridge openings because flow occurs in only one direction.

During overpumping a surging action can be achieved by "rawhiding," which is alternately lifting a column of water a significant distance above the pumping water level and then shutting off the pump and letting the water fall back into the well through the pump column. The pump should be started at reduced capacity and gradually increased to full capacity to minimize the danger of sand locking. This cycle is repeated as rapidly as the power unit and starting equipment permit.

To avoid pump damage the control box should be equipped with a starter lockout, so that the pump cannot be engaged when it is back-spinning. During rawhiding, the fluid produced occasionally should be pumped to a waste-holding tank to remove the sediment that has entered the well via surging. Rawhiding requires removal of a check value that normally is installed just above the pump-bowl sections. The permanent pump never should be used for rawhiding because the high sediment content accelerates pump wear. A comparison of three development methods is contained in Appendix 11.B (DVD).

DEVELOPMENT OF OPEN-BOREHOLE WELLS

The combination of water jetting and air-lift pumping is recommended for open-borehole or bedrock wells. Inflatable packers can be used to isolate productive zones so that development efforts can be focused on certain portions of the borehole. It has been shown that much of the water entering an open borehole in bedrock enters through fracture zones.

One technique for cleaning wells completed in sandstone aquifers combines air-lift pumping, air jetting, and rawhiding; this overcomes development difficulties in stratified aquifers having layers cemented by silica, calcium, iron, or fine material such as clay. A borehole of this nature is depicted in Figure 11.19. Ledges form where the sandstone is most resistant and well-cemented, and borehole enlargement occurs where more friable layers erode. As shown in the figure, erodable sand lies on top of the ledges. If the well is put into production after bailing or air development, it often continues to produce sediment. This problem stems from the inability to remove all of the loose material in the well, because the development procedures do not extend far enough from the well-bore. Borehole-camera surveys have shown that this loose sediment is removed well away from the borehole when air-lift pumping, air jetting, and rawhiding are used in combination.

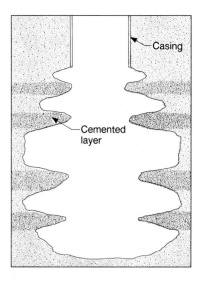

Figure 11.19. Borehole configuration caused by drilling in weakly consolidated sandstone containing well-cemented layers. Loose sand collects on the upper surface of the cemented layers.

ALLOWABLE SEDIMENT CONCENTRATION IN WELL WATER

Sediment in water supplies can be destructive to pumps and to water-discharge fittings such as valves and irrigation nozzles. One of the requirements of a production well is that it not produce sediment; however, occasionally sediment production occurs. The American Water Works Association (AWWA 2006) suggests that, for municipal-supply wells, water should contain less than 5 ppm of total suspended solids by volume. For many applications, however, varying concentrations can be required. Pump manufactures suggest that less than 1 ppm by volume is acceptable to minimize pump damage and increase service life.

The concentration of suspended sediment usually is estimated using a centrifugal sand sampler (Figure 11.20), or an Imhoff cone (Figure 11.21). The Imhoff cone is considered less accurate because of the small and instantaneous sample volume used. Accuracy of the Imhoff-cone method can be improved by increasing the frequency of sampling. The sediment concentration is determined by averaging the results of 5 samples taken during an aquifer test after the well is installed, at the times listed below.

1. 15 min after start of test
2. After 25% of the total aquifer-test time has elapsed
3. After 50% of the total aquifer-test time has elapsed
4. After 75% of the total aquifer-test time has elapsed
5. Near the end of the aquifer test

Such averaging takes into account the fact that at startup wells can have some sediment pumping that dissipates over time. It is helpful to record and graph this information to help determine whether further development is necessary.

Figure 11.20. The concentration of suspended sediment can be estimated using a centrifugal sand sampler that is mounted on the discharge pipe.

To obtain accurate measurements, a water sample must be of reasonable volume. Following is an example (in U.S. customary units) of how to collect a representative volume of water.

Figure 11.21. An Imhoff cone is used to estimate sediment concentration, but the small volume of the cone limits its accuracy.

Example

The recommended volume of water to be tested for sediment is determined by multiplying the flow rate, in gpm, by 0.05. At 300 gpm, the sample is 300 times 0.05, which equals 15 gal.

For yields greater than 1,000 gpm, the test volume should be 50 gal; for yields less than 20 gpm, 5 gal should be tested.

The amount of sediment collected in each sample can depend greatly on how the water sample is collected. For flow from a straight, horizontal pipe, most of the sediment can be at the bottom of the pipe; if the sample is collected there then the sediment concentration is higher than the average of the total stream. Conversely, a sample taken at the top might show a lower-than-average concentration. For accurate results, samples of the entire flow should be collected over a specific time interval.

Collection of an integrated sample becomes difficult as the flow volume increases. With large flow rates the use of a centrifugal sand sampler is recommended. When using a centrifugal sand sampler, the sample should be collected through a connection at the midline of the pipe. The sediment in the sample should be allowed to settle out, and then the sample should be weighed and compared with the total volume of water collected. In cases when the control of suspended solids is critical, automatic particle counters are used to measure the amount of sediment. Particle counters commonly are found in municipal water supplies and water-treatment plants.

The acceptable sediment concentration depends on the use of the water. The National Ground Water Association (NGWA) has recommended the following limits, most of which are widely accepted in the water-well industry (NGWA 1998).

- Sediment concentration of 1 ppm (by volume) for water to be used directly in contact with, or in the processing of, food and beverages.
- Sediment concentration of less than 2 ppm (by volume) for wells discharging directly into municipal water-treatment or distribution mains.
- Sediment concentration of 5 ppm (by volume) for water for homes, institutions, municipalities, and industries.
- Sediment concentration of 10 ppm (by volume) for water for sprinkler irrigation systems, industrial evaporative cooling systems, and any other use where a moderate amount of sediment is not especially harmful.
- Sediment concentration of 15 ppm (by volume) for water for flood-type irrigation in applications where the amount of sand pumping will not harm the well and pump.

In many instances, an Imhoff cone or sand tester is not available at the well site; however a 5-gal (19-ℓ) bucket can be used to collect sediment and obtain a rough estimate of sand content. In a 5-gal (19-ℓ) bucket, 10 ppm (by volume) equals approximately 0.04 teaspoons (tsp) (0.18 ml) of sediment, which is approximately the amount of sand that can cover a dime (or a circle that has a 0.7-in (18-mm) diameter) (Figure 11.22).

Figure 11.22. Amount of sand collected in a 5-gal (19-ℓ) bucket sample of water that is equivalent to 10 ppm of sand by volume.

AQUIFER-STIMULATION TECHNIQUES

In many parts of the world, the only groundwater available comes from bedrock. Assuming that the bedrock contains sufficient water storage to serve a water-supply need, the shortfall of a well's actual yield compared with the bedrock's potential yield can arise from either the well's construction or the well's connectivity to natural water-conducting features. Methods for improving the performance of the well itself through well development are discussed above. This section addresses select methods of improving the performance of the bedrock via aquifer stimulation.

Well stimulation is a technique used to improve the connectivity of a well to the water conductors in the bedrock. If the water transmission in the rock comes from sparse fractures, then the well could pass through the fracture network without intersecting a conductor having sufficient transmissivity to produce the desired yields. This effect can be a consequence of either the well having an unfavorable orientation with respect to the conducting fractures or the well's passage through a portion of a heterogeneous, conductive fracture that has poorly transmissivity. In either case, aquifer stimulation is an attempt to improve the connectivity of the well to fractures by opening natural or existing fractures, or by creating artificial fractures.

Hydrofracturing (as offered by water-well contractors) is most applicable to materials that are hard, competent, and indurated; and that ultimately derive whatever permeability offered in the form of interconnecting cracks, fractures, and joint systems. Hydrofracturing also can have benefits in low-permeability sedimentary rocks where the hydraulic fracture can sufficiently enhance the natural permeability to allow acceptable production.

The opening of fractures using hydrofracturing can have a dramatic effect on well performance. The essence of this behavior is expressed by the cubic law of parallel plate flow (Snow 1968), which states that a fracture's transmissivity varies with the cube of its opening.

$$T = \rho g(e^3/12\mu) \tag{11.1}$$

Where:

    T = the fracture transmissivity;

    e = aperture, or the distance between assumed parallel plates (m);

    ρ = fluid density;

    g = gravitational acceleration; and

    μ = the fluid's dynamic viscosity.

Although the cubic law applies ideally to perfect, smooth parallel plates, its essential behavior holds for natural fractures where a 10-fold increase in aperture produces a 1,000-fold increase in well yield (Bear 1993). Thus, a hydrofracture contractor is highly motivated to maximize the fracture aperture and the open area it provides, because small changes in fracture width can greatly enhance flow rate.

Hydrofracturing of Open-Hole Wells to Increase Production

Hydrofracturing injects water at pressures that are sufficient to open existing fractures or create new ones. After the high-pressure water injection has opened the fractures, they can remain open due to erosion of fractures' natural filling materials, propping due to natural fracture roughness, or propping due to injected proppants (materials injected to keep the fracture open). These newly opened fractures improve the well's yield by providing connections to the transmissive portions of the fracture network, or by providing a large surface area accessing porous, low-permeability rock.

The original 1947 patents for the "hydrofrac" process are held by Amoco (Howard & Fast 1970). During the past 60 years, the technology, equipment design, and procedures used in hydrofracturing have steadily improved to the point where hydrofracturing is a commonly used well-development tool. A review of hydrofracturing is presented in Williamson & Woolley (1980).

There are two critical pressure values needed for hydrofracture design: (1) the breakdown pressure, which is the pressure required to initiate fracture opening or create fractures; and (2) the shut-in pressure, which is the pressure required to propagate and keep fractures open. Both values depend on the stresses that are present in the rock and the properties of the rock.

In situ stresses arise from several factors, including gravitational effects from the weight of the rock, tectonic forces arising mainly from crustal deformation, and effects of variable topography and rock properties. Gravitational loading is approximately 1 psi per ft of depth. It increases with depth by the product of rock density, gravitational acceleration, and overburden thickness. Vertical stresses generally follow the rule of thumb for depth (1 psi per ft), but the horizontal stresses can be considerably more or less, depending on the tectonic setting.

Breakdown Pressure

The breakdown pressure is the pressure required to initiate fractures, and is a function of both the minimum and the maximum horizontal stresses acting on the wall of the well (Doe et al. 2006). The creation of a new fracture occurs when the internal pressure within the hole exceeds the sum of the minimum stress concentration around the hole and the rock tensile strength.

Due to the stress effects of the well geometry, hydraulic fractures generally initiate as vertical fractures along a vertical well, but propagate with distance perpendicularly to the minimum stress direction. When the minimum stress is vertical, the result is a rotation to a horizontal fracture. When the minimum stress is horizontal, the fracture should remain vertical and propagate in the direction of the maximum principal stress.

The breakdown pressure for natural fractures occurs when the mechanical load on the fracture face exceeds the stress acting on that face. The pressure required to produce this load can be less than the stress acting on the fracture face for two reasons: (1) there is a decrease in the fluid pressure with radial distance, due to friction losses in the fracture; and (2) prior to opening, the fracture is partly closed or sealed, thus the injection pressure acts only over part of the fracture face. Consequently, initiating the opening of the natural fractures requires higher pressures than the in situ stresses. Once fractures begin to open, the injection pressure required to extend the natural fractures drops sharply; re-opening a previously injected fracture also requires much lower pressure values.

Shut-In Pressure

The shut-in pressure is the pressure required to open or close fractures, and mainly is a function of the stress acting on the fracture surfaces. New, artificial hydraulic fractures tend to open and propagate perpendicular to the minimum in situ stress direction, which can be either vertical or horizontal. The increase in the minimum stress with depth is called the fracture gradient.

The shut-in pressure of natural fractures is determined by the resolution of the in situ stresses on the fracture plane. The fractures closest to being perpendicular to the minimum stress direction are the ones most likely to open and propagate.

In the absence of knowledge of rock properties or in situ stress values, it is reasonable to expect fracture initiation to require 1,000 psi to 2,000 psi more than the minimum stress value, and that extension and propagation will occur near the minimum stress value. A general estimate of minimum stress (the fracture gradient) is 1 psi of surface pressure per ft of depth (U.S. customary units). This could be an underestimate in hard rocks of the East Coast states (U.S.A.) where stresses can be very high. It could be an overestimate in parts of the western United States which are being stretched tectonically, or in mountainous areas where topographic effects relieve and reduce stresses.

Summary of Downhole Pressure

The downhole pressure observed at any particular point represents its resistance to the flow of water into the rock mass. If the injection rate is held constant and the downhole pressure drops, then it can be assumed that fracture development is occurring in the form of increased aperture, enhanced fracture interconnection, or the removal of fine sediment from any fractures. Downhole pressure behaves in a variety of ways. Figure 11.23 presents several graphs of downhole pressure versus time (at the same injection rate), and is followed by suggested interpretations.

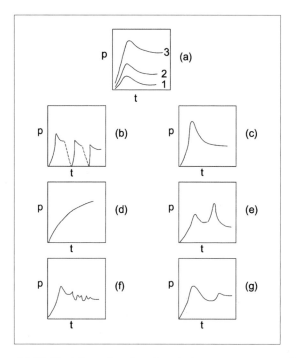

**Figure 11.23. Sketches showing downhole pressure versus time
(Boyle 2000).**

- Figure 11.23(a) shows 3 different single-packer depth settings
  (starting shallow and working deeper) and the associated increase in
  breakdown pressure reflecting 3 different fracture openings. Curve
  1 represents the shallowest depth and curve 3 is the deepest.
- Figure 11.23(b) presents a single-packer depth setting with multiple
  injection efforts (the decrease in breakdown pressure with time
  suggests that the fracture remains open, with continued development
  during each injection effort).
- Figure 11.23(c) indicates that the geologic materials are dense but
  brittle, because a significant pressure was required to open the
  fracture. The stabilized downhole pressure represents the minimum
  pressure required to keep the fracture open.
- Figure 11.23(d) shows plastic material or an intensely fractured zone
  that has the ability to accept the injection rate.

- Figure 11.23(e) illustrates a second breakdown pressure occurring because the initial fracture encountered a "dead end" and forced a second fracture to open.
- Figure 11.23(f) presents fluctuations in pressure due to the repeated flushing and the movement of fines within the fracture.
- Figure 11.23(g) indicates a pressure increase reflecting the arrival of a propping agent at the fracture. The addition of the proppant occupies some of the space within the fracture, resulting in an increase in the resistance to flow into the fracture.

Equipment and Setup Required for Hydrofracturing

The basic hydrofracturing equipment setup consists of a potable water supply, an injection pump, one or more packers, a means for installing the packer assembly, and valves and gauges to control and manage the injection fluids and associated pressures (Figure 11.24). Additional discussion of equipment design and hydrofracturing procedures is presented by Smith (1989). Hydraulic fracturing involves the use of high-pressure equipment and never should be attempted without the supervision of experienced operators. Improper use of equipment can result in serious injury or death. Hydraulic fracturing never should be attempted using compressed air, which can cause (among other hazards) the explosive ejection of equipment from the well if packers are not seated properly. Particular care should be taken with all components, including injection hose and pipe, general fittings, valves, and gauges. Any high-pressure components also must be properly rated for the anticipated pressures and working conditions. Importantly, to avoid the whiplash effects of a rupture on a high-pressure line and for the safety of on-site personnel, all high-pressure hoses should be secured.

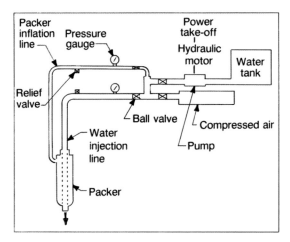

Figure 11.24. Diagram of the equipment used in a small hydrofracturing operation (Waltz & Decker 1981).

Not all conditions can be anticipated, therefore a pressure-relief valve that has a pressure rating that is less than the lowest prescribed rating of all components in the system also should be installed. As a rough guide for breakdown pressure (in U.S. customary units), drilling professionals use 1 psi of surface pressure per foot of fracturing depth plus 1,500 psi, although this varies with rock strength and stress conditions.

It is important to pay attention to the collection and interpretation of "real-time" fracture data, including injection rate, injection-pump pressure, downhole pressure, total volume of water injected, amount and size of proppant used, packer pressure, and water pressures above and below the packer. All of the parameters of pressure and flow can be recorded using electronic pressure transducers and flow meters that can be connected to a PC for data recording. Recording the surface pressure is sufficient for inferring downhole pressure, provided that head losses in the equipment are not excessive. If the head losses are large, as in high-rate cases or with the use of small-diameter tubing, downhole pressure measurement should be used. The operator should calibrate the equipment for head loss. This is done easily by recording the back pressure on the system with the packers deflated in the hole or with the equipment laid out at the surface.

The water used for a hydrofracture project must be clean and potable, and deliverable to the project site. Various types of pumps are available for hydro-fracturing, and a positive-displacement, piston-type pump typically is used. Such pumps are available in a variety of flow-rate and pressure configurations, ranging from 5 gpm (0.3 ℓ/sec) to 200 gpm (12.5 ℓ/sec) and up to 5,000 psi (345 bars). Sometimes a low–flow rate, high-pressure pump is used to initiate a fracture, and then a higher–flow rate, lower-pressure pump is used to further develop the fracture. Improvements in high-pressure pumps for pressure washers have made high-pressure capacity equipment available at reasonable costs.

The packer is the key component in hydrofracturing. Numerous packer designs exist, but inflatable packers have become the general standard for water-well hydrofracturing. Inflatable packers typically have higher inflation ratios, are lighter, and are more controllable than other types of packers. The packers selected should be rated for at least 20% more than the expected hydrofracture pressures, and the packer manufacturer's instructions must be followed in detail. High-pressure operations with packers should use water inflation and not compressed air. Water is inherently safer and requires less inflation pressure at the surface due to the hydrostatic pressure of the water in the inflation line. Operators should be aware of the possibility that water-inflated packers might not deflate, however, if the water level in the well is low and the internal pressure due to the water in the inflation lines exceeds the water pressure outside of the packers. In such cases an operator should consider a double inflation line and the use of compressed air to remove water from the inflation system and allow deflation of the packers.

If the rock is not fractured naturally, a straddle packer assembly tends to create fractures by splitting the borehole along its length. A single-packer arrangement in rock that is not fractured creates stress concentrations at the bottom of the hole. This causes a fracture that runs perpendicular to the borehole.

A single-packer arrangement can be more dangerous to use than a straddle packer system. If the single packer is not sufficient to withstand the high pressure in the test interval, then the assembly could blow out of the hole. This situation also can happen with straddle packers if the lower packer leaks and pressure builds up below the packer system.

Packers can be installed using either flexible hose or rigid pipe. The hard-pipe installation procedure is the most common, especially in cases where multiple packers are used. The packer can be installed using a pump rig, a drill rig, or a custom variation.

Proppants generally are not used for fractured, hard-rock domestic wells; however they are used in some sedimentary formations to keep the fractures open after the formation has been hydrofractured. Proppant can be added to water as it is pumped into a well. Commonly used proppants include sand and beads made from plastic, ceramic, or glass. Viscosifiers sometimes are used to help carry the proppants deeper into the fractures.

Use of NuWell® 220 Clay Dispersant for Opening a Fracture During Hydrofracturing

Water chemistry can play a part in the closure and plugging of fractures due to mineral precipitation, and in the generation of clay minerals. In some geologic settings, mobile fine-grained sediment can bridge and block fracture openings. Flow reduction as a result of mineral precipitation is dependant in part on the rock types present and the groundwater chemistry. Clay minerals can develop along faults and shear zones due to hydrochemical alteration.

The high injection-flow rates associated with the hydrofracturing process can dislodge many obstructions. The effectiveness often is observed during flushing or initial pumping from a well, when water with high sediment content is observed in the discharge.

Hydrofracturing combined with the use of NuWell® 220 Clay Dispersant (NW-220) has been successful for increasing the yield of wells. In a study conducted by Gleeson et al. (2005), a well was flow-tested, hydrofractured by conventional means, flow-tested again, and then redeveloped using NW-220 dispersant (Figure 11.25). Final flow-testing showed a 20% increase in the production of the well. This was achieved by removing from the fractures the fines and clays that could not be removed during the initial fracturing and development. The application of NW-220 also can be beneficial for newly drilled wells, to address drilling debris that has penetrated the fractures. Another example of the use of NW-220 to improve well yields is contained in Appendix 11.C (DVD).

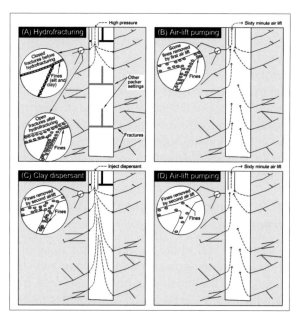

**Figure 11.25. (A) Hydrofracturing opening a fracture; (B) air-lift pumping
removing some of the fine sediment along an open fracture; (C) injection of
NuWell® 220 dispersant; (D) fracture cleaned by NW-220
(Gleeson et al. 2005).**

Site Considerations for Hydrofracturing

The purpose of hydrofracturing is to create a flow conduit between the borehole
and natural water-bearing and water-transmitting fractures in the vicinity of the
well. The effectiveness of hydrofracturing is enhanced when professionals have
an understanding of some basic hydrogeologic concepts and also are aware of
specific site characteristics. Ideally, hydrofracturing opens up a fracture in a well
that is completed adjacent to a similar fracture system—below the water table—
to tap into the more-permeable fractures that are not penetrated by the well.

Following are some of the important hydrogeologic concepts that should be
considered prior to undertaking hydrofracturing projects.

- ◆ Groundwater flow is dependant on the presence and interconnection
of fracture systems. Regionally, factors such as fracture frequency,
orientation, length, interconnection, continuity, and the presence of

    individual fractures (versus fracture zones) all control groundwater flow. Locally, fracture aperture at the borehole, fracture smoothness and irregularity, mineralization, and the degree of subsurface weathering and clay formation are the dominant factors (Domenico & Schwartz 1990). Fracture characteristics tend to show wide variation in character over short distances.

◆   There are more fractures and larger ones found near the earth's surface than at depth (Davis & DeWiest 1966; Trainer 1987), along with a consequent decrease in permeability with depth. This permeability decrease largely is due an increase in the stresses with depth. Laboratory experiments on fracture flow suggest that aperture reduction is non-linear with stress, with most of the closure happening at lower stresses or within a few hundred feet of the surface. On a regional scale, there exist fractures that are part of tectonic activity and that can be very continuous both laterally and vertically (Brace 1980). Vertical stresses of overlying rock (most crystalline rock materials have a density of between 140 lb/ft^3 (2,240 kg/m^3) and 180 lb/ft^3 (2,880 kg/m^3)).

◆   Without a source of recharge the largest, most open, most continuous fracture cannot be a significant source of water. Typically, most of the recharge of a domestic water well is derived from within about a 0.6-mi (1 km) radius from the well (Boyle 2000).

    In evaluating the suitability of a well to be hydrofractured successfully, the likely hydrogeologic considerations should be evaluated along with physical characteristics of the site. It also is important to consider the distance from, elevation above, and orientation and continuity of fractures between the well and surface-water features. An example of a poor candidate for hydrofracturing is a well that is 100 ft (30 m) deep with a depth to static-water level of 90 ft (27 m), that is situated on top of a hill. The well is located 300 ft (100 m) above and 0.6 mi (1 km) from the nearest stream (which only flows on an intermittent basis). Given such a list of hypothetical field conditions, even common sense indicates that a well of this type is not a good candidate for hydrofracturing.

    Appendix 11.D (DVD) contains a series of articles by Henry Baski on the practical aspects of hydrofracturing.

Use of Acid for Aquifer Stimulation

Acid can be used for well and aquifer development both in limestone or dolomite aquifers and in some semi-consolidated aquifers that are cemented by calcium carbonate. Many wells drilled in carbonate aquifers have open-borehole completions and are amenable to acid treatment. Mineral acids are the predominant acids used for treatments, and are discussed in Chapter 13. Acid dissolves carbonate minerals and this dissolution can extend into fractures in the aquifer around the open borehole, increasing the hydraulic conductivity of the rock mass. Placement of the acid in the borehole can be accomplished via jetting or gravity injection using a tremie tube or drill string. Alternatively, a service company can be hired to perform an acid injection—especially injection that is performed under pressure (Figure 11.26). Injection of acid can be extremely dangerous and should be done only by experienced professionals.

Figure 11.26. Acid is pumped into well to open fractures in a limestone aquifer.

Use of Explosives for Aquifer Stimulation

In an attempt to develop greater aquifer-fracture density, explosives sometimes are used to "shoot" bedrock wells. Acceptable results can be obtained if blasting procedures are appropriate for the rock type and the size and depth of the well. Due to the many unknown factors, however, it is difficult to predict whether a shooting operation will produce beneficial results, especially when performed in sedimentary rocks such as sandstone. Blasting and bailing techniques have been used in an attempt to reduce sand production and to enhance yields from wells constructed in weakly consolidated sandstones. Blasting and bailing techniques typically are used after other development methods have been applied.

To reduce sand production, some drilling professionals blast a sandstone aquifer to create a cavern around the borehole. In theory, the average flow velocity toward the borehole will be so low that no sand is transported. In many cases, however, sand production does not stop because the aquifer materials continue to slough off and fill the enlarged cavern. The inability to reduce sand production to acceptable levels indicates that these procedures might not be cost effective.

Blasting and bailing also are used to increase the yield by enlarging the effective well diameter. Walton (1962) has shown, for example, that yields increased an average of 29% after blasting and bailing techniques had been applied. In many cases, however, the blasting and bailing procedure can take months to perform and adds significantly to overall costs. Thus, blasting a sandstone aquifer might not increase the yield enough to justify the additional expenses, and this procedure also might not eliminate a sand-pumping problem. A more-extensive description of blasting in wells to increase production is given in Driscoll (1978). To control sand production, an increasing number of friable sandstone wells has been screened rather than blasted, even though some loss of specific capacity can occur.

It is important to note that this book does not contain all the acceptable safety procedures related to blasting, and that certain circumstances require additional precautions. The suggestions given here also do not supplement or modify any state, municipal, federal, and insurance requirements or codes regarding blasting. For old wells, in many cases replacement using proper well design, completion, and development is more economical—and certainly is safer—than redevelopment attempted using blasting.

SUMMARY

Well development is the most important part of well construction, and proper well development restores the formation and repairs the damage caused by all drilling processes. The application of multiple development techniques generally is required to fully develop a well. A well can be considered fully developed when the specific capacity does not increase with additional development effort.

Greater open area of the screen intake and the use of dispersants (e.g., NW-220) reduce development time and help create wells that are less expensive to own and operate. Wells that are not fully developed often experience biofouling problems. In some bedrock aquifers, well yield can be enhanced using well-stimulation methods such as hydrofracturing or acidization to open fractures. In summary, the best well design cannot achieve maximum efficiency unless the well is properly developed.

ACKNOWLEDGMENTS

The author wishes to acknowledge the contributions of Mr. Ray Boyle of Well Improvement Company and Dr. Thomas Doe of Golder Associates for their contributions and reviews regarding the section on hydrofracturing.

Outside reviewers provided valuable comments, and include: Mr. Eric J. Harmon PE, Principal, HRS Water Consultants, Inc.; Mr. Hank Baski, President, Baski, Inc.; Mr. Tom Downey, President, Downey Drilling, Inc.; and Richard E. Schramm, Chairman, Schramm, Inc. Mr. Raymond L. Schreurs, Johnson Screens (retired), also provided a review and comment on the chapter.

CHAPTER 12
Groundwater Pumps

Robert Pritchard
Servtech, Inc.

INTRODUCTION

After the construction and development of a groundwater well are complete, the next step is to enable the removal of groundwater for its beneficial use. Pumps and their related drivers (electric motors and engines) most commonly are used to perform this task. A pump can be defined as a machine that imparts energy to a fluid. In this case the fluid is groundwater. The energy transferred from the driver to the pump and then on to the fluid enables performance of work, such as raising water to a higher vertical level to remove it from the well, forcing water into a pipeline, filling a storage tank, or filling a pressure tank.

Pumps use various methods to impart energy to the pumped fluid, and currently the most prevalent pump type used in the water industry is the centrifugal pump (Figure 12.1). Other pump designs, such as rod pumps (as found on windmills), piston pumps, progressive cavity pumps, and others have been used extensively. Within the last century, however, centrifugal pumps have grown rapidly in popularity due to the development of reliable high-speed electric motors, distributed electrical power systems, and internal combustion engines. Centrifugal pumps, along with electric induction motors, are widely used.

The discussion here is not intended to be a detailed, technical approach to pumps (others already have accomplished this; for other sources of information, see Table 12.7 at the end of this chapter), but rather an introduction to the basic concepts and characteristics of pumps commonly used in water wells that might help professionals to properly select, apply, and maintain pumps, thus enabling the beneficial use of groundwater. In this chapter all equations and examples use U.S. customary units.

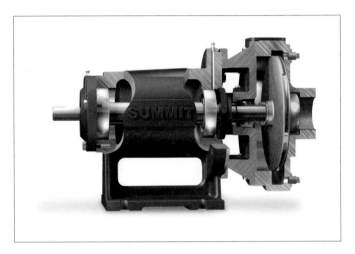

Figure 12.1. Cutaway view of a standard centrifugal pump (Summit Pump, Inc.).

CENTRIFUGAL PUMP BASIC COMPONENTS

Simply described, a centrifugal pump is a rotary machine consisting of four basic parts (Figure 12.2).

- ◆ **Impeller:** The rotary element of the pump that imparts energy to the fluid.
- ◆ **Pump casing (or diffuser):** The stationary element that directs the incoming and outgoing pump fluid flow.
- ◆ **Shaft:** The rotary connection between the driver (motor or engine) and the pump impeller.
- ◆ **Driver:** The motor or engine providing the rotational energy that turns the pump shaft which, in turn, rotates the pump impeller.

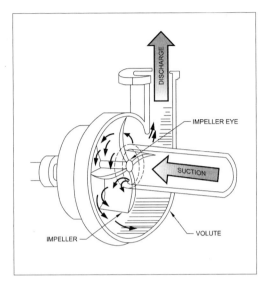

Figure 12.2. Water flow and rotation of a typical centrifugal pump.

CENTRIFUGAL PUMP OPERATION

The centrifugal pump impeller has a number of vanes or blades, usually curved in form, that are arranged in a circular array around a circular inlet opening at the center (known as the impeller eye) (Figure 12.2, Figure 12.3). The pump casing surrounds the impeller and usually is in the form of a scroll or volute curve. In some pumps, a diffuser with a series of flow guide vanes or blades surrounds the impeller. The impeller is attached to the pump shaft, which is rotated via the driver and supported by a bearing system.

To operate a centrifugal pump, the pump is filled with fluid, the driver is started, and the impeller is rotated via the pump shaft. The vanes or blades of the impeller cause the liquid to rotate with the impeller, and also impart a high velocity to the fluid as it is ejected. The fluid is thrown through the impeller vanes outward into the pump casing. This outward flow of water through the impeller reduces pressure at the impeller inlet, which allows more fluid to be forced in through the suction opening of the pump casing by atmospheric pressure or an external pressure.

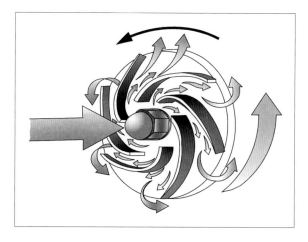

Figure 12.3. Centrifugal impeller operation.

CENTRIFUGAL PUMP IMPELLER TYPES

Overview

The following "rules of thumb" provide a good summary of operational factors associated with centrifugal pumps.

- The faster the rotating speed, the greater the wear potential and the shorter the component life. Wear factor is increased by the square of the ratio of the higher speed divided by the lower speed, and the ratio is cubed. Selecting a pump speed of 1,800 RPM instead of 3,600 RPM, for example, in some environments can result in an eightfold increase in pump life.
- The "deeper" the impeller vanes, the greater the flow gallons per minute (gpm) (cubic liters per second (ℓ^3/sec)) produced.
- The larger the diameter of the impeller, the greater the water exit velocity and resultant pressure (head) developed.
- A unit's design can greatly reduce its life when pumping water that is corrosive or contains a high suspended-solids concentration (high silt and sand content).

◆   The discharge pressure increases if the flow through the impeller
     is at more of a right angle to the pump shaft (radial flow).
◆   If the flow directed by the impeller is more parallel to the pump
     shaft (axial flow), then the volume increases and there is less wear
     on the components.
◆   Shrouding or enclosing the impeller vanes allows for greater pres-
     sure development (head), but also reduces the pump's tolerance for
     pumping solids contained in the pumped fluid. The impeller shroud
     reduces efficiency versus an open or semi-open impeller design that
     can be run with closer tolerances. This shroud, with a radial seal
     ring, however, enables the pump to be operated efficiently in
     abrasive conditions, or conditions where the impeller adjustment
     cannot be maintained, such as deep well turbine pumps, that have
     line shafts that stretch due to discharge head changes.

Thousands of different impeller designs and configurations are based upon
the flow (gpm) of head (ft of head), solids handling, net positive suction head
required (NPSHR), maximum allowable diameter, and other requirements of the
specific pumping application. Figure 12.4 illustrates impeller shapes and pump
specific speeds.

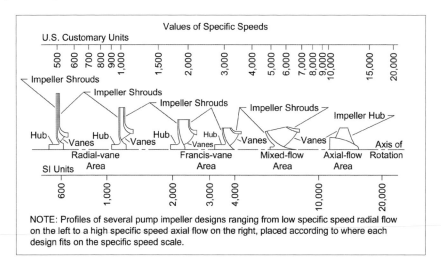

Figure 12.4. Impeller designs and pump specific speeds.

According to the Hydraulic Institute Standards (HIS), the concept of pump specific speed is a correlation of pump capacity, head, and speed at optimum efficiency, which classifies the pump impellers with respect to their geometric similarity. Specific speed (designated N_s) is expressed as a unitless rate. In this chapter, pump specific speed is mentioned to illustrate the shape, direction of flow, and broad classification of impellers.

The specific speed determines the general shape or class of the impeller, as depicted in Figure 12.4. As the specific speed increases, the ratio outlet to the inlet or eye diameter decreases. This ratio becomes 1.0 for a true axial flow impeller. Radial flow impellers develop head principally through centrifugal force. Pumps having greater specific speeds develop head partly by centrifugal force and partly by axial force. A higher specific speed indicates a pump design with head generation more by axial forces and less by centrifugal forces.

An axial flow or propeller pump with a specific speed of 10,000 or greater generates its head exclusively through axial forces. Radial impellers, for example, generally are low-flow high-head designs, whereas axial flow impellers are high-flow low-head designs.

The Francis-vane impeller (Figure 12.5) has specific speeds of approximately 1,200 to 5,000 with higher discharge heads per stage, and a horsepower curve that has a smaller variation throughout its operating range. The Francis-vane design makes it very suitable for booster and deep-well applications that require the pump to start against a closed discharge, as in many booster wells, or an open discharge as in deep-well applications.

The Francis-vane design is the predominant style impeller used in most vertical turbine pumps for the water industry. The turbine is designed for use in units ranging from one-stage to 30 or more stages (individual bowl and impeller units bolted together). Multi-stage design easily can achieve more than 2,000 ft of discharge head, given appropriate design and materials.

Another significant variance that is described by the specific-speed number is the rate of change in horsepower required at the impeller as it operated on each side of the best efficiency point. In low–specific speed impellers, the horsepower can increase dramatically as the flow increases, with the potential for overloading the motor when overpumping or when the pump is operating against an open discharge. The horsepower demand also drops, however, as the impeller moves toward shut off. In a high–specific speed impeller where axial flow predominates, the horsepower requirement drops as flow increases, but dramatically increases as the impeller moves toward shut off. In the

Francis-vane impeller, the horsepower usually is at its peak near the best efficiency point and drops off as flow increases or decreases from this point. This design is very useful in many applications.

For the reasons outlined, the Francis-vane impeller is the predominant design for water-well and medium- to high-pressure booster applications, or anything with a variable-load application. Generally, manufacturers simply call the Francis-vane design a "vertical turbine pump."

**Figure 12.5. Francis-vane impellers
(General Pump Company of Los Angeles).**

Impeller Types

Radial Flow Impeller

A radial flow impeller directs its discharge at (roughly) a right angle to the impeller suction centerline and pump shaft (Figure 12.6). This impeller design is utilized in relatively low-flow and high-head applications. It often is used in residential submersible pump design at flow rates of 5 gpm to 30 gpm, for example, with multiple stage designs capable of producing up to 2,000 ft of head. These stages are known as "pancake" type due to their thin vane depth (low flow), flat shape, and right-angle direction of impeller discharge. In the energy sector, very high head pumps have been developed by oil industry submersible pump manufacturers by multi-staging up to hundreds of radial-type stages, with head capacities exceeding 10,000 ft.

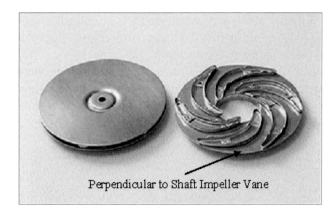

Figure 12.6. Radial flow impeller (Grundfos Pumps).

Mixed Flow Impeller

Mixed flow pump impellers direct discharge in a combination of radial (right-angle, higher head) and axial (parallel, higher flow) flow directions to enable moderate pumping rates at medium heads (Figure 12.7). This type of stage frequently is used in vertical turbine pumps to provide flow rates from 50 gpm to 10,000 gpm, with heads ranging from 10 ft per stage to 300 ft per stage. This type of impeller commonly is found in pumps used in larger groundwater irrigation wells, municipal wells, mine dewatering wells, industrial wells, booster pumps, and a variety of other surface pump uses and configurations.

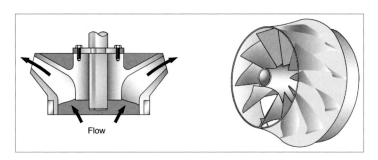

Figure 12.7. Mixed flow impeller.

Axial Flow Impeller

Axial flow pump impellers (Figure 12.8) direct the fluid discharge in a direction that is more parallel to the impeller suction and centerline of the pump shaft. Axial flow impellers are used for high-flow and low-head requirements, and often are used in ditch-water transfers, canals, lake-water transfer, storm-water removal, flood control, and other high-flow applications—flow rates of many thousands of gallons per minute at a few feet of head often occur. Some axial-type impellers also are called "propeller-style" impellers.

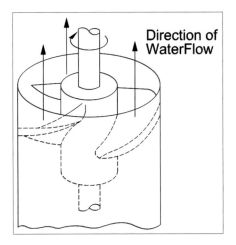

Figure 12.8. Large axial flow impeller.

CENTRIFUGAL PUMP IMPELLER CONFIGURATIONS

Within the three general flow versus head impeller designs listed above, there are several additional modifications that often are made to an impeller. Modifications include the presence and type of "shrouding" of the impeller vanes. Three general types of impeller vane shrouding configurations are used, and each type is used for specific pump characteristics and requirements, and has its own designation: open impeller, semi-open impeller, or enclosed impeller.

Open Impeller

An open impeller has no side walls surrounding or enclosing the pump impeller vanes (Figure 12.9). Open impellers consist of a series of vanes attached to a central impeller-eye hub. Open impeller centrifugal pumps are particularly suited for—but not restricted to—liquids containing abrasive solids. Abrasive wear on an open impeller is distributed over the diametrical area swept by the vanes. The resulting total wear has less effect on pump performance than the same total wear concentrated on the radial ring clearance of an enclosed impeller. Open impellers resist both plugging and clogging; this type often is used, for example, in mine slurry pumps where fluids with high solids contents are pumped intentionally to transport those solids via a pipeline.

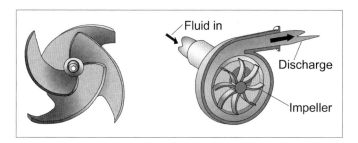

Figure 12.9. Open impeller.

Semi-Open Impeller

An impeller having a shroud or sidewall on one side only (usually on its back) also is designed for handling fluids containing solids (Figure 12.10, Figure 12.11). This type of impeller is used in applications where the solids content of the pumped fluid is lower than in those applications where an open impeller might be used, but where solids still are present in significant quantities.

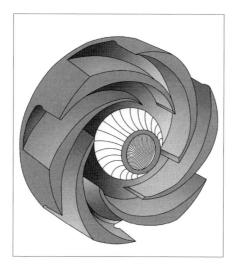

Figure 12.10. Semi-open impeller.

A semi-open impeller can produce higher heads than can an open impeller. Additionally, many vertical turbine irrigation pumps, for example, are equipped with semi-open impellers to successfully pump groundwater that contains silts and small sand-sized particles without plugging. This type of impeller also often is used for intake pumping of water from rivers, where the solids content of the fluid varies with the river level and season. Most importantly, the open and semi-open impeller designs permit restoration of "near-new" pump running clearance and performance, obtained by readjusting the impeller to pump-bowl clearance after wear has occurred. These adjustments can be made without removing or dismantling the pump assembly. The advantage of semi-open impellers is lost on vertical turbine pumps that are set at depths greater than 50 feet, where enclosed vanes with radial seal rings predominate. Enclosed vanes are used due to line shaft stretch that occurs under variable thrust loads in the operating cycle. In deep installations, this shaft stretch can range up to 1 in or more. There are very few semi-open impeller designs available from manufacturers today in the mid-size vertical turbine pumps that range in diameter from 8 in to 20 in.

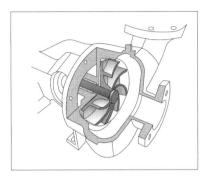

Figure 12.11. Semi-open impeller pump cutaway.

Enclosed Impeller

An impeller having shrouds or sidewalls extending from the impeller vane's outer edges inward to the suction opening or impeller-eye hub is called an enclosed impeller (Figure 12.12). This type of impeller provides higher head capacities than does the semi-open impeller, but it is not as resistant to solids wear or solids plugging. Enclosed impellers often are used in vertical turbines, submersibles, multi-stage boosters, shallow-well jet pumps, and single-stage centrifugal pumps.

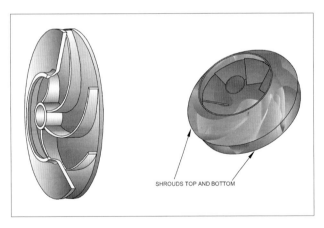

SHROUDS TOP AND BOTTOM

Figure 12.12. Enclosed impeller.

BASIC CENTRIFUGAL PUMP TYPES

Volute Pump

A volute pump has a casing built in the form of a volute curve, where the spiral starts with a small cross-sectional area near the impeller periphery and increases gradually to the pump discharge outlet (Figure 12.13). This is the simplest form of a centrifugal pump, and it typically is used where suction lifts are small and in applications having relatively low head.

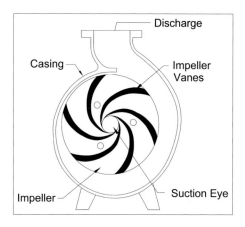

Figure 12.13. Volute pump.

Diffusion Vane or Turbine Pump

A diffusion vane or turbine pump is constructed with a pump casing that includes a series of guide vanes or blades surrounding the impeller (Figure 12.14). Diffusion vanes have small openings near the impeller that gradually enlarge to the diffuser-case diameter. This pump type has diffusion vanes to direct the output of fluid from the impeller discharge. One impeller discharging into one pump-bowl diffuser is considered a one-stage assembly.

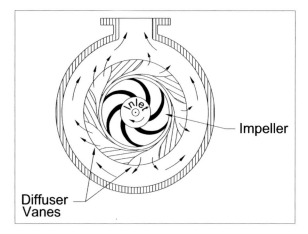

Figure 12.14. Diffusion vane or turbine pump.

Multi-Stage Pump

A multi-stage pump has two or more impellers that are attached to a common shaft and act in series in a single casing (Figure 12.15). Multiple stages can be assembled vertically or horizontally, but what they all have in common is that the fluid discharge of a stage directly flows into the suction of the next stage, which results in a "series" configuration that increases the pump output head. In this design, the flow rate of each stage is the same, but the output head capacity of one stage is multiplied by the number of stages present. For example, a pump stage design that is rated at 120 gpm at 64 ft of head per stage and which has 3 stages has a flow of 120 gpm, but the total head at the discharge of the pump is 3 times 64 ft or 192 ft.

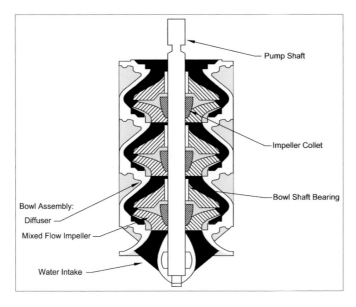

Figure 12.15. Multi-stage pump, 3 stages.

PUMP PERFORMANCE CURVES

Centrifugal pumps are designed to produce specific flow rates and discharge heads (pressure) within the constraints of impeller design, physical size, diameter, rotating speed, and driver horsepower. Pump manufacturers provide pump performance curves that are a graphic illustrations of these pump performance characteristics. These curves can be used to help select the best pump for a specific site.

Pump performance curves typically are created using pumping capacity (gpm) plotted as the base horizontal axis, total dynamic head (TDH) (ft or m) plotted on the left vertical or y-axis. Pump efficiency (as a percentage) and pump brake horsepower (BHP) often are plotted on the right vertical axis along with NPSHR; and in some cases thrust factor or "K" values are plotted on the top horizontal or x-axis. It is important to note, however, that all of these pump performance values including TDH, percent pump efficiency, BHP, NPSHR, and K are plotted in relation to flow rate (gpm).

To create this graphical representation of a pump's performance, pump manufacturers test a specific pump under various conditions of flow and head, from zero (0) flow (shutoff head) up to maximum flow (runout). A pump performance curve is shown in Figure 12.16. In this example, the pump has been tested at 9 different conditions of flow, and its resultant head and other data were recorded as noted in Table 12.1 (in U.S. customary units), along with additional pump-performance calculated values.

Table 12.1. Sample Pump-Test Data

Test Data Point	Flow Rate (gpm)	Total Dynamic Head (ft)	Pump Efficiency (%)	Net Positive Suction Head Required (ft)	Brake Horsepower (BHP)
1 (shutoff)	0	235.5	—	5	—
2	20	234	42	6	2.81
3	40	233.7	50	8	4.72
4	60	230.4	58	10	6.01
5	80	222.3	64	12	7.01
6	100	210	68.2	14	7.77
7	120	192	70	16	8.31
8	140	168	67	18	8.86
9 (runout)	160	141.9	63	20	9.1

With different impeller designs the permissible operating range or minimum to maximum "flow range" changes. As the specific speed increases radial flow, to mixed flow, to axial flow, the safe operating range becomes limited for several reasons. A low specific speed impeller (800 to 1,500), for example, can be run from near shutoff to runout without much effect on stability. Conversely, a Francis-vane impeller should not be operated for any period at a point that is greater than 10% to each side of the best efficiency point (BEP) of that particular impeller. Operating outside the 10% range can cause noise, vibration, and flow instability, resulting in potentially significant component failure. A mixed flow impeller–type pump should be operated much closer to its design point, and the limited operating range of an axial flow impeller–type pump is even greater.

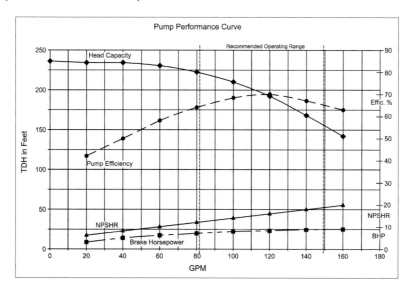

Figure 12.16. Sample pump performance curve (Servtech).

PUMP SELECTION

Head Capacity

The "head capacity" curve is the primary graphical data that can be used to start the pump-selection process. To create the head capacity portion of the pump performance curve, each test-data point set of flow (gpm) and head (ft) values is plotted on a graph. In the present example, note that the diamond-shaped data points that represent each flow-head data point taken from Table 12.1 are plotted graphically in Figure 12.16. A curved line then is drawn through the test-data points to create the head capacity curve. The far-left data point of zero flow and maximum head is known as shutoff head, in the example in Table 12.1, the shutoff head is 235.5 ft. The far-right data point of maximum flow at minimum head is known as runout, and in the example in Table 12.1, runout is 160 gpm at 141.9 ft (TDH).

Pump Efficiency

During a pump test, pump efficiency also is determined and collected for each test-flow (gpm) point. Pump efficiency also can be plotted on the graph as a separate curve and, in the example shown in Figure 12.16, the values are located using the upper right-hand axis. The data points from Table 12.1 are plotted on the pump performance curve in Figure 12.16. The pump efficiency curve data points are represented by the dark dots and a dashed line connects each data point. The peak efficiency of the pump is known as its best efficiency point (BEP). In the example, the BEP is approximately 70% and it occurs at a flow rate of 120 gpm (Figure 12.16). This point represents the highest-efficiency conversion of input energy to useful output pump work. Part of the "best fit" selection of a particular pump design is to match the selected pump BEP with the site's required pumping rate. The closer the match between desired pump flow rate and the selected pump BEP flow rate, the lesser the amount of energy used and the horsepower load on the driver.

Pump Brake Horsepower

Pump brake horsepower (BHP) is the amount of horsepower required at the pump shaft to create the desired pump work. It is calculated below using the test data derived from the factory pump-performance test.

$$BHP = \frac{\text{gpm} \cdot \text{TDH (ft)}}{3,960\,(\text{a constant}) \cdot \text{Pump Efficiency (as a decimal)}}$$

$$BHP = \frac{\text{gpm} \cdot \text{TDH}}{3,960 \cdot \text{Pump Efficiency}} \tag{12.1}$$

For example, the BHP for test-data point 6 (Table 12.1) is determined as follows.

$$BHP_{Test\,6} = \frac{100 \text{ gpm} \cdot 210 \text{ ft TDH}}{3,960 \cdot 0.682} = 7.77$$

This formula and the previously noted test data can be used to calculate and plot the BHP required for each test flow (gpm) data point. In the example shown in Figure 12.16, the BHP data points are noted by small rectangles and a dashed line is drawn between the data points to create a brake horsepower curve. From this BHP curve, the maximum horsepower required for pumping conditions can be determined, and then a driver can be sized accordingly. For example, the sample curve shows a peak BHP of 9.10, and at the BEP the BHP is 8.31.

If the goal is to provide a reliable, long-lasting pump system, a 10-HP motor would be chosen for this pump. This particular motor provides a "non-overloading" pump-and-motor combination, which allows operation anywhere on the pump curve without overloading the selected motor. This selection provides for a long motor life.

Net Positive Suction Head Required

Net positive suction head required (NPSHR) is the total head in feet of fluid that must be present at the pump suction to prevent pump "cavitation." Cavitation is the formation and collapse of vapor-filled cavities in the pumped fluid (Figure 12.17), and occurs when the pump suction pressure is near the vapor pressure of the pumped fluid. Cavitation can cause severe pitting and physical and mechanical damage to the pump components. Figure 12.18 shows pump damage due to cavitation.

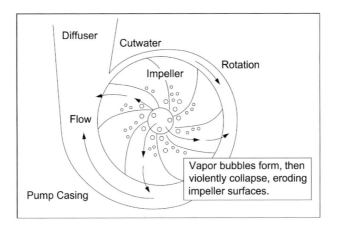

Figure 12.17. Cavitation damage.

**Figure 12.18. Cavitation wear on an enclosed impeller
(General Pump Company of Los Angeles).**

The NPSHR is a characteristic of the pump design that has a definite value in feet of head for a given flow rate. For each specific pump site there exists some value of net positive suction head available (NPSHA). The goal is to select a pump with an NPSHR lower than the NPSHA at the site. Cavitation can occur when the pump's NPSHR is equal to or greater than the NPSHA.

In Table 12.1, note that the NPSHR for the sample pump at a BEP flow rate of 120 gpm is 16 ft; as the pump flow increases the NPSHR also increases. At 160 gpm the NPSHR is 20 ft. If, for instance, a pump similar to the pump in the example is to be used at a specific site, then it is imperative that the NPSHA (specific to the site) exceeds the pump's NPSHR. For "real-world" conditions it is important to assume the worst-case conditions for NPSHA and also for the pump's NPSHR, because pumps often are operated at pumping rates greater than their BEP or their designed pumping rate.

It also is important to maintain a margin of safety by having 2 ft or more of the site's NPSHA exceed a pump's NPSHR. Again using the example pump, this would require having a minimum NPSHA of 22 ft (2 ft greater than the NPSHR at the pump's maximum flow rate).

The submersion requirements to stop cavitation vary by specific speed—the higher the specific speed the less submergence required for the pump to operate properly. For this reason some manufacturers install a low specific speed impeller on the suction end of a multi-stage vertical turbine booster.

There are other factors affecting potential of cavitation of an impeller. The condition the impeller or the material used to manufacture it can influence the potential for cavitation to occur.

For example, a cast iron or bronze impeller that is pitted due to corrosion or abrasion, forms pockets that induce cavitation where it normally does not occur. If there is a potential for cavitation to occur, then using coatings or stainless steel can reduce or eliminate its potential for occurrence.

Cavitation often results in a sound that has been described as "pumping rocks." This noise is the sound of the destructive collapse of the air bubble on the impeller vane surface, resulting in pitting. One approach for eliminating the "pumping rocks" sound is to introduce a small quantity of air into the pump inlet. This action also reduces the associated impeller and bearing damage—at a much-reduced pump efficiency, of course.

Another potential cause of cavitation is prerotation of the liquid. Prerotation sometimes is associated with vortexing, and can cause cavitation and significantly reduced pump capacity. This problem is related to specific speed; the higher the number the greater the risk of prerotation. In the case of axial flow and mixed flow pumps, they can be outfitted with "umbrellas" on the suction side of the pump to reduce the potential for cavitation.

Francis-vane type pumps used in water well–type applications can have their own unique problems associated with suction. Vertical turbine well pumps can be equipped with a suction pipe and strainer. Some manufacturers and drilling professionals specify or supply a 2-ft suction pipe and strainer. This suction strainer design easily reduce pump efficiency by as much as 2%. As such, it is recommended that a suction pipe that is—at minimum—10-ft (3-m) long and at least one diameter larger than the pump-discharge diameter be welded to the end of the intake pipe. The intake pipe should consist of a wire-wrap strainer. In some cases an engineered suction pipe designed based on well-performance criteria (Figure 12.19), can significantly enhance both pump and well performance by preventing prerotation and cavitation.

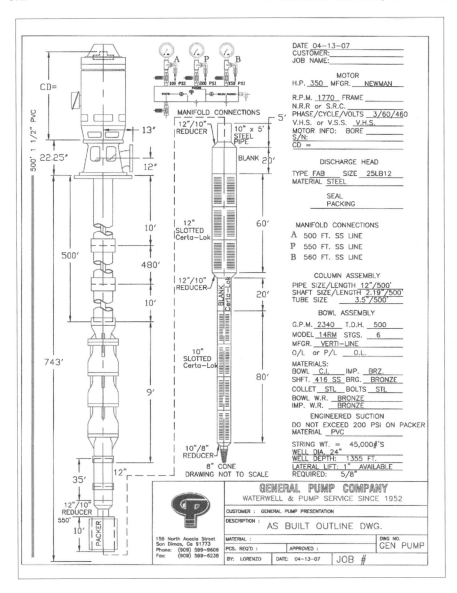

Figure 12.19. Engineered suction and pressurized packer assembly (General Pump Company of Los Angeles).

Cavitation or prerotation in water wells can be eliminated by sufficient submergence, typically 20 ft to 50 ft, and a minimum of a 10-ft (3-m) long suction pipe on the pump suction, or by using a motor shroud on submersible pumps.

Other Groundwater-Well Pump-Selection Considerations

Normally, pump selection starts with determining the required flow (gpm), head (TDH), brake horsepower (BHP), and the positive suction head required (NPSHR) for the application. There are other less-frequently examined but crucial components for optimal well-pump selection, and these are discussed in the following sections.

Minimum Pump Submergence

Minimum pump submergence is the smallest vertical distance—measured between the pump impeller eye and the pumping water level—that allows the pump to operate without creating a vortex. Vortexes can pull air into the pump suction intake and cause a loss in performance and possibly damage the pump.

Pump Diameter Versus Well-Casing Diameter

Pumps utilized for groundwater wells must fit the specific wells to be equipped, and are subject to the limitations of a given well diameter. For example, residential water wells often are drilled and cased using nominal 4-in diameter well casing, which results in the use of 3.75-in maximum outside diameter pumping equipment. If the column of water in the well is sufficient, the TDH requirement can be such that a pump rotating at a speed of 3,600 revolutions per minute (rpm) is required to build the desired TDH or create the desired flow capacity.

Typically, the larger the pump impeller diameter, the higher the pump efficiency and the greater head per stage that the pump can develop. Selecting the largest-diameter pump bowl assembly that also allows for adequate annular space in the well casing results in a more efficient pump. As demonstrated in the BHP calculations, a more-efficient pump results in the smallest BHP requirement. Minimizing the BHP requirement lowers power costs for pump operation, and also potentially results in a smaller motor, controller, and cable.

In the case of a multi-stage pump, selecting the largest-diameter pump also results in the fewest number of stages, potentially reducing the pump's cost and decreasing the number of moving parts (which can increase reliability and pump life).

In a well where the pump intake (suction pipe) is located in the well screen, and where water is entering the well above the pump, the pump diameter versus well casing diameter—along with other criteria—can be critical to the life of the pump and well. In such situations, the following guidelines should be used.

- In most well environments water flows horizontally before it flows vertically. This can cause disproportionately high velocities at the pump suction, resulting in sanding and potential casing deterioration, along with screen plugging.
- If the well is producing a significant percentage of its water from above the pump, then the potentially high vertical velocities— caused by too small a clearance between the pump and casing— might increase well sanding, vortexing, and air induced into the water stream and the pump suction. If clearance is too small then it conceivably could reduce well pressure and pump efficiency, and overpump the formation below the suction.

Proper pump design for the application, along with the appropriate suction pipe on line shaft turbines, can alleviate these problems.

Pump Rotational Speed

The pump's rotational speed as measured in rotations per minute (rpm) can help determine its NPSHR, life span, reliability, resistance to abrasive wear, driver cost, pump cost, and construction materials. The rule of thumb used in choosing a pump for the highest reliability is to select a pump with the slowest rotational speed (in rpm) that also provides the pump performance required. The NPSHR, abrasive wear from solids, and the criticality of dynamic balance (as defined below) all increase with pump speed. Pump cost often is decreased as rotational speed increases because fewer pump stages are needed, and the stages potentially can have smaller diameters.

Hydraulic Thrust Requirement and Capacity

The pumping of water creates hydraulic thrust in the direction opposite to that in which water is flowing (Figure 12.20). Some pump manufacturers provide thrust data that can be plotted on the pump performance curve, and also might provide what is known as a "K" factor. The "K" factor can be multiplied by the

TDH of the pump to calculate the pounds (lb) of hydraulic thrust. For the sample pump data from Table 12.1, the "K" factor is 3.11; the maximum thrust requirement is calculated by multiplying the shutoff head (ft) by 235.5 ft, which equals 732.4 lb of thrust. Once the maximum thrust requirement is known, it is critical to insure that the pump design and the driver design have a thrust bearing capable of adequately handling the thrust requirement.

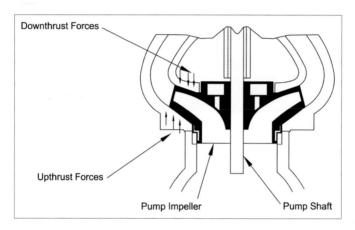

Figure 12.20. Pump impeller thrust forces.

On deep-well turbine pumps the weight of the rotating assembly, impellers, all pump shafting, and motor weight, along with the hydraulic thrust factor, need not be included in calculating total thrust bearing load.

Many new vertical hollow-shaft motors for vertical turbine pumps use spherical roller-bearings arrangements (Figure 12.21), and fewer radial angular-contact bearings. The spherical roller bearings do not have a significant radial load component, and require constant downward load to maintain proper ball contact so as to not have sliding or angular movement of the inner bearing. This downward load usually is supplied by a spring preload on the bearing. Any small—even momentary—up thrust, combined with any radial load component (imbalance), can cause bearing or gear mesh problems on these drivers resulting in destructive vibration.

**Figure 12.21. Spherical motor bearing
(General Pump Company of Los Angeles).**

Upthrust can occur when the pump operating discharge head is relatively low. This situation results in the pump operating in the ranges found on the right-hand side of the pump performance curve. If the pump's impellers can "float" or move axially in response to thrust, then the top of the impeller can rub when in upthrust, thus causing mechanical wear and premature pump failure. Operating in "downthrust" can occur when the pump operating discharge head is relatively high. The pump then operates in the ranges shown on the left-hand side of the pump performance curve.

Downthrust can be diminished by drilling small pressure-relief holes in the rear shroud of the impeller, but this practice also reduces overall pump efficiency. There often is a "recommended operating range" area shown on the pump curve that corresponds to flow and head conditions that allow for acceptable pump thrust conditions (see the sample in Figure 12.16).

In deep-well turbine applications, line shaft stretch as a result of downthrust due to the "K" factor of the impeller multiplied by discharge head, affects shaft diameter selection more than shaft horsepower ratings does. In deep settings (several hundred feet or more) extra-large diameter shafting can be required to reduce differential shaft stretch, in some cases along with extra lateral (end play) in the pump bowls. At the cost of reduced efficiency, the impellers can be thrust balanced along with associated modifications to the pump bowls (*see* Figure 12.22).

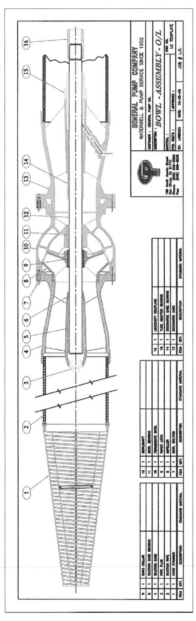

Figure 12.22. Bowl assembly diagram (General Pump Co. of Los Angeles).

Mechanical Balance

The pump and driver must be mechanically balanced sufficiently well to allow minimal vibration during operation. This protects the integrity of the rotating elements such as pump impeller, shaft, bearings, and seals. Mechanical balance usually rises in importance as the pump diameter, horsepower, rotating speed, and physical size and mass increase. Frequently, medium- to large-diameter pump impellers are "dynamically balanced" to help insure that they rotate without excessive vibration when operated at design speed. Dynamic balancing usually involves removing small amounts of the pump impeller shroud via grinding.

It also is crucial for the pump shafting and the driver shafting to be straight and aligned, and for the pump and driver base to be of sufficient mass and rigidity to resist excessive vibration. To help insure mechanical balance check pump shafts for straightness; shaft couplings for concentricity; and driver bases to insure alignment, mounting dimensions, concentricity, and parallelism.

PUMP CONSTRUCTION MATERIALS

Corrosion Resistance

Pumps are constructed using a variety of materials, including numerous alloys and varieties of cast iron, steel, stainless steel, bronze, combinations of nickel-aluminum-bronze, and plastics. The material used must provide adequate resistance to corrosion damage that can be caused by the site's specific water chemistry and composition. To preserve the water quality, pumps for potable-water use also must be constructed using non-contaminating materials such as lead-free alloys.

Abrasion Resistance

Abrasive wear of pump components (Figure 12.23) is caused by pumping water that contains solids having a Brinell hardness greater than that of the pump materials. Selecting a harder base material for pump construction can reduce abrasive wear. An alternative is to select an elastic material that can provide resilience to solids wear. As noted, open and semi-open impeller designs are more tolerant of solids in the water than is the enclosed impeller design.

The rotating speed of the pump assembly also affects the rate of solids wear; the higher the rotating speed, the greater the rate of abrasive wear. Therefore, if solids are present, selecting the lowest rotating speed that still provides the required pump performance can extend pump life.

In choosing an impeller, materials having a finer grain structure do better in an abrasive environment than do those that only are harder. For example, 316 stainless steel (softer) has a finer grain structure than bronze (hard), and provides longer pump life. The ideal composition is a metal that is both hard and has a fine grain structure. In the case of shafts or seal rings for pumps, stainless steel 17-4 PH is recommended. If pumping solids is a problem then selecting a pump with a higher specific speed will extend pump life.

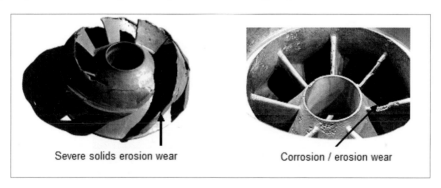

Severe solids erosion wear   Corrosion / erosion wear

Figure 12.23. Examples of pump wear (University of California–Davis).

Mechanical Strength

All pump materials must be able to safely withstand the pertinent mechanical forces, including pump pressure, horsepower, bearing capacity, and tensile strength. When selecting a specific pump the following limits should be checked.

* **Bowl or pump casing pressure rating.** The pressure rating for the pump bowl or casing must be greater than the pressure rating for the shutoff head of the pump. It is preferable to have an adequate

safety margin in the pressure rating of the pump bowl or casing that can withstand pressure transients created by a water hammer (a concussion of moving water against the sides of a containing pipe or vessel if the direction of water is changed suddenly).

- **Shaft horsepower rating.** The pump shaft must be capable of developing the peak horsepower and torque requirements of the pump assembly at the rated rotating speed (rpm) of the unit.
- **Tensile strength.** The pump casing, fasteners, discharge head, and motor mounting base all must be rated to withstand the tensile stress created by the hydraulic forces at any point on the pump performance curve, and must adequately support the weight of the assembly.

Figure 12.24 shows large impeller and shaft assemblies that require significant engineering to minimize unexpected failures.

**Figure 12.24. Large impeller and shaft assembly
(U.S. Bureau of Reclamation).**

PUMP DRIVER CHARACTERISTICS

Pump selection also is affected by the constraints and limitations of the pump driver. The most common rotating speeds for the most widely used electric induction motors used with 60-hertz (Hz) power systems, for example, are nominal 1,800 rpm and 3,600 rpm models. These motors experience "slip" which results in actual rotating speeds of approximately 1,750 rpm and 3,550 rpm (subject to the actual motor characteristics). The end result is that pumps commonly are sized and designed based upon their performance at one of these nominal rotating speeds.

TOTAL DYNAMIC HEAD

The following section discusses how to calculate the total dynamic head (TDH) required for a specific flow rate. Head usually is measured in feet (meters).

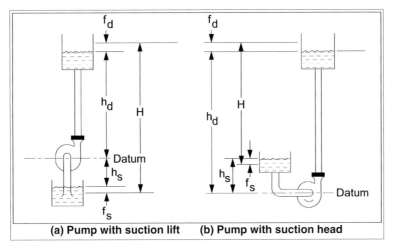

(a) Pump with suction lift   (b) Pump with suction head

Figure 12.25. TDH diagrams showing various parameters.

For Figure 12.25(a), the total TDH for a pump with a suction lift can be calculated using equation 12.2. Equation 12.3 can be used to calculate the TDH for the case of a pump with a suction head (Figure 12.25(b)).

$$TDH = h_d + h_s + f_d + f_s + V_h \qquad\qquad (12.2)$$

$$TDH = h_d - h_s + f_d + f_s + V_h \qquad\qquad (12.3)$$

Where:

$h_d =$ Static discharge head (ft or m) (vertical distance between the pump intake centerline and the liquid at its point of discharge (ft or m), including discharge pressure required);

$h_s =$ Static suction head or lift (ft or m) (vertical distance from the surface of the well water to the pump intake centerline);

$f_d =$ Discharge friction head (ft or m) (the head required to overcome the friction losses in the pipe and fittings in the discharge piping system);

$f_s =$ Suction friction head (ft or m) (the head required to overcome the friction losses in the pipe and fittings in the suction piping system, if present); and

$V_h =$ Velocity head (ft or m) (the head required to attain pump discharge water velocity) (in groundwater–well pump applications this head normally is not significant and can be ignored).

Centrifugal Pump Suction Lift TDH Sample Calculation

The following example demonstrates how to calculate the TDH (in U.S. customary units) of a simple suction-lift centrifugal pump, as shown in diagram (a) in Figure 12.25, assuming the following requirements.

- Flow rate = 120 gpm
- Pumping water level (PWL) = 10 ft
- Suction pipe length = 30 ft
- Discharge and suction pipe diameter = 3 in
- Elevation from pump to discharge = 20 ft
- Discharge pipe distance = 100 ft
- Discharge pressure required = 40 psi

From diagram (a) in Figure 12.25 the following can be stated using equation 12.2.

$$TDH = h_d + h_s + f_d + f_s + V_h$$

From the example the following can be determined.

h_d = Elevation from pump to discharge plus discharge pressure required (ft)

= 20 ft + 92 ft (40 psi · 2.31 ft of water per psi)

= 112 ft

h_s = Suction lift (ft) = 10 ft (PWL)

f_d = Discharge friction head (ft)

= 100 ft of pipe · 3 ft friction loss per 100 ft of 3-in pipe (from friction loss tables for 3-in pipe)

= 3 ft

f_s = Suction friction head (ft)

= 30 · 3 ft friction loss per 100 ft of 3-in pipe (from friction loss tables for 3-in pipe)

= 1 ft

The centrifugal suction pump example yields the following.

$$TDH = 112 \text{ ft} + 10 \text{ ft} + 3 \text{ ft} + 1 \text{ ft} = 126 \text{ ft}$$

For pumps that have a suction head instead of a suction lift, the TDH calculation is similar, as shown in the following example of a typical domestic submersible-pump system (Figure 12.26).

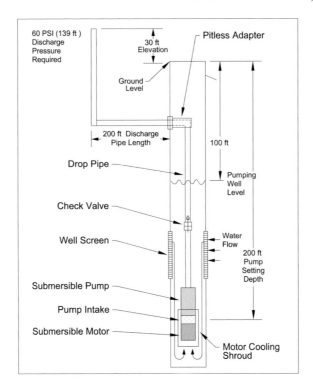

Figure 12.26. Typical domestic submersible-pump system (Servtech).

Submersible Well Pump TDH Sample Calculation

This example shows how to calculate the TDH of a simple submersible well-pump application that has the following characteristics.

- Flow rate = 120 gpm
- Pumping water level = 100 ft
- Pump set depth = 200 ft
- Discharge pipe diameter = 3 in
- Discharge pipe distance = 200 ft
- Discharge pressure required = 60 psi
- Elevation from top of casing to discharge = 30 ft

As noted on diagram (b) in Figure 12.25, the appropriate calculation of TDH for a pump with a suction head is as shown in equation 12.3.

$$TDH = h_d - h_s + f_d + f_s + V_h$$

h_d = Vertical distance from pump intake to discharge + discharge pressure required

= Pump set depth + elevation from pump to discharge + discharge pressure required

= 200 ft + 30 ft + 139 ft (60 psi · 2.31 ft per psi) = 369 ft

h_s = Vertical distance from the well water to the pump intake

= Pump set depth – pumping water level

= 200 ft – 100 ft = 100 ft

f_d = Discharge friction head in ft

= (Pump set depth + discharge pipe distance) · friction loss ft per 100 ft of pipe

= (200 ft + 200 ft) · 3 ft friction loss per 100 ft of 3-in pipe

= 12 ft

f_s = Suction friction head in ft

= Not significant for submersible groundwater pumps

For this example the following calculation results.

TDH = 369 ft + 100 ft + 12 ft = 481 ft

COMMON GROUNDWATER WELL PUMPS

Figure 12.27 shows various types of centrifugal pumps and configurations. Table 12.2 illustrates some of the most common types of groundwater pumps, their flow and head abilities, and the type and size well where they typically are used. The subsequent sections describe the common pump types. Appendix 12.A (DVD) provides a more in-depth discussion.

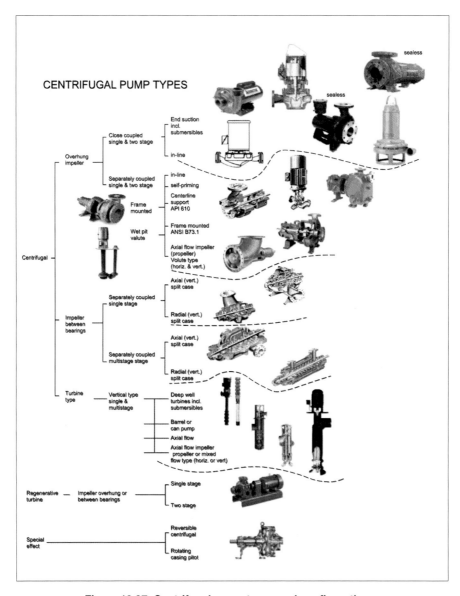

Figure 12.27. Centrifugal pump types and configurations.

Table 12.2. Groundwater Pump and Well Comparison

Type of Well	Nominal Well Diameter (in)	Nominal Well Depth (ft)	Type of Pump	Nominal Flow (gpm)	Impeller Type	Pump Selection Considerations	Motor Selection Considerations
Environmental; Sampling	2 to 4	10 to 200	Multi-stage submersible	0.5 to 2	Enclosed; Radial flow	Contaminant-free construction	2-in to 3.75-in max. OD limits HP
Domestic; Residential	3 to 6	10 to 30	Shallow-well jet; Single stage	5 to 25	Enclosed; Radial flow	Lead-free construction materials; Suitable for potable water; Maximum suction lift 25 ft	120 to 240 VAC single-phase power typical limits max HP
Domestic; Residential	4 to 8	30 to 2,000	Multi-stage submersible	5 to 90	Enclosed; Radial flow	Lead-free construction materials; Suitable for potable water; Allowable flow range; Solids-related wear resistance; NEMA standard motor base and coupling; Corrosion resistance	Minimum cooling flow past the motor casing; Submersible cable voltage drop; Thrust-bearing capacity; Nominal 4-in motors max 10 HP; NEMA standard base, shaft; Lightning protection

Type of Well	Nominal Well Diameter (in)	Nominal Well Depth (ft)	Type of Pump	Nominal Flow (gpm)	Impeller Type	Pump Selection Considerations	Motor Selection Considerations
Agricultural	6 to 36	10 to 1,000	Vertical lineshaft turbine; Multi-stage submersible	50 to 5,000	Open; Semi-Open; Enclosed; Mixed flow	Pump efficiency, power costs; Solids content of the water; NPSH requirements; Verticality of the well; Pump submergence; Lineshaft lube type; Lineshaft bowl lateral; Driver HP available; Water temperature, chemistry	VLT or submersible; Thrust-bearing capacity; VLT shaft adjustment; VLT non-reverse ratchet; Minimum cooling flow past the submersible motor casing; Submersible cable voltage drop; Submersible motor rpm; Submersible motor voltage; Submersible maximum diameter
Agricultural	6 to 36	1,000 to 3,000	Multi-stage submersible	50 to 5,000	Enclosed; Mixed flow	Pump efficiency, power costs; Solids content of the water; NPSH requirements; Pump submergence; Driver HP, rpm, and diameter available; Water temperature, chemistry	Minimum cooling flow past the motor casing; Submersible cable voltage drop; Motor rpm; Thrust-bearing capacity; Maximum diameter; Motor voltage

Type of Well	Nominal Well Diameter (in)	Nominal Well Depth (ft)	Type of Pump	Nominal Flow (gpm)	Impeller Type	Pump Selection Considerations	Motor Selection Considerations
Municipal; Mining; Industrial	6 to 36	100 to 10,000	Vertical lineshaft turbine; Multi-stage submersible	50 to 10,000	Open; Semi-Open; Enclosed; Mixed flow	Solids content of the water; Verticality of the well; Depth to water; Pump submergence; Lineshaft lube type; Lineshaft bowl lateral; Driver HP and rpm available; Water temperature, chemistry	VLT or submersible; Thrust-bearing capacity; VLT shaft adjustment; VLT non-reverse ratchet; Minimum cooling flow past the submersible motor casing; Submersible cable voltage drop; Submersible motor rpm; Submersible motor voltage Submersible maximum diameter

Jet Pump

A jet pump combines the pump-design principle of a diffusion vane centrifugal pump with that of a jet ejector, which consists of a jet nozzle and venturi (Figure 12.29, Figure 12.30). The jet pump is used extensively for residential water supply in areas having shallow water tables. There are two jet pump configurations: shallow-well units have the jet ejector located within the pump assembly, the deep-well units that have the jet ejector located separately from the pump within the well.

The centrifugal pump portion of the jet pump creates suction and flow, part of which passes through the jet ejector. The jet nozzle (a smooth reduction in diameter) accelerates the water, causing a pressure drop which creates additional suction. As it exits the jet nozzle, water passes through the venturi and its velocity decreases and its pressure increases. A portion of the suction water is recirculated in this process, and the remainder flows out the discharge of the pump. This design enables a shallow-well jet pump to increase its effective suction lift to as much as 28 ft (at sea level), depending upon the elevation of the installation. Higher elevation causes less-effective suction lift.

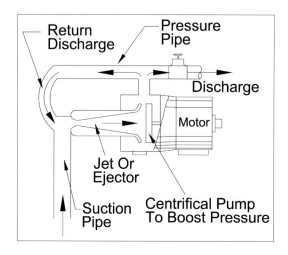

Figure 12.28. Shallow-well jet pump flow.

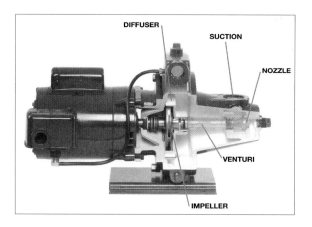

Figure 12.29. Shallow-well jet pump cutaway (MacDonald Pump Co).

Deep-well jet pumps (Figure 12.30) can be utilized down to a depth of approximately 150 ft by placing the jet ejector in the well at the end of the suction and pressure lines. Jet pumps often are supplanted by submersible pumps due to their lower potential maintenance needs. Additional information regarding the design of jet pumps is contained in Appendix 12.A (DVD).

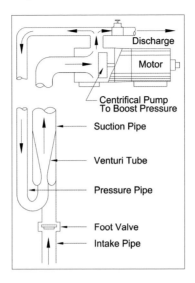

Figure 12.30. Deep-well jet pump.

Vertical Lineshaft Turbine Pump

Overview

Vertical lineshaft turbine (VLT) pumps are extremely common and durable. They are designed so that the pumping assembly is submerged in the well and connected to the pump discharge head by the column pipe, and is connected by the lineshaft to the vertical motor at the surface (Figure 12.31). The motor sits on top of the discharge head and rotates the lineshaft which then rotates the impeller assembly. This creates flow out of the pump assembly into the column pipe and through the discharge head (Figure 12.31). The pumping assembly of a vertical turbine pump consists of one or more impellers housed in a single-stage or multi-stage unit called a bowl assembly. Each stage provides a certain amount of lift; a sufficient number of stages (bowl assemblies) are assembled to meet the head requirements of the system. When designing a pump system, the number of stages required is proportional to the head and horsepower requirements, although the discharge rate and efficiency remain constant. Additional information regarding design issues associated with VLT pumps is contained in Appendix 12.A (DVD).

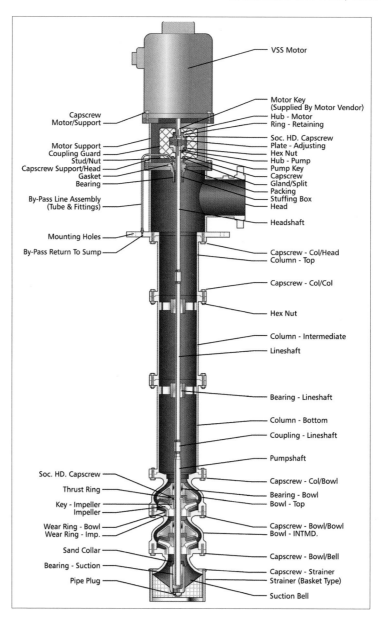

Figure 12.31. Water-lubricated VLT assembly (Goulds Pumps).

Submersible Pump

Overview

Submersible pumps now are commonly used in groundwater wells. Their use has increased due to numerous factors including the market pressure to reduce drilling costs using smaller-diameter casing, well "straightness" requirements, deep practical well-production depths, a lower-skilled installation workforce requirement, and the increasing reliability of submersible motors. This type of pump ranges from single-stage to multi-stage assemblies (Figure 12.32). The small (less than 25 hp or 3,600 rpm) submersible has become a simple "throwaway" design. The larger 60 hp to 1,000 hp submersibles used in municipal applications for security and noise abatement are quite complex and require a fully qualified professional to assemble, adjust, and install them. Additional information regarding the design of submersible pumps is contained in Appendix 12.A (DVD).

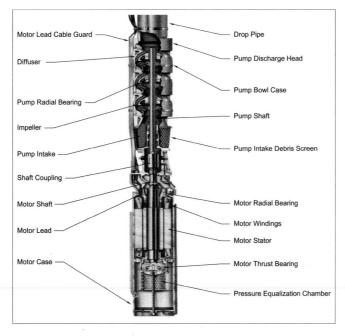

Figure 12.32. Submersible pump and motor.

PUMP SELECTION AND APPLICATION SUMMARY

The selection and application of centrifugal pumps is very challenging and requires the knowledge and experience of pump professionals. The reliable supply of groundwater requires the wise use of pumps, the associated motors, and all other equipment that completes a pumping system.

Professionals should strive to select and apply the "best-fit" pump systems for the particular applications and sites, bearing in mind the following goals.

- Achieve high pump efficiency to minimize BHP, thereby minimizing the driver size and long-term energy costs.
- Create high motor efficiency to minimize long-term energy costs.
- Afford longevity, mechanical integrity.
- Provide long-term value.
- Insure public safety.
- Protect water quality.

Table 12.3 provides additional sources of information regarding pumps.

Table 12.3. Sources for Additional Information

Organization	Web Site
ANSI	http://www.ansi.org/
API	http://www.api.org/
ASME	http://www.asme.org/
AWWA	http://www.awwa.org
Conversion utility	http://joshmadison.net/software/convert/
Fluide Design	http://www.fluidedesign.com/
FlowCalculator	http://www.flowcalculator.com/
Hydraulic Institute	http://www.pumps.org/
Impeller Net	http://impeller.net/
NEMA	http://www.nema.org/
NFPA (NEC)	http://www.nfpa.org/
Pump World	http://www.pumpworld.com/
Pump Ed 101	http://www.pumped101.com/
Pump-Flo	http://www.pump-flo.com/
Pumps & Systems	http://www.pump-zone.com/
U.S. Dept. of Energy	http://www1.eere.energy.gov/industry/index.html

The appendices for this chapter include a variety of reference materials, and all are contained on the DVD accompanying this book.

- Appendix 12.A. Common Groundwater Well Pumps and Pump-System Components
- Appendix 12.B. Malfunctions in High-Capacity Centrifugal and Turbine Pumps, Possible Causes, and Solutions
- Appendix 12.C. Pump Technical Guides
- Appendix 12.D. Pump Installation Guide
- Appendix 12.E. Vertical Line Turbine (VLT) Pumps Guides
- Appendix 12.F. Pump Maintenance Guides
- Appendix 12.G. Submersible Motors Guide
- Appendix 12.H. Motor Control Guides

ACKNOWLEDGMENT

Mr. William M. Tweed, President, General Pump Company of Los Angeles, provided a valuable review of and additions to this chapter; his efforts are greatly appreciated.

CHAPTER 13
Well Blockage and Rehabilitation

John Schnieders, PhD, CPC
Water Systems Engineering Inc.

It is extremely important to control well blockage; when the flow pathways or pore spaces of a well gradually are plugged and water flow is lost, the costs of maintaining production escalate. Larger pumps often are installed or the operating period is lengthened to meet demand, thus increasing the expenditure for electrical power.

The major loss in water-well production is due to blockage of screen openings and flow spaces in the filter pack or in the immediate formation (which is an area equal to one half the diameter outside the borehole wall). Blockage most often consists of mineral deposits and biological formations—referred to as biofilm. Biofilm primarily is a combination of mineral and biological accumulations, but it is termed "incrustation" in both the singular sense and for formations and deposits that occur in combination.

THEORY OF WELL BLOCKAGE

Water flowing toward a well comes into contact with more surfaces and collides with more ions, crystals, and colloids; this provides opportunities for water to pair with dissimilar charges and form conglomerate and mineral compounds. The compounds that occur ultimately form crystals that are particulate matter too heavy to stay in solution. Eventually falling out of solution, the crystals continue to grow until the flow paths for groundwater are blocked. This phenomenon can be uniform, such as the formation of calcite (calcium carbonate), or it can be an accumulation of separate crystals that are held together with clays or organic matter also deposited by the flow of the water.

The major accumulation—which is the truer definition of incrustation—is the attachment of the newly formed crystals to the surface by the adhesive action of a polysaccharide material produced by bacteria. The production of this natural polymer (sticky slime) by the bacteria is the beginning or the forming of incrustation. All bacteria produce exopolymer and attach to a surface so that the bacterial colony is not swept away by the flow of water. This attachment serves to form a habitat for the bacteria. It is a collection of bacteria and the polysaccharide exopolymer (or biofilm), and provides a place where the bacteria can multiply and live. The sticky polysaccharide is not water-soluble and is not easily washed from the area. Oxygen diffuses through the surface of the structure for the aerobic organisms and water flows through the latticework carrying oxygen and food and removing waste products, enabling the biofilm colony to grow. The slime also is a protective mechanism of the bacteria and can be produced in amounts from 30 to 100 times the weight of the organism.

Incrustation is the combination of mineral and biological deposits forming a complex matrix. This matrix at times also can include natural clays, bentonite, and other colloidal-like material filtered from the flow of water. Additional discussion of incrustation is contained in the section titled, "Types of Blockage." To assess the likelihood of mineral or biological incrustation, water samples from the well should be collected (see Appendix 13.A (DVD) for a description of sampling and a sampling form).

ANALYSIS OF GROUNDWATER

Overview of Laboratory Analysis

A groundwater analysis should cover all the inorganic parameters that usually are associated with a standard water-quality analysis, and also should include a profile of bacterial activity. Consider including microscopic evaluation of the water for detecting sands or silica crystals, clays, and bacteria that are more easily identified visually. Table 13.1 and Table 13.2 show typical standard commercial-laboratory analyses—including all of the elements of a laboratory report—to enable evaluation of the potential type and degree of incrustation that could be found in the well.

Table 13.1. Typical Water Analysis and Control Report

	Well No. 1 Casing After 3 min** (mg/ℓ)	Well No. 1 Aquifer Pumping 3–4 hr*** (mg/ℓ)
Phenolphthalein alkalinity*	0	0
Total alkalinity**	148	172
Hydroxide alkalinity	0	0
Carbonate alkalinity	0	0
Bicarbonate alkalinity	148	172
pH Value	7.6	7.8
Chlorides (as Cl)	45	49
Total Dissolved Solids	291	297
Conductivity (µS/s)	454	464
Total Hardness***	184	180
Carbonate hardness	148	172
Non-Carbonate hardness	36	8
Calcium*	128	116
Magnesium*	56	64
Sodium (as Na)	53	66
Potassium (as K)	2.6	3.0
Phosphate (as PO_4)	0.2	0.3
Iron Ferrous (as Fe_{2+})	0.0	0.0
Iron total (as Fe)	0.5	0.4
Copper (as Cu)	0.0	0.0

	Well No. 1 Casing After 3 min** (mg/ℓ)	Well No. 1 Aquifer Pumping 3–4 hr*** (mg/ℓ)
Tannin/Lignin	0.0	0.0
Nitrate (Nitrogen)	0.1	0.1
Sulfate (as SO₄)	0.4	0.6
Silica (as SiO₂)	20	20
Manganese (as Mn)	0.1	0.1
Saturation Index	- 0.21	+ 0.01
Total organic carbon (TOC)	1.8	0.7
Chlorine (as Cl)	0.0	0.0
Oxidation-reduction potential	208 mV	210 mV

* As $CaCO_3$.

** Pump the well (after sitting idle 8–12 hr) for a period sufficient to remove the water from the drop pipe and to retrieve casing water.

*** Pump the well a period sufficient to remove water from the casing and begin drawing water from the aquifer (3–4 hr).

Table 13.2. Typical Bacterial Analysis

	Well No. 1 Casing After 3 min	Well No. 1 Aquifer Pumping 3–4 hr
Plate count (colonies/ml)	No growth	15
Sulfate-reducing bacteria	Positive	Positive
Anaerobic growth (% of total count)	20%	20%
ATP (cells per ml)	522,500	62,000
Bacterial identification		Aquaspirillum dispar, Bacillus

Microscopic

Casing
Moderate bacterial activity, moderate amount of crystals, no sheathed or stalked bacteria noted, no iron oxide.

Aquifer
Low bacterial activity, moderate amount of crystals, no sheathed or stalked bacteria noted, no iron oxide.

Inorganic analysis together with the saturation index and the oxidation-reduction potential (see Chapter 5 for a discussion of these topics) give values that can be used to determine the probability of certain precipitation reactions. Values for manganese and iron, for example, can be used to suggest precipitation of oxides of these chemicals when the saturation indices for these compounds are exceeded, especially when the oxidation-reduction potential for the water is high or if iron-oxidizing bacteria are present. A negative saturation index along with the moderate levels of calcium suggest only a limited possibility of calcium-carbonate precipitation in the well environment. As discussed below, however, certain physical phenomena can increase the probability of precipitation resulting in considerable buildup of calcite.

Biological analyses or, more specifically, bacteriological analyses are important because they provide information regarding the probability of bacterial plugging of the well. Additionally, the types of bacteria present might provide clues about the possibility of surface-water infiltration. Some tests provide a means of quantifying the bacteria present; others do more for the identification of specific organisms. Tests such as the simple heterotrophic plate count (HPC) which determines the colony-forming units (CFUs) per milliliter of water, and the test for adenosine triphosphate (ATP) can be used to determine the amount of bacteria per milliliter. Both of these tests quantify the number of bacteria present; the question then becomes how the data are interpreted.

Heterotrophic Plate Count

The heterotrophic plate count provides the number of colonies of bacteria formed on an agar plate after the plate has been streaked with a specific amount of the water to be tested. The water is spread out over the surface of the agar, and colonies grow wherever a bacterial cell or group of cells lands. The colonies that form during a 24-hr period are counted, and this count then is reported as colony-forming units per milliliter (CFUs per ml) (variation in the HPC can be seen in *Standard Methods for the Examination of Water and Wastewater* (APHA & AWWA 2005)). The count is useful because most labs perform it in the same manner and, if recorded and observed over time, variations in the counts can be used as indications of potential changes in the well environment. Any variation in the testing procedure, however, can make it almost impossible to make comparisons between the results obtained.

Additionally, the underlying theory of the plate count revolves around the premise that all bacteria present will grow and divide, thus producing a colony to be counted. The method also does not take into consideration bacteria that land together and result in growth that is counted as only one colony. It is thought, for example, that as few as 1 bacterium or as many as 500 bacteria could land together and produce only 1 colony. In the field of microbiology it also now is widely assumed that fewer than 10% of the bacteria in a water sample can be cultured, and many professionals think that this figure actually is less than 1%.

Nevertheless, many labs do use standard procedures for HPC counts, and if the random nature of growth is accepted then the tests should reflect the general population change taking place in the well. When growth increases and plugging is expected, the HPC plate should show a numerical increase in the colony count.

Adenosine Triphosphate Determination

The adenosine triphosphate (ATP) count determines the amount of adenosine triphosphate in a specific water volume after the cell walls of the bacteria have been destroyed (lysed). Adenosine triphosphate is present only in living cells, and after the cell wall has been lysed it remains in the surrounding water for only 15 sec to 20 sec. The number of live bacteria present can be determined by using the value for the average amount of ATP in a bacterial cell count. There are some problems in using this method of counting bacteria. It does sidestep many of the errors often seen in the counting or quantifying of bacteria in a water sample, however, and also is one of the most reliable tests used.

Identifying the major populations present provides some benefits, and can be accomplished using various microbial techniques as well as direct microscopic evaluation. Although microscope work cannot be used to identify many bacteria, it can be used to determine the presence of the iron-oxidizing stalked or sheathed bacteria and other branching or filamentous organisms. The presence of such organisms should be considered when determining the parameters required to rehabilitate a well. A microscopic evaluation also can be used to pinpoint iron-oxide accumulation, sand infiltration, protozoan presence, and other abnormalities that can be corrected during rehabilitation. As is the case for any technical report, an appropriate professional should be consulted for proper evaluation of the test results.

TYPES OF BLOCKAGE

Incrustation and blockage of water flow in a well system take many forms, but generally are categorized as biological blockage, mineral blockage, and physical blockage. Biological blockage usually is slimy and predominately composed of bacterial growth. Mineral blockage results from the precipitation of, for example, calcium salts, iron oxides, and manganese oxides. Physical blockage refers to deposits or incrustations that usually are composed of migrating particulates such as sand and clays brought into the well zone through over-pumping or the natural movement of water through the aquifer.

The soft biological deposits can be observed on all the surfaces of the well such as the casing and screen but, for the most part, these deposits form blockage when existing in the filter pack and formation in the vicinity of the well. Some bacteria—particularly the branching type—are known to inhabit the borehole wall. When *Gallionella* (an iron-oxidizing stalked bacteria) deposits are first formed, they often are found in a soft form on or near the screen or intake areas of the well. The iron oxyhydroxide dehydrates (chemically loses water) and form a very hard matrix.

In most cases, blockage is a composite of biological material and minerals formed either as deposits of water constituents, such as calcium and carbonates, or from the adhesion of particulate matter or sand. This matrix begins with the formation of sticky, slimy biofilm (from bacterial growth) which then matures to a denser hard form as minerals compose more and more of its mass. Some biomasses (particularly in water with low total dissolved solids) remain primarily organic in nature but they, too, grow denser with age and become formidable barriers to water flow.

CAUSES OF BLOCKAGE

There are many reasons that incrustation forms in water-well systems, however the primary cause of blockage is the quality of the water. Water with high dissolved solids tends to deposit certain minerals when an environmental change moves the saturation index (*see* Chapter 5) to the positive, resulting in the precipitation of materials such as carbonates and sulfates. Changes that move the index toward the negative result in corrosion of the metal well structure, and the accumulation of iron oxide as incrustation. Reducing reactions also can take place in the aquifer where minerals containing metals are dissolved, the metal ions then move toward the well and are oxidized, forming deposits such as iron or manganese oxides.

Bacteria in the water passing through the well form biofilms which grow and become biological blockage that plug flow-ways. These biofilms also entrap mineral particles which further enhance the growth of the incrustation. The well—in a sense—acts as a giant filter, and any particulate or biological entity moving through it is subject to being filtered out, resulting in the blockage of the flow path wherever the filtered material is trapped.

EFFECTS OF TEMPERATURE, PRESSURE, AND VELOCITY CHANGE

The groundwater in most aquifers is balanced and the saturation index is near neutral. Under neutral conditions, precipitates are not expected to form and deposits are not expected to dissolve. During whatever period it took to form the aquifer, changes occurred as the water moved more toward a balanced state. These changes, which were chemical or biological in nature, primarily were initiated by more basic changes in temperature, pressure, and velocity. These same basic phenomena continue to initiate change.

Velocity change, such as that resulting from over-pumping, can initiate dissolution of soft mineral deposits in the aquifer, the products of which move toward the well in an unbalanced state. This same over-pumping, or even simply the extraction of water from an aquifer, can produce changes in pressure which result in degassing.

This pressure change and off-gassing of dissolved gases from the water entering the well also result in changes to the saturation index, usually pushing it toward the positive side. A positive saturation index brought about by either an increase in a specific ion or a rise in the pH can result in precipitation of products such as calcium carbonate and calcium sulfate.

Temperature changes also affect the saturation index. As the temperature increases, minerals such as calcium carbonate and calcium sulfate are less soluble, and if they are at or near their respective saturation levels then these compounds precipitate. In addition to the chemical changes that can occur, slight variations in temperature can encourage the growth of certain organisms or changes in the bacterial fauna of an aquifer or well environment. The new dominant bacteria might change the pH of the water or directly affect the concentration of certain minerals present. Examples of direct change are the reduction or oxidation of iron by bacteria, which result in the deposition or solubilizing of the iron. The soluble iron then moves toward the well and—after oxidation in the well proper—results in deposition (possibly triggering "red water" complaints when the oxidized iron appears in the water-distribution system).

CHEMICAL BLOCKAGE

Chemical blockage is the form of incrustation usually brought about by a chemical activity or change, and in most cases it results in the formation of mineral crystals and a subsequent plugging of the flow paths. The more common forms of incrustation are carbonates (calcite), sulfates (gypsum), and both iron and manganese oxides.

Carbonate

Carbonate deposits—most notably calcium carbonate and sometimes magnesium and iron—are potential incrustations in a well, as determined by the alkalinity; hardness (calcium, magnesium, and iron); total dissolved solids; and pH.

Key to Determination

The key to determining the possibility of carbonate formation's existence is the saturation index (*see* Chapter 5). A positive number can indicate that carbonate deposits have formed in the well systems; a negative number can indicate the potential for some corrosion activity. Deposits of carbonate can be the primary blockage if a water's pH is greater than 7.5, the hardness is greater than 250 mg/ℓ, and its alkalinity is greater than 220 mg/ℓ.

Calcium Sulfate (Gypsum)

The potential for the formation of gypsum as blockage in a well is measured using the same parameters as those used for carbonates, plus those for noncarbonate hardness and sulfates.

Key to Determination

If the saturation index is positive (indicating the potential for calcite deposits), the non-carbonate hardness is greater than the carbonate hardness, and the sulfate levels are in excess of 100 mg/ℓ, then gypsum or sulfate scale could deposit on the screens and in the filter pack or formation (especially if there is an increase in pumping rates or an increase in pH). Sulfate deposits could be the major blockage if a water's pH is greater than 7.5, the calcium concentration is greater than 175 mg/ℓ, the alkalinity is less than 50% of the calcium concentration, and the sulfate concentration is greater than 150 mg/ℓ.

Oxides

Oxidized metals—particularly iron and manganese—form oxides; oxides also are a form of corrosion by-products. Determining the potential for oxide formation can require having knowledge not only of the existence of iron and manganese levels in the aquifer but also of the potential for corrosion in the well. Here, again, the saturation index is helpful. A negative index reading indicates corrosive water and could point to the corrosion of carbon-steel piping as the source of iron. Iron or manganese concentrations in the aquifer also are a source of metals that can lead to oxide accumulation in the well.

Key to Determination

If the saturation index is negative and the oxidation-reduction potential (ORP) is less than 150 mV, then the water is corrosive and any metal in the system is subject to releasing ions (most probably iron) into the water to become a metal oxide; this process speeds up when more oxygenated water enters the well. The accumulation of iron oxide (typically red in color) and manganese oxide (typically black in color)—an outcome of the oxidation of the iron and manganese in the aquifer water—can result in considerable incrustation. Serious fouling can occur when iron levels in the aquifer water are as low as 1.0 mg/ℓ and manganese is 0.1 mg/ℓ or greater. Oxides such as brucite (a magnesium hydroxide mineral) can form with calcite deposits if the magnesium-calcium ratio is approximately 1:1, the alkalinity is greater than 220 mg/ℓ, and the hardness is less than 250 mg/ℓ.

PHYSICAL INCRUSTATION

Physical incrustation includes sand, clays, and particulate matter from the formation, as compared with incrustation due to minerals precipitated in the well systems. This group also can include bentonite and some of the synthetic polymers used as drilling fluids during the well-construction period. As water moves toward the well, sand and fine-grained sediments (e.g., silt) are transported by the higher velocity developed near the well. Eventually these fines and sands impact the filter pack, and can enter the well through the screen. Sand can impact the pump adversely, and result in erosion or corrosion of pump parts and screen and slot openings; larger openings lead to more sand moving into the well.

Clays also move toward the well—especially if they comprise a large part of the formation and if water velocity is increased by increased pumping rates. Clays, bentonite, and synthetic drilling fluids left in the well filter pack during construction all can become part of incrustations. Physical incrustations can act as focal points for additional incrustations resulting from biological and chemical processes. The occurrence of all three types of incrustation can severely block the water flow to the well.

Microscopic examination of water samples drawn from a pumping well often provides evidence of bentonite, natural clays, and sand accumulating in the well. Proper drilling-fluid management and well development during well construction go a long way in maintaining a clean filter pack and good water flow.

The Kiwa Water Research organization in the Netherlands has undertaken significant research into the causes of mechanical well clogging. Appendix 13.B (DVD) contains a presentation on mechanical (physical) well clogging and a research dissertation on the processes for investigating clogging.

BIOLOGICAL INCRUSTATION

It has been estimated that more than 80% of typical well blockage is caused to some extent by biological growth, and both laboratory work and field experience confirm this percentage (at minimum). It therefore is critical to understand the role that bacteria play in the well environment and the resulting biological incrustation.

Biofilm

All bacteria produce polysaccharides—the long-chain polymers that the bacteria use to adhere to surfaces, to entrap nutrients, and as a means of protection. A free-swimming bacterium has a biological need to attach itself to a surface to grow and procreate (Figure 13.1). As soon as the bacterium lands on a surface it begins to produce the polysaccharide material needed to attach itself to that surface. Later, as the cell divides, more exopolymer is produced until many cells live in the formation and all are covered with this protective layer. Such formations—made up of the slimy polysaccharide and living bacteria—are known as biofilms and are the typical habitat for bacteria; they are present wherever there is both water and a surface enabling adherence.

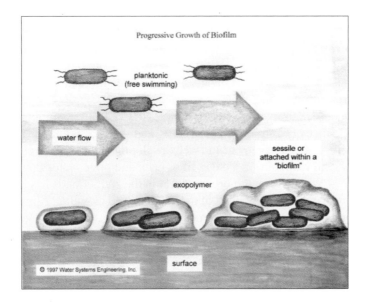

Figure 13.1. Progressive growth of biofilm.

Biological incrustations and their growth are the primary causes of most blockages. Sticky, slimy biofilm is an ideal place for particulates to adhere, and it promotes the growth of crystals that require a strong attachment to assist them in becoming mineral deposits. Biofilms also respond to conditions in the well. Increases in oxygen content from aeration due to cascading water, for example, often result in excessive growth of certain bacterial populations. Food sources coming into the well with the groundwater can encourage growth and can increase biofilms, thus blocking more flow pathways. Velocity increases due to higher pumping rates often result in thicker biofilm because the bacteria produce more exopolymer in an attempt to avoid being pulled into the flow—and each bacterium is capable of producing 30 to 100 times its own weight in exopolymer. Figure 13.2 shows flow pathways being blocked by the growth of biofilm.

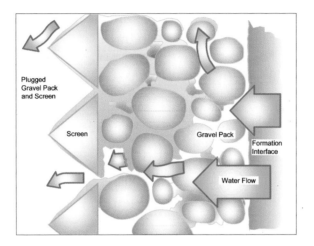

Figure 13.2. Blockage of flow paths by biofilm.

Bacteria Growth

The growth rate of bacteria varies considerably, however the average is between 20 min and 3 hr, and the exponential growth rates of bacteria (Figure 13.3) can cause rapid changes in the well environment. Odor and color problems can occur overnight, and the growth of bacteria often results in a well losing capacity rapidly.

In colder climates, typical groundwater temperatures can slow bacterial growth in wells, and in warmer climates temperatures can make wells more susceptible to rapid bacterial growth. Other factors, such as the availability of nutrients, also play a significant role in biological blockages.

The example presented in Figure 13.3 shows that, in less than 3 hr, each bacterium multiplied 1,000 times (this figure is based on bacteria doubling every 20 min). If all factors—such as food and byproduct removal—are perfect and the flow pathways are 50% plugged, then it would take only one generation of bacteria to fill the remaining pathways. Although 20-min transition periods are unlikely, the significant deterioration of wells occurring in only a few weeks often can be explained by the fact that a biogrowth quickly can produce excessive populations.

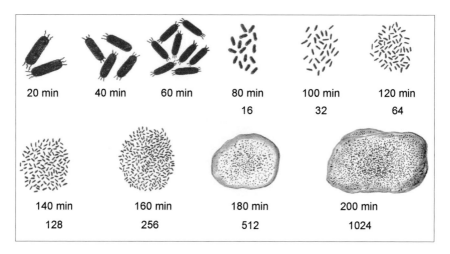

Figure 13.3. Illustration of the exponential growth of bacteria; in slightly longer than 3 hr, each bacterium multiplied 1,000 times (Water Systems Engineering, Inc.).

An excess bacteria population occurring in a well often results in taste and odor problems or in a measurable reduction in well production due to blockage of the pore space or the screen. Most wells are capable of sustaining production even when only 50% of the flow pathways are open. The capacity being pumped is not limited until the blockage begins to close the remaining 50% of the pathways. Additionally, it can take many years for the first 50% to become plugged, but the remaining 50% could be closed much more rapidly.

CHARACTERISTICS OF IRON DEPOSITS

Iron deposits primarily are iron oxides, however some iron carbonates and iron sulfides are formed under specific conditions. In general, these deposits should be considered to be chemical incrustations, but the oxidation reaction—which produces the oxide—could be driven either chemically or biologically.

Oxidation

The simplest oxidation of iron is the oxidation of the dissolved iron, Fe(II) or ferrous iron, which usually enters the well in groundwater. Ferrous iron is present in the aquifer from the reduction of iron oxhydroxides coupled with the oxidation of organic matter. The reduction of Fe(III) to Fe(II) is attributed to the bioenergetic activity of iron-reducing bacteria. The corrosion of casing or screen can result in the production of Fe(II). Direct oxidation of steel casing and screens is promoted in the hydrogen-rich (acidic) environment in the lower anoxic areas of the well. This environment primarily is the result of biological activity, because the fermentative and sulfate-reducing bacteria are responsible for the low pH of this zone.

The Fe(II) generated from either organic or inorganic resources easily is oxidized to Fe(III) as water enters the more aerobic zones in a well. The production of ferric oxide ($Fe_2O_3 \cdot (x)H_2O$) results in a slick, slimy, very insoluble compound that is characterized by a red color. This viscous red material can cover the casing, screen, and other well hardware. The chemical dehydration this material results in a very dense ferric-oxide deposit. These deposits form in the more aerobic zones of the well, and plug screens and piping.

Biologically driven Fe(II) oxidation takes place near the interface of the anoxic/aerobic water, because the iron-oxidizing bacteria are aerobic. The iron oxidizers obtain their energy from the oxidation of iron. They must operate primarily in this area to satisfy their need for oxygen and the Fe(II) ion, which otherwise would chemically oxidize very quickly into the oxygen-rich water of the aerobic zone.

The iron-oxidizing or iron-related bacteria are divided into two distinct groups which, in a sense, dictate where deposits form. The iron bacteria most frequently responsible for the direct blockage of well screens and filter packs are stalked or sheath-forming bacteria. The most well known of this group is *Gallionella ferruginea* (Figure 13.4). *Crenothrix, Leptothrix,* and *Sphaerotilus* also occur commonly, however they facilitate the accumulation of Fe(III) oxide via different mechanisms.

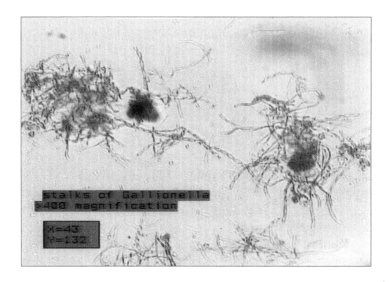

Figure 13.4. Stalks of *Gallionella ferruginea*.

Biofilm

The other iron-related bacteria usually are grouped in the slime-former designation and are members of many of the heterotrophic species that inhabit wells. These bacteria are somewhat more ubiquitous in the well system but typically collect in the aerobic portion of the aquifer directly adjacent to the well. There—much nearer to the aquifer formation—they are able to build biofilms that are more structurally sound. These bacteria are responsible for accumulation of ferric (III) oxides, primarily in the formation adjacent to the well.

Stalks of the *Gallionella*, as shown in Figure 13.4, easily can form bridges that block screens and other flow areas. The mass formed is composed of iron oxyhydroxides and sheaths glued together with the bacteria-produced polysaccharide exopolymer. In the initial stages deposits are soft, but as the iron compounds dehydrate the deposits become quite dense and extremely difficult to dislodge. Brushing followed by acid treatment usually is the cleaning method of choice.

Iron Sulfide

Another iron deposit that is driven bacteriologically is iron sulfide, which often accumulates in wells as a result of the synergistic anaerobic activity of fermentative bacteria and sulfate-reducing bacteria. A source of iron and oxidized sulfur also must be available. Hydrogen, which is present from the metabolic activities of fermentative anaerobes, usually combines with the reduced sulfur produced by sulfate-reducing bacteria. This results in the production of hydrogen sulfide. When considerable Fe(II) is present, iron sulfide also forms and accumulates in the area.

FIELD TESTING OF INCRUSTATIONS

Analysis of the well water is far more important for determining the type of blockage that can be present in a plugged well, but samples of incrustation occasionally are obtained. Without the availability of a complete on-site field laboratory, the analysis usually is restricted to the results of acid dissolution of the incrustation.

The color and density of the sample can provide insight into the type of incrustation encountered.

- Black color indicates an iron sulfide or a manganese deposit.
- Dark to reddish-brown color usually indicates a ferric (III) iron deposit.
- Bright-yellow color most probably indicates a sulfur deposit and usually is seen high up on the drop piping and casing, often above the water level.
- Light-tan color can indicate dolomite (a mixture of calcium and magnesium carbonate).
- Very light to white color indicates a calcium carbonate deposit, and usually is seen along with other minerals that display additional colors.

- ◆ Very heavy or dense material usually indicates a deposit that is predominately mineral.
- ◆ Very light or low-density deposit usually indicates that considerable biological material is present.

Placement of a few drops of hydrochloric (muriatic) acid on the incrustation might elicit some additional information.

- ◆ Considerable foaming or frothing indicates the presence of a carbonate (calcium, magnesium, or iron).
- ◆ Hydrogen sulfide gas or rotten-egg odor indicates the presence of iron sulfide.
- ◆ A strong chlorine odor indicates the possible presence of manganese dioxide.
- ◆ No occurrence of effervescence, frothing, or odor usually indicates the presence of iron oxide, calcium sulfate, or silica.

A number of simple field tests are available from various vendors, and can be used to check for iron, manganese sulfate, calcium, and phosphates. Using a field test kit and as little hydrochloric acid as possible, a water-well professional can dissolve a small amount of the deposit. Diluting the dissolved material with deionized water reduces the acid strength and provides a volume sufficient for testing. Positive tests for any of the parameters listed above should confirm some of the other observations.

TIMELY MAINTENANCE

Cleaning

Preventative maintenance (PM) performed on any operating system can save considerable time and cost. Preventative maintenance for water-well systems for the most part has been relegated to pump maintenance and occasional observation on the condition of casing and screen. Periodic cleaning of the casing, screen, and the bottom of the well would go a long way in preventing blockage and the loss of water quality and quantity. The biggest impediment to periodic cleaning is the need to remove the pump, and the cleaning of the well and filter pack therefore has been limited to the scheduling of pump removal and repair.

Even in these cases, the necessity of cleaning the well seems poorly understood. Often the pump is removed and repaired and only a token chlorination of the well is conducted—usually to meet basic regulatory requirements. Failure to perform a simple cleaning often results in a tremendous loss in the areas of both maintenance and good well operation.

The incrustation or blockage of water flow to a well occurs over time, with the initial blockage forming on or near the screen. In the case of an open-borehole well, the blockage occurs at the interface where water enters the wellbore. This area, as discussed above, is subject to mineral incrustation due to precipitation following pH change as the aquifer water is degassed, or from oxidation as ferrous (II) iron enters the more oxygenated water of the well. Various bacterial activities also encourage deposits in the area of the borehole wall and well screen; as deposits occur, water flow into the well is slowed. The slowing of water flow also permits additional deposition. Bacterial growth, which often precedes the forming of mineral deposits, also proceeds more abundantly in slowed water channels. Gradually, blockage moves outward from the well center and becomes denser and more difficult to remove.

The gradual formation of the blockage to a great extent depends on the initial formation or deposit. If a periodic or "timely" cleaning is performed, then more severe and incapacitating blockage can be averted. Several considerations must be recognized, including the need to determine how often the blockage process (which occurs continually) reaches a point at which cleaning becomes critical. Additionally, deposit occurrence probably takes place more frequently than does the required pump maintenance, therefore it is important to establish how cleaning can be achieved without incurring the cost of pump removal.

Periodic water tests can be used to track potential formation of deposits and increases in bacterial growth rates. Historical records of wellfield operational data also often illuminate the incidence of fouling in well systems. If a well shows a loss in specific capacity or a water-quality loss (e.g., 10% or greater) on a certain cycle, such as every 6 yr to 8 yr, then cutting the cycle in half is reasonable. A cleaning performed at the halfway mark (3 yr to 4 yr) requires far less chemical and mechanical effort.

Light cleaning can be used successfully to remove the initial deposits of both mineral and bacteriological incrustations; the difficult task is completing the cleaning without removing the pump. Avoiding pump removal results in less-costly periodic cleaning and less downtime. Under such circumstances well maintenance occurs more often. Although the actual design of a light cleaning system is beyond the scope of this chapter, some ideas are presented below.

Treatment Fluids

Laboratory studies and field use have demonstrated that movement or circulation of treatment fluids (usually consisting of an acid and a biodispersant) within the casing and screened zones results in dissolution of the initial deposits of mineral and bacteria. These deposits then can be removed by pumping the fluid to a waste-holding area. In the more shallow wells, plastic piping can be installed alongside the pump, and against the casing or borehole wall. One pipe is fitted to reach to the well bottom and one pipe is extended to the top of the screen. A surface pump is used to circulate a light acid (1% to 3% concentration) and biodispersant (such as Johnson Screens NW-310) mixture (0.5% to 3%) downhole. After the solution has been circulated for 6 hr it is pumped from the well. The well's content is pumped to a waste-holding area until the well's pH has returned to normal (pH 7). The well then can be returned to service.

Another method is the use of a single pipe to deliver the treatment fluids into the lower zones of the well and then injecting nitrogen gas to facilitate water movement or mechanical agitation to improve cleaning. After the nitrogen is periodically agitated for 4 hr to 6 hr, the treatment fluids can be pumped from the well using the installed well pump. The extracted fluids are pumped to a waste-holding area.

In smaller well systems, treatment fluids are added and then circulated using the well pump by directing the flow back downhole to supply agitation. Once cleaning has stopped, the water is pumped to a waste-holding area and the well is returned to standard operation. Although this method supplies some agitation, it is limited from reaching the deeper well zones.

Well designs now should include the installation of piping or other mechanisms to facilitate the addition of treatment fluids to both the well bottom and the active production zones. This type of installation also would facilitate the use of disinfection chemicals.

ACID TREATMENT

Acids, particularly mineral acids, primarily are used for the dissolution of mineral deposits or of incrustations that incorporate minerals into the biological matrix. Hydrochloric acid and sulfamic acid currently are used most frequently for treatment, however phosphoric acid is becoming more popular due to the availability of a food-grade type, the handling safety, and the very limited corrosiveness of this acid versus hydrochloric and sulfamic acids (which often are used with inhibitors). Without the addition of an inhibiting agent (such as Johnson Screens NuWell 310®), extensive corrosion can take place in the well.

Organic acids are used during well cleaning because of their reported effect on bacterial exopolymer. This use could be overstated, however, and using organic acids often results in the production of less-soluble by-products. More than 80% of incrustations found in well systems contain heavy concentrations of minerals. The acids typically used for their effect on biological accumulations are hydroxyacetic acid and acetic acid. These acids produce acetates when they come into contact with calcium minerals such as calcite and (to a lesser extent) gypsum. The acetate salts have limited solubility and, as a result, remain in the well system following washout of the acid cleaner.

Acetates and organic acids are excellent carbon sources for use by future bacterial growth. Citric acid and hydroxyacetic often are used in conjunction with a strong mineral acid (such as hydrochloric acid) to aid in solubilizing iron deposits, and work as chelating agent helping to keep the iron in the solution to be discharged with the treatment fluids. The citric and hydroxyacetic do have some solubilizing effect against the softer iron oxyhydroxide deposits, however activity against the more dense dehydrated iron oxides is limited even with hydrochloric acid use. The citric acid and the salts of hydroxyacetic acid are excellent food sources for heterotrophic bacteria.

During the last few years, the development of dispersants (such as the Johnson Screens NW-310 and NW-320 products) has provided a much more efficient method of improving dissolution and removal of both iron and biological substances. Table 13.3 provides some of the basic information concerning the various acids currently in use.

Hydrochloric Acid

Of the three mineral acids used most often as solvents of mineral deposits during well cleaning, hydrochloric acid (HCL) is the most universal. Although it is a very low-cost acid, it is very corrosive both to equipment and to human tissue. The acid (hydrogen chloride) actually is a gas and the fumes from the acid solution are dangerous. These fumes can cause deterioration of equipment and electrical wiring when they condense with water vapors on such surfaces. Inhaled, the fumes are caustic to lung tissue. In addition to the personal safety issues posed the acid is very corrosive to steel (especially stainless steel). Inhibited hydrochloric acid—or the use of inhibitors—often give water-well professionals a false sense of protection. Inhibitors have a very short life (4 hr to 6 hr) in a strong-acid cleaning operation; and when the inhibitors are exhausted, the equipment and the well are left completely unprotected.

Table 13.3. Characteristics of Common Acids

Characteristic	Phosphoric	Sulfamic	Hydrochloric	Hydroxy-acetic	Citric
Appearance	Clear liquid	White crystal	Slightly yellow liquid	Clear liquid	White crystal
Formula	H_3PO_4	HSO_3NH_2	HCl	CH_2OHCOO	$C_6H_8O_7$
Molecular weight	98.0	97.1	36.47	76.05	192.12
Type	Mineral	Mineral	Mineral	Organic	Organic
Hazardous fumes	None	None	High	Some	None
Relative strength	Strong	Strong	Strong	Weak	Weak
pH at 1%	1.5	1.2	0.6	2.33	2.6
Relative reaction time (1 = fast 10 = slow)	4–5	< 2	1	4–5	4–5
Corrosiveness to: Metals Skin/tissue	Slight Moderate	Moderate Moderate	Very high Severe	Slight Slight	Slight Slight

Characteristic	Phosphoric	Sulfamic	Hydrochloric	Hydroxy-acetic	Citric
Reactivity vs. Carbonate scale Sulfate scale Fe/Mn oxides Biofilm	Very good; Good to poor; Good; Poor	Very good; Good (initially); Fair; Poor	Very good; Good to poor; Very good; Poor	Poor to fair; Very poor; Good; Moderately good	Poor; Very poor; Chelate Poor
Quantity (lb) of 100% Acid Required to Dissolve 1 lb of Calcium Carbonate	0.65 lb	2.0 lb	0.73 lb	4.5 lb	4.0 lb

Sulfamic Acid

Sulfamic acid is a granular acid (such as NW-100) and usually is used to treat smaller wells (those smaller both in diameter and in depth). Its ease of transportation and handling make this a good chemical for smaller service companies. Sulfamic acid use poses a major problem if calcium sulfate is present in the well or if the water contains a high concentration of calcium hardness and sulfate. Sulfamic acid, once dissolved, is subject to hydrolysis, which is a reaction that converts the very soluble sulfamate ion to sulfate—in actuality producing sulfuric acid. Although this is a strong acid, the presence of the sulfate ion prevents further dissolution of gypsum or other sulfate mineralization, and (if calcium is present) promotes precipitation of these salts when the pH rises.

Phosphoric Acid

Phosphoric acid dissolves most, or all, of the same products as hydrochloric acid, particularly if a strong organic dispersant (e.g., NW-310) also is used. Phosphoric acid reacts more slowly, however, and its food-grade quality is available to a greater extent than is any other acid. Typically available in concentrations of 75% and 85%, using such high concentrations means that smaller quantities of this acid are handled and transported. No gaseous fumes are emitted, however sprays or liquid mists are acidic. Corrosion activity against most metals is very limited as compared to that of hydrochloric or sulfamic acids. Phosphoric acid also always should be used with a strong polymeric (nonphosphate) dispersant, because this prevents the formation of phosphate salts that could enhance bacterial activity if the salts are left in the well or aquifer.

Determining the Quantity of Acid to Use

Determination of the quantity of mineral acid to be used in well treatment should be based on the potential for calcite, gypsum, and iron or manganese oxide to form in the particular well. Water analysis indicates the potential for formation of any or all of the substances, and also is used to determine the required concentration of acid. Table 13.4 lists some basic parameters that can be used in selecting the strength of a mineral acid. Carbonates have the greatest potential for neutralizing acids; therefore their presence is the controlling factor. Calcium sulfate or gypsum and both iron and manganese oxides require a minimum pH of 2.0 to be able to provide reasonable dissolution of the incrustation.

Table 13.4. Concentration of Acid Required for Various Minerals' Potential

Mineral	Acid Concentration
High carbonate and sulfate potential	10% to 12%
Some carbonate or sulfate, or strong iron or manganese	8% to 10%
Moderate mineral potential with no heavy deposits	6% to 8%
No mineral deposit expected and water pH below 7.0	3% to 5%
No alkalinity and water pH below 6.0	3%
Recently acid cleaned, but using a biodispersant for biogrowth removal	1%

After determining the concentration of the acid to be used, the volume of acid needed must be calculated. The volume of the area to be cleaned is calculated using the standing-well volume (defined as depth of the well minus depth to the static water level) plus the volume of the filter pack multiplied by the porosity of the filter pack. A rule of thumb to use is 1.5 times the standing well volume. In well systems with unusually large filter packs, or with an underreamed filter-packed area, the actual calculation should be made, because calculations using 1.5 times standing well volume do not include the enlarged system. The 1.5 factor also is useful for calculations for open-borehole wells. The additional volume aids considerably in penetrating the aquifer immediately surrounding the wellbore, which often is the area experiencing the severe biological impact.

CHLORINE TREATMENT

Chlorine—or one of its formulations—is the oxidizer of choice for water-well disinfection. Technically, it is available as chlorine gas or as 5%, 10%, 12%, and 15% solutions of sodium hypochlorite. Chlorine also is found in a powder form as calcium hypochlorite. The powder or granular form has 65% to 70% available chlorine. Chlorine gas typically is not used in well chlorination, due to both the safety problem of handling the product and the difficulty in the application of a gaseous product to a well environment. Sodium hypochlorite is widely used due to its ease of application (because it is a liquid). Calcium hypochlorite is used when its high level of chlorine (which reduces cost) and its longer shelf life are required. Sodium hypochlorite solutions lose 5% to 10% of their activity for every 30 days of storage.

Chlorine is available for use as a disinfectant, both as the hypochlorite ion and as hypochlorous acid. The hypochlorous acid form is a minimum of 100-times more effective as a disinfectant, particularly against free-swimming planktonic bacteria. The pH of the cleaning solution determines the availability of the two forms (shown in Figure 13.5).

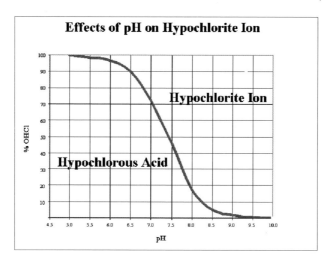

Figure 13.5. Effects of pH on hypochlorite ion.

Chlorine Gas and pH Control

When chlorine gas is used it produces an acid reaction which lowers the pH of the water and essentially delivers hypochlorous acid. This can be reversed in very alkaline waters. Sodium and calcium hypochlorite, however, both have caustic products as part of their formulation, so their use increases the pH of the cleaning solution and only the hypochlorite ion is formed. Buffering acids can be used to neutralize the caustic hypochlorite product and the natural alkalinity of the water to maintain a pH of 6.5 at the point that maximum hypochlorous acid is formed. Chlorine gas is released if the pH is allowed to fall below 5.0, therefore the reaction must be calculated carefully and monitored to prevent the release of this dangerous gas. Several commercial products are available but the only worthwhile products are those formulated to take into consideration the alkalinity of the water and the quantity of the hypochlorite product used.

The following formula might simplify pH-control calculations.

$$\begin{array}{c}\text{Quarts of}\\ \text{NuWell 410}^{\circledR}\end{array} = \frac{\begin{array}{c}\text{actual}\\ \text{alkalinity}\end{array}}{100\ \text{mg}/\ell} \cdot \frac{\begin{array}{c}\text{chlorine}\\ \text{concentration}\end{array}}{200\ \text{mg}/\ell} \cdot \frac{\text{volume}}{250\ \text{gal}} \qquad \textbf{(13.1)}$$

Example

Water total alkalinity	=	150 mg/ℓ
Standing well volume (SWV)	=	900 gal
Total disinfectant volume (TDV)	=	3,600 gal
Desired chlorine level	=	200 mg/ℓ

$$\frac{150}{100} \cdot \frac{200}{200} \cdot \frac{3,600}{1,000} = \quad 5.4\ \text{quarts of NuWell 410}^{\circledR}$$

Although chlorine use or well disinfection at times is absolutely necessary, if it is used to excess the application can be debilitating to the well system. One of the important parameters of the saturation index is pH. As the pH rises, carbonates and other minerals begin to precipitate. The flooding of the well environment with a chlorine solution causes a dramatic rise in the pH level, resulting in increased precipitation of insoluble carbonates, sulfates, and oxides in the well. If calcium hypochlorite is used, then the reaction takes place even in water that is low in hardness because the calcium hypochlorite supplies the calcium necessary for calcite or gypsum deposition. The use of pH-controlled chlorination and sodium hypochlorite therefore greatly reduces the formation of deposits in and around the well. If NW-410 is used to buffer the solution, it also supplies dispersant for calcium or hard-water control and surfactants to improve penetration.

Chlorine (or any strong oxidizing agent) attacks the polysaccharide polymers produced by the bacteria. The attack often creates insoluble by-products which tend to increase the density and decrease the penetration of the bacterial biofilm formation (Figure 13.6). Continued chlorinating procedures might cause or increase the blockage effect of the bacterial slime, particularly in an aquifer where mechanical shear (e.g., brushing) is not available to help dislodge the biological matrix. Using lesser quantities of chlorine for disinfection can reduce this effect.

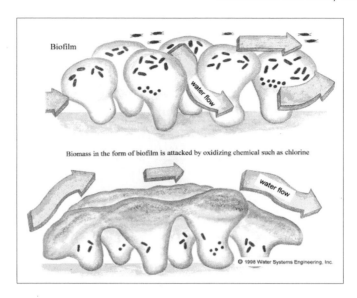

**Figure 13.6. Effects of chlorine on biofilm
(Water Systems Engineering, Inc.).**

Chlorine Levels

Laboratory tests have demonstrated that a higher degree of coliform removal is achieved when chlorine concentration is between 50 mg/ℓ and 200 mg/ℓ. Tests examined treatment of well systems over a wide chlorine dosage (20 mg/ℓ to 5,000 mg/ℓ). The conclusions indicate that strong oxidation of top layers of the biofilm prevented penetration to the levels where coliform resided. The lower levels of available chlorine, together with mechanical activity and adequate contact time, resulted in better penetration and more-effective removal of coliform.

Pretreatment

The pretreatment and method of chlorine application are other factors that greatly influence the success rate of water-well disinfection. The well—like any surface to be disinfected—should have any debris removed and all incrustation eliminated prior to the application of the hypochlorite solution. The correct method for disinfecting a well is to remove the pump and evacuate all the debris from the well bottom. The well casing and screen areas should be brushed to remove incrustation. Evacuating (air lifting or pumping) the well bottom and screen area further improves the disinfection process.

After the level of chlorination is selected, the necessary chlorine solution volume should be calculated. Although smaller wells often are chlorinated by adding the chlorine solution directly to the well, little success is achieved because the chlorine solution is not dispersed throughout the column and frequently never reaches the lowest zone. Larger wells often continue to fail when only relatively small volumes of solution are tremied into the various zones.

Chlorination Procedure

The highest degree of successful chlorination is achieved by preparing a volume of chlorine solution equal to 4 times the standing well volume. The ideal procedure is to prepare this treatment volume in a blending tank at the selected chlorine level—at a pH of 6.5—and then to tremie the solution into all zones of the well. Place 25% of the volume at the well bottom, 25% at the halfway position in the screen zone, and 25% at the top of the screen; use the remaining 25% to wash the upper portion of the well above the static water level. In open-borehole wells, equal portions of treatment fluids should be placed at the well bottom, halfway up the water column, and at the static water level. A portion also should be used to disinfect the upper level of the well, and the pump and any column piping or other hardware that is removed from the well should be disinfected.

After the chlorine solution is in place a surge block or tight-fitting swab should be used to surge the solution, effectively washing most surfaces and forcing the solution into the formation and filter pack. Surging should be conducted for no less than 30 min for each 20-ft section of screen or casing below the screen area. In open-borehole construction, use of a jetting device which recirculates the hypochlorite solution usually is preferable for preventing damage to the borehole wall.

Evacuation of the well should be performed using an air-lift method or high-capacity pump to remove the oxidizing solution and any loosened debris. Air-lifting or pumping should begin at the well bottom then the equipment should be raised every 10 ft to 20 ft when each area is clean.

If pump removal is not planned, then the hypochlorite solution should be tremied into place by placing the tremie line alongside the pump. Agitation should be accomplished, for example, by recirculating the treatment fluids downhole with an auxiliary pump or, in smaller well systems, by diverting the well discharge back down the well. Most coliform and other bacteria reside in the bottom portion of the well (many wells are constructed with a sump or dead space) and the rehabilitation professional must inject chlorine and also utilize some mechanical force to disrupt this area and enable contact between the organisms and the disinfectant treatment fluids.

ALTERNATIVE TO POLYPHOSPHATE TREATMENT

Phosphate compounds (e.g., inorganic phosphate salts) primarily are used as silt and clay dispersants during well developments, and also are found in many drilling fluids. In recent years, use of phosphates has become somewhat controversial because they stimulate bacterial growth. It originally was thought that phosphates were removed during the evacuation of the well. The interaction of phosphates with calcium, however, usually produces insoluble salts and these salts remain in the well, often resulting in bacterial problems over extended periods of time. Phosphate chemicals are available in a wide range of products (which are classified as acid or alkaline). Determining which product is most effective in a particular area could be difficult, and often is decided over time via trial and error. In areas where there exists considerable calcium carbonate potential, acidic phosphate products can cause dissolution of formations and the subsequent production of by-products of limited solubility, resulting in formation blockage.

Polymer solutions such as Johnson NuWell 220® Clay Dispersant have replaced phosphates, especially in large well-development projects. Additionally, because of their high activity their use is quite economical. Polymers applicable for well development usually are referred to as drilling-fluid control agents or polymeric dispersants. Phosphate products are used at between 0.5% and 2.0% by weight of well volume, and the polymer products (which are liquids) are used at 0.2 % to 0.4 % of well volume.

SONAR-JET™ METHOD OF WELL REHABILITATION

The Sonar-Jet™ well-rehabilitation method employs two controlled physical actions that work simultaneously.

- A mild "harmonic" (kinetic) frequency of shockwaves designed to gently loosen hardened mineral, bacterial, or other types of deposits; and
- A pulsating, horizontally directed, gas pressure jets fluid at a high velocity back and forth through the perforations to deep-clean aquifer zones.

The shockwaves loosen crust-like deposits and the gas jets repetitively surge fluids in the well back and forth through the perforations.

Other vendors offer similar types of well-development programs, however the types of cleaning operations are more appropriate for near-well, hardened deposits (mineral deposits) and have not been effective on soft, biofouling plugs, which can be forced outward into the aquifer by the harmonic step of the Sonar-Jet™ method.

SUMMARY

Most wells—given sound integrity of the well structure and continued viability of the source aquifer—can be rehabilitated to near normal operating capacity. Wells often actually can be improved. If proper cleaning procedures and re-development are used, then capacities can be raised to as much as 20% to 30% more than the original production rate.

Water wells usually are cleaned with an acid because the most responsive blockage is mineral deposits. Mineral removal returns the greatest increase in capacity, however most blockage initiates with biological involvement from biofilm formation. If the biological involvement is not removed, then reformation of mineral blockage occurs rapidly and loss of capacity occurs more quickly.

The key to any good rehabilitation program is a proper diagnosis and choice of treatment chemistry and mechanical application. Although physical and video inspection is important, a biological and chemical analysis is invaluable.

Appendix 13.C (DVD) provides an overview of well rehabilitation. This appendix also contains information regarding various chemicals manufactured by Johnson Screens that can be used to rehabilitate a well. This information is provided primarily for the water-well professional. Appendix 13.D (DVD) is a computer program that can be used by water-well professionals to design a chemical treatment process for the cleaning and disinfection of water wells.

CHAPTER 14
Groundwater Monitoring and Remediation Wells

Robert J. Sterrett, PhD
Engineering Management Support Inc.

During the past 20 years, the state of practice regarding monitoring and remediation of groundwater has evolved significantly, especially regarding non-aqueous phase liquids (NAPLs). The practice of groundwater monitoring has become somewhat prescriptive. Many U.S. states, for example, have published guidance documents with respect to the design and installation of groundwater monitoring wells. ASTM International also has published a standard (D 5092-04) for the design and installation of groundwater monitoring wells. Additionally, for groundwater remediation there are presumptive remedies for certain suites of chemicals that can be found in groundwater.

In this same period, the field of groundwater remediation also has advanced significantly. In the early 1980s, extracting and treating groundwater (pump and treat) to achieve regulatory standards was a standard and accepted approach to the remediation of groundwater. By the late 1980s and early 1990s, the practice of pumping and treating groundwater was found to not be cost effective for remediating groundwater to regulatory limits (e.g., a drinking-water standard) (National Research Council 1994).

Alternatives to the pump-and-treat method include barrier technologies, in situ treatment technologies (biological, thermal, and chemical), and natural

629

attenuation. Currently, groundwater pumping and treatment systems primarily are used for hydraulic containment, with the objective of controlling the migration of chemically impacted groundwater and preventing the expansion of plumes. Groundwater extraction systems also are used to reduce chemical concentrations within a plume or the source area. Although pump-and-treat systems can be used to restore groundwater quality, application generally is limited to sites that exist in the simplest hydrogeologic settings (e.g., small areas in homogeneous and isotropic aquifers that are composed of coarse-grained materials). In summary, pump and treat generally more often is considered to be a containment technology rather than a mechanism for significant mass removal.

This chapter does not attempt to provide groundwater sampling techniques or to cover all available groundwater remediation technologies—entire books have been devoted to those subjects. The U.S. Environmental Agency and other U.S. agencies have issued numerous guidance documents on site characterization and remediation. Select documents are provided on the accompanying DVD in the appendices for this chapter. This chapter instead focuses on the design of groundwater monitoring wells and groundwater extraction wells. A brief discussion of chemical transport is provided in the following sections and then well design is examined. Water-well professionals must have a basic understanding of chemical transport to be successful in placing wells appropriately.

CHEMICAL MOVEMENT

Advection

Once in the aquifer, the primary driving force for chemical movement in most cases is created by the hydraulic gradient that produces groundwater flow. Chemicals entering groundwater are transported downgradient, typically forming a plume of chemically impacted groundwater. This type of chemical movement is termed "advection." Other factors, such as hydrodynamic dispersion, also influence the shape of the plume.

Hydrodynamic Dispersion

Hydrodynamic dispersion includes mechanical mixing and molecular diffusion. These two processes cause a spreading (dispersion) of the chemical over a much larger area than advection alone would; consequently, they also cause a dilution of the chemical away from the source area (Figure 14.1). Mechanical mixing processes include velocity differences within the pore openings, velocity differences caused by the difference in the size of the pores through which the water molecules move, and the degree of tortuosity (length) of the pore channels.

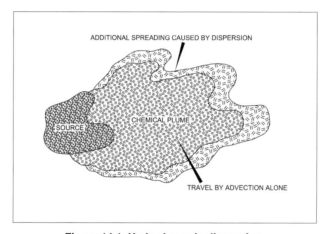

Figure 14.1. Hydrodynamic dispersion.

Molecular diffusion (chemical dispersion) also can occur. In the absence of any groundwater movement, a slug of highly concentrated chemical moves outward from its origin toward points of lower concentration. This type of dispersion occurs due to the kinetic activity of the ionic or molecular constituents. The effect of molecular diffusion on chemical dispersion usually is much less than are the effects of mechanical mixing processes, except in the case of very low groundwater velocities. In most instances, it probably can be ignored when estimating the spread of chemicals—except in the situations of flow in geologic materials with low hydraulic conductivities (e.g., clay) or in areas of low hydraulic gradients.

Density

The density of the chemical constituent that enters the subsurface plays a part in determining the vertical dimensions of the plume. If a chemical entering an aquifer in its pure (non-aqueous) form is denser than water, then it sinks slowly as it disperses transversely and longitudinally. The density and solubility of the chemical in relation to water—as well as the groundwater flow velocities and vertical hydraulic gradients—govern the vertical penetration of the plume into the aquifer as the chemical moves downgradient (Figure 14.2, Figure 14.3)). If the concentration of the chemical is below its solubility limit, then the transport of the chemical is governed by advection and dispersion.

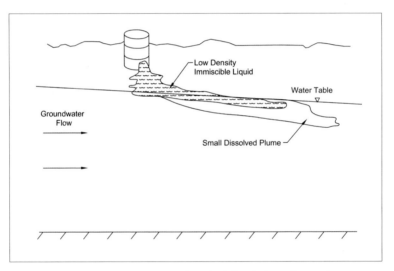

Figure 14.2. Diagram showing a chemical that is less dense than water entering an aquifer.

The concept of density of a chemical is important in the placement of the screen for observation wells. As indicated in Figure 14.2, a well screened at the bottom of the aquifer will miss detecting the plume. Figure 14.3 shows that the density of the chemical is sufficient to move along the dip underlying aquitard opposite the direction of groundwater flow.

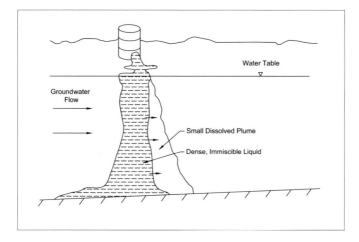

Figure 14.3. Diagram showing a chemical that is more dense than water entering an aquifer.

Chemical and Biochemical Reactions

Many chemical and biochemical reactions take place in the subsurface environment. The reactions reduce the concentrations of a chemical introduced in the subsurface and yield transformation products that differ from the chemical originally introduced. The most important of these processes are solution-precipitation, oxidation-reduction, adsorption-desorption, acid-base reactions, hydrolysis, volatilization, and microbial cell synthesis. Some of these reactions take place in the vadose zone before the chemical reaches the aquifer. Once in the aquifer, different chemicals in the same plume travel at different velocities depending on their reactions with the geologic media.

One important process is adsorption-desorption. The adsorption of a chemical tends to retard the velocity of the chemical of interest. Fetter (2001) provides a more thorough description of adsorption mechanisms and the resulting retardation of the chemical in relation to the average groundwater velocity (see Chapter 2 for a discussion of groundwater velocity). Figure 14.4 illustrates the differences between the velocity of a reactive chemical and that of a conservative chemical (a chemical that does not react with the geologic materials, such as chloride). Figure 14.4 also shows the effects of dispersion; a chemical is detected earlier than when it is predicted by using the average groundwater velocity.

Investigations of chemical fate and transport in groundwater should include an analysis of the chemical or biological reactions taking place, and the effects of these reactions on the concentrations of the chemical.

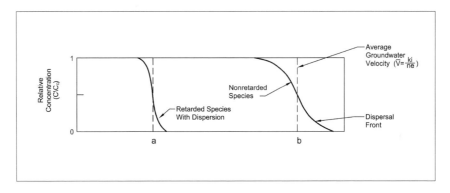

Figure 14.4. Illustration showing the differences between the velocity of a reactive chemical and of a conservative chemical, including the influence of dispersion.

Many factors play a part in the movement of a chemical in groundwater. The migration of a plume of a particular chemical is impacted by a variety of processes or circumstances such as the anisotropic-isotropic properties of the geologic materials, advection rate, hydrodynamic dispersion processes, and the potential for reaction with the subsurface materials. As such, it often is exceedingly difficult to perform a straightforward analysis of the movement and resultant spatial distribution of chemicals in groundwater.

Assessing Plumes of Chemicals in Groundwater

Openings in rocks or unconsolidated materials are not regularly spaced, and the permeability of the aquifer material varies both vertically and horizontally. Thus the transport of chemicals is highly variable. Despite this fact, it is necessary to estimate the groundwater flow direction within the aquifer so that the source of chemicals and the direction of plume movement can be assessed.

Usually the general direction of groundwater flow in shallow aquifers can be established based on the local topography (by using topographic maps or aerial photos) and the presence of streams or rivers—which often act as groundwater discharge boundaries. The local groundwater flow direction can be established by installing 3 small-diameter wells or piezometers into the aquifer. Water levels measured in the wells then establish a plane; the dip of this plane is the calculated direction of groundwater flow.

In porous, isotropic, and homogenous geologic materials, the direction of groundwater flow is indicated by determining the hydraulic gradient based on the relative water table or potentiometric surfaces derived from water-level measurements in the wells. In aquifers with significant anisotropy—especially fractured rock—the direction of groundwater flow (and chemical migration) might not be parallel to the hydraulic gradient (Fetter 2001). This is an important concept, because a plume of chemicals could migrate in a direction that is very different from the hydraulic gradient. See Chapter 2 for further discussion of groundwater flow direction.

LOCATING MONITORING WELLS

Regulatory guidance in the United States in the mid-1980s recommended the installation of a minimum of 4 wells at a site. Generally, 1 well is located up-gradient and 3 are downgradient from the site. Except at the smallest and simplest of sites, however, 4 wells seldom are sufficient for assessing the extent of chemicals released at a site.

The overall objective of a site investigation is to assess the lateral and vertical extent of detectable concentrations of chemicals of interest in soil and groundwater. After this assessment is made, a determination of the fate and transport of chemicals in the subsurface also is made so that all receptors (e.g., drinking-water wells, ecologically sensitive areas) can be protected. Achieving this objective might require the installation of wells at multiple depths and locations.

In practice, the number of wells required to adequately monitor a specific site varies depending on the local hydrogeology. Selection of appropriate depths depends on the density of the chemical of interest, anisotropic characteristics of the aquifer, hydraulic gradients (vertical and horizontal), and hydrostratigraphy of the site. Wells generally are located within the source area to assess source concentrations, and downgradient of the source to assess the extent of detectable concentrations of chemical. Background groundwater conditions also generally are monitored, especially if metals are chemicals of concern and geochemical indicators of natural biodegradation are being evaluated. The overall goal of a groundwater monitoring program is to develop a three-dimensional conceptual model of the site and a temporal evaluation of chemical concentration trends. Additional discussion on site characterization is contained in Appendix 14.A (DVD).

DESIGNING MONITORING WELLS

The particular design of a monitoring well depends on the hydrogeology of the site as well as on the characteristics of the chemicals of interest. Monitoring wells should be designed such that both water levels and samples can be collected—a design requirement that is in contrast to the design of a piezometer.

A piezometer is a well that is designed primarily to measure pore pressures (e.g., water levels or potentials). As such, the size of the borehole and the well (screen length and diameter) should be minimized to reduce the time-lag needed to achieve water-level equilibrium conditions between the formation and the piezometer. This minimization enables representative water-level measurements to be made.

Many monitoring wells are constructed of 2-in (51-mm) diameter casing and screen, however selection of the most appropriate diameter depends on numerous site-specific factors. For shallow monitoring wells or those used for measuring water levels only, 2-in (51-mm) diameter or smaller well screens and casing might be suitable, and they are appropriately sized to accommodate a transducer (a water-pressure measuring device) or electronic probe. Deeper wells and those where some form of aquifer test is necessary might require that the screen and casing be at least 4 in (102 mm) in diameter and be able to accommodate a pump. Wells that are larger in diameter not only are more expensive to install but also are more expensive to sample, especially if chemically impacted purge water requires treatment or disposal at a regulated facility.

Before installing the wells, there should be a clear objective for the design and location of each well. It is highly recommended that monitoring wells not be used as extraction wells because the design criteria are different for each well type. A monitoring well is not designed to be efficient and, if used as an extraction well, increased costs can result due to the design. Appendix 14.B (DVD) contains three guidance documents for the design of monitoring wells. Note that many states in the United States have guidelines for the design and installation of monitoring wells. The guidance documents included in the appendix provide examples.

Material Criteria for Monitoring Wells

Materials used for monitoring wells must be selected with care, because many common screen or casing materials—such as PVC, low-carbon steel, and stainless steel—can react with groundwater and impact the water-quality data. Monitoring well casing and screen materials should meet the following requirements (California Environmental Protection Agency 1995).

- ◆ Materials should maintain their structural integrity and durability in the environment in which they are used during their operating life. Monitoring well casings and screens should be resistant to chemical and microbiological corrosion and degradation in chemically impacted water or background waters.
- ◆ Well casings and screens should be able to withstand the physical forces acting upon them during and following their installation and during their use. These forces include those due to suspension in the borehole; grouting; development; purging, pumping, and sampling; and the forces exerted by the surrounding geologic materials.
- ◆ Materials should not chemically alter groundwater samples—especially with respect to the analytes of concern—as a result of their sorbing, desorbing, or leaching of analytes. If a metal such as chromium is an analyte of interest, for example, then the well casing or screen should not increase or decrease the amount of chromium in the groundwater. Any material that leaches from the casing or screen should not be an analyte of interest, and should not interfere in the analysis of an analyte of interest.

The selection of appropriate materials for monitoring-well casings and screens should include consideration of several site-specific factors including (California Environmental Protection Agency 1995):

- ◆ Geologic environment,
- ◆ Geochemical environment (both soil and groundwater),
- ◆ Anticipated well depth,

- Types and concentrations of suspected chemicals, and
- Design life of the monitoring well.

Materials used for monitoring wells should have the following characteristics.

- Screens are constructed from a material that is inert in the water being tested.
- Open area is maximized to facilitate development and provide rapid sample recovery.
- Slot sizes retain filter pack or natural formation consistent with capability to develop the well.
- Slot openings, slot design, open area, and screen diameter permit effective development.
- The diameter is appropriate for the intended purpose or for accommodating a specific pump or sampling equipment.

Table 14.1 lists the major types of materials used for monitoring wells, along with usage recommendations. Selection of the screen and casing material generally depends upon the chemical nature of the groundwater and the objective of the monitoring. It is important to note that the cost of a monitoring well is a fraction of the long-term costs for water-quality analyses. Therefore the most suitable well materials and construction practices should be selected for monitoring wells. The cost of the screen or casing material also is minor as compared to the cost of collection and analysis of water samples from the well.

Stainless steel offers the greatest combination of high strength, rigidity, and inertness when exposed to most common chemicals. Stainless steel should not be used in groundwater containing heavy metals, however, because leaching of chromium or other metallic components might occur. Materials composed of PVC are suitable for most monitoring applications, except where certain organic chemicals such as methyl ethyl ketone (MEK), toluene, trichloroethylene, and xylenes are present in elevated concentrations (typically on the order of parts per million). Teflon™ is suitable for most constituents, but its high cost and low strength properties can limit its use. In common applications Teflon™ seldom is used for groundwater monitoring wells.

Galvanized steel and carbon steel seldom are used in environmental studies where the emphasis is on the fate and transport of chemicals. The lack of use primarily is due to corrosion and resulting by-products of corrosion. Steel casing can be used for piezometers (water-level measurements only). Table 14.2

presents general recommendations for well casing and screen materials (Lapham et al. 1997). See Chapter 9 for additional discussion regarding well materials.

Table 14.1. Common Monitoring-Well Casing and Screen Materials

Type	Advantages	Disadvantages
Stainless Steel (SS)	◆ Least absorption of halogenated and aromatic hydrocarbons ◆ High strength at a great range of temperatures ◆ Excellent resistance to corrosion and oxidation (this differs between types of stainless steel) ◆ Readily available in all diameters and slot sizes	◆ Heavier than plastics ◆ Might corrode and leach some chromium in highly acidic waters (corrosion products mostly are iron compounds with some trace metals) ◆ Might act as a catalyst in some organic reactions ◆ Screens are costlier than those constructed of plastic
Polyvinyl-chloride (PVC)	◆ Lightweight ◆ Excellent chemical resistance to weak alkalies, alcohols, aliphatic hydrocarbons, and oils ◆ Readily available ◆ Lower cost than stainless steel and Teflon™ ◆ Easy to handle and assemble	◆ Weaker, less rigid, and more temperature sensitive than metallic materials ◆ Slot sizes might decrease over time in the presence of elevated concentrations of petroleum hydrocarbons ◆ Could adsorb some constituents from groundwater ◆ Might react with and leach some constituents from groundwater ◆ Poor chemical resistance to ketones, esters, and aromatic hydrocarbons if concentrations are elevated

Type	Advantages	Disadvantages
Polyvinyl-chloride (PVC) (continued)		◆ Leaking of volatile organic compounds such as THF, MEK, and cyclohexanone into groundwater can occur when glued joints are used (threaded joints with O-rings generally are used) ◆ Can deform due to heat of hydration if neat cement is used as an annulus seal ◆ CFCs can volatilize into the atmosphere within the unsaturated zone, potentially posing problems for studies of gas and moisture transport through the vadose zone
Polytetra-flouro-ethylene, Teflon™ (PTFE)	◆ Good resistance to attacks by most chemicals ◆ Lightweight ◆ High impact strength ◆ Ideal material in corrosive environments where inorganic solids or high concentrations of solvents (e.g., TCE, PCE) are present	◆ Screen slot openings could decrease in size over time due to compression ◆ Tensile strength and wear resistance are low as compared to other engineered plastics ◆ Expensive as compared to other plastics and to stainless steel ◆ Potential problems with creating a seal between the casing and annular space, because of the low coefficient of friction and "anti-stick" properties of the material

Table 14.2. Recommendations of Types of Well and Well Screen Materials for Different Geologic and Geochemical Conditions

Do Not Use	Use
PTFE, if well depth exceeds 225 ft (68.6 m) to 375 ft (114 m)	PVC or SS
PVC, if well depth exceeds 1,000 ft (305 m) to 2,000 ft (610 m)	SS
SS, if pH < 7.0	PVC or PTFE
SS, if DO >2 ppm	PVC or PTFE
SS, if H_2S > 1 ppm	PVC or PTFE
SS, if TDS > 1,000 ppm	PVC or PTFE
SS, if CO_2 > 50 ppm	PVC or PTFE
SS, if Cl > 500 ppm	PVC or PTFE
PVC, if a neat PVC solvent or softening agent[*] is present, or if the aqueous concentration of the PVC solvent or softening agent exceeds 0.25 times its solubility in water	SS or PTFE
Solvent-bonded joints for PVC casings	Threaded PVC casings
Welded stainless joints[**]	Threaded SS casings
Any PVC well casing that is not NSF-ASTM approved—D-1785 and F-480	ASTM-NSF-approved PVC well casings—D-1785 and F-480
Any stainless-steel casing that is not ASTM approved—A312	ASTM-approved SS 304 and SS 316 casings—A312

[*] Known PVC solvents and softening agents include tetrahydrofuran, cyclohexane, methyl ethyl ketone, methyl isobutyl ketone, methylene chloride, trichloromethane, 1,1-dichloroethane, 1,1,1-trichloroethane, trichloroethylene, benzene, toluene, acetone, and tetrachloroethylene.
[**] Do not weld on site.

(modified from California Environmental Protection Agency 1995)

Screens used for monitoring often are placed in geologic materials that have low hydraulic conductivities (e.g., clayey sands). In these situations, the open area of the screen should be maximized and should allow acceptable filtration so that the well can be properly developed. It is important to note that, in clayey sands, the well might never be developed to the point of producing sediment-free water. In such cases, a small slot size and small screen size generally are used with an appropriately sized filter pack. A properly developed well results in less sampling time. Many regulatory agencies dictate sampling methods that require a water sample be taken only after 3 to 10 well volumes have been removed, therefore the amount of time dedicated to taking a single sample can be excessive if low–open area screens are installed. Note that low-flow sampling techniques tend to negate the need to purge (and dispose of) excessive amounts of water. A description of low-flow sampling procedures is provided in Appendix 14.C (DVD).

Screen slot sizes must retain a high percentage (95% to 100%) of the filter pack or natural formation for all 2-in (51-mm) wells, because effective development of small-diameter wells is particularly difficult. For larger-diameter monitoring wells, the slot sizes can follow the recommendations for water wells more closely (*see* Chapter 9). Development is most effective when the slot openings are distributed uniformly around the circumference of the screen, so that the development action can reach as much of the formation and filter pack as is possible. The configuration of the slot should permit the maximum development energy to reach the formation.

Slot openings should widen inward (e.g., PVC vee wire, stainless-steel vee wire) so that finer formation materials are pulled through the screen during development. Slots that are cut straight through the casing tend to become plugged with fine material during development, thereby reducing the open area of the screen significantly. This is especially true for 2-in (51-mm) diameter or smaller screens where development effort already is relatively inefficient. Plugging of the slots increases the time required to obtain a representative water sample from the formation.

The transport of chemicals within a geologic unit generally occurs in the more permeable zones, therefore these zones should be monitored. This can be accomplished by using multiple wells with short screen segments. The scientific need to screen and sample thin, individual zones, however, must be balanced by costs and practicability. Commonly, a nest of wells is installed in single borehole or multiple boreholes to gather water samples from several depths in the aquifer (Figure 14.5). This method can be used to assess the vertical components of chemical concentrations and hydraulic gradients. Note that multiple wells completed in a single borehole can create problems with cross-contamination of water samples if the seals between zones are compromised and allow waters from the various zones to mix. If depths of investigation are relatively shallow, then it probably is more cost effective to drill separate boreholes for each monitoring well.

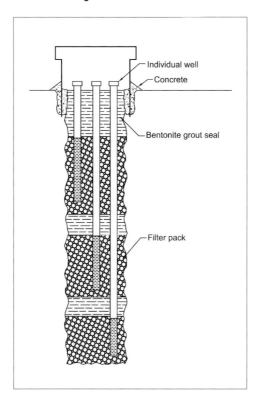

Figure 14.5. Multiple well completions within a single borehole (Morrison 1983).

Screens used to collect water samples typically are 5 ft (1.5 m) to 10 ft (3.3 m) in length, because samples should come from specific depths. Obtaining high yields is not the main objective of a monitoring well, but the well yield should be sufficient so that a reliable water sample can be collected. Screens that monitor groundwater quality at the top of the water table usually are 10 ft (3.3 m) to 15 ft (5 m) long, depending on anticipated long-term changes in groundwater elevation. Some of the screen always remains above the water table in the vadose zone. Wells that are screened across the water table are used to monitor for the presence of NAPLs that are less dense than water (for example petroleum hydrocarbons such as gasoline or diesel). If monitoring groundwater quality in a landfill, it is recommended that the well screen be placed below the water table so that water samples are not impacted by landfill gases.

Filter Pack Design and Well-Slot Selection

Monitoring wells often are installed in formations that have a wide range of particle sizes (which makes it difficult to design an effective filter pack). Filter-packing procedures recommended for water wells generally are suitable for monitoring wells. Unlike a production well, where 10% of the filter pack is developed out of the pack, the slot size for a monitoring well is selected to retain 100% of the filter pack. The design of a typical filter-packed monitoring well is shown in Figure 14.6.

To minimize the entrance of fine silts, sands, and clays into a monitoring well, the grain-size distribution curve for the filter pack is selected by multiplying the 70% retained size of the finest formation sample by 3 or 4. This leads to selection of a more conservatively sized filter pack than would be used for a water well. Selection of too fine a pack reduces the yield of the well, causing longer sampling times. Uniformity coefficients from filter-pack material should range from 1 to 3 (see Chapter 2 for discussion on uniformity). Suggested well-screen slot size and filter-pack material combinations are presented in Table 14.3 (modified ASTM D 5092-04).

All filter-pack material should be purchased from suppliers that have properly cleaned and bagged the material. Some investigations can require acid washing or steam cleaning of the pack to remove contaminants adhering to the filter-pack particles. At minimum, the pack should be washed with freshwater from a source that has a known water quality.

Often a project requires drilling and installing the monitoring well in one phase of work or mobilization. In this situation, the filter pack and well screen must be ordered prior to the collection of soil samples for laboratory testing of grain size. Information regarding the nature of subsurface conditions can be obtained from regional studies or from other sites in the area.

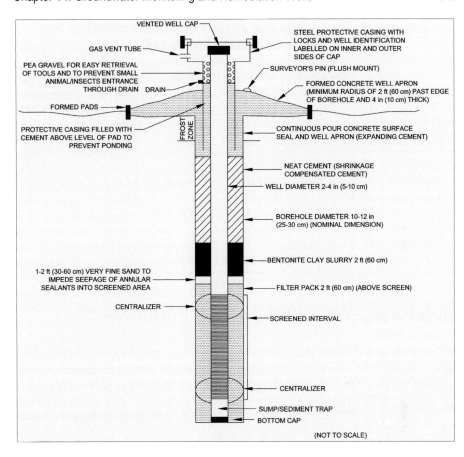

VENTED WELL CAP

STEEL PROTECTIVE CASING WITH
LOCKS AND WELL IDENTIFICATION
LABELLED ON INNER AND OUTER
SIDES OF CAP

GAS VENT TUBE

PEA GRAVEL FOR EASY RETRIEVAL
OF TOOLS AND TO PREVENT SMALL
ANIMAL/INSECTS ENTRANCE
THROUGH DRAIN   DRAIN

SURVEYOR'S PIN (FLUSH MOUNT)

FORMED CONCRETE WELL APRON
(MINIMUM RADIUS OF 2 ft (60 cm) PAST EDGE
OF BOREHOLE AND 4 in (10 cm) THICK)

FORMED PADS

PROTECTIVE CASING FILLED WITH
CEMENT ABOVE LEVEL OF PAD TO
PREVENT PONDING

FROST ZONE

CONTINUOUS POUR CONCRETE SURFACE
SEAL AND WELL APRON (EXPANDING CEMENT)

NEAT CEMENT (SHRINKAGE
COMPENSATED CEMENT)

WELL DIAMETER 2-4 in (5-10 cm)

BOREHOLE DIAMETER 10-12 in
(25-30 cm) (NOMINAL DIMENSION)

BENTONITE CLAY SLURRY 2 ft (60 cm)

1-2 ft (30-60 cm) VERY FINE SAND TO
IMPEDE SEEPAGE OF ANNULAR
SEALANTS INTO SCREENED AREA

FILTER PACK 2 ft (60 cm) (ABOVE SCREEN)

CENTRALIZER

SCREENED INTERVAL

CENTRALIZER

SUMP/SEDIMENT TRAP

BOTTOM CAP

(NOT TO SCALE)

Figure 14.6. A single-well completion monitoring-well design.

Table 14.3. Recommended Filter-Pack Characteristics for Common Screen Slot Sizes

Opening in (mm)	Slot No.	Sand Pack Mesh Sizes	1% Passing Size (D-1) mm	Effective Size (D-10) mm	30% Passing Size (D-30) mm	Range of Uniformity Coefficient
0.005 (0.125)	6	100	0.09 to 0.12	0.14 to 0.17	0.17 to 0.21	1.3 to 2.0
0.010 (0.25)	10	20 to 40	0.25 to 0.35	0.4 to 0.5	0.5 to 0.6	1.1 to 1.6
0.020 (0.50)	20	10 to 20	0.7 to 0.9	1.0 to 1.2	1.2 to 1.5	1.1 to 1.6
0.030 (0.75)	30	10 to 20	0.7 to 0.9	1.0 to 1.2	1.2 to 1.5	1.1 to 1.6
0.040 (1.0)	40	8 to 12	1.2 to 1.4	1.6 to 1.8	1.7 to 2.0	1.1 to 1.6
0.060 (1.5)	60	6 to 9	1.5 to 1.8	2.3 to 2.8	2.5 to 3.0	1.1 to 1.7
0.080 (2.0)	80	4 to 8	2.0 to 2.4	2.4 to 3.0	2.6 to 3.1	1.1 to 1.7

(modified ASTM D5092-04)

Monitoring-Well Installation Procedures

All screens and casings used for monitoring wells should be either certified clean and bagged from the manufacturer (such as those manufactured by Johnson Screens); steam-cleaned; or high-pressure, hot-water washed (depending on the material selected) using water from a source with known quality (chemistry). Working components of the drilling rig (drillpipe, subs, collars, kelly, and all parts of the rig chassis near the borehole) also should be cleaned, and generally are steam cleaned. Soap, such as Alconox™, can be added to the cleaning water. A decontamination pad should be used and the wash fluids gathered and contained. These cleaning operations should be verified by the driller or on-site geologist and noted in the field log.

The methods used for joining screens to casing and for assembling the casing string also must insure the prevention of water movement from various zones into the casing, where it would impact the integrity of the sample from the target zone. No solvent welds should be used; all plastic screens and casing must be joined using threads and couplings or flush threads. All F480 joints must have an O-ring in the joint.

A primary objective of monitoring-well construction is insuring that chemically impacted groundwater does not enter any geologic formations that are not impacted. Although some minor amount of cross-contamination might occur during drilling and well installation, the integrity of individual formations must be protected thereafter. This usually is accomplished by placing either bentonite or cement grout in the borehole above the filter pack in both single- and multiple-screen wells. Drill cuttings should not be placed in any open-borehole annulus. To prevent downward migration of the bentonite or cement into the screen, the filter pack usually is extended at least 2 ft (0.6 m) above the top of the screen. The filter pack should not extend into any overlying forma-tion, because this would permit downward vertical seepage in the pack, which would either dilute or add chemicals to the water being monitored.

For monitoring wells being installed in a geologic unit below a chemically impacted zone, the potential for cross-contamination can be eliminated by using the well design shown in Figure 14.7. First, the 6-in (152-mm) casing is in-stalled into the clay layer. After thoroughly flushing the casing and changing the drilling fluid, the borehole then is extended and a 2-in (52-mm) diameter moni-toring well is installed and filter packed. Cement or bentonite grout is placed as shown in Figure 14.7. A protective surface casing with a locking cap is installed before the cement has hardened, and the locking cap usually is vented.

The well should then be developed as thoroughly as possible after the grout has had sufficient time to set (for cement grouts, this generally takes two days, but it can take up to 72 hr, depending upon the type and density of the grout) (California Environmental Protection Agency 1995). Well-development methods and equipment that alter the chemical composition of the groundwater should not be used on monitoring wells. Development methods that involve adding chemical dispersants typically are not recommended. Generally accepted well-development techniques include: bailing, surging with a surge block, pumping (and over pumping), or combinations of these methods. Air-lift can be acceptable if steps are taken to prevent compressor oils from entering the well.

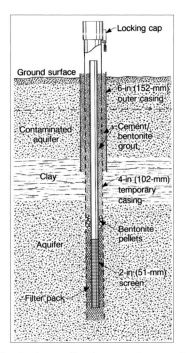

Locking cap

Ground surface

6-in (152-mm) outer casing

Contaminated aquifer

Cement/ bentonite grout

Clay

4-in (102-mm) temporary casing

Bentonite pellets

Aquifer

2-in (51-mm) screen

Filter pack

Figure 14.7. Monitoring well using a surface casing to prevent cross-contamination of a lower aquifer by chemical movement from an upper aquifer.

Development not only removes the borehole damage (*see* Chapter 11) and fines, but also increases the yield so that reliable samples can be collected in the shortest time. Development also is important to insure that the ambient water quality is maintained in the sample container until the water can be analyzed. Any sediment in the sample container, for example, potentially can react with the water, altering the actual chemical quality.

A cement seal around the top of the wellbore is recommended even if the annular seal is carried to the surface. The cement seal is shaped so that surface water flows away from the casing. If plastic casing is used, a short section of metal surface casing should be installed around the top section of the plastic pipe and be extended 2 ft (0.6 m) to 5 ft (1.5 m) into the ground. The metal casing prevents accidental damage to the plastic pipe. The top of the casing should be fitted with a locking cap. In areas where it is not possible to have well casings extending above the ground surface, such as in parking lots or public areas, small well vaults (or surface housings) can be used (Figure 14.8).

Figure 14.8. Well vault (Site Services, Inc.)

Frost heaving can be a major problem for small-diameter PVC monitoring wells installed in areas that have cold climates. As the soil freezes during the winter, it expands upward occasionally pulling the casing apart. Damage caused by frost heaving can be minimized by placing a metal surface casing to a depth of from 5 ft (1.5 m) to 10 ft (3 m). A steeply inclined cement cap should be placed around the surface casing. If frost action exerts pressure on the cement, the surface casing can rise without disturbing the monitoring well's casing.

DIRECT-PUSH MONITORING AND REMEDIATION WELLS

Another advancement in groundwater sampling methods that has occurred in the past few years is the use of small-diameter monitoring wells that are installed by direct-push technologies. As discussed in Chapter 3, direct push is a technology which uses a probe that is directly inserted and pushed into the ground. Direct-push drilling rigs can be used to install groundwater monitoring and remediation wells.

A well that is installed by direct-push technology generally consists of a 1-in (25.4-mm) diameter schedule 80 PVC screen and riser pipe. Wells that are up to 2 in (52 mm) in diameter also can be installed using direct-push technology.

The diameter of a bore in which the well is inserted typically is 0.2 in (5 mm) larger than the outer diameter of the well screen and riser (BP Corp. & U.S. EPA 2002), and the well screen is installed without a filter pack. If HDPE is an acceptable material, then a SCHUMAprobe™ screen can be installed. Additional information on this type of screen material is contained in Appendix 14.D. A prepacked well also can be installed, however it requires a slightly larger borehole. Monitoring wells installed by direct push cost significantly less, and more wells can be installed in a relatively short time as compared to a traditional installation using a hollow-stem auger rig or other rotary drilling method. Appendix 14.E (DVD) contains an evaluation of direct-push versus conventional monitoring wells.

AQUIFER REMEDIATION

Overview

If a local groundwater supply has been impacted by chemicals, then action must be taken to (1) find and eliminate the source of chemicals, (2) contain the chemicals in the area already affected, and (3) restore the water quality of the aquifer to a level that insures beneficial uses. A combination of methods of containment and treatment are ways to enhance aquifer remediation. Containment of the source of chemicals often is the first step in aquifer remediation.

Containment

Containment usually involves a hydraulic means of preventing the spread of chemicals, generally through withdrawal of chemically impacted water. Withdrawal of groundwater can reverse the local groundwater gradient, thereby preventing the advance of the chemical front. The common approach is to place extraction wells at the leading edge of impacted groundwater to prevent further migration. Another approach is to place extraction wells along the axis of the plume to prevent or minimize migration.

In cases where the source of chemicals might contain dense non-aqueous phase liquids (DNAPLs), extraction wells could be located within—or just downgradient of—the zone of suspected DNAPL to prevent the further migration of high concentrations of chemicals. The DNAPL is considered to be a source of dissolved chemicals to groundwater, and the remediation of the DNAPL can be a long-term effort. As this effort is progressing, the downgradient extraction wells prevent the further migration of the higher concentrations of chemicals. The water removed usually is treated before use or discharge.

The design of a groundwater extraction well is similar to that of a water-supply well in that the filter pack and screen-slot size should conform to standard design practice (*see* Chapter 9). A well designer should recognize that the environment in which the well is placed can have adverse geochemical conditions that impact the integrity of the well. Chlorinated solvents such as tetrachloroethylene (PCE) and trichloroethylene (TCE) in relatively high concentrations will impact the integrity of well or screen constructed of PVC. As such, stainless steel could be a more appropriate material in such circumstances. A well designer also must recognize that the groundwater extraction well will be in place for a long time—perhaps even for decades. Given this fact, efforts should be expended to design an efficient well to minimize operating costs. Additional information on groundwater pump and treat systems is contained in Appendix 14.F (DVD).

IN SITU REMEDIATION

In situ remediation of groundwater is preferred to groundwater extraction and treatment due to the lower costs and the fact that the groundwater and aquifer materials are treated as a unit. It is recognized that many chemicals, such as the chlorinated solvents, sorb to the organic fraction of the aquifer materials. In a typical groundwater extraction and treatment program, the chemicals of concern within the aquifer are found in various forms. They are dissolved within the groundwater, sorbed to organic materials, exist as a separate phase, or are found as a dissolved phase but within pores that are not well connected to the more permeable portions of the aquifer where the most flow occurs. The dissolved chemicals within the larger pores are removed more readily than the other forms in the subsurface. The concentrations of chemicals in extracted groundwater are initially high; with time, the concentration declines, however it still might not achieve a remediation goal (e.g., a drinking-water standard).

If the extraction well is shut off for a period of time and then is restarted, an increase in extracted concentrations might be observed. This phenomenon occurs because the chemicals dissolved in groundwater within the larger pores are removed more readily by advection, but the chemicals attached to the aquifer particles must desorb into the groundwater or diffuse from the pores that are not well-connected into the zones of flowing groundwater. Desorption and diffusion are relatively slow processes in comparison to advection; but it is these processes that prevent the rapid remediation of groundwater. As such, since the early to mid 1990s the emphasis of groundwater remediation has been directed toward in situ remediation. A brief discussion of some methodologies is provided in the following sections.

Biosparging and Air-Sparging Wells

One type of in situ remediation is the introduction of treatment fluids (e.g., chemical reagents or nutrients) into the subsurface. To enhance the degradation of organic compounds—such as petroleum hydrocarbons—oxygen is added into the subsurface, usually by pumping air into specially designed wells. This technique is called biosparging.

If the primary purpose is to cause the in situ volatilization and stripping of the chemicals from groundwater, then higher flow rates of air are used and the process is called air sparging. The vapors are captured in the vadose zone using soil-vapor extraction wells (Figure 14.9). Air sparging–biosparging wells typically are installed to a depth that is within or below the target treatment zone, and have short screen lengths—generally on the order of 2 ft (0.6 m) to 5 ft (1.5 m). Air is forced into the well via a compressor and the air bubbles migrate upward through the aquifer, increasing the oxygen content of the groundwater and assisting in the volatilization of the chemical. This technology primarily is applicable in aquifers that are relatively homogeneous and coarse-grained. In situations when the geologic materials are finer grained, a trench often is excavated and a horizontal screen is placed in the trench. The trench is constructed below the water table and the permeable backfill within the trench creates a zone that is sufficiently permeable and homogeneous to allow the upward migration of air through the impacted groundwater that moves through the trench. Additional information on air sparging is contained in Appendix 14.G (DVD).

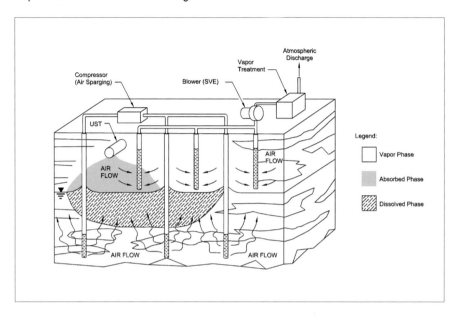

Figure 14.9. Diagram of air-sparging system.

Horizontal Wells

The installation of vertical wells might not be feasible in certain situations due to constraints such as the presence of buildings or other obstacles. In other cases, it might be desirable to pump groundwater or inject groundwater, air, and chemical reagent or nutrients along a horizontal line in the subsurface. In these types of situations it can be more cost effective to drill horizontal wells for the air sparging, biosparging, groundwater extraction, or other in situ remediation programs (Figure 14.10). Horizontal wells can be used to target lenticular zones for extraction or the injection of air or other fluids that can be used to facilitate the degradation or removal of chemicals. Additional information on horizontal drilling and the design of horizontal wells and horizontal air-sparging wells is contained in Appendix 14.H (DVD). Several of these documents are provided courtesy of Directed Technologies Drilling, Inc.

Materials that are used for well screens and casings for horizontal wells are the same as those used for vertical wells. If a conductor casing is not used to install screen materials, however, then pipe-based screens often are used to increase tensile strength. Collapse strength, tensile strength, and flexural strength are factors that should be considered in selecting materials for horizontal wells. The costs of horizontal-well installation vary depending on site-specific factors. The range of costs for drilling horizontal remediation wells is about two-to-four times greater than the average cost of horizontal directional drilling for regular utility installation (Purdue University, Division of Construction Engineering & Management 2000).

A disadvantage of horizontal wells for air sparging is their high potential for nonuniform aeration. Nonuniform aeration results in the concentration of airflow into the geologic materials in only one part of the screened interval. This situation can be minimized through the use of a well-screen material that distributes airflow more uniformly. Johnson Screens manufactures the high-density porous polyethylene well screen, SCHUMASOIL®, which has an open surface area of 25% to 36%. The uniform construction of this type of well screen leads to a uniform distribution of airflow as shown in Figure 14.10. Additional information on SCHUMASOIL® is contained in Appendix 14.I (DVD).

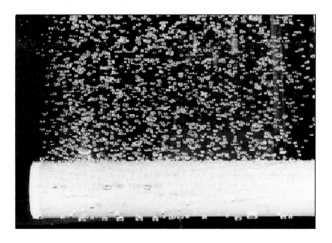

Figure 14.10. The uniform distribution of air bubbles from a SCHUMASOIL® screen.

Soil Vapor Extraction Wells

Soil vapor extraction (SVE) wells are installed in the vadose zone to remove volatile constituents such as chlorinated solvents and gasoline. In the operation of this type of well, oxygen is introduced into the subsurface, and this can assist in the degradation of organic chemicals such as petroleum hydrocarbons. The design of an SVE well is very similar to that of a standard groundwater extraction well. Its purpose is to move as much air through the well screen as possible. Thus, the maximum open area should be specified for the well. United States EPA (1994) guidance specifies that the filter-pack material and screen slot size must be consistent with the grain size of the surrounding soils. Experience has shown that a screen and filter pack larger than that specified for a groundwater extraction well can be used. It is not uncommon to have 0.060-in and 0.080-in slot screens for soil vapor extraction wells. Pea-sized gravel then can be used for the filter pack material, primarily for borehole stability.

Such SVE wells usually are constructed of PVC casing and screening, and well diameters typically range from 2 in (51 mm) to 6 in (304 mm) depending on flow rates and depth. A 4-in (102-mm) diameter casing and screen are most common. In general, 4-in (102-mm) diameter wells are favored over 2-in (51-mm) diameter wells because the larger-diameter wells are capable of higher extraction flow rates and generate less frictional loss. Additionally, the cost of valves and flow meters is less for 4-in (102-mm) wells than for larger-diameter casings. More information on enhancements of soil vapor extraction is contained in Appendix 14.J (DVD).

SUMMARY

The design of a monitoring or remediation well should be based on the physical nature of the site, the depth and characteristics of chemicals of concern, the overall groundwater quality, and the objectives of the monitoring or remediation program. It also is recommended that regulatory agencies be consulted with respect to well design and permit requirements. General references regarding remedial actions at contaminated sites are contained in Appendix 14.K (DVD). Additional information and links to other sites that provide relevant documents can be found on the U.S. Environmental Protection Agency website: www.epa.gov.

ACKNOWLEDGMENTS

Mr. Thomas M. Hanna, CPG, Johnson Screens, contributed information for Table 14.1 and provided a review of this chapter. Mr. John M. Norris, PG, Vice President, Kennedy/Jenks Consultants, and Mr. Paul V. Rosasco, PE, Principal Engineer, Engineering Management Support Inc., provided reviews and valuable comments.

CHAPTER 15
Alternative Uses for Wells and Well Screens

Albert J. Smith
Johnson Screens

Well screens are used for purposes other than the typical water-supply or extraction wells, including usage for aquifer storage and recovery (ASR) wells, and collector, horizontal, and dewatering wells. An overview of these topics is provided in this chapter. Several authors contributed to this chapter, and each is identified at the beginning of the section written by that author.

AQUIFER STORAGE RECOVERY WELLS

R. David G. Pyne
ASR Systems LLC

The growing urgency for achieving water-supply sustainability has set in motion many projects designed to increase water storage. In the United States, however, most good dam and reservoir sites already have been developed, and environmental pressures make it increasingly difficult to develop new dam sites. Siltation, seepage, and evapotranspiration losses from surface reservoirs often are significant. Consequently, greater attention is being directed to underground water storage. The goal is to insure sustainable water supplies by managing aquifer recharge and balancing groundwater withdrawals.

In the recent past, most groundwater development has been focused on removing water from the ground. As a result, water levels in many aquifers have fallen dramatically, causing saltwater intrusion, land subsidence, large depressions in the potentiometric surface, and expensive pumping lifts for groundwater production. Storage volumes potentially available underground often are several times the volumes that can be developed above ground within the same area of land. It is becoming increasingly important to efficiently get water back into the ground, and to provide sustainable water supplies to meet global needs.

Conjunctive use of surface reservoirs and wells takes full advantage of the ability of surface reservoirs to rapidly capture storm water when it is available and then, between storm events, transfer this water at slower rates into aquifers. Such use generally enables surface reservoirs to be maintained at lower levels so they can capture as much water as possible. Aquifers provide the majority of storage. The most cost-effective combination of surface and aquifer storage should be established at each site, and pumping costs to recover the water from the aquifer also should be considered.

Some groundwater-recharge areas are fortunate to have permeable soils that convey water relatively inexpensively from infiltration ponds to the water table. Hydrogeologic constraints in many areas, however, preclude cost-effective surface-recharge practices. In these areas, managed aquifer recharge requires the use of wells to get the water into the aquifer. Historically, injection wells or recharge wells were used; however such wells tend to clog—sometimes very rapidly. Quite often, redevelopment of these wells has been problematic due to inadequate casing diameter barring the installation of a high-capacity pump. To overcome this problem, aquifer storage recovery technology was developed; for example, providing a pump in an injection well so that periodic redevelopment can be quickly accomplished as needed every few days, weeks, or months. The same pump then is used for recovery of the stored water. The advent of ASR technology generated the anticipation that dedicated injection wells and recharge wells will decline in number and importance. Additionally, the opportunity to successfully recharge aquifers through ASR wells could cause a continuing rapid increase in the number of ASR wells and the variety of their applications.

Since 1968, more than 300 ASR wells have been constructed at more than 70 wellfields in the United States (Figure 15.1), plus many others in Australia, Canada, India, Israel, The Netherlands, England, South Africa, Namibia, and other countries. These wells differ from conventional production or injection wells in that they are used for both recharge and recovery. During times when good-quality water is available in excess of local need, it is recharged into a suitable aquifer through a well. The stored water is recovered from the same well as needed.

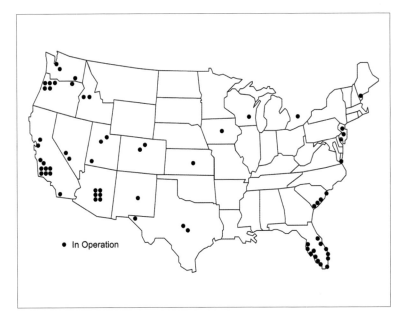

Figure 15.1. Locations of operating ASR wellfields in the United States and lower Canada, March 2005.

ASR wells can be operated in a wide range of geologic settings such as sand, sandstone, clayey sand, limestone, dolomite, alluvial deposits, glacial deposits, fractured quartzite, basalt, and conglomerates. Most storage aquifers are confined or semi-confined aquifers, however a few are deep, unconfined aquifers. The shallowest depth to the top of an ASR storage zone is about 30 ft (9.1 m) while the greatest depth to the base of an ASR storage zone is about 2,700 ft (823 m). The thickness of most ASR storage zones ranges between about 50 ft (15.2 m) to 400 ft (122 m). ASR well yields tend to range typically between 1.0 MGD (3,800 m³/d) and 3.0 MGD (11,356 m³/d) although yields of up to 8 MGD (30,283 m³/d) have been achieved in karst limestone aquifers.

Storage aquifers can be freshwater, brackish water, or saline water. Approximately one third of all ASR wells utilizes aquifers that contain brackish water or water of a quality that is unsuitable for drinking except after some form of treatment is performed. Typical ambient groundwater constituents present at high concentrations can include iron, manganese, hydrogen sulfide, fluoride, and nitrate. Storage in an aquifer containing seawater has been successfully demonstrated at Clayton, South Australia, and also in Marathon, Florida (U.S.A.), although a portion of the stored water typically is not recovered. A majority of ASR wells store water in freshwater aquifers, however it is unusual to have no significant difference in quality between the recharge water and the ambient groundwater in the storage zone.

A principal reason for the successful application of ASR technology at so many sites is that it is cost effective relative to other water-storage, peak-demand, and emergency water-supply alternatives. As a general guideline, ASR typically costs less than half the capital cost of other comparable alternatives. In several cases the capital cost savings have been close to 90%, particularly where ASR storage is substituted for surface-reservoir storage. Higher unit capital costs are associated with construction of single wells, new wells, deep wells, and low-yield wells. Lower unit capital costs are associated with simultaneous construction of multiple wells to achieve economies of scale, retrofitting of existing wells for ASR purposes, shallow wells, and high-yield wells. Operating costs are roughly comparable to those for conventional water-supply wellfields.

Although storage of water to meet seasonal peak demands, emergency demands, and for long-term water banking have been the principal applications of ASR, many other applications have been identified. These include restoration of groundwater levels, controlling subsidence, maintaining water-distribution system pressures and flows, preventing saltwater intrusion, deferring expansion of water facilities, storage of reclaimed water during wet-weather periods when irrigation demand is reduced, diurnal storage, and thermal-energy storage.

The growing acceptance of the viability and cost-effectiveness of ASR has caused an increase in the size of individual projects. At many sites, single ASR wells are being expanded into ASR wellfields. Currently, the largest ASR wellfield in the world is in the Las Vegas Valley Water District, Nevada (U.S.A.). It includes 46 ASR wells and 32 injection wells with a combined recovery capacity of 157 MGD (594,000 m³/d). Other large operational ASR wellfields include Calleguas Municipal Water District, California (U.S.A.), which currently has 18 wells with a recharge capacity of 48 MGD (182,000 m³/d) and a recovery capacity of 64 MGD (243,000 m³/d); it is being expanded to 26 wells. The San Antonio Water System, Texas (U.S.A.) operates a 30 MGD (114,000 m³/d) ASR wellfield, which is being expanded to 60 MGD (228,000 m³/d). In Florida (U.S.A.), the Comprehensive Everglades Restoration Program includes plans for more than 330 ASR wells, with a combined recovery capacity of 1,700 MGD (6,400,000 m³/d).

Several aspects of the design and operation of ASR wells, wellhead facilities, and wellfields are unique. Achieving a reasonable understanding of these aspects helps insure that a project is successful. A brief summary of selected technical topics is included here. More-detailed information is available in Pyne (2005).

ASR-Well Construction Materials

A key issue in well construction is selection of the correct materials for construction of casings and screens, such as carbon steel, epoxy-coated carbon steel, stainless steel, fiberglass, and PVC.

ASR wells are more prone to oxidation than are other types of wells. Water levels vary greatly between recharge and recovery operations, creating much greater wetted surface area on the casing, pump column, and other downhole equipment as compared to that found in conventional production wells. This is in addition to potential external casing corrosion due to contact with brackish groundwater or corrosive soils. To the extent that the wetted surface area might be carbon steel, and the water in contact with the steel can vary in dissolved oxygen content, chlorine residual, and possibly salinity, a greater potential for corrosion exists. Corrosion products are swept into the well during recharge, contributing to clogging of the well screen and surrounding portions of the aquifer. At the beginning of recovery, or during periodic backflushing operations, oxidation products and other particulates pumped from the well must be discharged to a waste-holding area or receiving water-body in an acceptable manner. Depending upon the construction materials, it could be necessary to pump the well to a waste-holding area at a high rate for up to 2 hours to achieve water quality acceptable for water distribution. With non-ferrous or stainless-steel materials this could be reduced to a few minutes, which greatly reduces the complexity of ASR operations.

The ability to discharge backwash waters from ASR wells to a waste-holding area or receiving water body in an environmentally acceptable manner is one of the most important contributing factors for an assessment of ASR feasibility at any particular site. Table 15.1 lists backflushing frequencies for different locations and geologic materials for sites in the United States. When the expected flow rate, total volume, or frequency of discharge is deemed unacceptably high, it is necessary to reconsider site feasibility and whether the appropriate construction materials were selected. This often is an important consideration when an existing well with a carbon-steel casing is to be retro-fitted for ASR operations. Wells with carbon-steel casing have lower capital costs, but this initial savings could be offset by the higher cost for ASR operations due to increased backflushing frequency and duration. Conversely, many ASR wells are operational with carbon-steel casing, having achieved an acceptable solution for discharging rusty-colored, turbid water. After the turbidity and rust-coloring both decline to acceptable levels, recovered water then is disinfected and directed to the water-distribution system.

Table 15.1. Backflushing Frequencies at Selected ASR Wellfields

Site	Backflushing Frequency	Lithology
Wildwood, NJ	Daily	Clayey sand
Gordons Corner, NJ	Daily	Clayey sand
Peace River, FL	Seasonal	Limestone
Cocoa, FL	Seasonal	Limestone
Port Malabar, FL (now Palm Bay, FL)	Monthly	Limestone
Las Vegas, NV	Seasonal	Alluvium
Chesapeake, VA	Bimonthly	Sand
Seattle, WA	Weekly	Glacial deposits
Calleguas, CA	Monthly (approx.)	Sand
Highlands Ranch, CO	Monthly	Sandstone

Some ASR wells have been constructed with fusion-bond epoxy-coated carbon-steel casing and pump column, which substantially reduces the surface area subject to corrosion. At each welded connection in the casing, however, a band of uncoated exposed steel remains, and any corrosion is focused upon the exposed areas—including any scratches or pinhole openings in the coating—accelerating corrosion at these points. In the piping industry, such pinhole openings are termed "holidays." Corrosion can cause failure of the casing and downhole equipment.

To eliminate corrosion concerns, some ASR wells have been constructed with PVC casings. These wells have been constructed at depths up to about 1,300 ft (400 m) using the diameters as large as 17.4 in (44.2 cm) OD, SDR-17 casing with an inside diameter of about 15.3 in (38.9 cm). Most PVC casings with this diameter, however, are set at depths of less than about 800 ft (244 m). Greater depths are attainable with smaller-diameter casings. Considerable care is required during installation and cementing of the casing because the heat of hydration weakens the collapse strength. Another consideration for PVC column pipe joints is the resistance to torque that must be accounted for by the downhole submersible pump. PVC generally is not suitable for vertical turbine pumps.

PVC pipe also has been used successfully for many years for pump columns with diameters up to 8 in (20.3 cm). Care is required to insure that adequate consideration is made for tensile strength of the column pipe connections, particularly with deeper pump settings and high-horsepower motors.

Because of the current unavailability of larger PVC casing diameters and to the rapid increase in cost of stainless-steel casing in recent years, the use of fiberglass casing for high-capacity wells has received increased attention. At least one ASR well has been constructed using fiberglass casing, and others are planned. The connections for fiberglass and PVC casings have relatively large outer diameters, requiring a large borehole diameter to allow proper cementing. Prior to setting long strings of fiberglass and PVC casing, it also is important to insure that the boreholes are straight and plumb.

Stainless-steel well casings are relatively expensive, however they provide the strength and durability required to insure a long service life. This is true particularly in areas and applications where carbon-steel casings are prone to failure, or where non-ferrous casings are potentially vulnerable to earthquake damage. In areas where the expected service life of a carbon-steel casing might be short (e.g., 10 yr to 15 yr), using a stainless-steel casing to potentially achieve a service life exceeding 100 years can be desirable. Where suitable well sites are small or scarce, a long-lasting well ultimately could be advantageous when compared to having to plug and abandon a less-expensive well due to corrosion failure, and having to re-drill a replacement well a few feet away on the same site or at another location.

ASR-Well Water-Level Measurement and Casing Diameter

It is important to be able to reliably measure water levels during recharge, recovery, and under static conditions in ASR wells. The resulting water-level data enables tracking of well clogging, specific capacity, specific injectivity (recharge flow rate divided by increase in pressure head) and the need for periodic backflushing of the well to remove accumulated particulates. There typically is a great range in water levels in ASR wells.

A recommended design measure is to provide two independent methods for water-level measurement. Typical options can include a pressure transducer, a bubbler tube, or a dedicated tube for insertion of an electric tape. If practical, using a dedicated tube between the pump column and the casing could be less costly than the larger inner casing required to accommodate both the pump bowls and a tube.

Where stainless-steel column pipe is utilized, the connections can be either flanged or threaded pipe. Threads on stainless-steel pipe tend to "gall," however. This results from the metal transferring between the coupling and the pipe such that, once galling starts, the connection cannot be turned any further. Use of Nitronic 60 threaded couplings reduces the galling potential. Use of flanges is more conventional but can create the need for a larger casing diameter.

In general, selection of casing diameter for ASR wells requires careful consideration, because several factors tend to increase the minimum required diameter for accommodating downhole piping and equipment.

Mechanical Integrity Testing

Regulatory agency requirements at some ASR sites in the United States have included the need for periodic mechanical integrity testing, otherwise known as "MIT tests." The intention is to demonstrate that the well's inner casing does not lose water to the surrounding formations as a result of typical pressures occurring during ASR recharge, and that groundwater does not move into the well through the casing during recovery. Carbon steel–cased wells, in particular, tend to corrode with time due to chemical or galvanic corrosion, therefore a steel casing that is sound initially still could fail eventually. Failure potentially could contaminate overlying aquifers or the ASR storage zone by providing a cross-connection through the well casing. When this occurs, mitigation measures include plugging and abandoning the well, or relining it with a smaller inner casing.

The MIT test typically is conducted on a well during its construction, following cementing of the inner casing and prior to drilling out the cement plug. Alternatively, the test can be conducted on the completed well after first installing a packer at the base of the casing. The casing is filled with liquid, pressurized to between 50 psi (345 kPa) and 100 psi (690 kPa), and then monitored for 30 min to 1 hr. If the pressure holds for that period (plus or minus about 10%) then the test is considered acceptable. If the pressure dissipates rapidly—indicating a leak—then it is the drilling contractor's responsibility to either repeat the test or resolve the problem. Resolution potentially could include plugging the well and reconstructing a new well.

Steel-cased wells—where the joints have been properly welded or threaded together—usually have no difficulty passing the test. For a PVC-cased well the pressure might decline due to slight expansion of the casing, even without a leak. Recognizing the negligible risk of aquifer contamination due to ASR operations, regulatory agencies in one U.S. state recently have required and accepted MIT test results without imposing strict criteria for success. Initial test results then are available for comparison with the repeat tests that probably will be required in the future. The subsequent tests typically are expensive and require removing the pump from the well, setting a packer in the casing, and then conducting the test. If the results from later tests are substantially different from results of the initial tests, then a basis exists for evaluating the extent of the potential leakage and determining appropriate remedial measures.

Selection of ASR Storage Intervals

Generally, ASR wells store water in aquifers where groundwater velocities are low. Consequently, the stored water bubble stays around the well and therefore is available for recovery. For a few ASR wells, the recharge-water quality and the ambient groundwater quality are similar, in which case groundwater velocity need not be a significant consideration in the selection of the storage interval. The potential for surface contamination is reduced and recharge pressures can be above land surface where ASR storage is in artesian aquifers. Deep aquifers with little natural recharge that are being "mined" quite often make excellent ASR storage zones. The deeper aquifers are more expensive to develop and, quite often, also have poor water quality so that competing uses for such aquifers are minimal. Some ASR wells are operating satisfactorily in water-table aquifers, particularly in areas where depth to static-water level is substantial, for example exceeding about 130 ft (40 m).

In consolidated (rock) formations that can produce water without the pumping of sediment or solids, an open-hole well completion is low cost and can be effective. Typical formation lithologies are sandstone and karst or fractured limestone. For such formations, the primary porosity in sandstone or secondary porosity in limestone typically provide most of the water-storage volume for ASR wells. The void spaces between the sand grains in the sand-stone, or the intergranular or vuggy porosity in the limestone provide water storage. Secondary porosity—due to fracturing and solution openings—typically provides most of the water conveyance to and from the ASR well during recharge and recovery. In basalt rock aquifers, the relatively productive intervals between the successive lava flows provide virtually all of the porosity. In unconsolidated formations, screen intervals must be selected using naturally developed or gravel-pack well completions. Whether the ASR storage zone is in consolidated or unconsolidated geologic materials, certain factors should be considered during selection of the appropriate storage interval.

The simplest case is one in which the ASR storage zone under consideration contains water of similar quality to that which will be recharged, and has no potential geochemical problems. In such a case, the ASR-well design is similar to a conventional production-well design. If screened, the screen length tends to be slightly longer, to maximize well efficiency and to minimize the rate of plugging. For open holes, the borehole length tends to fully penetrate the production interval for the same reason.

For the case where the storage zone is brackish or contains water of such quality that mixing should be minimized, the selection of the storage interval requires greater care. Thin intervals that have excellent vertical confinement are best suited for minimizing mixing. Figure 15.2 shows a geologic cross section for the Marathon, Florida (U.S.A.), ASR test well which successfully stored treated drinking water for emergency water-supply purposes. Storage was in a confined sand production interval 40 ft (11 m) thick and containing seawater with a TDS concentration of 39,000 mg/ℓ. To insure the ability to recover the desired volume of water during emergencies it was necessary to add a small trickle flow of drinking water to the well (at least 42 gpm (0.2 m^3/min)) during extended storage periods to compensate for density stratification losses. In less-extreme cases of water-quality difference, thicker storage intervals with less confinement could be sufficient to provide the desired recovery efficiency.

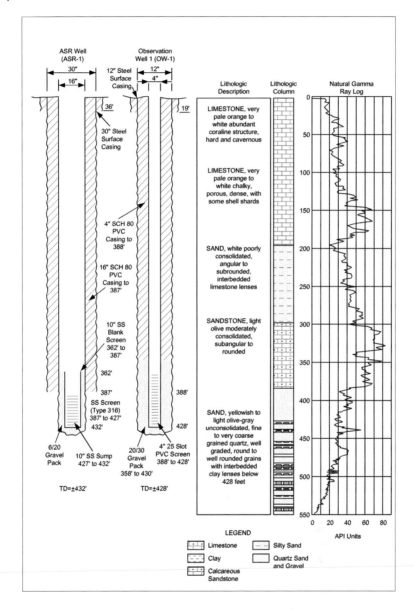

Figure 15.2. ASR well construction details and lithology at a well near Marathon, FL (U.S.A.).

Where the choice of storage intervals is limited, well and wellfield design can, to some extent, adapt to the limitations imposed by nature. Multiple wells or horizontal directionally drilled wells can enable ASR development of a zone that has sufficient storage-volume capacity but low yield to individual wells. This condition could be due to low transmissivity, shallow depth, subsidence concerns, or potential upconing of brackish water from below the storage zone during ASR. The cost of additional wells frequently is small as compared to the cost of alternative surface-water storage or other sources of peak water supply.

If several potential storage zones are available, then it is appropriate to consider the volumes and rates required for storage and recovery and select the storage interval that best matches ASR objectives. In some cases, storage in multiple intervals is appropriate, with each utilizing separate ASR wells at the same site. This practice is termed "stacking."

Where the storage zone has great thickness or poor confinement and contains poor-quality groundwater, acceptable recovery performance sometimes can be achieved by operating at high rates and for long durations during recharge. The volume stored then might be sufficient to displace the poor-quality water away from the well—both vertically and laterally—so that a useful recovery volume can be achieved during each subsequent recovery season. This can take several annual cycles of operation, each showing an increase in recovery efficiency. Alternatively, a large initial storage volume could be recharged following construction. This might be considered to be the formation of a buffer zone, analogous to initial filling of a surface reservoir. Once the buffer zone is formed, or the "surface reservoir" is filled, ASR operations at the ultimate recovery efficiency can proceed. This is known as the "target storage volume" (TSV) concept (discussed below).

Recovery efficiency is defined as the percentage of the water volume stored in an operating cycle that subsequently is recovered in the same cycle, while meeting a target water-quality criterion in the recovered water. The recovery efficiency attainable depends upon the hydraulic and water-quality characteristics at each site. Although 100% recovery efficiency is a reasonable target and is obtained in most cases of storage in brackish aquifers, lower recovery efficiency might occur in some situations. An economic analysis then can indicate whether the lost investment in the water not recovered is offset by the value of the water recovered when it is needed. Usually this is the case, because water typically is stored at times of the year when marginal costs of water production (cost per unit volume)—including electricity, chemicals, and residuals disposal—are low.

When the water is recovered, the marginal value usually is quite high, reflecting local alternatives for supplemental peak-demand water supply.

The most complex issues pertaining to storage zone selection are with aquifers, or portions of aquifers, that have potential geochemical challenges. One solution is to design the ASR well to case the production intervals that can result in severe geochemical problems, if this can be achieved without losing much of the potential production capacity of the well. Formations that are known to contain high concentrations of arsenopyrite (FeAsS), iron, manganese, or other metals, sometimes can be cased. If a formation cannot be cased without losing significant well yield, it might be necessary to implement pretreatment, such as pH adjustment, or operational measures, such as formation of a buffer zone around the well, to control the occurrence of the above-listed metals in the recovered water. Obtaining and analyzing continuous wireline cores (see Chapter 3 for a description of wireline coring) at new ASR well-field sites is expensive but is very helpful in better defining and resolving potential geologic and geochemical issues.

Typically, coring, core analysis, geophysical logging, and water-quality testing in selected depth intervals provide the detailed information needed to make a reasonable judgment regarding well design and to avoid geochemical problems. In the absence of these data, it is difficult to know which intervals are contributing the undesirable water quality. Consequently, the design of subsequent ASR wells can benefit from experience gained with the first such well installed at any new site. In such circumstances initial construction and testing of an exploratory well is appropriate.

Other geochemical problems can include potential precipitation of calcium carbonate within the well casing, screen, and pump column. Rarely has this been a real problem, however at least one ASR well has lost capacity due to such precipitation. This is thought to have been caused by a combination of factors, including high velocities and resultant large head losses within a deep-set pump column, and within a very long, small-diameter well casing during recharge. An excess of calcium carbonate in the recharge water, added to control pipe corrosion, also were contributing factors.

ASR-Well Screen Design

Filter-pack wells initially were utilized because of their low cost and also due to a requirement to reduce sand pumping while using wide-slot screens having torch-cut perforations, louvers, mill slots, and punch openings. The filter pack must be well-rounded and typically composed of silica sand. Design criteria for the grading of the filter pack can vary depending upon the types of aquifers encountered and empirical sizing based upon historical success. The slot size normally is designed to hold back 90% to 100% of the filter-pack material. Wire-wrap screens are very successful with a filter-pack envelope due to their large percentage of open area; such screens typically have open area of from 10% to 50%, whereas louvers, perforations, torch slots, etc., can have open area of from 2% to 10%.

A well screen that is installed without a gravel pack is considered to be a naturally developed well. Continuous-slot wire-wrap screens have been used successfully for many years in wells developed naturally. The slot size selected for the screen can be selected using several different criteria, as discussed in Chapter 9.

In recent years, there has been discussion regarding whether the screen and filter-pack design for an ASR well in an unconsolidated aquifer should be any different than that intended for a standard production well. Normal ASR operations can be viewed as the long-term cyclic redevelopment of the well screen, with consequent increased potential for movement and settling of the surrounding formation.

A case can be made that the screen slot size for an ASR well should be slightly larger than that used in a typical production well and the filter pack should be as thin as practicable, so that during pumping and redevelopment the filter pack clears more readily of any particulates introduced during recharge. When taking this approach, it is necessary to add 1 or 2 tubes from the ground surface to the top of the filter pack, and to periodically confirm the depth to the top of the filter pack. Filter-pack material then is added as necessary to compensate for that which is washed through the screen during recovery. If this is not done, then the formation material could collapse around the screen during ASR operational changes from recharge to recovery. It is helpful to use a non-ferrous feed tube or tubes to prevent the original filter pack from being iron-cemented to the inside of the mild-steel tube—ultimately rendering it useless for observation or refills. The use of tubes should be considered very carefully, because problems can arise in installing thinly packed filter-media systems. A properly designed well and filter pack should negate the use of such tubes.

Some uncertainty always will exist, however, as to whether using one or more tubes adequately can protect the well against collapse. The best solution is to design the screen identically to that for a production well, so that there is no increased likelihood of filter-pack movement through the screen. Whether a well is used for production or for ASR, pumping sand is an operating problem to be avoided.

To date, the Las Vegas, Nevada (U.S.A.), and Glendale, Arizona (U.S.A.), ASR wellfields are the only known applications of constructing new ASR wells in an alluvial aquifer using natural screen development instead of a filter pack. At the Las Vegas site, many difficulties were encountered with this method due to the geologic nature of the aquifer. The semi-consolidated aquifer material did not fully collapse upon the screen to form a continuous natural filter pack, instead leaving voids around the screen. All development methods were unsuccessful, because any energy applied was redirected up and down the borehole following the path of least resistance. During recovery, the four wells constructed in this manner produced considerable amounts of sand at startup and continued to produce small amounts of sand during extended operation, necessitating the use of sand separators to remove sand from the recovered water. Comparisons indicated that the efficiency of these four wells was substantially less than for adjacent wells drilled using conventional production-well completion methods with a screen and filter pack. The results of the Las Vegas research indicate that the formation must be able to fully collapse onto the screen to make naturally developed wells successful. Addition of a formation stabilizer between the screen and the formation often is utilized for this purpose in semi-consolidated formations.

Efficient screen design is important, but effective screen development is critical for achieving high efficiency for any well. Removing the drilling fluid from the well using chemicals to break down the fluid, along with using mechanical surging and jetting, is a standard procedure. For some applications the use of biodegradable drilling mud can be a good solution. For other applications it might be necessary to surge and pump large volumes of water backward and forward through successive segments of the screen for an extended period— sometimes for several days or more—to properly develop the well. See Chapter 11 for further discussion of well development.

Prepacked well screens (e.g., Muni-Pak™) are available to overcome the challenge of filter-pack installation in a horizontal well, or to use in lieu of a tremied filter pack in a vertical well. The filter-pack material is confined between two stainless-steel screens, providing great strength and also abrasion resistance. There exists some concern that the surrounding formation might not be effectively developed through such a screen using conventional surge block and jetting tools, because much of the development energy would be dissipated within the screen. These concerns have been addressed; field experience shows that these screens enhance development. To date, the results of using prepacked screens in wells have been good, and advantages include:

- Development through a thin filter pack;
- No tremie pipe is needed for addition of lost filter pack;
- A smaller hole is required;
- The mud damage to the aquifer is closer to the screen and therefore easier to remove; and
- Installation of a filter pack is unnecessary.

Additional discussion on prepacked screens is contained in Chapter 9.

Target Storage Volume and Recovery Efficiency

The target storage volume (TSV) is defined as the stored water volume required for recovery to meet the objectives of the ASR program, plus a buffer-zone volume of water required to separate stored water from surrounding ambient groundwater (Figure 15.3). The buffer zone is analogous to the walls of a storage tank or the dam associated with a surface reservoir. Usually it is formed from the same water being stored and is left in place underground instead of being recovered. The volume of the TSV depends upon several hydrogeologic factors associated with the storage zone (thickness, hydraulic characteristics, lithology, water quality) and also on hydrologic factors associated with meeting ASR-program objectives, such as recovered storage volume needs. Objectives are based upon variability in supply; demand and quality of the source water; duration of storage; and the associated potential for loss of stored water.

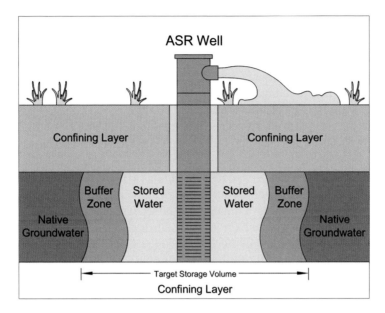

Figure 15.3. ASR target storage volume.

Estimation of the TSV primarily is based upon experience, and the unit of measurement used is a day. A general range for TSV is 50 MG (190,000 m³) to 350 MG (1,330,000 m³) per MGD (3,785 m³ per day) of installed recovery capacity. The lower end of the range tends to be for thin sand and sandstone aquifers containing freshwater or slightly brackish water. This situation would be found for ASR systems designed to meet seasonal variations in demand. The higher end of the range tends to be for thick, heterogeneous, or karst limestone aquifers containing brackish water, for ASR systems designed to meet seasonal variations in water supply, demand, and quality. In particular, where the source water supply is unreliable, the TSV increases as needed to insure a sustainable supply from ASR storage.

The TSV approach is applicable for situations where mixing and dispersion are the predominant mechanisms for changes in water quality underground during storage. Formation of the buffer zone insures that mixing and dispersion occur at a sufficient distance from the ASR well so that water-quality changes during recovery are acceptably small. It therefore is important to not recover the buffer zone volume once it is formed.

A noticeable reduction in recovery efficiency can occur where there exists significant hydraulic gradient. Some loss of stored water also could occur if there is a significant density difference between the recharge water and the native groundwater. In these relatively unusual situations, the TSV approach should be combined with additional wellfield design and operational measures to compensate for potential losses of stored water.

When the storage zone has water quality that is fresh and essentially is the same as the stored water, then no buffer zone is required. In this case, the TSV equals the stored water volume required for recovery. Where the storage zone has water quality with a TDS exceeding about 5,000 mg/ℓ, the density difference between the stored water and the surrounding ambient groundwater can reduce recovery efficiency. Adding a small flow of recharge water during extended storage periods can compensate for losses occurring due to density stratification.

Where lateral movement in the storage zone causes the stored water bubble to move away from the well, it might be advisable to construct a line of ASR wells oriented along the groundwater flow path. Recharge would be toward the upstream end of the wellfield and recovery would be toward the downstream end.

A significant advantage of the TSV approach is that it pushes the mixing zone between stored water and ambient groundwater away from the ASR well. The mixing zone is where geochemical reactions are most likely to occur. Such geochemical reactions tend to attenuate with distance from the ASR well, and if they can be controlled then recovery water quality during initial cycles improves.

The TSV approach to ASR well development at most sites will reduce the cost and duration of cycle testing and expedite achievement of ultimate recovery efficiency. The TSV should be developed upon completion of well construction and baseline hydraulic and aquifer performance testing, and prior to initiating cycle testing. Through forming the TSV, cycle testing can be abbreviated and the ASR well can be placed into full operation sooner.

Whether the TSV approach is followed to rapidly achieve full recovery efficiency, or whether this is achieved over a period of several years and several operating cycles, it is normal for recovery efficiency at an ASR well to reach approximately 100%.

At a few ASR sites there exists some concern that TSV formation could push end products of subsurface geochemical and microbial reactions away from the ASR well, potentially contaminating adjacent portions of the aquifer. Water-quality data obtained from monitor wells generally support the conclusion that such reaction products typically are not found more than a few tens of feet (or meters) away from the ASR well, even though the buffer zone might extend several hundred feet (meters). Research is needed to better understand geochemical and microbial reactions occurring within a radius of about 150 ft (46 m) of an ASR well. Until such research is conducted it is likely that, for many new ASR wells, one or more small-volume geochemical test cycles will be appropriate to characterize aquifer water-quality response prior to forming the TSV.

ASR WELLHEAD AND WELLFIELD DESIGN AND OPERATION

Several features of ASR wellhead and wellfield design and operation also are unique, however such discussion extends well beyond the scope of this section. Figures 15.4 and 15.5 show typical wellhead completions for ASR systems.

Figure 15.4. Kiawah Island Utility, Kiawah Island, SC (U.S.A.), with PVC casing and SS316 wellhead.

Figure 15.5. City of West Palm Beach, FL (U.S.A.), 8 MGD recharge and recovery capacity.

Additional ASR information is available at www.asrforum.com, or in Pyne (2005).

HORIZONTAL COLLECTOR WELLS

Samuel M. Stowe
President, Collector Wells International, Inc.

For more than 70 years, horizontal collector wells (also referred to as Ranney™ wells and radial collector wells) have been used to develop water from a variety of sources, including groundwater, induced infiltration (e.g., riverbank filtration), and—in coastal areas—even seawater. They have also been used for groundwater recharge–aquifer storage and recovery programs. Collector wells typically are constructed in unconsolidated sand and gravel deposits, and generally consist of a central, reinforced concrete–caisson wet well that serves as the pump station, with horizontal well screens projected out into the aquifer. A general cross-sectional view of a typical collector well is shown in Figure 15.6, below.

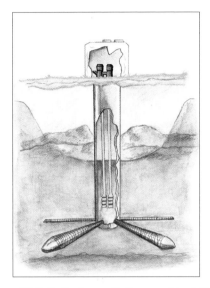

Figure 15.6. Collector-well diagram (Hunt 2002).

In the 1920s, petroleum engineer Leo Ranney originated the concept of the horizontal collector well. He created a horizontal drilling approach to develop oil in relatively shallow oil-bearing rock formations, and demonstrated it in places like northern Texas (U.S.A.), Ohio (U.S.A.), Pennsylvania (U.S.A.), and in Australia. Ranney theorized that if wells (open boreholes or screened) could be placed into a formation horizontally, then more of the well could be exposed to the producing formation and, thus, higher yields per single horizontal well could be developed than could occur when using a single vertical well.

Mr. Ranney modified his horizontal drilling process to enable the installation of horizontal bores into unconsolidated deposits to develop water supplies. The first horizontal collector well was constructed for the London Water Board (England), in about 1933. Following that installation, Ranney introduced horizontal collector-well technology to continental Europe, where the concept flourished and utilities installed numerous collector wells using the original installation method bearing the inventor's name (The Ranney Method), whereby perforated pipe well screens were jacked horizontally into aquifer formations. This method was used exclusively until about 1946, when Swiss engineer Dr. Hans Fehlmann modified the jacking process to enable continuous wire-wound well screens to be installed in a collector well for the City of Bern, Switzerland. Dr. Fehlmann's technology involved projecting a solid pipe into the formation and then inserting a wire-wound well screen—designed to conform to the grain size of the formation—into the pipe. The projection pipe then was retracted, exposing the formation to the wire-wrap well screen. Thus, this process enabled the matching of finer-grained formations with a more hydraulically efficient screen.

In 1953, German engineers modified this installation process to include the installation of an artificial filter pack around the well screens to accommodate finer-grained formations. This process also involves a solid pipe that is projected full-length into the formation. A special well screen is then inserted into the pipe, and gravel materials are pumped into the annulus between the projection pipe and the screen while the projection pipe is retracted. The use of an artificial filter pack provides a transition between fine-grained formation deposits and larger, more-efficient screen openings.

These two advances in collector-well technology improved the hydraulic efficiency of collector wells, reduced sand pumping, and permitted collector-well laterals to be installed in a wider range of geologic formations. Both the Fehlmann and filter-packing technologies were brought to the United States in the mid-1980s and, since then, have been used extensively. In 1985, two collector wells were built in the midwestern United States using the process developed by Dr. Fehlmann and, concurrently, the first gravel-packed collector well screens used in the North America were installed in New Jersey (U.S.A.).

Collector wells can be used in virtually any unconsolidated geologic formation that contains sand, gravel, cobbles, etc. and in consolidated (rock) formations, if conditions are appropriate. Collector wells offer advantages in situations where aquifer formations are stratified or shallow, because the entire well screen can be installed in the most hydraulically efficient zone within the aquifer, thus minimizing head losses. The well screen is installed horizontally so it can be placed near the base of the aquifer, maximizing the amount of available drawdown and the possible yield. Additionally, because the length of screen is not restricted by the aquifer thickness, more screen can be installed— minimizing head losses through the screen, and minimizing the rate of screen plugging.

Since the first collector well was installed in 1933 in England, hundreds of collector wells have been installed throughout the world, including more than 300 in the United States. These have ranged from single-well installations to multiple-well installations for a single utility, such as the more than 100 collector wells installed for the City of Belgrade in the Republic of Serbia. The individual well capacities (yields) have ranged from about 70 gpm (0.0044 m³/sec) to 27,700 gpm (1.75 m³/sec) while total wellfield capacities have approached

100 MGD (4.38 m³/sec) in several instances. The largest single collector well in the world, installed for the Board of Public Utilities in Kansas City, Kansas (U.S.A.), has been pumped at rates of up to 55 MGD (2.4 m³/sec). A second collector well in Kansas City; one in Prince George, British Columbia (Canada); and one in Sonoma County, California (U.S.A.), have yields that approach this rate.

Collector-Well Design

The expected yield and subsequent design of a collector well are determined in much the same way as for vertical wells—by using data obtained from exploratory test drilling and aquifer testing. The commonly used investigative field and analytical procedures are discussed at length in preceding chapters that involve groundwater exploration (Chapter 3) and well hydraulics (Chapter 6). Specialized analytical equations for calculating the expected yields from horizontal collector wells are presented in Hantush (1964) for various hydrogeological settings. Numerical models also can be used to estimate yields and travel times.

Phased, multi-faceted investigations are structured to collect pertinent data to evaluate yield, quality, and ultimately the design of a horizontal collector well. A collector well is designed to infiltrate water from the adjacent surface water source, using the streambed and riverbank deposits to naturally filter out suspended materials from the source water. The first, obvious, requirement is that the collector wells be placed in close proximity to a source of recharge, such as a river. During the feasibility and siting stages of a project, a number of criteria must be considered, including the following.

- Availability of water from a surface-water source that can recharge the aquifer
- An efficient hydraulic interconnection between the river and the aquifer
- A suitable aquifer, capable of conveying infiltrated water to the well
- Suitable water quality in the aquifer and source surface water
- Sustainable flow in a river or inflow to a lake for the anticipated withdrawal rates

In general, studies can be comprised of 4 phases, including:

Phase 1. Site reconnaissance, and review of existing data;
Phase 2. Test drilling;
Phase 3. Aquifer testing; and
Phase 4. Design and reporting.

The initial phase should define project objectives (yield, quality, water use), identify project concerns (treatment and regulatory issues), and collect available data for preliminary hydrogeological screening and feasibility determination. If the initial phase indicates a reasonable probability that potential favorable conditions exist for the project objectives, then subsequent phases can be designed to collect site-specific data for comprehensive analysis. Subsequent phases should include test drilling, hydraulic interval testing, streambed characterization, water-level monitoring, and detailed aquifer and water-quality testing.

The testing procedures typically involve test drilling and aquifer tests that are conducted for a period of at least 48 hr, or until stabilization occurs. The hydraulic characteristics of the aquifer and streambed are determined and boundary conditions assessed so that long-term well performance can be calculated. This testing provides the necessary information to predict well-production rates. Production rates, in turn, dictate well-design criteria such as caisson diameter and depth, screen elevation, screen slot-opening design, number and orientation of well screens, well-screen diameter, and recommendations for setting pumping levels for long-term performance to meet projected demands.

The key parameters for any riverbank filtration evaluation are aquifer transmissivity and streambed permeability. A good understanding of these parameters and the hydrogeological setting enable the proper evaluation of expected yield and water quality from a horizontal collector well and enable thorough evaluation of design options. Determining the ability of the aquifer to provide sufficient riverbank filtration to recharge water pumped from a horizontal collector well is key to ensuring that long-term capacities can be sustained, and that target water quality can be maintained through a balance of infiltrated surface water and groundwater.

Collector-Well Construction

The caisson is constructed by forming and pouring concrete sections (or lifts) at grade, and then excavating geologic materials from within the caisson and allowing the caisson walls to sink into the ground. One of the lower sections includes wall-port openings to be used for projecting the lateral well screens. As each lift section—usually 10 ft (3 m) to 12 ft (3.7 m) high—sinks into the ground, the subsequent sections are tied together with reinforcing steel and water stops, and then formed and poured. The sinking process continues until the lower portion of the caisson reaches the design depth for projection of the lateral well screens. After the caisson is placed to its design depth, a reinforced-concrete bottom-sealing plug is poured to enable the interior of the shaft to be dewatered for screen installation. The concrete caissons typically are con-structed with an inside diameter ranging from 10 ft (3 m) to 20 ft (6 m), or larger if necessary. The caissons can be installed to depths of 150 ft (46 m) using normal construction methods, and possibly deeper using special hydraulic-assist jacking equipment. The average depth of the caissons in the United States is 68 ft (21 m) and the average diameter is 13 ft (4 m). Figure 15.7 shows the general caisson-sinking process.

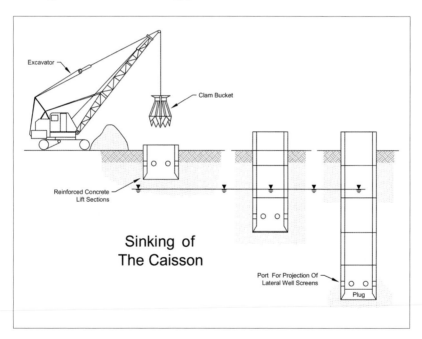

Figure 15.7. Caisson-sinking process.

After the bottom seal has set, the water in the caisson is pumped down and the lateral well screens are hydraulically jacked out into the aquifer formation from inside the caisson, using one of several methods, depending upon the nature of the aquifer formation, the anticipated yield of the well, and water-quality considerations. There are three principal methods for well-screen installation, using (1) perforated pipe, (2) wire-wrapped screen, or (3) filter-packed screen as shown in Figure 15.8 (Hunt 2002) and described below (Hunt 1985). Frequently, well screen that is 500 ft (150 m) to 1,000 ft (300 m) or longer is installed in a collector well. The largest collector well installed to date has more than 2,600 ft (800 m) of well screen installed, divided into two tiers.

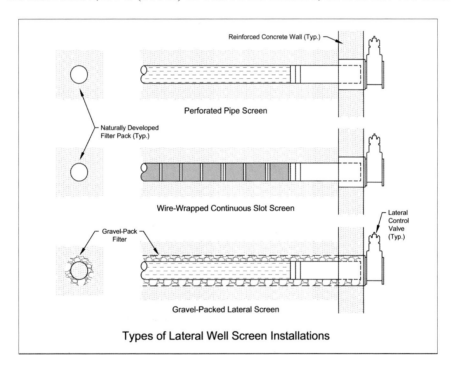

Figure 15.8. Diagram of collector-well screen designs.

Perforated-Pipe Screens

The original (Ranney) method for installing lateral well screens involves projecting pipe sections that have been perforated by punching or sawing. The pipe sections are attached to a digging head that is used to direct the projection of the lateral pipe. In this approach, the pipe sections are projected into the aquifer and then left in place. The openings on the pipe typically provide a maximum open area of 20%, which is limited because the pipe must have sufficient structural strength to accommodate the jacking forces used during projection. Perforated-pipe well screens having diameters of 8 in (20 cm), 10 in (25 cm), 12 in (30 cm), and 16 in (40 cm) have been projected out to a maximum length of about 350 ft (107 m). When using the Ranney Method, the perforated pipe most commonly is made of standard carbon-steel materials, due to cost. Occasionally, stainless-steel or special alloy materials are used. The minimum slot size that can be made using existing methods for perforating the pipe sometimes is too large to sufficiently retain fine-grained formation materials for efficient well development. Perforated pipe screens therefore primarily are used for aquifers containing coarser-grained deposits that have higher percentages of gravel.

Wire-Wrapped Screens (Projection-Pipe Method)

The projection-pipe method involves the use of a special heavy-duty projection pipe that is pushed into the aquifer formation. During the projection process, formation samples are collected and analyzed for grain-size distribution. Once the pipe has been placed in the aquifer to the desired distance, a wire-wrapped continuous-slot well screen (with slot openings selected to conform to the aquifer deposits encountered) is inserted inside the projection pipe. The projection pipe then is withdrawn so that it can be used in projecting the next lateral. For this installation method, the lateral lengths range from about 100 ft (30 m) to 250 ft (75 m), with 8-in (20-cm) or 12-in (30-cm) diameter screens installed. This screen design can use a variety of slot-size openings to accommodate almost any formation gradation, including fine- to medium-grained sands. These screens are developed by removing fine-grained deposits to create a natural filter pack around the well screens.

Using this method, the well screen provides the following advantages.

- The screen can have more open area (often 40% or more).
- The screen is more durable (usually composed of stainless steel).
- The screen has more flexibility in slot size, to accommodate a wider range of formation deposits.
- The installation method enables the selection of slot sizes for individual screen sections to conform to the specific gradation of the formation in which the sections are placed.
- The screening method allows the use of other screen materials (e.g., plastic) in selected applications.
- Screens can be installed in formations containing greater amounts of fine-grained (e.g., sand) deposits.

This installation method also provides the ability to use special well-screen materials that are applicable in saline and brackish environments. It also makes it possible to install laterals in formations containing large cobbles and boulders.

Filter-Packed Screens

Filter-packed screens are installed in much the same manner as is used for the wire-wrapped design, however an artificial filter-pack is installed around the well screen. When this method is employed, formation samples are collected as the pipe is projected. After the projection pipe has been pushed to the full design length, specially designed well screens (usually made of stainless steel) are inserted and an artificial filter pack is placed around the well screens as the projection pipe is withdrawn. Alternatively, a prepacked well-screen design that uses dual-screen sections and contains the artificial media between the two sets of screens (e.g., Johnson Screens Muni-Pak™), as shown below in Figure 15.9, can be installed. This enables the installation of a filter to act as a transition zone between a fine-grained formation and the slots in the well screen and to prevent ongoing sand intrusion into the well. This method has been used for both seawater and freshwater applications.

Figure 15.9. Johnson Screens Muni-Pak™ prepacked well screen.

The well screens typically are projected out into the aquifer in one of three patterns: (1) radial, with all laterals equally spaced in all directions; (2) fan, with laterals pointed toward a specific direction; or (3) a combination of radial and fan. The pattern selected depends upon several site variables and on the intended source (e.g., groundwater, induced infiltration).

Once installed, the well screens are developed to remove fine-grained formation materials from around the screens. This optimizes filter permeability, and improves flow hydraulics within the filter as the water nears the screen. The development process is performed along the full length of each lateral well screen section in an incremental manner to insure that all sections of the well screen are developed uniformly, and that the water produced has a minimum sand content. The development of any well is a critical part of optimizing performance and minimizing maintenance needs.

It is also possible to construct collector wells in consolidated (rock) formations, however certain modifications to the construction procedures outlined above are required to enable construction in rock to reach design lengths and depths. Special investigation also is needed to determine anticipated well yields, because the predominant flow in many rock formations results from intersecting fracture zones within the rock, which can be difficult—if not impossible—to predict.

Record Keeping

A comprehensive well-monitoring program should be established for all wells, whether they are vertical wells or collector wells. Several monitoring criteria are useful for developing an operational trend for a horizontal collector well located near a perennial stream. These criteria include total monthly pumpage, collector pumping level, water temperatures, specific capacity, differential drawdown, and river stage versus groundwater elevation. The information gathered helps to identify declining trends or other anomalies that can occur during the life of the well and to forewarn of impending situations where well capacity could fall below demand. Reviewing the collected and graphed data enables a determination of critical operating parameters, so that required maintenance can be scheduled at opportune times.

In addition to maintaining a record-keeping and monitoring program, it also is recommended that an in-well, underwater inspection be made of the collector well—under operating conditions—after the well has been in operation for about 7 years and once every 5 years thereafter. During these inspections, a scuba diver makes observations of physical conditions in the caisson and of the well-screen conditions in the sections of the laterals closest to the caisson. Flow measurements should be obtained from each of the laterals. As noted, pumping and water-level data also should be collected and reviewed.

The parameters described above can be utilized to properly analyze and understand the changing conditions throughout the production life cycle of a collector well, and enable a general comparison of screen efficiency, aquifer condition, and collector-well yield with time. When used in conjunction with periodic pumping tests and in-well inspections—from which more-exact computations and observations of screen efficiency and total yield can be determined—the condition of each collector well can be monitored accurately and continually.

Collector-Well Maintenance

As with any water well, a collector well eventually requires maintenance to restore lost well efficiency and capacity. Using the data collected and graphed as part of the monitoring program, declines in well performance can be observed and maintenance can be anticipated and scheduled for opportune times, thus minimizing disruption during normal service periods.

Maintenance is accomplished most effectively by inserting specialized equipment into the individual laterals while the central caisson is dewatered. The cleaning and redevelopment program removes debris from inside the well screen, accumulations from the well-screen slot openings, and deposits from outside the well screen in the aquifer and filter-pack materials. Through the use of specialized procedures, maintenance (well-screen cleaning and redevelopment) also can be performed while the collector well remains in service, which is important if the well is the only source of water supply for the utility. When using one of these methods, redevelopment and cleaning can take place while the collector well continues to pump into the system, uninterrupted. This illustrates the unique flexibility of a collector well.

Maintenance also can include installation of new or additional lateral well screens when older screens (usually made of mild steel) have corroded or deteriorated over time, or have become excessively plugged. Many of the older collector wells (constructed with mild-steel screens) require new lateral screens after about 40 years of operation. Most of the collector wells built in recent years, however, utilize newer technology that facilitates the use of stainless-steel well screens, which should last longer and be more resistant to normal corrosion processes.

Riverbank Filtration

As the design and construction process for the horizontal collector well evolved, it became evident that wells installed adjacent to—and sometimes underneath—surface-water sources were able to develop large quantities of water. As groundwater levels were lowered by pumping, the hydraulic gradients in the aquifer permitted water to be infiltrated from an adjacent river or lake, providing recharge into the aquifer to replenish water removed by pumping. This infiltration process pre-filters river water as it percolates through the riverbed sediments into the aquifer (recharging it) and, ultimately, into the well screens, and typically removes objectionable characteristics of the river water, such as turbidity and microorganisms. Because the "recharge water" from the river is infiltrated over such a large area, infiltration rates are extremely low and, in most cases, provide a high degree of filtration. This process of recharging aquifers and supporting well yields through natural filtration process generally is referred to as riverbank filtration (RBF). A typical RBF installation is shown in Figure 15.10.

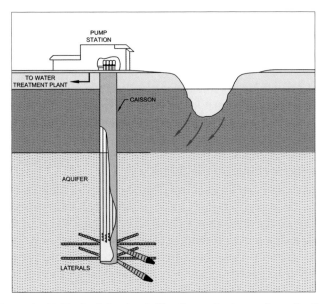

Figure 15.10. Typical riverbank filtration collector-well application.

During the first 50 years that collector wells were installed, they often were built immediately adjacent to surface-water sources to be in close proximity to the apparent source of recharge, and to take advantage of the filtering capacity of the riverbed sediments and aquifer to provide high-capacity and high-quality infiltrated water supplies.

In the 1990s, as U.S. regulatory agencies began evaluating issues relating to groundwater that is recharged by surface water, siting and design philosophies for collector wells were revised to:

  ◆ Improve the filtration of surface water;
  ◆ Locate wells to minimize the potential for contamination from surface-water sources;

- ◆ Improve caisson installation methods to minimize disturbance to the aquifer; and
- ◆ Improve surface-sealing techniques around the caisson.

The revised design philosophies involved the proper selection of the horizon (elevation) for projecting the lateral screens and sometimes locating the wells a sufficient distance back from the river to increase the degree of filtration and travel time for recharge water. The ability (or efficiency) of the streambed and aquifer to filter out objectionable microorganisms and to reduce the turbidity from surface-water sources varies from region to region and, certainly, from site to site. In most alluvial settings, it should be possible to achieve some degree of filtration to improve water quality. If adequate natural filtration occurs, then a riverbank filtration system can qualify as an approved alternative treatment technology by regulatory agencies and receive filtration-removal credits.

Other Collector-Well Applications

In addition to being used for municipal or industrial water supplies, collector wells are used for other applications including construction dewatering and for artificial recharge (such as in ASR programs), and as seawater collector wells. Collector wells have been installed at several coastal sites to develop a filtered seawater supply to be used for desalination and to provide filtered seawater for aquarium make-up water. Installing the well screens beneath beaches minimizes both environmental disturbance and impacts on local aquatic life. Filtering the raw seawater through the beach sands removes suspended particulates that would otherwise clog membrane filter treatment equipment, and serves as pre-treatment for the seawater-treatment process. An illustration showing a beach collector well for developing filtered seawater is shown in Figure 15.11.

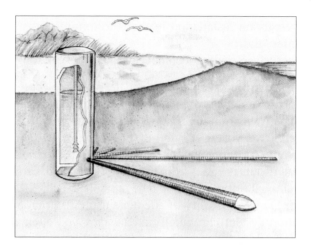

Figure 15.11. Typical seawater-collector well (Hunt 2002).

Collector wells also have been used since the 1940s as part of aquifer re-charging projects (Hunt 1984), including the following.

- *Louisville, Kentucky (U.S.A.).* A collector well was used to recharge treated city water into an alluvial aquifer to restore groundwater levels that had been falling due to over-pumping in the downtown area over a number of years.
- *Canton, Ohio (U.S.A.).* In an early ASR program, a series of 3 collectors was used to recharge water (developed by RBF) from a shallow surficial aquifer past a confining clay into a lower confined aquifer for storage. Two tiers of lateral well screens were used (above and below the confining layer) to convey the water past the clay layer in a passive manner.

Collector wells also have been constructed from a direct surface-water intake and can utilize either water source, depending upon groundwater levels, river-water quality, temperature needs, and system demands. Typical of this application is a combination collector well–intake constructed for an industry in Missouri (U.S.A.) that is about 85 ft (26 m) deep and which can produce 2,100 gpm (0.13 m^3/sec). Figure 15.12 is an illustration showing a typical combination-unit arrangement.

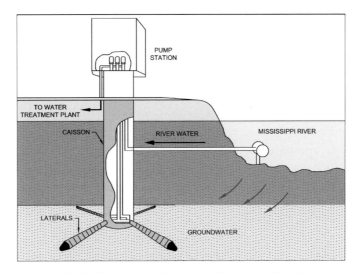

Figure 15.12. Typical combination collector-well intake unit.

INFILTRATION GALLERIES

Albert Smith
Johnson Screens

In some geologic environments, the aquifer thickness might not be sufficient to supply the required volume of water to vertical wells, even though the aquifer is hydraulically connected to a nearby surface-water body. A typical example is a river valley where thin alluvial deposits overlie bedrock. Although the hydraulic conductivity of the sediment is excellent, the transmissivity is severely limited because the deposits are so thin. In other situations, a thin layer of freshwater can overlie saltwater. Deep wells at this site would cause upconing of the saltwater, thereby degrading water quality.

Under these hydrogeologic conditions, infiltration galleries, which consist of one or more horizontally laid screens, can be either bank mounted or bed mounted in permeable alluvial materials. A significant quantity of water can be pumped from an infiltration gallery because the hydraulic conductivity of the natural material and the filter pack surrounding the screens is sufficiently high that the recharge rate is equal to the pumping rate. Because the screens are placed in open excavations, the usual practical depth limitation is about 25 ft (7.6 m) (Bennett 1970). Water entering the screen often is collected in a central vertical pumping station (sump) constructed near the end of the screens. A large-diameter sump can serve as a storage chamber if the infiltration rate is low (Figure 15.13).

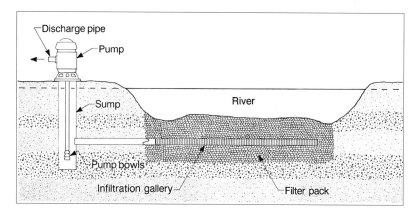

Figure 15.13. Cross section of typical pump station and infiltration gallery.

This discussion of infiltration galleries focuses on designs that are dependent on the sustained flow provided by a nearby surface-water source. The design and construction parameters are the same, however, for galleries not associated with a direct source of recharge, for example those placed in highly permeable sediments that are consistently recharged by rainfall.

The decision of whether to place the gallery adjacent to or under the surface-water body depends on several factors.

   ♦   **Yield requirements.** Galleries placed under a water body initially produce much greater yield than galleries placed adjacent to the water body. As the disturbed lake or river bed assumes its normal sedimentation regime, however, the transmissivity value falls as finer-grained particles infiltrate the filter-pack material surrounding the screens.

   ♦   **Water-quality requirements.** Galleries located adjacent to a water body usually receive water that has lower turbidity and fewer bacteria than bed-mounted galleries because the water has been filtered more extensively due to a longer flow path.

- ◆ **Construction difficulties.** It generally is more difficult to install a gallery beneath a stream or lake bed.
- ◆ **Maintenance considerations.** Maintenance and repairs are easier to perform on galleries installed adjacent to a water body. In general, more maintenance is required for bed-mounted galleries because stream current continually adds fine material to the top of the filter pack.
- ◆ **Stability of the river course or lake level.** River waters can move great distances over relatively short periods, and either carry away a gallery placed on the bank or completely cover a bed-mounted gallery with less-permeable material. Changes in the elevation of a water body also can affect where the gallery is placed. For example, the available head might drop considerably in intermittent streams during dry seasons of the year, but flow through the underlying sand and gravel usually continues.

Additional information on the design, installation, and maintenance of infiltration galleries is contained in Appendix 15.A (DVD).

DEWATERING

Paul C. Schmall, PE
Vice President, Chief Engineer, Moretrench American Corp.

Dewatering technology has advanced concurrently with improvements in water-well design and construction practices, new pump designs, and the development of alternative technologies such as ground freezing. The dewatering industry is extensive, and many contracting firms specialize in this business.

Dewatering wells are designed primarily to lower the groundwater level to a predetermined depth and to maintain that depth until all construction below the water table has been completed. In the past, almost all construction of buildings, subways, tunnels, sewer and water trenches, or earth-sheltered houses required some temporary or long-term dewatering. In most cases, it is more economical to dewater rather than surround an excavation with a continuous wall of sheet piling and pump from within the work area. Lowering the water table by pumping enables drilling professionals to work with heavy equipment, even in zones that formerly were saturated. Proper dewatering also eliminates the hazards of sand boils developing in the bottom of the excavation.

Dewatering techniques also can be utilized for the removal of contaminated groundwater or to control the spread or migration of groundwater contaminants as discussed in Chapter 14.

The main purposes for construction dewatering include the following (Cedergren 1977).

- ◆ Intercepting seepage that would enter an excavation site and interfere with construction activities.
- ◆ Improving the stability of slopes, thus preventing sloughing or slope failures.
- ◆ Preventing the bottom of excavations from heaving due to excessive hydrostatic pressure.
- ◆ Improving the compaction characteristics of soils in the bottom of excavations for basements, freeways, and other structures.
- ◆ Drying borrow pits so that excavated materials can be properly compacted in embankments.
- ◆ Reducing earth pressures on temporary supports and sheeting.

Despite advances in dewatering technology, it is almost impossible to predict subsurface conditions before a project is started, because near-surface geologic materials do not necessarily reflect the materials that are buried more deeply. It therefore is difficult to predict how much water must be removed and the effect of this removal on the engineering characteristics of the dewatered materials.

It is beyond the scope of this section to investigate the physical effects of dewatering on dewatered materials, but this aspect of any construction project is vital, and anyone involved with a dewatering project must become familiar with the behavior of subsurface materials under stress induced by dewatering. Preliminary determination of compressive strengths, Atterberg limits, shear strengths, and grain sizes must be completed for any major dewatering project. Stability of the dewatered materials is of prime concern; unexpected changes in pore water pressure—caused by dewatering—must never be allowed to produce "quick" conditions, in which the dewatered material loses its stability and then flows (e.g., quicksand).

The emphasis in this section is on traditional dewatering techniques utilizing both shallow- and deep-well systems. Knowledge of the hydrogeology at a site, basic hydraulic theory, and the practical elements of well design and construction are essential. Experience always plays a major role in successful dewatering engineering. Other dewatering methods are discussed by Powers et al. (2007) and the Water and Power Resources Service (1981).

Factors in Selecting a Dewatering System

Deep wells, well points, and to a lesser extent ejector wells (eductor wells) are the three most common dewatering tools. Selection of which type of dewatering design to use depends on many factors, including: hydrogeologic conditions at the site; length of time pumping is required at a site; volume of water to be removed; whether pumping equipment can be installed in the construction area; and availability of drilling and dewatering equipment. Experience also is important in selecting the dewatering design.

Characteristics of the water-bearing formation that must be determined before designing a dewatering system include the following.

- Whether the aquifer is confined or unconfined
- Depth and thickness of the aquifer
- Stratification, layering, or vertical drainage characteristics of the aquifer
- Transmissivity and storage coefficient of the aquifer
- Static water level
- Sources of recharge to the aquifer and the location of these sources

Additional discussion on some of these topics is contained in Appendix 15.B. Information required about the construction site includes the following.

- Dimensions of the area to be dewatered
- Depth to which the water levels must be lowered
- Construction techniques proposed and the ability to handle residual water from within the excavation area
- Plans for disposal of water pumped from the wells
- Whether the installation is to be permanent or temporary

This information, coupled with a firm knowledge of well hydraulics and groundwater-flow theory, enables a dewatering professional to develop a satisfactory design incorporating a minimum number of wells with optimum pumping rates, well depths, and well spacing. In any dewatering design, there generally is a maximum drawdown that can be permitted in each pumped well, and simultaneously there is a minimum drawdown that must be achieved everywhere within the excavation area. For large projects, selecting the proper number of wells, the well spacing, and the well yield—while staying within these two limits—can require numerous iterations of calculations and models.

Before the use of digital computers in dewatering design, all calculations and comparisons were completed manually. Due to time limitations, a dewatering professional frequently was forced to select the first solution that appeared to work, rather than selecting the optimal design which would have accomplished the dewatering goals at a lower cost.

Well-Point Dewatering Systems

The well-point system commonly is constructed as a group of closely spaced, relatively small-diameter shallow wells, connected to a common header pipe or manifold which is pumped by suction methods. Well points commonly are used for dewatering of trenches for sewers and water mains, and excavations for foundations that are below the water table.

Well-point systems frequently are used because in sandy soils; they are relatively easy to install by jetting methods and are adaptable to a wide range of site conditions. They are particularly suited to the following situations.

- Single-stage dewatering, where the pumping water level is within suction lift (i.e., 15 ft (4.5 m))
- Formations with low transmissivity (fine sand and silt); the vacuum applied to the well points enhances the drainage of silty and clayey soils that do not respond as well to gravity-drainage methods
- Shallow formations that overlie low-permeability formations; the close spacing of well points is very effective in lowering the water level as near as practical to a problematic geological interface

During operation of a well-point system, a central pump lifts water from each well point by applying a partial vacuum in the header and riser pipes. The partial vacuum or suction lift that the pump can maintain determines the drawdown that can be obtained in the water-bearing formation. The maximum drawdown obtainable is the difference between the suction limit of the pump (suction head) and the distance from the static water level to the center of the pump. These terms are shown in Figure 15.14.

In practice, the greatest suction lift that can be developed is about 25 ft (7.5 m), with friction losses in mechanical equipment and piping as well as the "mounding" of groundwater in the interior area of an excavation, most well-point systems are engineered on the basis of an effective suction lift of 15 ft (4.5 m). The elevation of the project site also influences the effective suction lift. The higher the elevation, the less the suction lift.

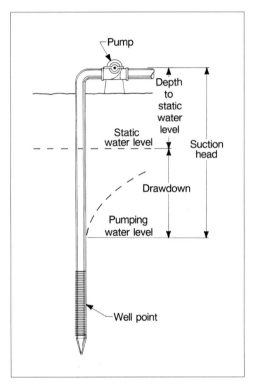

Figure 15.14. Relationships of suction head and drawdown for a suction well-point system.

The yield from fine soils always is low—so low, in fact, as to raise the question of whether practical dewatering can be achieved. In many cases, the need for a well-point system cannot be based upon the anticipated yield. Experience has shown that, for fine-grained soils, in many cases the removal of even a small volume of water can have a significant and very pronounced stabilizing effect on the material. A saturated, fine-grained soil exposed within an excavation can be unworkable and behaves as "flowing ground." The same fine-grained soil can demonstrate significant stability when the water content is drained to just below saturation, whereby the pore water pressures have been modified from positive to negative and the soil has been imparted with apparent cohesion.

The diameter of well points used in dewatering systems usually is either 1½ in (38 mm) or 2 in (51 mm); the yield can vary from a fraction of a gallon per minute to 50 gpm (272 m³/day). Well points typically are spaced 5 ft (1.5 m) to 12 ft (3.7 m) apart, depending upon the hydraulic conductivity of the saturated formation, the depth to which the water table must be lowered, and the depth to which the well points can be installed in the water-bearing formation (Powers et al. 2007). For fine-grained materials, the well-point spacing could be less.

For any given aquifer or ground condition, the actual spacing of the well points depends on the type of point used, the friction losses in the system, and the volume of water to be removed. For a major dewatering operation, total flow requirements should be estimated from constant-rate aquifer tests. The point spacing then is based on the total volume of water to be removed and the anticipated yield of an individual well point, when multiple well points are pumping.

The actual volume of water obtained from each point is a function of the available yield of the formation as well as the head losses in the screen, casing, and header system. Use of smaller diameter points results in greater friction losses at higher yields. In general, PVC points that use slotted screens have much higher friction losses than well points constructed with continuous-slot or wire-mesh screens.

The well-point system is a very versatile tool and can be adapted for a wide variety of soil or ground conditions. Most well-point dewatering systems for small projects can be installed without an exhaustive analysis of site-specific conditions. Length of the screen and diameter of the screen and pipe usually are dictated by the equipment available, which is reused on each project and typically is oversized. Spacing of the individual points generally is based on field experience for similar ground conditions. Testing for well-point yield and drawdown can be performed concurrently with the system installation, so that adjustments for varied ground conditions can be made in a timely manner. Additional discussion on the design and installation of a well-point system is contained in Appendix 15.B.

Deep-Well Dewatering Systems

At many construction sites, deep wells are used instead of well-point systems. Each well in deep-well installations usually produces many times the quantity of water produced by an individual well point in a well-point system; however, deep wells also can be effective with yields of a fraction of a gallon per minute. Deep wells can vary from approximately 20 ft deep to hundreds of feet deep. Design and construction techniques for water-supply wells are discussed at length in Chapter 9 and Chapter 10. The same general principles apply to deep wells used for dewatering.

Deep-well dewatering schemes are most appropriate in the following situations.

- ◆ Environments where pumping water levels or dewatered levels in the excavation are beyond the suction-lift capacity of a well-point system, or where multistage well-point dewatering is impractical.
- ◆ Formations that extend to depths considerably below the depth of the proposed excavation. These formations permit installation of deeper wells, provide more available drawdown, and produce larger yields from fewer wells.

An optimum deep-well dewatering system is one that utilizes a minimum number of efficient wells pumped at proper rates and spaced as strategically as practicable around the job site. Deep wells are advantageous in that they are not limited in effectiveness with depth and they can be installed outside of an excavation and activated in advance to pre-drain the site prior to excavation.

Deep-Well Dewatering-System Design

The method of cumulative-drawdown can be used to design a deep-well array provided that the aquifer is confined or the design drawdown is less than 20% of the initial saturated thickness in a water table aquifer setting (Powers et al. 2007). The method provides accurate information on drawdown within the area of interest, particularly if an aquifer test has been conducted.

In some situations, it is recommended that the deep wells not be placed to the bottom of the aquifer, because more water might have to be pumped to achieve the required drawdown. In many alluvial systems, for example, the hydraulic conductivity of lower sediments can be greater than that of the overlying sediments. If the screens are not set to the bottom of the aquifer, however, it is impossible to use the predictive methods described above, because they are predicated on the assumption that the wells are fully penetrating. The transmissivity value is established based on the total aquifer thickness, with no consideration of partial-penetration effects.

Dewatering-Well Installation Methods

Powers et al. (2007) indicate that the most common dewatering-well installation methods are jetting, reverse circulation rotary drilling, dual rotary drilling, mud rotary drilling, bucket-auger drilling, and hollow-stem auger drilling. Bucket-auger and mud rotary methods are the most commonly used for dewatering work.

Well installation via jetting methods requires a significant amount of equipment mobilization and setup, and is utilized uniquely on dewatering projects where a large number of wells is installed and the wells are within close proximity to each other. Jetting with the use of a heavy-wall jet casing (Figure 15.15) can be used for the installation of high-efficiency dewatering wells that are up to 24 in (60 cm) in diameter and 120 ft (40 m) in depth.

Figure 15.15. A jetted well installation (Moretrench).

Bucket-auger drilling—which is relatively quick and inexpensive for shallow drilling—probably is the most common method used for installing a dewatering well (Figure 15.16). The technique simply requires a cylindrical bucket with auger-type cutting teeth attached to a string of telescoping kelly bars. It can be performed with a truck-mounted rig, crane attachment, or a large crawler-mounted foundation drill. Bucket-auger drilling is very versatile and effective and is used in a broad range of soil types, but it is most effective in sand and gravel comprised of particle sizes up to 3 in (75 mm) and in soft to moderately stiff silts and clays. Cobbles and boulders cause problems, and very stiff clays and hardpans can be difficult to penetrate.

Figure 15.16. Bucket-auger drilling using a large truck-mounted foundation drill (Moretrench).

Dewatering-Well Construction

Powers et al. (2007) indicate that PVC well screen is used for most temporary dewatering projects where well yields are less than 1,000 gpm (3,785 ℓ/min) and 12-in (300-mm) diameter or smaller screen and casing can be used. Well screens are designed to limit velocities to below the critical value, as discussed in Chapter 9. Schedule 40 PVC, slotted, solvent-welded screen most commonly is used in low- to moderate-yield situations, and wire-wrap PVC screen is utilized in higher-yield situations. Although the anticipated yield of the formation might not require screens that have greater open area, development and well-mainten-ance efforts are more effective if the higher open-area screens are utilized.

Steel, galvanized-steel, or stainless-steel well screen is used most often where screen diameters are larger than 12 in (300 mm). Bridge-slot and louvered screens are relatively low cost, and commonly are used for temporary large-diameter dewatering well construction. These screens are best suited for gravel-packed wells where larger openings and higher entrance velocities could occur without excessive friction loss. In some cases the screens are pulled and reused.

Powers et al. (2007) also cite the use of wire-mesh screen for jetted wells, particularly in finer soils where openings smaller than 0.020 in (0.5 mm) are required. The open area of this screen material can be as much as 45%. Because of the small openings, the wire-mesh well screen is not recommended for drilled wells requiring development.

Prepacked screens are used in dewatering where the placement of a con-ventional filter pack is difficult, such as in an angled or horizontal borehole or where the borehole diameter is very close to the well screen diameter.

The annulus around the screen typically is filled with a filter pack consisting of sand or gravel. The best filter pack is one that is as coarse as possible but that does not continuously pass fines. Powers et al. (2007) indicate 3 in (75 mm) is the optimum filter-pack thickness for dewatering wells, but less than 3 in (75 mm) might be acceptable if the wells are shallow, the drilling technique can provide a straight borehole, and centralizers are used frequently. Filter packs thicker than 8 in (200 mm) present difficulty in development, particularly if the filter sand is relatively fine grained. Use of thicker filter packs is common for dewatering wells installed by bucket-auger drilling methods where borehole diameters typically are 24-in long or larger. Uniform filters (with a uniform coefficient less than 3) that can be placed by pouring without performing segregation typically are used for dewatering wells. Chapter 9 discusses the design of filter packs. Development of dewatering wells is similar to that of water-supply wells; development is discussed in Chapter 11.

Dewatering wells are used under varied conditions, and the appropriate construction details should be based on the specific conditions under which the well will function. A basic dewatering well (Figure 15.17) is best for short-term use such as fast-moving trench work; its service life can be less than a week and the pump is removed and reinstalled multiple times. Under such circumstances, rigorous design and installation procedures, as discussed previously, need not be followed. Such a well is quite modest in cost when drilled in favorable ground condition. Additionally, the cost of lengthy development procedures to enhance well efficiency could exceed that of drilling a greater number of wells that have lower efficiency.

The filter pack and well screen should be selected to suit the formation, although perhaps not with the care required for permanent water-supply wells. A small amount of sand produced from a well that will operate for less than a week might not be harmful. Filter design which results in significant sand pumping, however, must be avoided.

Figure 15.18 illustrates many of the construction details appropriate for dewatering wells that must function for lengthy periods of time during the construction of longer-term projects (e.g., power plants, subway structures). Depending on the degree of drilling difficulty and construction materials selected, the well could be significantly more costly than that of a short-term well such as that shown in Figure 15.17.

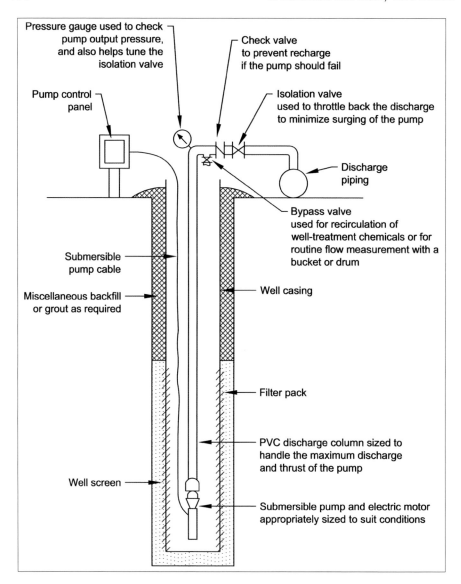

Figure 15.17. Basic dewatering-well construction details for systems intended for short-term use.

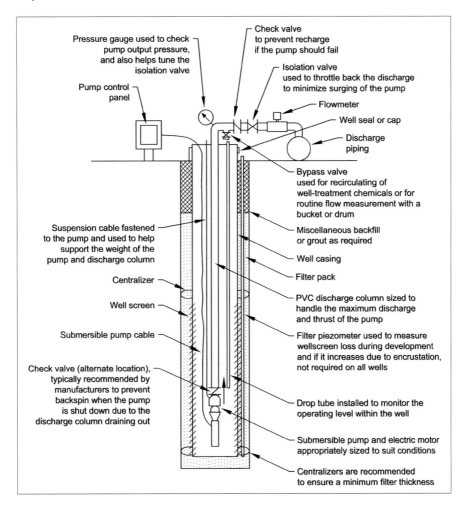

Figure 15.18. Basic dewatering-well construction details for systems designed for longer-term use.

Deep-Well Dewatering Applications in Low-Permeability Soils

Deep wells and ejectors (discussed below) are the most appropriate tools when dewatering to depths of more than 15 ft (4.6 m) in geologic materials of low permeability. Affordable smaller submersible pumps are available for residential use, therefore the cost of ejectors and deep wells for the same project can be very comparable. Ejectors require a significant amount of system piping and subsequent maintenance, and deep wells require electrical distribution to each well. Site conditions often dictate which technique is should be used.

Low-Yielding Deep-Well Systems

Low-yielding deep wells are difficult to maintain. The most common cause of submersible pump failure is inadequate motor cooling due to the limited flow of water past the motor because of the low yield of water from the geologic materials. Pump failure occurs even with small, fractional one-half and one-third horsepower pumps. The second most common failure associated with low-flow wells is due to the mechanical stresses to the pump and pump-motor connection due to surging. Surges occur when the pump capacity exceeds the well yield and the pump draws the internal water level down to the intake and "gulps" air.

A well-throttling valve always should be used to regulate or "tune" a surging pump output to the yield of the well. Should additional protective measures be warranted, electronic controllers can be utilized to automatically shut down a pump motor when the operating characteristics indicate lack of load (water), or "dry-running." These electronic pump protectors can be incorporated into a pump control panel or directly into the motor itself. They provide what is known in the industry as "dry-run protection." Powers et al. (2007) note that the most advanced technology for submersible pumps is the incorporation of both variable-frequency drives and dry-run sensors into small-horsepower submersible pumps. The low-load pump sensing of the electronic pump protector provides dry-run protection, and the variable-frequency driven motor provides a "soft start" to gradually speed up the pump and avoid the shock and stress of a high-torque start, so that repeated starts do not cause the mechanical stresses. This technology has been quite successful for dewatering applications. Additional information on pumps and accessory equipment is contained in Chapter 12 and its appendices.

Vacuum Wells

Vacuum can be applied to deep wells to enhance the drainage of finer-grained soils in a similar manner to well points. Figure 15.19 illustrates a well with a well head designed for the application of vacuum. A grout seal in the annular space prevents air from moving through the filter column. Vacuum can substantially increase the yield of the well and help overcome well loss. Powers et al. (2007) indicate that vacuum can increase well yield from low–hydraulic conductivity formations by as much as 20%. Vacuums have been measured in piezometers as far as 10 ft (3 m) away.

Figure 15.19. A vacuum-tight well head (Moretrench).

Vacuum is more effective in confined-aquifer situations. With water-table wells, the effectiveness of the vacuum usually is limited to the early stage of pumping when the aquifer still is substantially saturated. Normally when the well screen is exposed, air enters and overloads even large-capacity vacuum pumps.

Ejectors

Ejectors can be utilized effectively in situations where low well yields present difficult operating conditions. Powers et al. (2007) cite the use of an ejector system (sometimes referred to as an eductor system) as an adaptation of the residential jet-pump arrangement; multiple wells can be powered by a single pumping station rather than by individual jet pumps at each well.

The ejector itself is a nozzle and venturi pumping device that can be installed within a dewatering well or well point. It is driven by water pressure; essentially, high pressure is converted (at the nozzle) to a suction action which draws the water into the ejector body. Where the screen is exposed, the vacuum developed by the ejector can enhance drainage of low-permeability geologic materials.

Powers et al. (2007) indicate a significant advantage is the ability of the ejector to automatically develop a high vacuum in its screen and transmit it to the soil itself. The presence of horizontal varves or lenses of fine sand within a silt formation can greatly increase the effectiveness of a vacuum-dewatering system by enhancing the communication between the silt and the vertical sand columns around the ejectors. In such soil conditions, ejector well spacing of 5 ft (1.5 m) to 10 ft (3 m) is typical.

Ejectors typically are used if groundwater must be lowered more than 15 ft (4.5 m) (i.e., more than the effective suction lift of a well-point system), and the permeability of the soil is such that vacuum application is warranted. Ejectors are very inefficient and their application generally is cost effective only in low-yielding formations.

Ejectors are available commercially in both two-pipe and single-pipe configurations. The two-pipe ejector (Figure 15.20) requires fewer specialized parts and can be operated in a wide range of conditions. A typical commercially available two-pipe ejector can yield up to 12 gpm (45 ℓ/min) (Q_2), but requires a minimum 4-in (100-mm) diameter well screen and casing.

The single-pipe ejector (Figure 15.21) utilizes concentric supply and return pipes to save space. A single-pipe ejector can be installed freely in a fully screened well 3 in (75 mm) in diameter or in a 2-in (50-mm) well casing or well-point riser if a shorter screen is fastened to the well casing below the ejector assembly. Thus, the single-pipe ejector can provide the same pumping capacity from a smaller-diameter borehole. The ejector body can be equipped with a drawdown tube or tailpipe placed to the bottom of the well screen.

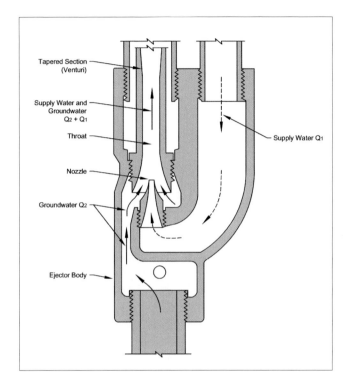

Figure 15.20. A two-pipe ejector.

An ejector system is a recirculating system driven with a single pumping station which consists simply of a tank and a high-pressure pump. The pump draws water from the tank and delivers it at high pressure to the individual ejectors through the supply header. The combined supply and return flow (which includes the well yield) returns to the tank through the return header. The yield of the system continuously overflows to discharge.

This type of system requires a significant amount of supply and return piping to convey the water to and from the ejector pumping station. The ejector's performance is very sensitive to piping friction, particularly on the return side of the system, and high supply pressures often must be maintained to offset the return friction. It is not uncommon to have supply pressures of 125 psi (862 kPa) (Powers et al. 2007). Ejector headers normally are constructed of steel or aluminum, although PVC sometimes is used in corrosive groundwater.

Smaller-diameter single-pipe ejectors usually are installed by the same methods utilized for well points, such as jetting or drilling. Two-pipe ejector wells typically are installed by mud rotary drilling techniques, to create a well with an 8-in or 12-in diameter.

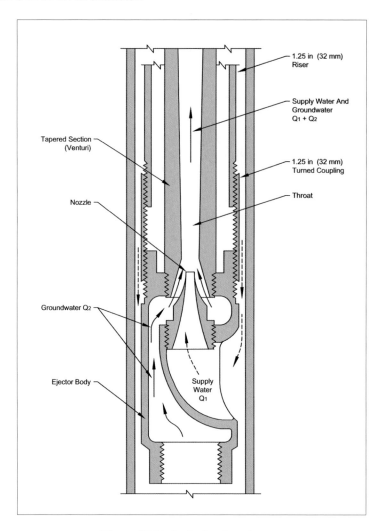

Figure 15.21. A single-pipe ejector.

Summary

Decisions on the number of wells required, well depths and diameters, and other construction details depend on numerous site-specific requirements and conditions. The time required to drain the aquifer can be predicted on the basis of the pumping test. Wells must be able to remove the required volumes of water from storage and maintain drawdown, even during periods of excess recharge (heavy rainfall events or temporary rises in nearby rivers).

The most critical factor involved in dewatering is the ability to predict drawdown at various pumping rates. Specific capacity can fall off significantly as drawdown increases and the saturated thickness decreases, therefore the results from a step-drawdown test can be helpful in gauging actual well yield under dewatered conditions. Careful analysis of both constant-rate and step-drawdown tests is important in estimating conditions during dewatering. See Chapter 6 for the limitations and advantages of both tests.

For complex dewatering conditions—which do not lend themselves to traditional calculations—the use of finite element or finite difference modeling is recommended, because this helps assure that the design produces optimum performance at the lowest cost. The use of a groundwater model also can include the complex calculations for dewatering in an unconfined aquifer condition where more than 20% of the aquifer is dewatered. In view of well construction, completion, and operation costs, the value of the time spent seeking an optimal dewatering design is clear.

INJECTION WELLS

Albert J. Smith
Johnson Screens

Injection wells are used for a variety of purposes, including water supply, saltwater control, groundwater control and remediation, solution mining, carbon-dioxide sequestration, liquid-waste disposal, geothermal energy, and in the oil and gas industry. Appropriate well-design and well-construction techniques vary according to the specific purpose of each well. The design and construction of injection wells is significant, because they are much more likely to fail than are typical water wells. If the wells are used for liquid-waste disposal, then a failure could lead to significant water-quality issues.

With the exception of entrance velocity and screen length, the design criteria given in Chapter 9 apply to injection wells. Thus, screen open area and screen length must be optimal. The average entrance velocity for injection wells should be 0.05 ft/sec (0.015 m/sec), therefore screens should be twice as long as for a withdrawal-well pumping the same volume of water.

The typical injection well should pump sand-free water, be efficient (maximum recharge at minimum pressure build-up), and be cost effective in terms of both initial investment and operational costs. There also are some special design features for the major types of injection wells. It has been suggested, for example, that because the water flow is from the inside out, the well-screen wire should be inverted. Inverted wire is not warranted because initial development and future rehabilitation both require the normal orientation of wire. Fines must be able to move through the non-clogging slot to be developed after installation so that maximum efficiency is obtained. Any other orientation, or the use of irrigator style (round wire on round rod) screens, cause more blockage and reduce open area. Best results are obtained with standard orientation using the highest open-area wire profiles. The use of injection wells for recharge is discussed in this chapter, and additional information regarding injection-well technology can be found in Tsang and Apps (2005).

Control of Saltwater Intrusion

In Florida (U.S.A.), Southern California (U.S.A.), Long Island, New York (U.S.A.), and other low-lying coastal areas, the high use of groundwater has enabled the normal freshwater-saltwater interface to move inland and nearer the ground surface. Initially, many communities faced with saltwater encroachment problems merely drilled new production wells farther inland. Efforts are being made to maintain groundwater levels by ponding surface runoff or river water so that it recharges the groundwater table (Figure 15.22(a)). Elsewhere, the installation of deep recharge wells has been able to control saltwater intrusion by creating a ridge of groundwater having a potentiometric surface sufficiently elevated to prevent saltwater intrusion while allowing pumping below sea level landward of the ridge (Figure 15.22(b)). Sometimes barrier wells near the shore are used to collect saltwater and induce a freshwater gradient toward the sea (Figure 15.22(c)). Thus recharge systems are extremely useful in maintaining the proper hydraulic gradient between freshwater and saltwater.

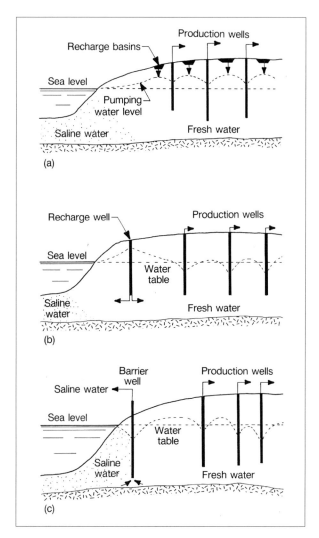

Figure 15.22. Diagrams showing: (a) Use of artificial recharge in the area of production wells in an unconfined coastal aquifer, the recharge water maintains the water table above sea level to prevent saltwater intrusion; (b) Use of injection wells to form a pressure ridge to prevent saltwater intrusion in an unconfined coastal aquifer; (c) Use of pumping wells at the coastline to form a trench in the water table, which acts as a barrier to further saltwater encroachment.

Solution Mining

In-situ mining is used to extract deposits of uranium, copper, sulfur, potash, halite, gypsum, and other minerals from ore bodies located deep beneath the earth's surface, without excavation of the overburden. Leaching of the minerals in place is accomplished by injecting chemically treated groundwater into the ore body, allowing the ores to dissolve, and then pumping the groundwater and dissolved minerals to the surface where the minerals then are precipitated. Both injection wells and recovery wells are used in this operation. In addition to eliminating the need for large excavations, in-situ mining can cause significantly less environmental damage. Additional information on solution mining can be found on the website for the Solution Mining Research Institute (http://www.solutionmining.org).

PRESSURE-RELIEF WELLS

Albert J. Smith
Johnson Screens

During the 1940s, it became common practice to relieve hydrostatic pressures resulting from dam or levee construction by installing wells landward of the structures. Dams or levees often are constructed on a thin layer of semi-permeable or impermeable materials underlain by a relatively thick layer of highly permeable material (usually alluvium). Driven by hydrostatic pressures in the reservoir, water flows from the reservoir through the underlying permeable sediment to the area landward of the structure (Figure 15.23).

Subsurface pressure can become so great that the saturated weight of the surface materials might not be sufficient to contain it. Excess pressure causes localized heaving of the soil; these areas are called "sand boils" and are characterized by "quick" conditions. The construction of pressure-relief wells prevents the occurrence of excessive seepage and the formation of sand boils at the surface (Middlebrooks & Jervis 1946).

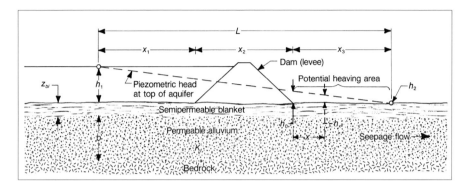

Figure 15.23. Cross section of a dam or levee structure showing the transmission of the static hydraulic head downriver or landward of the structure.

Pressure-relief wells, however, usually have little or no affect on the volume of seepage that passes through a dam or levee (Rutledge 1947). In a few instances, hydrostatic pressures are not a problem because the dam structure is "keyed" into bedrock. Thus, hydrostatic pressures in the reservoir cannot be transmitted to the area near the toe of the dam.

Prior to the installation of pressure-relief wells various types of horizontal drains were used to reduce near-surface pressures. These often proved to be ineffective, however, because much of the pressure buildup occurs deep beneath the land surface itself. To be effective, pressure reduction must take place in deep, highly permeable sediments below less-permeable surface or near-surface materials. The principal requirements for a relief well system are listed below (Turnbull & Mansur 1953).

- Wells must penetrate to the sediment layers having the highest transmissivity values.
- The wells must be installed close to each other so they can intercept a major part of the subsurface seepage, thereby minimizing pressures landward (downgradient) of the well installation.
- Wells must be efficient so that head losses are minimized.
- Wells should be designed and constructed so that movement of fine particles into the filter pack or screen is prevented.
- Wells should be resistant to chemical attack.

The design of a relief-well system is based on somewhat different principles than for a typical dewatering situation, in which pumping capacities easily can be adjusted to create the required drawdown conditions. Wells used to reduce pressure must be designed and installed so that each well in the system can accommodate its share of the total flow in the permeable zone beneath the dam or levee without the use of pumps or the creation of excessive head losses when flowing free. An exhaustive coverage of pressure relief–well applications is found in Appendix 15.C (DVD), The U.S. Army Corp of Engineers manual; it also describes the design and specification requirements of pressure-relief wells.

WELLS FOR HEAT PUMPS
Albert J. Smith
Johnson Screens

A heat pump is a mechanical device that extracts heat energy from a source such as air or water and makes it available for cooling or heating purposes. By definition a heat pump upgrades the ambient levels of heat in the heat source. That is, it increases or decreases the absolute temperature significantly with respect to that found in the heat source (Heap 1979). The function of a heat pump is to concentrate energy and make it available. The amount of energy required to run a heat pump usually is only one third to one fifth of the total heating or cooling energy provided by the pump (Kazmann & Whitehead 1980). The coefficients of performance— the ratio between the BTUs moved from the heat source to another location divided by the BTUs used in performing the work—are in the range of 3.5 to 4.5.

Groundwater is an excellent source for heating or cooling because the temperature essentially is constant at an approximate depth of 20 ft (6.1 m), mirroring the mean annual temperature at the surface. At depths greater than 100 ft (30.5 m), the temperature of the groundwater rises at a rate of 1°F (0.5°C) per 100 ft (30.5 m). Above 20 ft, the temperature changes slowly throughout the year, depending on the weather conditions at the surface. A water well must have adequate volume to provide the typical residential heat-pump requirement of 1 gpm (5.5 m³/day) to 3 gpm (16.44 m³/day). Additional information on groundwater heat pumps can be found on the website of the National Ground Water Association (http://http://www.ngwa.org) or on the website of the Geo-Heat Center (http://geoheat.oit.edu).

SURFACE-WATER WITHDRAWAL

Albert J. Smith
Johnson Screens

The volume of surface water removed for various purposes is far greater than the volume of groundwater. Modern filtering technology developed for groundwater use has been successfully adapted to meet the specific demands of surface-water removal.

It is clear that the surface-water environment is different from the groundwater environment. The chemical properties of surface water, for example, vary from place to place because of both the natural chemistry and the physical conditions. Consideration of biological factors is vital in all surface-water screen installations, whereas biological activity might be limited in many groundwater environments. The physical properties of the surface-water environment differ according to whether it is a river, lake, reservoir, or ocean. Waves, ice formation, salinity, temperature, turbidity, tidal effects, river gradients, pH, and navigation are just some of the important characteristics of surface-water bodies. Design of intake systems for specific sites requires careful evaluation of these characteristics.

Fundamental criteria for a water-intake system include:

◆ A reliable water source;
◆ Identification of a withdrawal point from that source; and
◆ Selection of the most appropriate screening device.

Choice of the water source usually is obvious because it must be close to the processing facility or project.

Three withdrawal-point options exist for most sites: (1) approach channel, (2) onshore, and (3) offshore (Figure 15.24). The withdrawal point should be selected so that sufficient water depth is available, plugging conditions are minimized, the fish habitat is protected, and costs are reasonable.

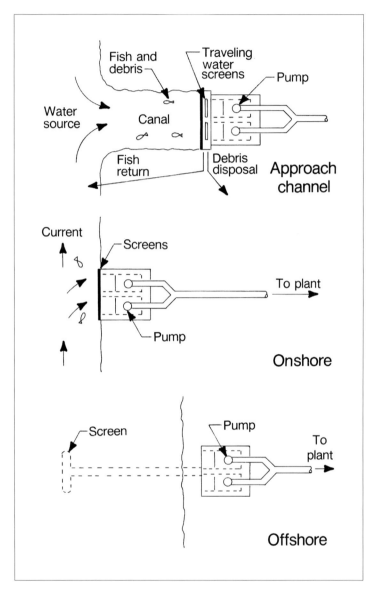

Figure 15.24. Inlet locations with respect to shoreline.

To keep the screen surface free of any foreign substances, the screen axis should be oriented parallel to current flow.

Potential icing conditions caused by surface, pack, and frazil (sheet) ice must be considered. Locating screens in deeper water generally eliminates most icing problems but, for shallow-water situations, circulation of warm water can prevent buildup of frazil ice. For potential ice-pack problems, appropriately placed trash racks or pilings are practical preventative measures.

Seawater Intakes

Screens placed in saltwater are affected by severe corrosion and biofouling, and thus require access for periodic maintenance and cleaning. Bulkhead-mounted screens on vertical rails provide easy access for maintenance and can be installed either onshore or offshore (Figure 15.25). In applications where bio-fouling is not a problem, 316L stainless steel is a minimum requirement; site conditions could require more-exotic alloys to provide adequate resistance to chemical corrosion. Performance of marine intakes is subject to a wide variety of site conditions and is difficult to predict; thus a test program to assess specific site conditions is recommended.

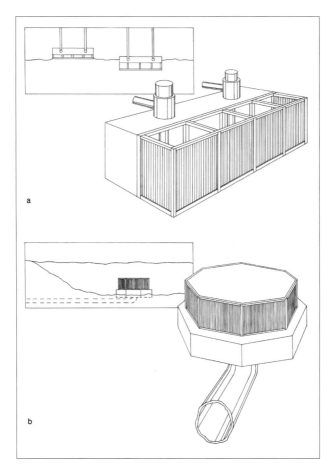

Figure 15.25. Diagram showing (a) stationary panels in onshore installation; and (b) stationary panels in a velocity cap.

Passive Screening

Passive screening is an engineering alternative for removing surface water, such as in the case of dams (Figure 15.26). Designed to minimize initial costs and re-duce maintenance, passive screening is based on two fundamental concepts: (1) reduced inflow velocity, and (2) use of natural currents or force of gravity for cleaning. Limiting the maximum intake velocity to 0.5 ft/sec (0.15 m/sec) minimizes the buildup of solid particles and aquatic organisms on the screen. Materials that do collect on the screen are held so lightly that they are swept away periodically by currents or are permeable to normal inflow. Low inflow velocities and minimum clogging conditions insure that the head loss across the screen surface is less than 0.1 ft (0.03 m) of water. The screen axis should be oriented parallel to current flow to provide the most-efficient cleaning conditions.

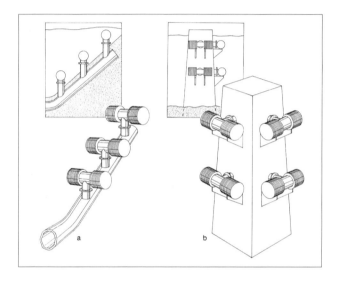

Figure 15.26. Diagram showing (a) dam face–mounted screens; and (b) tower-mounted screens.

In cases of extremely heavy debris loads or inadequate current conditions, an air-backwash system for auxiliary cleaning can be included as part of the screen assembly. Such systems consist of an air-distributor pipe within the screen cylinder that lifts materials off the screen surface using a sudden blast of air.

To improve the basic objectives of velocity reduction and natural cleaning, the passive screen is constructed of V-shaped wire to prevent back eddies, lost energy, and excessive head loss. The outer surface of the V-wire has a smooth, flat surface that presents no hazard to fish and easily can be kept clean by currents.

The following basic site and pumping parameters must be considered in the design of a passive screen system.

- Water source (river, lake, reservoir, or sea water)
- Water depth (including low, high, and mean levels)
- Approximate frequency of high and low water depths
- Velocity and direction of water currents
- General water quality
- Salinity and pH levels
- Icing possibilities
- Maximum pumping rate
- Pump-screen relationship (direct flow or gravity flow to well pump)
- Slot opening
- Intake-line size
- Connection type and size

Inflow velocities can be controlled to a maximum of 0.5 ft/sec (0.15 m/sec), with an average velocity of 0.35 ft/sec (0.11 m/sec), by designing the screen slots and diameter correctly. The basic concept of passive screening is that, by controlling the intake velocity to less than 0.5 ft/sec (15 cm/sec), the flow velocity away from the screen will be significantly lower. As the distance from the screen surface increases, inflow velocities toward the screen decrease exponentially so that, at a distance equal to one half the diameter of the screen, flow is less than 20% of the surface velocity. If a screen has an average inflow velocity of 0.5 ft/sec (15 cm/sec), flow occurring one-half the screen diameter away will be less than 0.10 ft/sec (0.03 m/sec), which is virtually undetectable.

A passive intake system consists of a cylinder screen with a length-to-diameter ratio historically equal to 1. Recent advances in the internal pipe of passive intake screens have allowed length-to-diameter ratios greater than 1, typically up to 1:3. The cylinder screen has a solid plate on one end and an adapter plate with the outlet pipe on the opposite end. The final assembly can be a single-cylinder unit or a "T-screen" assembly, as shown in Figure 15.27.

The drum screen normally is mounted vertically. Attachment of the screen assembly to the intake line usually is made with either a flange connection or a stud-ring connected to a flange. Other attachment arrangements are welded pipe, slip-on pipe, and Victaulic coupling. These screen configurations are shown in Figure 15.27. Individual screen cylinders can be replaced if damaged.

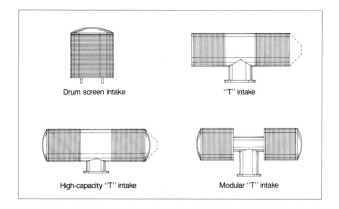

Drum screen intake

"T" intake

High-capacity "T" intake

Modular "T" intake

Figure 15.27. Various screen configurations for intake screens.

Important environmental conditions that affect the operation of a passive screen include the extent of the open-water areas, water depths, salinity and corrosion levels, fish and debris conditions, and potential for ice formation. The following recommendations should be observed.

- The main water body must feed the intake evenly and provide good-quality water. Dead-end approach channels should be avoided because they concentrate flow and collect debris and fish.
- Adequate water depth is a critical requirement for limiting maximum inflow velocity to 0.5 ft/sec (0.15 m/sec). Screens must be placed a minimum distance of one-half the screen diameter from any boundary, such as a surface, bottom, or solid wall, to achieve this flow. In addition, a distance of one diameter must be provided between adjacent screens.
- For long and reliable operating life, screens installed in freshwater commonly are made of 304 stainless steel. Marine or brackish waters usually require a higher grade of stainless steel such as 316 L. As a minimum requirement, site conditions could require more-exotic alloys. The best method to determine the proper alloy is to conduct testing at the site where the seawater intake will be located. If biofouling is a severe problem, Johnson Screens' Z-Alloy® might be required to inhibit rapid build-up of marine organisms.

APPENDIX 5.A
Common Water-Quality Issues

Andrew Nicholson, PhD
Geomega

WATER QUALITY

The primary purpose of a water analysis is to determine the suitability of water for a proposed use. Additionally, water produced during dewatering of mines and from construction sites must be disposed of, and there often are regulations governing the quality of this discharge water.

The three main classes of use are domestic (household), agricultural, and industrial. A supply intended for municipal use can include all three classes and accordingly requires a standard of quality that generally is higher than that needed for any one class. Conversely, water for use in a particular industry might require a quality that is substantially higher than that considered acceptable for a municipal supply. Groundwater quality, as discussed in Chapter 5, can lead to a variety of well-maintenance issues. Table 5.A.1 is a listing of groundwater-chemistry issues.

Table 5.A.1. Groundwater-Chemistry Issues

Water-Quality Issues	Controlling Issues	Elements of Concern	Section
Odor and taste	Redox, microbiology, well-construction material	Iron	Redox-sensitive elements
		Sulfate, sulfide	Redox-sensitive elements
		Organic compounds	Organic compounds
		TDS	Salinity
Hardness	Aquifer mineralogy, water source	Calcium, magnesium, carbonate	Hardness
			Reactive major compounds
Health issues	Water source, redox	Trace metals	Trace metals
		Trace organics	Organic compounds
Agricultural impacts	Water source, depth to water	Nitrogen compounds	Redox-sensitive elements
		Sodium	Conservative elements
		Chloride	Conservative elements
Saltwater intrusion	Distance from ocean, aquifer properties	Salinity, sodium, chloride	Conservative elements
Industrial impacts	Depth to water, type of industry, and contaminants	Trace metals	Trace metals
		Trace organics	Organic compounds
Well-Production Issues			
Scale formation	Degassing, groundwater composition	Calcium, magnesium, carbonate, TDS	Reactive major elements
	Redox, temperature	Manganese, iron	Physical parameters
Biofouling	Redox, bacteria, well-construction materials	Iron, manganese, sulfide	Redox-sensitive elements
Corrosion	Well-construction materials, redox reaction, water salinity	Iron, sulfide, manganese	Well rehabilitation
			Redox-sensitive elements
Turbidity	Well-construction material, well development, redox elements	Iron, manganese	Well rehabilitation

Drinking Water

Drinking water generally has the most stringent requirements for use. There are regulations for organic and inorganic compounds, as well as for microbial properties of the water. The World Health Organization (WHO) constantly updates these guidelines based on new information and has developed a list of more than 100 compounds (a portion is listed in Table 5.A.2). Each country has its own specific guidelines on water quality, and these should be consulted. Appendix 5.E (DVD) contains a complete compilation of EPA drinking-water criteria.

Table 5.A.2. Representative List of Guideline Values of Health Significance in Drinking Water

Constituent	Guideline Value (mg/ℓ)*
Inorganic Chemicals	
Arsenic (As)	0.01
Barium (Ba)	0.7
Cadmium (Cd)	0.003
Chromium (Cr)	0.05
Fluoride (F)	1.5
Lead (Pb)	0.01
Mercury (Hg)	0.001
Nitrate (as NO^{3-})	50.0
Selenium (Se)	0.01
Organic Chemicals	
Benzene	0.01
Toluene	0.7
Trichloroethene	0.07
Vinyl Chloride	0.0003
Endrin	0.0006
Lindane	0.002
Methoxychlor	0.02
2, 4-D	0.03

* Maximum contaminant levels are set according to health criteria. These levels are subject to further modifications (WHO 2006).

In addition to primary drinking-water standards based on health effects, many locations have secondary water-quality criteria that are based on aesthetic and practical issues. Table 5.A.3 shows some of the EPA secondary standards for drinking-water quality.

Table 5.A.3. U.S. Secondary Drinking-Water Regulations

Constituent	Recommended Level*
Chloride (Cl)	250 mg/ℓ
Color	15 color units
Copper (Cu)	1.0 mg/ℓ
Corrosivity	Noncorrosive
Foaming agents	0.5 mg/ℓ
Iron (Fe)	0.3 mg/ℓ
Manganese (Mn)	0.05 mg/ℓ
Odor	3 (threshold odor number)
pH	6.5 to 8.5
Sulfate (SO4)	250 mg/ℓ
Total dissolved solids (TDS)	500 mg/ℓ
Zinc (Zn)	5.0 mg/ℓ

* Recommended levels for these constituents mainly are to provide acceptable aesthetic and taste characteristics.

(U.S. EPA 1977)

Surface-Water Quality

Surface water and its quality are not a primary focus of this book, however groundwater interaction with surface water often is an important issue. Specific water-quality regulations are applied to surface-water bodies. These regulations vary based upon the governing jurisdiction of the water body, whether it is freshwater or saltwater, the ambient nature of the water body, water hardness, and for some elements the specific chemical species present in solution. Given these complexities, it is important to research site-specific criteria when dealing with any surface water–groundwater interactions. Note that water-quality criteria for cadmium, copper, lead, selenium, zinc, and mercury often are very low for surface-water bodies—and frequently are much lower than required by drinking-water standards.

Agricultural and Irrigation Water

Water for agriculture and irrigation use must not be toxic to crops or livestock. Additionally, the build-up of salts in soils and irrigation runoff waters is a major concern. The role of sodium adsorption in agricultural waters is discussed above. In addition to sodium other trace elements—particularly selenium—are of concern. Table 5.A.4 is a list of compounds that should be evaluated in irrigation water. Table 5.A.5 is a list of compounds and their recommended maximum allowable concentrations for irrigation water.

Table 5.A.4. Laboratory Determinations for Evaluating Water to be Used for Irrigation

Acidity-Alkalinity	Iron
Adjusted sodium adsorption ratio	Lithium
Ammonium-Nitrogen[1,2]	Magnesium
Bicarbonate	Nitrate-Nitrogen
Boron-Phosphate	Phosphorous
Calcium	Potassium
Carbonate	Sodium
Chloride	Sulphate
Electrical conductivity	

1. These levels normally do not adversely affect plants and soils. No data are available for mercury (Hg), silver (Ag), tin (Sn), titanium (Ti), or tungsten (W).
2. Not a problem when less than 0.75 mg/ℓ; increasingly problematic when between 0.75 mg/ℓ and 2.0 mg/ℓ; severe problem when greater than 2.0 mg/ℓ.

(adapted from Ayers & Westcott 1976)

Table 5.A.5. Recommended Maximum Concentrations of Trace Elements in Irrigation Waters

Element (Symbol)	For Waters Used Continuously on Soils (mg/ℓ)	For Use on Fine-Textured Soils of pH 6.0 to 8.5 for up to 20 Years (mg/ℓ)
Aluminum (Al)	5.0	20.0
Arsenic (As)	0.1	2.0
Beryllium (Be)	0.1	0.5
Boron (B)	2.0	2.0
Cadmium (Cd)	0.01	0.05
Chromium (Cr)	0.1	1.0
Cobalt (Co)	0.05	5.0
Copper (Cu)	0.2	5.0
Fluoride (F)	1.0	15.0
Iron (Fe)	5.0	20.0
Lead (Pb)	5.0	10.0
Lithium (Li)	2.5	2.5
Manganese (Mn)	0.2	10.0
Molybdenum (Mo)	0.01	0.053[*]
Nickel (Ni)	0.2	2.0
Selenium (Se)	0.02	0.02
Vanadium (V)	0.1	1.0
Zinc (Zn)	2.0	10.0

[*]   Only for acid fine-textured soils and acid soils with relatively high iron-oxide content.

**(National Academy of Science &
National Academy of Engineering 1972)**

Industrial Uses

Water-quality requirements for industrial waters vary widely according to potential use. Saltwater and brackish water, for example, commonly are used as cooling water, particularly when such water is not recycled and if it can be disposed of without polluting the environment. When disposal of these waters is a major problem, deep-well injection might provide the best (and often the only) disposal method available.

Industrial process waters must be of much higher quality than cooling waters. Municipal supplies generally satisfy the quality requirements of most process waters, with the exception of those waters used in boilers. About 60% of the water used by industry must be treated to meet quality standards (Fair et al. 1971). Sanitary requirements for water used in processing milk, canned goods, meats, and beverages exceed the requirements for drinking water.

In many cases, groundwater is desirable for particular uses because of its low, relatively constant temperature. In other cases, groundwater might be suitable because of its natural hardness. For example, distilleries, bakeries, and breweries prefer hard water; but even small amounts of iron, manganese, or calcium can cause tremendous damage if used in paper-making processes.

APPENDIX 9.C
Dimensions and Strengths of Steel Pipe

U.S. CUSTOMARY UNITS

Nom Size	OD (in)	ID (in)	Wall (in)	Wt/ft (lb)	Schedule	D/t	Collapse* (psi)	Yield (tons)	Tensile (tons)
	4.500	4.334	0.0830	3.92	5	54.2	261	20.2	34.6
	4.500	4.260	0.1200	5.61	10	37.5	627	28.9	49.5
	4.500	4.216	0.1420	6.61	WWC	31.7	900	34.0	58.3
4 PS	4.500	4.026	0.2370	10.79	40 (STD)	19.0	2,316	55.5	95.2
	4.500	3.938	0.2810	12.66	60	16.0	3,038	65.2	111.7
	4.500	3.626	0.4370	18.96	120	10.3	5,790	97.6	167.3
	4.500	3.826	0.3370	14.98	80 (XS)	13.4	3,993	77.1	132.2
	5.563	5.345	0.1090	6.35	5	51.0	304	32.7	56.0
	5.563	5.295	0.1340	7.77	10	41.5	498	40.0	68.6
5 PS	5.563	5.255	0.1540	8.90	WWC	36.1	681	45.8	78.5
	5.563	5.047	0.2580	14.62	40 (STD)	21.6	1,869	75.2	129.0
	5.563	4.813	0.3750	20.78	80	14.8	3,415	106.9	183.3
	5.563	4.563	0.5000	27.03	120	11.1	5,194	139.2	238.6

Nom Size	OD (in)	ID (in)	Wall (in)	Wt/ft (lb)	Schedule	D/t	Collapse* (psi)	Yield (tons)	Tensile (tons)
6 PS	6.625	6.407	0.1090	7.59	5	60.8	195	39.0	66.9
	6.625	6.357	0.1340	9.29	10	49.4	328	47.8	82.0
	6.625	6.255	0.1850	12.72	WWC	35.8	694	65.5	112.3
	6.625	6.250	0.1875	12.89		35.3	715	66.4	113.8
	6.625	6.125	0.2500	17.02		26.5	1,285	87.6	150.2
	6.625	6.065	0.2800	18.97	40 (STD)	23.7	1,585	97.7	167.4
	6.625	6.001	0.3120	21.04		21.2	1,919	108.3	185.6
	6.625	5.761	0.4320	28.57	80 (XS)	15.3	3,246	147.1	252.1
8 PS	8.625	8.407	0.1090	9.91	5	79.1	97	51.0	87.5
	8.625	8.329	0.1480	13.40	10	58.3	218	69.0	118.2
	8.625	8.249	0.1880	16.94	WWC	45.9	393	87.2	149.5
	8.625	8.125	0.2500	22.36	20	34.5	752	115.1	197.3
	8.625	8.071	0.2770	24.70	30	31.1	933	127.1	217.9
	8.625	8.001	0.3120	27.70		27.6	1,184	142.6	244.4
	8.625	7.981	0.3220	28.55	40 (STD)	26.8	1,259	147.0	252.0
	8.625	7.813	0.4060	35.64	60	21.2	1,917	183.5	314.5
	8.625	7.625	0.5000	43.39	80 (XS)	17.3	2,704	223.3	382.9
10 PS	10.750	10.482	0.1340	15.19	5	80.2	94	78.2	134.1
	10.750	10.420	0.1650	18.65	10	65.2	163	96.0	164.6
	10.750	10.374	0.1880	21.21		57.2	228	109.2	187.1
	10.750	10.250	0.2500	28.04	20	43.0	459	144.3	247.4
	10.750	10.136	0.3070	34.24	30	35.0	729	176.3	302.2
	10.750	10.125	0.3125	34.84		34.4	757	179.3	307.4
	10.750	10.020	0.3650	40.48	40 (STD)	29.5	1,045	208.4	357.2
	10.750	9.750	0.5000	54.74	60 (XS)	21.5	1,878	281.8	483.0
12 PS	12.750	12.420	0.1650	22.18	5	77.3	104	114.2	195.7
	12.750	12.390	0.1800	24.16	10	70.8	131	124.4	213.2
	12.750	12.375	0.1875	25.16		68.0	146	129.5	222.0
	12.750	12.250	0.2500	33.38	20	51.0	304	171.8	294.5
	12.750	12.125	0.3125	41.51		40.8	518	213.7	366.3
	12.750	12.090	0.3300	43.77	30	38.6	586	225.3	386.3
	12.750	12.000	0.3750	49.56	(STD)	34.0	776	255.1	437.4
	12.750	11.938	0.4060	53.52	40	31.4	917	275.5	472.3
	12.750	11.750	0.5000	65.42	(XS)	25.5	1,381	336.7	577.3
	12.750	11.376	0.6870	88.51	80	18.6	2,404	455.6	781.1

Nom Size	OD (in)	ID (in)	Wall (in)	Wt/ft (lb)	Schedule	D/t	Collapse* (psi)	Yield (tons)	Tensile (tons)
14 PS	14.000	13.625	0.1875	27.66		74.7	114	142.4	244.1
	14.000	13.500	0.2500	36.71	10	56.0	241	189.0	324.0
	14.000	13.375	0.3125	45.68	20	44.8	416	235.2	403.1
	14.000	13.250	0.3750	54.57	30 (STD)	37.3	633	280.9	481.5
	14.000	13.126	0.4370	63.30	40	32.0	880	325.9	558.6
	14.000	13.000	0.5000	72.09	(XS)	28.0	1,155	371.1	636.2
16 PS	16.000	15.625	0.1875	31.66		85.3	79	163.0	279.4
	16.000	15.500	0.2500	42.05	10	64.0	171	216.5	371.1
	16.000	15.375	0.3125	52.36	20	51.2	301	269.5	462.0
	16.000	15.250	0.3750	62.58	30 (STD)	42.7	467	322.1	552.2
	16.000	15.000	0.5000	82.77	40 (XS)	32.0	882	426.1	730.4
18 PS	18.000	17.625	0.1875	35.67		96.0	58	183.6	314.8
	18.000	17.500	0.2500	47.39	10	72.0	125	244.0	418.2
	18.000	17.375	0.3125	59.03	20	57.6	224	303.9	520.9
	18.000	17.250	0.3750	70.59	(STD)	48.0	353	363.4	622.9
	18.000	17.126	0.4370	81.97	30	41.2	507	422.0	723.4
	18.000	16.876	0.5620	104.67	40	32.0	881	538.8	923.6
20 PS	20.000	19.625	0.1875	39.67		106.7	43	204.2	350.1
	20.000	19.500	0.2500	52.73	10	80.0	95	271.5	465.3
	20.000	19.375	0.3125	65.71		64.0	171	338.2	579.8
	20.000	19.250	0.3750	78.60	(STD)	53.3	272	404.6	693.6
	20.000	19.000	0.5000	104.13	30	40.0	542	536.0	918.9
22 PS	22.000	21.500	0.2500	58.07	10	88.0	73	298.9	512.5
	22.000	21.375	0.3125	72.38		70.4	133	372.6	638.8
	22.000	21.250	0.3750	86.61	20 (STD)	58.7	214	445.8	764.3
	22.000	21.000	0.5000	114.81	30 (XS)	44.0	434	591.0	1,013.2
24 PS	24.000	23.500	0.2500	63.41	10	96.0	58	326.4	559.6
	24.000	23.375	0.3125	79.06		76.8	106	407.0	697.7
	24.000	23.250	0.3750	94.62	20 (STD)	64.0	171	487.1	835.0
	24.000	23.000	0.5000	125.49	(XS)	48.0	353	646.0	1,107.4
	24.000	22.876	0.5620	140.68	30	42.7	466	724.2	1,241.4
26 PS	26.000	25.500	0.2500	68.75		104.0	46	353.9	606.7
	26.000	25.375	0.3125	85.73	10	83.2	85	441.3	756.6
	26.000	25.250	0.3750	102.63	(STD)	69.3	139	528.3	905.7
	26.000	25.000	0.5000	136.17	20 (XS)	52.0	290	701.0	1,201.7

Nom Size	OD (in)	ID (in)	Wall (in)	Wt/ft (lb)	Schedule	D/t	Collapse* (psi)	Yield (tons)	Tensile (tons)
28 PS	28.000	27.500	0.2500	74.09		112.0	38	381.4	653.8
	28.000	27.375	0.3125	92.41	10	89.6	70	475.7	815.5
	28.000	27.250	0.3750	110.64	(STD)	74.7	114	569.5	976.4
	28.000	27.000	0.5000	146.85	20 (XS)	56.0	241	755.9	1,295.9
30 PS	30.000	29.375	0.3125	99.08	10	96.0	58	510.0	874.4
	30.000	29.250	0.3750	118.65	(STD)	80.0	95	610.8	1,047.0
	30.000	29.000	0.5000	157.53	(XS)	60.0	202	810.9	1,390.2
	30.000	28.750	0.6250	196.08	30	48.0	353	1,009.4	1,730.3
36 PS	36.000	35.375	0.3125	119.11	10	115.2	35	613.1	1,051.1
	36.000	35.250	0.3750	142.68	(STD)	96.0	58	734.5	1,259.1
	36.000	35.000	0.5000	189.57	20 (XS)	72.0	125	975.9	1,672.9
	36.000	34.750	0.6250	236.13	30	57.6	224	1,215.5	2,083.8

*   Note: Collapse pressures are based on standard wall thickness. Allowance for 12.5% minimum thickness deviation.

Collapse values assume:
   Yield Strength = 35,000; Tensile = 70,000; Modulus of Elasticity = $30 \cdot 10^6$;
   Poission Ratio = 0.3

DIMENSIONS AND STRENGTHS OF STEEL PIPE (SI UNITS)

Nom Size	OD (mm)	ID (mm)	Wall (mm)	Wt / meter (kg)	Schedule	D/t	Collapse* (kpa)	Yield (m-tons)	Tensile (m-tons)
4 PS	114	110	2.1	5.8	5.0	54.2	1,800.5	18.3	31.3
	114	108	3.0	8.4	10	37.5	4,322.3	26.2	44.9
	114	107	3.6	9.8	WWC	31.7	6,206.7	30.9	52.9
	114	102	6.0	16.1	40 (STD)	19.0	15,966.7	50.4	86.4
	114	100	7.1	18.8	60	16.0	20,942.8	59.1	101.4
	114	92	11.1	28.2	120	10.3	39,918.7	88.6	151.8
	114	97	8.6	22.3	80 (XS)	13.4	27,532.4	70.0	120.0

Nom Size	OD (mm)	ID (mm)	Wall (mm)	Wt / meter (kg)	Schedule	D/t	Collapse* (kpa)	Yield (m-tons)	Tensile (m-tons)
5 PS	141	136	2.8	9.4	5	51.0	2,093.2	29.6	50.8
	141	134	3.4	11.6	10	41.5	3,431.7	36.3	62.2
	141	133	3.9	13.2	WWC	36.1	4,695.6	41.5	71.2
	141	128	6.6	21.8	40 (STD)	21.6	12,885.0	68.3	117.0
	141	122	9.5	30.9	80	14.8	23,543.4	97.0	166.3
	141	116	12.7	40.2	120	11.1	35,808.6	126.2	216.4
6 PS	168	163	2.8	11.3	5	60.8	1,346.8	35.4	60.7
	168	161	3.4	13.8	10	49.4	2,262.8	43.4	74.4
	168	159	4.7	18.9	WWC	35.8	4,784.8	59.4	101.9
	168	159	4.8	19.2		35.3	4,926.8	60.2	103.2
	168	156	6.4	25.3		26.5	8,856.8	79.5	136.3
	168	154	7.1	28.2	40 (STD)	23.7	10,930.0	88.6	151.9
	168	152	7.9	31.3		21.2	13,228.8	98.2	168.4
	168	146	11.0	42.5	80 (XS)	15.3	22,382.8	133.4	228.7
8 PS	219	214	2.8	14.8	5	79.1	672.0	46.3	79.4
	219	212	3.8	19.9	10	58.3	1,499.9	62.6	107.3
	219	210	4.8	25.2	WWC	45.9	2,711.8	79.1	135.6
	219	206	6.4	33.3	20	34.5	5,187.7	104.4	179.0
	219	205	7.0	36.8	30	31.1	6,436.2	115.3	197.7
	219	203	7.9	41.2		27.6	8,164.7	129.4	221.8
	219	203	8.2	42.5	40 (STD)	26.8	8,677.2	133.3	228.6
	219	198	10.3	53.0	60	21.2	13,218.2	166.4	285.3
	219	194	12.7	64.6	80 (XS)	17.3	18,641.9	202.6	347.4
10 PS	273	266	3.4	22.6	5	80.2	647.5	71.0	121.6
	273	265	4.2	27.8	10	65.2	1,124.9	87.1	149.3
	273	263	4.8	31.6		57.2	1,574.2	99.0	169.8
	273	260	6.4	41.7	20	43.0	3,161.4	130.9	224.4
	273	257	7.8	51.0	30	35.0	5,024.1	159.9	274.1
	273	257	7.9	51.8		34.4	5,220.1	162.7	278.9
	273	255	9.3	60.2	40 (STD)	29.5	7,205.3	189.1	324.1
	273	248	12.7	81.5	60 (XS)	21.5	12,947.4	255.6	438.2

Nom Size	OD (mm)	ID (mm)	Wall (mm)	Wt / meter (kg)	Schedule	D/t	Collapse* (kpa)	Yield (m-tons)	Tensile (m-tons)
	324	315	4.2	33.0	5	77.3	716.2	103.6	177.5
	324	315	4.6	36.0	10	70.8	903.0	112.8	193.5
	324	314	4.8	37.4		68.0	1,005.7	117.5	201.4
	324	311	6.4	49.7	20	51.0	2,096.5	155.9	267.2
12	324	308	7.9	61.8		40.8	3,571.2	193.9	332.3
PS	324	307	8.4	65.1	30	38.6	4,042.8	204.4	350.4
	324	305	9.5	73.8	(STD)	34.0	5,352.6	231.5	396.8
	324	303	10.3	79.7	40	31.4	6,324.2	250.0	428.5
	324	298	12.7	97.4	(XS)	25.5	9,524.1	305.5	523.7
	324	289	17.4	131.7	80	18.6	16,574.3	413.3	708.6
	356	346	4.8	41.2		74.7	785.0	129.2	221.4
	356	343	6.4	54.6	10	56.0	1,659.7	171.4	293.9
14	356	340	7.9	68.0	20	44.8	2,869.9	213.3	365.7
PS	356	337	9.5	81.2	30 (STD)	37.3	4,365.4	254.8	436.9
	356	333	11.1	94.2	40	32.0	6,068.1	295.6	506.8
	356	330	12.7	107.3	(XS)	28.0	7,963.6	336.7	577.1
	406	397	4.8	47.1		85.3	547.9	147.9	253.5
16	406	394	6.4	62.6	10	64.0	1,178.4	196.4	336.7
PS	406	391	7.9	77.9	20	51.2	2,076.3	244.5	419.2
	406	387	9.5	93.1	30 (STD)	42.7	3,219.5	292.2	501.0
	406	381	12.7	123.2	40 (XS)	32.0	6,082.6	386.5	662.6
	457	448	4.8	53.1		96.0	397.0	166.6	285.6
	457	445	6.4	70.5	10	72.0	864.8	221.3	379.4
18	457	441	7.9	87.9	20	57.6	1,545.2	275.7	472.6
PS	457	438	9.5	105.1	(STD)	48.0	2,431.8	329.7	565.1
	457	435	11.1	122.0	30	41.2	3,493.9	382.8	656.2
	457	429	14.3	155.8	40	32.0	6,071.3	488.8	837.9
	508	498	4.8	59.0		106.7	296.7	185.3	317.6
	508	495	6.4	78.5	10	80.0	652.4	246.3	422.2
20	508	492	7.9	97.8		64.0	1,178.4	306.9	526.0
PS	508	489	9.5	117.0	(STD)	53.3	1,876.1	367.1	629.2
	508	483	12.7	155.0	30	40.0	3,737.0	486.3	833.6

Nom Size	OD (mm)	ID (mm)	Wall (mm)	Wt / meter (kg)	Schedule	D/t	Collapse* (kpa)	Yield (m-tons)	Tensile (m-tons)
22 PS	559	546	6.4	86.4	10	88.0	503.9	271.2	464.9
	559	543	7.9	107.7		70.4	917.8	338.0	579.5
	559	540	9.5	128.9	20 (STD)	58.7	1,474.6	404.5	693.4
	559	533	12.7	170.9	30 (XS)	44.0	2,995.0	536.2	919.1
24 PS	610	597	6.4	94.4	10	96.0	397.0	296.1	507.7
	610	594	7.9	117.7		76.8	728.1	369.2	632.9
	610	591	9.5	140.8	20 (STD)	64.0	1,178.4	441.9	757.5
	610	584	12.7	186.8	(XS)	48.0	2,431.8	586.0	1004.6
	610	581	14.3	209.4	30	42.7	3,212.8	657.0	1126.2
26 PS	660	648	6.4	102.3		104.0	318.3	321.1	550.4
	660	645	7.9	127.6	10	83.2	586.9	400.4	686.4
	660	641	9.5	152.7	(STD)	69.3	955.6	479.3	821.6
	660	635	12.7	202.7	20 (XS)	52.0	1,998.1	635.9	1090.2
28 PS	711	699	6.4	110.3		112.0	259.0	346.0	593.2
	711	695	7.9	137.5	10	89.6	479.7	431.5	739.8
	711	692	9.5	164.7	(STD)	74.7	785.0	516.7	885.7
	711	686	12.7	218.6	20 (XS)	56.0	1,659.7	685.8	1175.7
30 PS	762	746	7.9	147.5	10	96.0	397.0	462.7	793.2
	762	743	9.5	176.6	(STD)	80.0	652.4	554.1	949.9
	762	737	12.7	234.4	(XS)	60.0	1,392.2	735.7	1261.2
	762	730	15.9	291.8	30	48.0	2,431.8	915.7	1569.8
36 PS	914	899	7.9	177.3	10	115.2	239.4	556.2	953.5
	914	895	9.5	212.3	(STD)	96.0	397.0	666.3	1142.3
	914	889	12.7	282.1	20 (XS)	72.0	864.8	885.3	1517.7
	914	883	15.9	351.4	30	57.6	1,545.2	1102.7	1890.4

* Note: Collapse pressures are based on standard wall thickness. Allowance for 12.5% minimum thickness deviation.

APPENDIX 9.E
Collapse Pressures for
Thermoplastic Water-Well Casing

Minimum Wall Thickness and Collapse Pressure							
Nom PS (in)	OD (in)	SDR-41 (11 psi)	SDR-32.5 (22 psi)	SDR 27.6 (37 psi)	SDR-26 (44 psi)	SDR-21 (85 psi)	SDR-17 (163 psi)	SDR-13.5 (338 psi)
½	0.840	0.020	0.026	0.030	0.032	0.040	0.049	0.062
¾	1.050	0.026	0.032	0.038	0.040	0.050	0.062	0.078
1	1.315	0.032	0.040	0.048	0.051	0.063	0.077	0.097
1¼	1.660	0.040	0.051	0.060	0.064	0.079	0.098	0.123
1½	1.900	0.046	0.058	0.069	0.073	0.090	0.112	0.141
2	2.375	0.058	0.073	0.086	0.091	0.113	0.140	0.176
2½	2.875	0.070	0.088	0.104	0.111	0.137	0.169	0.213
3	3.500	0.085	0.108	0.127	0.135	0.167	0.206	0.259
3½	4.000	0.098	0.123	0.145	0.154	0.190	0.235	0.296
4	4.500	0.110	0.138	0.163	0.173	0.214	0.265	0.333
4½	4.950	0.121	0.152	0.179	0.190	0.236	0.291	0.367
5	5.563	0.136	0.171	0.202	0.214	0.265	0.327	0.412
6	6.625	0.162	0.204	0.240	0.255	0.315	0.390	0.491
6¼	6.900	0.168	0.212	0.250	0.265	0.329	0.406	0.511
8	8.625	0.210	0.265	0.313	0.332	0.411	0.507	0.639
10	10.750	0.262	0.331	0.389	0.413	0.512	0.632	0.796
12	12.750	0.311	0.392	0.462	0.490	0.607	0.750	0.944
14	14.000	0.341	0.431	0.507	0.538	0.667	0.824	1.037

Minimum Wall Thickness and Collapse Pressure							
Nom PS (in)	OD (in)	SDR-41 (11 psi)	SDR-32.5 (22 psi)	SDR 27.6 (37 psi)	SDR-26 (44 psi)	SDR-21 (85 psi)	SDR-17 (163 psi)	SDR-13.5 (338 psi)
16	16.000	0.390	0.492	0.580	0.615	0.762	0.941	1.185
18	18.000	0.439	0.554	0.652	0.692	0.857	1.059	1.333
20	20.000	0.488	0.615	0.725	0.769	0.952	1.176	1.481
24	24.000	0.585	0.738	0.870	0.923	1.143	1.412	1.778

Note: Hydraulic collapse pressure (shown below each SDR size above) remains constant for each diameter due to wall thickness variation.

Pressures and tensile strength (TS) values assume:

◆ No temperature derating;
◆ Dimensions equal table values shown;
◆ Tensile yield = 7,000 psi @ 73°F;
◆ Modulus of elasticity = 400,000 @ 73°F; and
◆ Poisson's ration = 0.40 @ 73°F.

Sch 40 PVC—Cell Class 12454									
Nom PS (in)	OD (in)	ID (in)	Min. Wall (in)	Wt/Ft (lbs)	WP[1]	BP	Clps[2]	Ten-sile[3] (lbs)	SDR Equiva-lent
1/8	0.405	0.269	0.068	0.051	810	2,350	4,880	50	6.0
1/8	0.540	0.364	0.088	0.086	780	2,280	4,410	90	6.1
3/8	0.675	0.493	0.091	0.115	620	1,890	2,340	120	7.4
1/2	0.840	0.622	0.109	0.170	600	1,820	2,060	180	7.7
3/4	1.050	0.824	0.113	0.226	480	1,510	1,120	230	9.3
1	1.315	1.049	0.133	0.333	450	1,420	910	350	9.9
1¼	1.660	1.380	0.140	0.450	370	1,180	510	470	11.9
1½	1.900	1.610	0.145	0.537	330	1,070	370	560	13.1
2	2.375	2.067	0.154	0.720	280	910	220	750	15.4
2½	2.875	2.469	0.203	1.136	300	990	290	1,190	14.2
3	3.500	3.068	0.216	1.488	260	860	190	1,560	16.2
3½	4.000	3.548	0.226	1.789	240	790	140	1,880	17.7
4	4.500	4.026	0.237	2.118	220	740	120	2,220	19.0
5	5.563	5.047	0.258	2.874	190	650	80	3,010	21.6
6	6.625	6.065	0.280	3.733	180	590	60	3,910	23.7
8	8.625	7.981	0.322	5.619	160	520	40	5,880	26.8
10	10.750	10.020	0.365	7.966	140	480	30	8,340	29.5

			Min.		Pressures (psi)			Ten-	SDR
Nom			Wall	Wt/Ft				sile[3]	Equiva-
PS (in)	OD (in)	ID (in)	(in)	(lbs)	WP[1]	BP	Clps[2]	(lbs)	lent
12	12.750	11.938	0.406	10.534	130	450	25	11,020	31.4
14	14.000	13.126	0.437	12.462	130	440	23	13,030	32.0
16	16.000	15.000	0.500	16.286	130	440	23	17,040	32.0
18	18.000	16.876	0.562	20.587	130	440	23	21,550	32.0
20	20.000	18.814	0.593	24.183	120	420	20	25,310	33.7
24	24.000	22.626	0.687	33.652	120	400	18	35,220	34.9
¼	0.540	0.302	0.119	0.105	1,130	3,090	12,580	120	4.5
3/8	0.675	0.423	0.126	0.146	920	2,610	7,020	160	5.4
½	0.840	0.546	0.147	0.213	850	2,450	5,620	240	5.7
¾	1.050	0.742	0.154	0.289	690	2,050	3,090	320	6.8
1	1.315	0.957	0.179	0.424	630	1,910	2,410	470	7.3
1¼	1.660	1.278	0.191	0.586	520	1,610	1,390	650	8.7
1½	1.900	1.500	0.200	0.711	470	1,470	1,040	790	9.5
2	2.375	1.939	0.218	0.984	400	1,290	670	1,090	10.9
2½	2.875	2.323	0.276	1.500	420	1,340	770	1,660	10.4
3	3.500	2.900	0.300	2.010	380	1,200	540	2,230	11.7
3½	4.000	3.364	0.318	2.452	350	1,110	420	2,710	12.6
4	4.500	3.826	0.337	2.938	320	1,050	350	3,250	13.4
5	5.563	4.813	0.375	4.078	290	940	250	4,520	14.8
6	6.625	5.761	0.432	5.610	280	910	230	6,210	15.3
8	8.625	7.625	0.500	8.522	250	810	160	9,430	17.3
10	10.750	9.564	0.593	12.635	230	770	130	13,990	18.1
12	12.750	11.376	0.687	17.384	230	750	120	19,250	18.6
14	14.000	12.500	0.750	20.852	230	750	120	23,090	18.7
16	16.000	14.314	0.843	26.810	220	740	120	29,680	19.0
18	18.000	16.126	0.937	33.544	220	730	110	37,140	19.2
20	20.000	17.938	1.031	41.047	220	720	110	45,450	19.4
24	24.000	21.564	1.218	58.233	210	710	100	64,470	19.7

Sch 40 PVC—Cell Class 12454

1. Working pressure (WP) is for unthreaded pipe (derate 50% for threaded), safety factor = 3.5.
2. Collapse (clps) includes 25% safety factor.
3. Tensile strength (TS) assumes 90% safety factor.

APPENDIX 9.H
Recommended Minimum Thickness for Carbon Steel Well Casing

Depth (ft)		Nominal Casing Diameter (in)				
From	To	8	10	12	14	16
0	100	0.2500	0.2500	0.2500	0.2500	0.2500
100	200	0.2500	0.2500	0.2500	0.2500	0.2500
200	300	0.2500	0.2500	0.2500	0.2500	0.2500
300	400	0.2500	0.2500	0.2500	0.2500	0.3125
400	600	0.2500	0.2500	0.2500	0.2500	0.3125
600	800	0.2500	0.2500	0.2500	0.3125	0.3125
800	1,000	0.2500	0.2500	0.2500	0.3125	0.3125
1,000	1,500	0.2500	0.3125	0.3125	0.3125	0.3750
1,500	2,000	0.2500	0.3125	0.3125	0.3125	0.3750

Depth (ft)		Nominal Casing Diameter (in)				
From	To	18	20	22	24	30
0	100	0.2500	0.2500	0.3125	0.3125	0.3125
100	200	0.2500	0.2500	0.3125	0.3125	0.3125
200	300	0.3125	0.3125	0.3125	0.3125	0.3750
300	400	0.3125	0.3125	0.3125	0.3750	0.3750
400	600	0.3125	0.3125	0.3750	0.3750	0.4375
600	800	0.3125	0.3750	0.3750	0.3750	0.4375
800	1,000	0.3125	0.3750	0.3750	0.4375	0.5000
1,000	1,500	0.3750	0.3750	0.3750		
1,500	2,000	0.3750	0.4375	0.4375		
(AWWA Standard, ANSI/AWWA A100-06)						

745

Depth (ft)		Carbon Steel Casing Collapse (psi)				
From	**To**	**18**	**20**	**22**	**24**	**30**
0	100	126	95	134	107	58
100	200	126	95	134	107	58
200	300	226	172	134	107	95
300	400	226	172	134	172	95
400	600	226	172	215	172	143
600	800	226	274	215	172	143
800	1,000	226	274	215	254	202
1,000	1,500	355	274	215		
1,500	2,000	355	397	315		

Note that collapse values are calculated using the Timeshenko equation for wall thickness listed above.

ABBREVIATIONS AND SYMBOLS

A, area

a, array spacing

ABS, acrylonitrile butadiene styrene

adj. SAR, adjusted sodium adsorption ratio

ADV, acoustic doppler velocimeter

AMD, acid mine drainage

API, American Petroleum Institute

ANSI, American National Standards Institute

ASR, aquifer storage and recovery

ASTM International, formerly American Society for Testing and Materials (**ASTM**)

ATP, adenosine triphosphate

AWS, American Welding Society

AWWA, American Water Works Association

B, buoyancy factor

b, aquifer thickness

BE, barometric efficiency

BEP, best efficiency point

BHFTC, borehole fluid temperature and conductivity tool

BHP, brake horsepower

BQ, head loss attributable to laminar flow

btu, British thermal unit

C, coefficient of discharge

C, constant

°C, degrees Celsius

Cas, casing axial compressive strength

CBL, cement bond log

cfm, cubic foot (feet) per minute

CFU, colony-forming unit

CFUs per ml, colony-forming units per milliliter

cfs, cubic foot (feet) per second

Clp, collapse resistance

cm³, cubic centimeters

CMC, carboxymethylcellulose

COD, chemical oxygen demand

cpm, counts per minute

CPS, counts per second

CPT, cone-penetration tools

CQ^2, head loss attributable to turbulent flow

Cts, casing tensile strength

CW, continuous weld pipe

D, depth

D, outside diameter of pipe

d, depth to water

d, diameter

d, inside diameter of pipe

Df, density of fluid

Dm, density of casing material

DNAPL, dense, non-aqueous phase liquid

D_o, casing outside diameter

DO, dissolved oxygen

DSAW, double submerged arc weld pipe

DTH, downhole hammer

E, efficiency of well

E, Young's modulus

e, aperture of a fracture

e, eccentricity constant

e, exponential function

EC, electrical conductance

ECD, equivalent circulating density

Eh, reduction potential

EPA, United States Environmental Protection Agency

EXP, explosion-proof enclosure

°F, degrees Fahrenheit

FEC, fluid electrical conductivity

FLA, full-load motor amps

Fs, force exerted by soil

ft, foot (feet)

ft^2, square foot (feet)

ft^3, cubic foot (feet)

ft-lb, foot-pound

ft/min, foot (feet) per minute

ft/sec, foot (feet) per second

Fw, upward force on a soil column caused by reservoir pressure

g, acceleration of gravity

g, gram(s)

gal, gallon(s)

GIS, geographic information systems

gpd, gallon(s) per day

gpd/ft, gallon(s) per day per foot

gpd/ft^2, gallon(s) per day per square foot

gpm, gallon(s) per minute

gPg, grains per gallon

H, total head (L)

h, head (L)

h, height

HCSWB, Hydrogeologic Classification System for Water-Well Boreholes

HDPE, high-density polyethylene

HEC, hydroxyethylcellulose

HFI, high-frequency induction

HIS, Hydraulic Institute Standards

h_L, head loss

hp, horsepower

HP, high power

HPC, heterotrophic plate count

hr, hour(s)

HTH, calcium hypochlorite

Hz, hertz

I, current

I, hydraulic gradient

IAP, ion activity product

Ic, critical gradient

ID, inside diameter

IMA, inrush motor amps

in, inch(es)

in^2, square inch(es)

in^3, cubic inch(es)

J, joule

K, hydraulic conductivity (L/t)

k, intrinsic permeability (L^2)

°K, degrees Kelvin

kg, kilogram(s)

km, kilometer(s)

km^2, square kilometer(s)

km^3, cubic kilometer(s)

kPa, kilopascal(s)

kVA, kilovolt-amp(s)

kVAR, kilovar(s)

kW, kilowatt(s)

ℓ, liter(s)

ℓ^3**/sec,** cubic liters per second

L, length or distance

L, engaged thread length

lb, pound(s)

LNAPL, light, non-aqueous phase liquid

LSI, Langelier Saturation Index

LVF, liquid-volume fraction

m, meter(s)

m^2, square meter(s)

m^3, cubic meter(s)

m/day, meter(s) per day

m^2**/day,** square meter(s) per day

m^3**/day,** cubic meter(s) per day

m^3**/sec,** cubic meter(s) per second

m/min, meter(s) per minute

m/sec, meter(s) per second

mb, millibar(s)

MEK, methyl ethyl ketone

meq/ℓ**,** milliequivalent(s) per liter(s)

MeV, million electron-volts

MG, million gallons

MGD, million gallons per day

mg/ℓ**,** milligram(s) per liter(s)

MHZ, megahertz

mi, mile(s)

mi², square mile(s)

mi³, cubic mile(s)

min, minute(s)

MIT, mechanical integrity test

ml, milliliter(s)

mm, millimeter(s)

mm², square millimeters

mm³, cubic millimeters

MPF, motor power factor

MTBE, methyl tert-butyl ether

NAPLs, non-aqueous phase liquids

NDMA, n-nitroso-dimethylamine

NEMA, National Electrical Manufacturers Association

NGWA, National Ground Water Association

NPSH, net positive suction head

NPSHA, net positive suction head available

NPSHR, net positive suction head required

NPT, non-recessed taper tapped

NSF, National Sanitary Federation

NTU, Nephelometric Turbidity Units

NW-220, NuWell® 220 Clay Dispersant

NW-310, NuWell® 310 Bioacid Dispersant

NW-320, NuWell® 320 Biocaustic Dispersant

NW-400, NuWell® 400 Non-Ionic Surfactant

NWWA, National Water Well Association

OA, open area

OD, outside diameter

ODP, open and drip-proof enclosure

ORP, oxidation-reduction potential

oz, ounce(s)

P, pullout strength

Pa, pascal

PAC, polyanionic cellulose

PAHs, polyaromatic hydrocarbons

PCBs, polychlorinated biphenyls

PCE, tetrachloroethylene

pCi, picocurie

pCi/ℓ, picocurie per liter

Pcr, perfect cylinder collapse

Pd, design collapse

PDC, polycrystalline diamond compact

Pf, fracture strength

P.F., power factor

PHPA, partially hydrolyzed poly-acrylamides

PM, preventative maintenance

ppb, part per billion

ppm, part per million

psi, pounds per square inch

psig, pounds per square inch at gauge

PTFE, polytetraflouroethylene (Teflon™)

PVC, polyvinyl chloride

PWL, pumping water level

Q, discharge (L^3/t)

q, flow through each foot of aquifer width

Q/s, specific capacity

qt, quart

R, radius

R, radius of influence

R, resistance

r, radius

r, distance from center of a pumped well to a point where the drawdown is measured

RBF, riverbank filtration

rpm, revolutions per minute

rps, revolutions per second

RQD, rock-quality designation

S, coefficient of storage

s, drawdown

s', residual drawdown

SAR, sodium adsorption ratio

SC, specific conductance

SCBF, scanning colloidal borescope flowmeter

SCFM, standard cubic feet per minute

SDR, standard dimension ratio

sec, second(s)

SI, International System of Units (Système international d'unités)

SOC, synthetic organic chemical(s)

SP, spontaneous potential

SPA, sodium polyacrylates

SPR, single-point resistance

sp. gr., specific gravity

SR, styrene rubber

SRB, sulfate-reducing bacteria

S_t, ultimate tensile strength of material

STP, Standard Penetration Test

SVE, soil vapor extraction

SWL, static water level

SWP, spiral weld pipe

S_{yp}, material strength yield strength

T, temperature

T, transmissivity (L^2/t)

t, wall thickness

t, time

TBHP, total brake horsepower

TCE, trichloroethylene

TD, total depth

TDH, total dynamic head

TDS, total dissolved solids

TE, tidal efficiency

TEFC, totally enclosed fan cooled

TSV, target storage volume

U, minimum pipe tensile strength

u, $1.87r^2S/Tt$

u, Poisson's ratio

UL, Underwriters Laboratory

U.S. EPA, United States Environmental Protection Agency

USGS, United States Geological Survey

V, velocity

V, voltage

v, volume

VAC, AC volts

VDL, variable density log

VOC, volatile organic compound

W, width

w, width

Whp, water horsepower

WP, weather protected enclosure

W(u), well function of u; represents an exponential integral

x, unit length

Y, minimum pipe yield strength

Yp, material yield strength

z, elevation above a certain datum

zbl, thickness of impermeable materials placed landward of structure

‰ parts per thousand

α, alpha

β, beta

γ, gamma

δ, delta

Δ, delta

η, porosity

γ, specific weight

μ, dynamic viscosity

μg/ℓ, micrograms per liter

μmhos/cm, micromhos per centimeter

μsec, microsecond

ρ, fluid density

ρ, density

ρ, resistivity

ρ$_w$, density of water

Glossary*

A

absolute pressure.** Atmospheric pressure added to gauge pressure.

acid. Any chemical compound containing hydrogen capable of being replaced by positive elements or radicals to form salts. In terms of the dissociation theory, it is a compound which—on dissociation in solution—yields excess hydrogen ions. Acids lower the pH. Examples of acids or acidic substances are hydrochloric acid, tannic acid, and sodium acid pyrophosphate.

acidize.* To add and circulate acid in a well or open borehole to remove scale and to open the aquifer to improve water production characteristics. Commonly used to treat limestone or other carbonate formations. Acids that are used to acidize wells include citric acid, sulfamic acid, sulfuric acid, and hydrochloric acid. Typically, the acid is injected into the formation under pressure, where it etches the rock and enlarges the pore spaces and passages through which the fluids flow. Chemical inhibitors can be combined with the acid to prevent corrosion of the pipe.

adapter. Connects and aligns the power end of an ANSI pump to the wet end.

adsorption. The assimilation of gas, vapor, or dissolved matter by the surface of a solid.

advection. The process by which solutes are transported by the bulk motion of flowing groundwater.

affinity laws. The laws that predict how capacity, head, and horsepower are affected by changes in the centrifugal pump impeller diameter or shaft speed.

aggregation. The formation of aggregates. In drilling fluids, aggregation results in the stacking of the clay platelets face to face; as a result, viscosity and gel strength decrease.

---

* Some of the terms and definitions in this Glossary were provided by the National Ground Water Association (reprinted from the *National Ground Water Association's Illustrated Glossary of Drilling Terms,* with permission of the National Ground Water Association © 2004; indicated by an asterisk (*)); and the United States Geological Survey (USGS; indicated by two asterisks (**)).

air stripping. A mass transfer process in which a substance in solution in water is transferred to solution in a gas, usually air.

airlift.* To lift water or drilling fluid to the land surface using compressed air. Associated with airlifting water, such as airlift development or an airlift test.

alignment. Condition where the centerline of the pump is perfectly aligned with the centerline of the driver (usually an electric motor). Also refers to the straightness of a borehole and well.

alkaline. Any of various soluble mineral salts that have a pH greater than 7 and which are found in natural water and arid soils. In water analysis, this represents the carbonates, bicarbonates, hydroxides, and occasionally the borates, silicates, and phosphates in the water.

alluvial. Pertaining to or composed of alluvium, or deposited by a stream or running water.

alluvium. A general term for clay, silt, sand, gravel, or similar unconsolidated material that has been deposited comparatively recently in geologic time by a stream or other body of running water as a sorted or semi-sorted sediment in the bed of the stream or on its floodplain or delta, or as a cone or fan at the base of a mountain slope.

ambient heat. The heat in the area where equipment is located.

ambient pressure. The pressure in the area where equipment is located.

American National Standards Institute (ANSI). An organization that serves as administrator and coordinator of the United States private sector voluntary standardization system.

anion. A negatively charged ion that migrates to an anode (such as in electrolysis).

anion exchange. Ion exchange process in which anions in solution are exchanged for other anions from an ion exchanger.

anisotropic. Having some physical property that varies with direction.

annealing.** To soften metal by heating it to a predetermined temperature that is below its melting point.

annular velocity.* The velocity of a fluid moving in the annulus.

annulus. The space between the drill string or casing and the wall of the borehole or outer casing.

anode. Any positively charged electrode, as in an electrolytic cell, storage battery, or electron tube.

ANSI. *See* American National Standards Institute.

ANSI standard.** A set of specifications developed by the American National Standards Institute.

API. American Petroleum Institute.

aquiclude. A saturated but low-permeability geologic material that does not yield water freely to a well or spring. This term has been replaced by aquitard.

aquifer. A formation, group of formations, or part of a formation that contains sufficient saturated permeable material to yield economical quantities of water to wells and springs. Aquifers store and transmit water.

aquifer stimulation. A type of development that is performed in semi-consolidated and consolidated formations to alter the formation physically to improve its hydraulic properties.

aquitard. A geologic formation, group of formations, or part of a formation through which virtually no water moves.

artesian aquifer. A confined aquifer where the elevation of the water level in the aquifer is greater than the bottom of the confining unit. If the pressure in the confined aquifer is sufficient that the water-level elevation in a well is greater than the land surface, then the well is termed a flowing artesian well.

artesian well. A well deriving its water from a confined aquifer in which the water level is above the bottom of the confining layer. If the water level is above the land surface, then it is an artesian flowing well.

artificial recharge. Recharge induced by human activity for the storage of water.

atmospheric pressure. At sea level this measurement is 14.7 psi.

attapulgite clay. A colloidal, viscosity-building clay that consists of hydrous magnesium aluminum silicates.

Attenberg limits. A basic measure of the nature of a fine-grained soil. Depending on the water content of the soil, it can appear in four states: solid, semi-solid, plastic, and liquid.

B

back-off sub.* A reverse-threaded section of pipe that is connected to the top of a section of casing or other object that is to be positioned within a borehole or well. After the object is placed in position, the drillpipe or other tubing (which is threaded into the back-off sub) is turned to the right, and is unscrewed from the reverse-threaded shoe. Also called "let-down shoe."

backwash (well development). The surging effect or reversal of water flow in a well. Backwashing removes fine-grained material from the formation surrounding the borehole, which can enhance well yield.

bactericide. A substance that kills bacteria.

bail.* To remove sediment or other debris from a well or borehole with a bailer. Bailing also is used for development of smaller wells.

bailer.* A cylindrical device suspended from a wire rope or cable, which is used to remove sediment or other material from a well or open borehole. A bailer can be equipped with various types of valves or trap doors at its base, to allow sediment to enter the bailer and be retained within it while the bailer is pulled to the land surface. Types of bailers include dart valve bailers, flapper valve bailers, suction bailers, and scows.

bar. Metric term for one atmosphere of pressure.

barite. Natural finely ground barium sulfate used for increasing the density of drilling fluids.

barrier fluid. High-pressure fluid that is circulated between two mechanical seals. To prevent air pockets, the fluid should enter through the bottom and leave through the top.

basalt. A general term for dark-colored iron- and magnesium-rich igneous rocks, commonly extrusive but locally intrusive.

base exchange. The displacement of a cation bound to a site on the surface of a solid (for example in silica-alumina clay-mineral packets) by a cation in solution.

bearing. Supports the rotating shaft and allows it to turn with a minimum amount of friction. Can be either a sleeve or an anti-friction type.

bedload. The part of the total stream load that is moved on or immediately above the stream bed, such as the larger or heavier particles (boulders, pebbles, gravel) transported along the bottom. The part of the load that is not in suspension or solution continuously.

bedrock. A general term for the rock, usually solid, that underlies soil or other unconsolidated material.

bentonite. A colloidal clay largely comprised of the mineral sodium montmorillonite (a hydrated aluminum silicate).

B.E.P. *See* best efficiency point.

Bernoulli equation. The total energy in a fluid consists of three components: pressure head, velocity head, and elevation head (energy derived from the elevation of the water body). The sum of these energy heads is expressed by the Bernoulli equation.

best efficiency point (B.E.P.).* The point where the power coming out of the pump (water horsepower) is the closest to the power coming into the pump (brake horsepower) from the driver. This also is the point at which there is no radial deflection of the shaft caused by unequal hydraulic forces acting on the impeller.

BHP. *See* brake horsepower.

bit.* The cutting tool attached to the base or bottom end of the drill string that breaks the formation into smaller pieces (cuttings) during drilling. Bits come in various sizes and shapes, and are designed for either soft, medium, or hard formations. Common bit types include hammer bits, tricone bits (including button bits and mill tooth bits), drag bits, and core bits. Other bit types include the fishtail bit, roller-type bit, three-way bit, two cone, Mother Hubbard bit, star bit, crackerjack bit, pilot bit, spudding bit, side bit, T-bit, Z-bit, and paddy bit.

bit balling.* The situation when clay sticks to the drill bit and covers the teeth, resulting in reduced drilling rate.

blooey line.* A flow line used in air drilling. The cuttings are blown out of the pipe with air pressure.

blowout. An uncontrolled escape of drilling fluid, gas, oil, or water from the well, caused by formation pressure that is greater than the hydrostatic head of the fluid in the borehole.

bowls.* Pump impellers.

braden head.* 1. A device that is used during inner-string grouting or pressure grouting operations. The braden head is situated at the top of the well casing, where it allows a drill pipe to be extended into the well while the well head is sealed and the annulus between the well casing and drill pipe is pressurized. Also termed casing head, cement head, or largen head. 2. To conduct inner-string grouting or pressure grouting operations using a braden head.

braided stream. A stream that divides into an interlacing network of several small branching and reuniting shallow channels separated from each other by branch islands or channel bars, resembling the strands of a complex braid.

brake horsepower (BHP).* The amount of horsepower consumed by a pump, as measured using a pony brake or dynamometer.

bridge.* An obstruction in the drill hole or annulus. A bridge usually is formed by: caving of the borehole wall; intrusion of a large boulder, sediment, or other debris into the borehole; swelling of clay sections; or by filter-pack materials during well completion. Bridging also can occur in the formation during well development.

bridge plug.* A downhole tool (composed primarily of slips, a plug mandrel, and a rubber sealing element) that is run and set in casing to isolate a lower zone while an upper section is tested, cemented, stimulated, produced, or has material injected into it. Can be used to close off a borehole or casing opening. *See also* bridge seal.

bridge seal.* An artificial plug set to seal off specific zones in the abandonment of a well.

Brinell hardness.** A method of measuring the hardness of metal parts and hard seal faces. Hardness greater than 350 makes standard machining operations (turning, boring, drilling, tapping) uneconomical.

Brinell scale. A scale that characterizes the indentation hardness of materials through the scale of penetration and an indenter, loaded on a material test piece. It is one of several definitions of hardness in materials science.

buried valley. A depression in an ancient land surface or in bedrock that is covered by younger deposits, particularly a preglacial valley filled with glacial drift.

bushing. A close fitting support device used to restrict flow between two liquids, thermally isolate a hot liquid, support the rotating shaft, break-down pressure, etc.

C

capillary fringe. The zone at the bottom of the vadose zone where groundwater is drawn upward by capillary force.

carbide. The compound formed when carbon combines with an element. The carbides of metal are very hard and often are used as a mechanical seal face.

carbonate. A mineral compound characterized by a fundamental anionic structure of CO_3^{-2}. Calcite is an example of carbonate.

carbonate rock. A rock consisting chiefly of carbonate minerals, such as limestone and dolomite.

casing centralizer.* A device, commonly made of spring steel, stainless steel, or PVC, secured around the casing at regular intervals to center it in the hole. Casing that is centralized allows a more uniform filter pack or grout sheath to form in the annulus around the pipe.

casing jacks.* Hydraulic jacks that can be used to pull casing, drill pipe, or other tubing strings from the borehole. Casing jacks are capable of exerting a very great pulling force, so the driller must take care not to pull the casing or other tubing string in half.

cathode. Any negatively charged electrode, such as in an electrolytic cell or storage battery.

cation. An ion having a positive charge and, in electrolytes, one that characteristically moves toward a negative electrode.

cation exchange. Ion exchange process in which cations in solution are exchanged for other cations from an ion exchanger.

cavitate.** Cavities or bubbles form in a fluid low-pressure area and collapse in a higher-pressure area of the pump, causing noise, damage, and a loss of capacity.

cavitation. A phenomena of cavity formation, or the formation and collapse (especially in regard to pumps), that occurs when the absolute pressure within the water reaches the vapor pressure, and causes the formation of vapor pockets.

cement basket.* A metal, canvas, or rubber device that is placed on the outside of a casing string to prevent cement or other materials from moving below that depth. *See also* shale trap.

cement shoe.* A check-valve device that is used when pumping cement grout into an annulus using inner string or pressure grouting. The cement shoe contains a check valve which prevents the cement from flowing back into the drill pipe, even if the pressures are uneven across the shoe. Also termed "float shoe."

cementing. *See* grouting.

centistokes. The kinematic unit of viscosity. Viscosity in centipoises divided by the liquid density at the same temperature gives kinematic viscosity in centistokes.

centrifugal separator. Uses centrifugal force to throw solids out of the fluid. Sometimes called a cyclone separator.

chlorine (Cl$_2$). A gas, chlorine is used widely in the disinfection of water and as an oxidizing agent.

circulate.* To cause drilling fluid (such as drilling mud, foam, or compressed air) or other fluids (e.g., water, cement) to pass through the drill string, annulus, and mud pits (in the case of circulated drilling mud). *See also* direct circulation; reverse circulation.

clastic. Pertaining to a rock or sediment composed principally of broken fragments that are derived from pre-existing rocks or minerals, and that have been transported some distance from their places of origin.

coefficient of permeability. A term that has been replaced by "hydraulic conductivity." *See* hydraulic conductivity.

coefficient of storage. The volume of water an aquifer releases from or takes into storage per unit surface area of the aquifer per unit change in head.

coefficient of transmissivity. *See* transmissivity.

collapse strength.* A measure of the property of a casing or other tubing to resist collapse when subjected to horizontal exterior stress during and after installation (i.e., collapse stress).

collar.* A thick-walled, heavy section of drill pipe. Collars are located near the base of the drill string (near the bit) to maintain plumbness and provide weight on the bit while drilling.

collar locator.* A device used to locate drill pipe with a greater wall thickness, such as collars and tool joints. A collar locator operates on the principle of electrical resistivity.

colloid. Extremely small solid particles, 0.0001 to 1 micron in size, which do not settle out of a solution; intermediate between a true dissolved particle and a suspended solid which does settle out of solution.

condition the borehole.* To circulate drilling fluid through the borehole while rotating the drill string to remove cuttings and slough material, and also to improve the condition of the wall cake.

conductor casing.* A relatively short string of large-diameter pipe which is set to keep the top of the borehole open and provide a means of returning the upflowing drilling fluid from the wellbore to the surface drilling-fluid system (mud pit or slush pit) until the first casing string is set in the well. Installation of conductor pipe typically is termed "collaring the hole." Conductor casing usually is cemented to provide well control. Also called "conductor pipe." *See also* surface casing.

cone of depression. A depression in the water table or potentiometric surface that has the shape of an inverted cone and that develops around a well from which water is being withdrawn. This defines the area of influence of a well.

confined aquifer. A formation in which the groundwater is isolated from the atmosphere at the point of discharge by impermeable geologic formations. Confined groundwater generally is subject to pressure that is greater than atmospheric pressure.

conglomerate.** A coarse-grained sedimentary rock composed of fragments larger than 2 mm in diameter.

contamination. The degradation of natural water quality as a result of human or natural activities. There is no implication of any specific limits, because the degree of permissible contamination depends upon the intended end use (or uses) of the water.

convection. A natural circulation due to the thermal variations in a fluid.

conventional core drilling.* A type of drilling that involves the continuous or periodic recovery of core samples from a borehole without the use of a wireline. A disadvantage of this type of core drilling is that the drill pipe must be brought out (tripped out) of the hole to recover each core sample.

core.* 1. A continuous columnar sample of the lithologic units extracted from a borehole. Such a sample preserves stratigraphic contacts and structural features that are obtained for geological or other analysis. 2. To drill a donut-shaped boring, which will accommodate the collection of a cylindrical formation sample, called a core. Usually a core barrel assembly is substituted for the drilling bit and procures a sample as it penetrates the formation. *See also* wireline-core drilling; conventional core drilling.

core barrel.* A tubular device that is placed at the bottom of the air or mud rotary drill string, just above the core bit, to obtain a cylindrical formation sample in either consolidated or unconsolidated formations. After the core barrel has been filled with a formation sample as the core bit advances the hole, the core barrel is removed from the borehole on a wireline (*see* wireline-core drilling), or by tripping the drilling string out of the hole (*see* conventional core drilling). Core barrels can be single or double walled and of a swivel or rigid type.

corrosion. The act or process of wearing-away metals by chemical action.

critical speed. Any object made of an elastic material has a natural period of vibration. When a pump rotor or shaft rotates at any speed corresponding to its natural frequency, minor unbalances are magnified. These speeds are called the critical speeds.

crossover sub.* A short section within a drill string that allows two "unlike" sections of drillpipe, collcars, or subs to be joined. Crossover subs are used to join pin-to-pin, box-to-box, different diameter pipe, or different threads.

cyclone.* A device used in some types of reverse rotary drilling that separates the solids (cuttings) from the air in a large cone-shaped chamber that causes a venturi to divide solids from vapors.

D

Darcy's law. A derived equation for the flow of fluids, based on the assumption that the flow is laminar and that inertia can be neglected.

deflocculation. Breakup of a flocs of gel structures by use of a thinner.

density. Matter measured as mass per unit volume. It can be expressed, for example, in pounds per gallon (lb/gal), pounds per cubic ft (lb/ft^3), and kilogram per cubic m (kg/m^3).

desander.* A special cone-shaped vessel (hydrocyclone) operated by a pressurized high-speed stream of drilling fluid, imparting centrifugal force on sand and other particles (larger than 74 microns), removing them from the fluid stream and discharging them to waste. This process controls mud density, mitigates formation damage, and reduces equipment wear.

desilter.* A centrifugal device (hydro-cyclone) used to remove very fine (2,200 to 140 microns) particles of silt, etc. from the drilling fluid to keep the amount of entrained solids at the lowest point possible. Generally, the lower the solids content of the drilling fluid, the faster the rate of penetration, which minimizes the well development required. A desilter is very similar to a desander, except that it is smaller in diameter and designed to remove finer sediment.

develop a well.* To surge, bail, pump, swab, airlift, jet, or otherwise conduct opera-tions at a well that will increase the well's specific capacity by removing fine sediment and drilling fluids, and by creating a well-packed and graded filter-pack envelope around the well.

development. The act of repairing damage to a formation that was caused by drilling procedures.

deviation.* The difference (in degrees) of the wellbore from vertical or from the intended target. The angle of deviation, angle of drift, or drift angle is the angle (in degrees) that shows the variation from the vertical (or intended) target as revealed by deviation survey instruments.

deviation log.* A geophysical log that pro-vides an indication of the horizontal drift of a borehole from plumb. Deviation logs differ from inclinometer surveys in that they are conducted after the borehole has been drilled to its total depth, as opposed to logs per-formed intermittently during the drilling process. A deviation log also provides an indication of the plumbness of all portions of the borehole; an inclinometer survey applies only to a discrete location in the borehole. Deviation logs differ from gyroscopic surveys in that they are based on magnetic deflection rather than on gyroscopic varia-tions, and they are valid only in open well-bores, not in a cased well. *See* deviation.

diatomaceous earth. A light-colored, soft, siliceous earth composed of the shells of diatoms (a form of algae). Some deposits are of lake origin, but the largest are of marine origin.

direct circulation.* To circulate drilling fluid, compressed air, or other fluids (such as water or cement) downward through the drill pipe, out through the drill bit, upward through the annulus between the drill pipe and borehole, and through the mud pits (when appropriate).

discharge area (groundwater).** Area where subsurface water is discharged to the land surface, to surface water, or to the atmosphere.

discharge head. The outlet pressure of a pump operation.

dispersant.* Any chemical added to the drilling fluid that promotes breaking up the floes or separating the particles in the drilling fluid.

dispersion. The spreading and mixing of chemical constituents in groundwater caused by diffusion and mixing due to microscopic variations in velocities within and between pores.

dissociation. A chemical process that causes a molecule to split into simpler groups of atoms, single atoms, or ions. The water molecule (H_2O), for example, breaks down into H+ and OH- ions.

drainage basin. The land area from which surface runoff drains into a stream channel, or system of channels, or drains into a lake, reservoir, or other body of water.

drawdown. The distance between the static water level and the pumping water level in a well.

drawworks.* The winch or winches that are used to hoist the drill string up and down the borehole.

drill collar.* Large-diameter, heavy, thick-walled, stiff steel pipe placed in the drill string between the drill pipe and the bit. Drill collars aid in drilling a straight hole by stiffening the bottom hole assembly or lower drill string, controlling the angle of the bit, and by putting a controlled weight on the bit while maintaining the drill pipe portion of the drill string in tension. *See* collar.

drill pipe.* Seamless steel tubing used to rotate the bit and circulate the drilling fluid or, in some cases, to put the drilling weight on the bit. In some rotary drilling techniques, the drill pipe also transmits weight to the bit and conveys air or fluid that removes drill-pipe cuttings from the borehole and cools the bit. The joints of pipe are easily handled and uniform lengths are coupled together by tool joints, often with special thread systems.

drilling fluid. A water- or air-based fluid used in a drilling operation to remove cuttings from the hole, clean and cool the bit, reduce friction between the drill string and the sides of the hole, and seal the borehole.

drive point. *See* well point.

dual walled.* Referring to the type of drill pipe composed of two concentric pipe walls. The annulus between the two walls is open to the interior of the drill pipe, near the base of the drill string, to allow the reverse circulation of compressed air. Also termed "dual tube."

ductility. The property of a metal that allows a great deal of mechanical deformation without cracking.

E

effective size. The 90% retained size of a sediment as determined from a grain-size analysis; 10% of the sediment is finer and 90% is coarser.

electrical conductance. A measure of the ease with which a conducting current can be caused to flow through a material under the influence of an applied electric field. It is the reciprocal of resistivity and is measured in mhos per ft (m).

electrical resistivity. The property of a material which resists the flow of electrical current measured per unit length through a unit cross-sectional area. Its unit of measure is ohm-ft (ohm-cm).

electrolysis. A process involving chemical change caused by the passage of an electric current through a liquid.

electrolyte. A chemical that dissociates into positive and negative ions when dissolved in water, increasing the electrical conductivity.

encrust. *See* incrust.

endurance limit. The point beyond which a metal fatigues without increased stress.

ephemeral stream.** A stream or part of a stream that flows only in direct response to precipitation. It receives little or no water from springs, melting snow, or other sources; its channel is at all times above the water table.

equipotential line. A contour line on the water table or potentiometric surface; a line along which the total head of groundwater in an aquifer is the same. Fluid flow is normal to these lines in the direction of decreasing fluid potential.

erosion. The general process or group of processes whereby the materials of the earth's crust are moved from one place to another by running water (including rainfall, waves and currents, glacier ice, or water moved by wind).

evaporation. Volatilization of water in which the phase change from liquid to vapor occurs.

evapotranspiration. The loss of water from a land area through transpiration of plants and evaporation from the soil.

extrusive rocks. Igneous rocks formed from magma that flows onto the earth's surface. The magma cools rapidly, producing rock with a fine crystalline structure.

F

fault. A fracture or a zone of fractures along which there is displacement of the sides relative to one another and parallel to the fracture.

filter. A device used to remove solid particles from liquid. It removes particles smaller than those removed by a strainer.

filter cake. The suspended solids that are deposited on a porous medium during the process of filtration.

filter pack. Sand or gravel that is smooth, uniform, clean, well-rounded and siliceous. The pack material is placed in the annulus of the well between the borehole wall and the well screen to prevent formation material from entering the screen.

filtration. The process of separating suspended solids from liquid by forcing the liquid through a porous medium. Two types of fluid filtration occur in a borehole during the drilling process: dynamic filtration when fluid is circulating, and static filtration when fluid is at rest.

fish.* 1. An object that has been lost in a well or borehole, such as a logging probe, drill tools, drill bit, or pump. 2. The operation of recovering a lost object from a well or borehole.

fishing.* To attempt the retrieval of an object from the borehole (e.g., a twisted-off drill pipe, a pump, a dropped wrench).

flashing. A rapid change in liquid state from a liquid to a gas.

flocculation. The agglomeration of finely divided suspended solids into larger (usually gelatinous) particles; the development of a "floc" after treatment with a coagulant by gentle stirring or mixing.

flooded suction. When a liquid source is higher than the pump, the liquid flows to the pump by gravity. Preferable for centrifugal pump installations.

floodplain. The surface or strip of relatively smooth land adjacent to a river channel, constructed by the present river and covered with water when the river overflows its banks. It is built of alluvium carried by the river during floods and deposited in the sluggish water located beyond the influence of the swiftest current.

flow lines. Lines indicating the direction followed by groundwater toward points of discharge. Flow lines are perpendicular to equipotential lines in isotropic, homogeneous materials.

flowing artesian well. A well that is screened in a confined aquifer and that has a water level that is above the land surface, allowing the well to flow. *See also* artesian well.

fluid. A material that assumes the shape of its container; can be either a liquid or a gas.

flush threads.* Pipe threads that are engineered to allow the outside diameter of the threaded pipe to be consistent, without larger-diameter couplings or tool joints at the threaded connections.

fluvial deposit.** A sedimentary deposit consisting of material transported by suspension or laid down by a river or stream.

foam.* A circulating fluid used in air rotary drilling that consists of water and a foaming agent (surfactant) or other additives that are injected into the airline.

foot valve.** A type of check valve with a built-in strainer. Used at the point of the liquid intake to retain liquid in the system, preventing the loss of prime when the liquid source is lower than the pump.

formation stabilizer. A sand or gravel placed in the annulus of the well between the borehole wall and the well screen to provide temporary or long-term support for the borehole.

fouling. The process in which undesirable foreign matter accumulates in a bed of filter media or ion exchanger, and clogs pores and coats surfaces, thus inhibiting or retarding the proper operation of the bed.

frac.* 1. To stimulate (improve) the well production by increasing the secondary porosity and permeability of the producing formation. Under high hydraulic pressure, during a frac operation, a fluid (typically water—which then is termed hydrofrac— or nitrogen gas) is introduced into the borehole under enough hydraulic pressure to fracture the formation material. A proppant material (e.g., sand, aluminum pellets, glass beads) can be circulated into the borehole to prop the fractures open so that they remain open after the hydraulic pressure has been released. 2. To induce excessive hydraulic pressure (head) into the borehole while drilling. The excessive hydraulic head results from the hydrostatic head of the drilling fluid column plus the circulating pressure (circulating density), which can exceed the fracture gradient of the formation and cause fracturing to occur, resulting in lost circulation conditions.

friction head.** The pressure expressed in pounds per square inch or in feet of liquid required to overcome the resistance to the flow in the pipe and fittings.

G

gasket. Used between two static surfaces to provide a seal. Made from a variety of deformable materials.

gel. A state of a colloidal particle suspension, in which shearing stresses below a certain finite value fail to produce permanent deformation. Gels commonly occur when the dispersed colloidal particles have a great affinity for the base fluid.

gel strength.* The thixotropic property of a drilling fluid that allows it to form a "gel" (i.e., increase its viscosity) when it stops moving. Good gel strength prevents the drilled cuttings from falling around the drill pipe—potentially sticking to it—when circulation is stopped. The minimum shearing stresses that will produce permanent deformation of a colloidal suspension. The ability of the drilling fluid to support and suspend the cuttings. The use of bentonite in the drilling fluid greatly increases these characteristics.

glacial drift. A general term for unconsolidated sediment transported by glaciers and deposited directly on land.

glacial outwash.** Stratified detritus (chiefly sand and gravel) "washed out" from a glacier by meltwater streams and deposited in front of or beyond the end moraine or the margin of an active glacier.

glaciofluvial. Pertaining to the meltwater streams flowing from retreating glacier ice and especially to the deposits and landforms produced by such streams.

graded. An engineering term pertaining to a soil or an unconsolidated sediment consisting of particles of several or many sizes, or having a uniform or equable distribution of particles from coarse to fine.

grain per gallon (gpg). A common basis for reporting water analyses in the water-treatment industry in the United States. One grain per U.S. gallon equals 17.12 milligrams per liter.

groundwater flow system.** The underground pathway by which groundwater moves from areas of recharge to areas of discharge.

grout. A fluid mixture of cement and water (neat cement) of a consistency that can be forced through a pipe and placed as required. Various additives, such as sand, bentonite, and hydrated lime, can be included in the mixture to meet certain requirements. Bentonite and water sometimes are used for grout.

grouting. The operation by which grout is placed between the casing and the sides of the wellbore to a predetermined height above the bottom of the well. This process secures the casing in place and excludes water and other fluids from the wellbore.

H

hardness (water). A property of water causing formation of an insoluble residue when the water is used with soap. This primarily is caused by the presence of calcium and magnesium ions.

harmonic vibration.** Vibrating in harmony with something nearby. This can be a significant problem for bearings in stationary or non-running equipment.

head. Energy contained in a water mass; it is produced by elevation, pressure, or velocity.

head loss. The head energy lost due to friction occurring as water flows.

heaving sand.* Saturated sands encountered during drilling when the hydrostatic pressure of the formation is greater than the borehole pressure, causing the sands to move up into the borehole. Also termed "flowing sand" and "running sand."

heterogeneous. The state of being nonuniform in structure or composition throughout.

hollow-stem auger.* The type of drilling rig that uses the auger method together with a hollow drill string through which soil samples can be collected and well casing can be installed. Cuttings are removed and the borehole is advanced in hollow-stem auger drilling by the mechanical action of the auger flights on the drill string.

homogeneous. The state of being uniform in structure or composition throughout.

hydration. The act by which a substance takes up water by absorption or adsorption.

hydraulic conductivity.** The capacity of a geologic material to transmit water. It is expressed as the volume of water at the existing kinematic viscosity that will move in unit time under a unit hydraulic gradient through a unit area measured at right angles to the direction of flow.

hydraulic gradient. The rate of change in total head per unit of distance of flow in a given direction.

hydrocarbon. A petroleum product consisting of hydrogen and carbon.

hydrogeologic. Those factors that deal with subsurface waters and related geologic aspects of surface waters.

I

ID. Inside diameter.

igneous rocks. Rocks that solidified from molten or partly molten material (i.e., from a magma).

Imhoff cone.* A cone-shaped container with a graduated scale on its side (similar to a beaker) that is used to measure the proportion of sand content in pumped groundwater (or another fluid).

impeller.** Equipment that attaches to the end of the shaft to impart energy to the fluid being pumped. Available in open, semi-open, and closed designs.

impeller vane.** Located between the eye and the discharge side of the impeller. Directs the flow of the liquid to the outside diameter of the impeller.

incrustation. The process by which a crust or coating is formed.

inducer. A small axial-flow vane that attaches to the impeller of a centrifugal pump to increase the net positive suction head available.

infiltration.** The downward movement of water from the atmosphere into soil or porous rock.

interference. The condition occurring when the area of influence of a water well comes into contact with or overlaps that of a neighboring well, such as two wells pumping from the same aquifer or which are located near each other.

internal drainage.** Surface drainage whereby the water does not reach the ocean, such as drainage toward the lowermost or central part of an interior basin or closed depression.

internal recirculation. A loss of efficiency caused by liquid flowing through wear rings or the impeller to volute clearances.

intrusive rocks. The igneous rocks formed from magma that is injected beneath the earth's surface. These rocks generally have large crystals that are created by slow cooling of the material.

ion. An element or compound that has gained or lost an electron, and thus no longer is neutral electrically and instead carries a charge.

isotropic. Term describing a medium that exhibits properties having the same values when measured along axes in all directions.

J

jetting.* 1. To develop a well by applying high-velocity horizontal streams ("jets") of water or compressed air to the well screen. Jet development can be conducted with the application of chemical additives, and with simultaneous pumping or air lifting. 2. The drilling method that involves breaking up and removing sediment from the borehole by use of a high-velocity stream of water or compressed air, but without the mechanical action of a drilling bit. 3. The action of causing erosion by fluid impingement on the formation. Borehole enlargement and instability can result in unconsolidated formation by pumping the drilling fluid in turbulent flow.

joint.* 1. A single length of drill pipe, drill collar, or tubing that has threaded connections at both ends. Several joints screwed together constitute a stand of pipe (e.g., single, double, triple). 2. The point at which two pieces of pipe or a pipe and a fitting are connected.

K

karst topography. A type of topography that is formed on limestone, gypsum, and dolomite by dissolution. It is characterized by sinkholes, caves, and underground drainage.

KB. *See* kelly bushing.

kelly.* The heavy steel member (usually square or hexagonal) that is suspended from the swivel, passes through the rotary table, and is connected to the topmost joint of drill pipe to turn the drill string as the rotary table turns. The kelly is hollow so fluids can be circulated through it into the drill pipe (during direct circulation) or kelly hose (during reverse circulation).

kelly bushing (KB).* The steel object that fits within the rotary table, and grips and supports the kelly. Also called "drive bushing."

L

laminar flow. Water flow in which the stream lines remain distinct and the flow direction at every point remains unchanged over time. It is characteristic of the movement of groundwater.

landfill. A general term indicating a disposal site of refuse, dirt from excavations, and miscellaneous refuse.

leachate. The liquid that has percolated through solid waste and dissolved soluble components.

leaky confined aquifer. Confined aquifers that lose or receive water from the surrounding formations.

limestone. A sedimentary rock consisting chiefly of calcium carbonate, primarily in the form of the mineral calcite.

lost circulation. A result of drilling fluid escaping from the borehole into the formation.

lubricant. Any fluid that will maintain a film thickness of one micron or more at its operating temperature and load.

M

marker bed. A rock unit that is distinctive and easily recognized across long distances in the subsurface.

Marsh funnel.* A device with a specifically sized orifice and a screen at the top to remove large particles and that holds a specific volume of drilling fluid. It is used to measure drilling fluid viscosity where the time required for a known volume of drilling fluid to drain through an orifice is measured and calibrated against a time for draining of an equal volume of water.

Marsh funnel viscosity. Commonly called funnel viscosity. The Marsh funnel viscosity is reported as the number of seconds required for 1 qt (946 ml) of a given fluid to flow through the Marsh funnel.

metal fatigue. Breakage of a metal that is caused by the bending and flexing of a metal part beyond its endurance limit.

metamorphic rocks. Any rock derived from pre-existing rocks by mineralogical, chemical, or structural changes—essentially in the solid state—in response to marked changes in temperature, pressure, shearing stress, and chemical environment, generally at depth in the earth's crust.

mho. Unit of conductance that is equal to the reciprocal of the ohm.

molecular diffusion. Dispersion of a chemical that is caused by the kinetic activity of the ionic or molecular constituents.

molecule. A stable configuration of atomic nuclei and electrons bound together by electrostatic and electromagnetic forces. It is the simplest structural unit that displays the characteristic physical and chemical properties of a compound.

moraine. A mound, ridge, or other distinct accumulation of unsorted, unstratified glacial drift—predominantly till—deposited chiefly by direct action of glacier ice.

mud pit.* The pit (either an aboveground metal tank or an excavated belowground pit) that contains the drilling fluid. The mud pit is a series of earthen pits or metal open top tanks through which the drilling mud is cycled to allow drilled cuttings and sediments to settle out. If necessary to maintain system volume and quality, additives are mixed with the mud in the pit and the fluid temporarily is stored there before being pumped back down the borehole. Also termed settling pit, shaker pit, shale pit, and suction pit, depending on the primary purpose.

mud pump.* A pump used to circulate the drilling fluid (mud) system on a drilling rig. Usually a single- or double-acting piston pump with two or three cylinders. The pistons travel in replaceable liners and are driven by a crankshaft actuated by an engine or motor. A centrifugal-type pump often is used on special application rigs, in cases where it can efficiently operate within its limitations. Also termed "slush pump."

N

naturally developed well. A well in which the screen is placed in direct contact with the aquifer materials and no filter pack is used.

neat cement.* 1. A mixture of Portland cement (ASTM C-150) and water in the proportion of 5 to 6 gallons of clean water per bag (94 lb or 1 ft³) of cement. 2. A slurry of cement and water, containing no aggregate.

net positive suction head available (NPSHA).* The suction head available to prevent cavitation of the pump. Defined as atmospheric pressure, gauge pressure, static pressure, vapor pressure, friction loss in the suction piping.

net positive suction head required (NPSHR).* Suction head required to stop a pump from cavitating. The pump manufacturer provides this number. Testing with cold freshwater generated the number, therefore it sometimes can be lowered when pumping hot water or some hydrocarbons.

nominal. A term used to describe standard sizes for pipe ranging from ⅛ in (3.2 mm) to 12 in (305 mm). The nominal size is specified on the basis of the inside diameter. Depending on the wall thickness, the inside diameter can be less than or greater than the number indicated.

nongraded. An engineering term pertaining to a soil or an unconsolidated sediment consisting of particles that essentially are the same size.

NPSHA. *See* net positive suction head available.

NPSHR. *See* net positive suction head required.

O

observation well. A well drilled in a selected location for the purpose of observing parameters such as water levels and for the collection of water samples.

OD. Outside diameter.

ohm. Unit of electric resistance.

outwash plain. A broad, gently sloping sheet of glacial outwash.

overburden. The loose soil, silt, sand, gravel, or other unconsolidated material overlying bedrock, and which is either transported or formed in place. Also termed "regolith."

overshot tool. A fishing tool attached to wireline tool string, tubing rods, or drill pipe that is lowered over the outside of a "fish" in the wellbore. A friction device in the overshot, usually a basket or a spiral grapple, firmly grips the fish, enabling it to be pulled from the hole.

oxidation. Is a chemical change in which electrons are lost by an atom or group of atoms.

P

packer.* 1. A downhole pneumatic, mechanical, or hydraulic pressure device used to close off an annular opening such as between the casing and borehole or between concentric casings. 2. A device used to isolate a desired portion of a borehole.

partial penetration. Condition occurring when the intake portion of the well is less than the full thickness of the aquifer.

pathogenic. The condition of being capable of causing disease.

perched water table. Upper surface of unconfined groundwater existing above the regional water table, and separated from an underlying main body of groundwater by an unsaturated zone.

percolate. The act of water seeping or filtering through the soil instead to the water table.

percolation. The downward movement of water when the soil's capacity to hold water is exceeded.

permeability. The property or capacity of a porous rock, sediment, or soil for transmitting a fluid. A measure of the relative ease of fluid flow under unequal pressure.

pH. A measure of the acidity or alkalinity of a solution. It numerically is equal to 7 for neutral solutions, increasing with increasing alkalinity and decreasing with increasing acidity. Originally was an acronym for "potential of hydrogen."

phreatic water. All water in the zone of saturation. Synonym for groundwater.

pilot hole.* A boring that is drilled and subsequently reamed out to a larger diameter. Pilot holes sometimes are drilled and tested as a preliminary step during the installation of a water-production well. The testing of a pilot hole can include lithologic logging (description of drilled cuttings), geophysical logging, and depth-specific water sampling. Exploratory borings sometimes also are drilled and tested prior to production-well installation, but exploratory borings differ from pilot holes in that they are abandoned after testing rather than being reamed out.

playa. The flat-floored bottom of an undrained desert basin that at times becomes a shallow lake.

playa lake.** A shallow, temporary lake in an arid or semiarid region, covering or occupying a playa in the wet season but drying up in summer. A temporary lake that upon evaporation leaves or forms a playa.

pollution. Condition when the contamination-concentration levels restrict the potential use of a water supply.

polymer. A substance formed by the union of two or more molecules of the same type that are linked end to end into another compound having the same elements in the same proportion, but that has a higher molecular weight and different physical properties.

porosity. The percentage of the bulk volume of a rock or soil that is occupied by interstices, whether isolated or connected.

potentiometric surface. An imaginary surface representing the total head of groundwater in an aquifer that is defined by the level to which water will rise in a well.

pressure head. The pump head exerted by atmospheric pressure, or any additional pressure that might be in the vessel.

pump-and-surge development.* The well development process that involves alternately pumping and surging a well. This is accomplished by pumping the well at sequentially increasing pumping rates, and intermittently applying the pump clutch to allow the water in the pump column pipe to backflow into the well to provide a surging action that helps to flush out fine-grained sediment and augment the well development process. To accommodate the pump-and-surge development process, the pump equipment is installed without a foot valve. Also termed backwashing development, overpumping development, and pumping development.

pumping test. A test conducted to determine aquifer or well characteristics. The preferred term is "aquifer test."

Q

quick condition. A condition of soil in which an increase in pore-water pressure decreases particle-to-particle attraction and significantly reduces the soil's bearing capacity.

R

radius of influence. The radial distance from the center of a well to the point where there is no lowering of the water table or potentiometric surface (the edge of its cone of depression).

rawhide.* A method of developing a well by pumping the well using equipment without a foot valve installed to prevent backflow through the pump. The pump clutch is used intermittently to allow back-washing of the well through the pump's column pipe. *See* pump-and-surge development.

recharge. The addition of water to the zone of saturation. Also refers to the amount of water added.

recharge area (groundwater).** An area within which water infiltrates the ground and reaches the zone of saturation.

redox. A chemical reaction in which an atom or molecule loses electrons to another atom or molecule. Also called oxidation-reduction. Oxidation is the loss of electrons; reduction is a gain in electrons.

regolith. A general term for the layer of fragmental and unconsolidated rock material that nearly everywhere forms the surface of the land and overlies or covers the bedrock.

residual drawdown. The difference between the original static water level and the depth to water at a given instant during the recovery period.

reverse circulation. The circulation of the drilling fluid down the annulus and back up to the surface through the drill stem; the opposite of direct circulation. Reverse circulation is used to accommodate special applications, such as large-diameter holes, unstable boreholes sensitive to high uphole velocities and pressures, or the need for better formation samples with an accurate depth of origin and minimum contamination due to caving.

Reynolds number. A dimensionless number that is a ratio of inertial forces to viscous forces.

runoff. That part of precipitation flowing to surface streams.

S

sandstone. A sedimentary rock composed of abundant rounded or angular fragments of sand set in a fine-grained matrix (silt or clay) and united relatively firmly by a cementing material.

sedimentary rocks. Rocks resulting from the consolidation of loose sediment that has accumulated in layers.

shale. A fine-grained sedimentary rock, formed by the consolidation of clay or silt. It is characterized by finely laminated structure and is sufficiently indurated so that it does not fall apart on wetting.

shale shaker.* A vibratory device that removes the larger cuttings from the drilling fluid as it exits the hole. The shaker is composed of one or more sized, controlled vibrating mesh wire screens (usually inclined). Cuttings removed by the shale shaker are discharged to waste in the shale pit. Also termed "mud screen" and "shaker."

shale trap.* A ring or cone composed of rubber or other material that is placed outside the casing to prevent slough materials from falling down the annulus during casing installation.

shear strength.* A measure of the shear value of a fluid, and a measure of the gelling properties of a fluid. Also termed "gel strength."

shear stress.* The component of stress that acts tangential to a plane through any given point in a body.

shut-off head.** The maximum head that a pump can generate with a given impeller outside diameter and horsepower driver.

sieve analysis. Determination of the particle-size distribution of a soil, sediment, or rock by measuring the percentage of the particles that passes through standard sieves of various sizes.

slurry. A thin mixture of liquid, particularly water, and any of several finely divided substances, such as cement or clay particles.

sonic drilling. A continuous core drilling method that uses vibrosonic energy to pulverize drilled material and push it outward from the borehole. This allows the borehole to be advanced without the use of drilling fluid, and without the deposition of drilled cuttings at the land surface.

spear*. A fishing tool used to retrieve pipe lost in a well. The spear is lowered into the borehole on a string of pipe (drill pipe) or cable, and ultimately into the lost pipe (the fish).

specific capacity. The rate of discharge of a water well per unit of drawdown, commonly expressed in gpm/ft or m^3/day/m. It varies with duration of discharge.

specific conductance.** A measure of the ability of a liquid to conduct an electrical current.

specific gravity. The weight of a particular volume of any substance compared to the weight of an equal volume of water at a reference temperature.

specific heat. The amount of calories or BTUs (British thermal units) required to raise a quantity of a liquid one degree.

specific retention. The ratio of the volume of water that a given body of rock or soil can hold against the pull of gravity to the volume of the body itself. Usually expressed as a percentage.

specific speed.** A formula that describes the shape of a pump impeller. The higher the specific speed the less NPSHR.

specific yield. The ratio of the volume of water that a given mass of saturated rock or soil yields by gravity to the volume of that mass. This ratio is expressed as a percentage.

static water level. The level of water in a well that is not affected by withdrawal of groundwater.

storage coefficient. *See* coefficient of storage.

storativity. *See* coefficient of storage.

stratigraphy. The study of rock strata and of their distribution, deposition, and age.

suction head.** Exists when the liquid source is above the centerline of the pump.

suction lift.** Exists when the liquid source is below the centerline of the pump.

sump.* 1. An enlarged area in the flow ditch made to allow cuttings to settle or to place a pump to lift the fluid up to the solids-control system. 2. An interval of excess borehole that has been drilled below the interval to be cased, or an excess portion of blank casing at the bottom of the well screen. The sump in a well or borehole serves to contain sediment that enters the well during casing installation or well development and use. The use of sumps is discouraged as they are areas for potential growth of bacteria.

surface casing.* The cased section of a borehole from ground level to a predetermined point. The surface casing typically is about 20 ft to 40 ft in length, and is of a larger diameter than the borehole to be drilled. The surface casing is installed prior to drilling the well to stabilize the shallow, unconsolidated formations found in the upper sections of the borehole. The annulus of the surface casing is sealed to prevent contaminants at the land surface from migrating into the well. It is not to be confused with a pump conductor pipe nor with a large caisson in an offshore area, which encloses several unique surface casings at the surface. *See also* conductor casing.

surfactant. A substance capable of reducing the surface tension of a liquid in which it is dissolved. Used in air-based drilling fluids to produce foam, and used during well development to disaggregate clays.

surge block.* A plunger-like tool consisting of solid or perforated pipe sandwiched between leather or rubber discs; used in well development.

system curve.** A description of required pump performance; the point where the system curve intersects the pump curve and shows where pumping will occur.

system head.** The head caused by friction in the piping valves and fittings.

T

TDH. *See* total dynamic head.

tensile strength. The resistance of a material to a force tending to tear it apart.

till. Predominantly unsorted and unstratified drift, generally unconsolidated, deposited directly by and underneath a glacier without subsequent reworking by meltwater. It primarily consists of a heterogeneous mixture of clay, silt, sand, gravel, and boulders ranging widely in size and shape.

top-head drive.* A type of rig that utilizes a hydraulic drive head at the top of the drill pipe to provide the rotating force (torque). A kelly is not required for use with a top-head drive.

tortuosity. Sinuosity of the actual flow path in porous medium. It is the ratio of the length of the flow path divided by the length of the sample.

total discharge head. A combination of the suction head and the head produced by the pump.

total dissolved solids (TDS). A term that expresses the quantity of dissolved material in a sample of water, either the residue on evaporation, dried at 356°F (180°C) or, for many waters that contain more than about 1,000 mg/ℓ, the sum of the chemical constituents.

total dynamic head (TDH). A combination of static discharge and suction heads as well as friction and velocity heads and losses.

total head. Summation of pressure and elevation heads. Also the amount of head produced by a pump.

transmissibility. *See* transmissivity.

transmissivity. The rate at which water is transmitted through a unit width of an aquifer under a unit hydraulic gradient. Transmissivity values are given in gpm through a vertical section of an aquifer 1 ft wide and extending the full saturated height of an aquifer under a hydraulic gradient of 1 in the U.S. customary system. The SI system defines transmissivity in cubic meters per day through a vertical section of an aquifer 1 m wide and extending the full saturated height of an aquifer under a hydraulic gradient of 1.

transpiration. The process by which water absorbed by plants (usually through the roots) is evaporated into the atmosphere from the plant surface.

tremie.* 1. A tubing string (typically about 2 to 3 inches in diameter) that is temporarily installed into the annulus outside the well casing during well construction. The tremie pipe is used for installing annular material such as filter pack sand and cement grout seals. 2. To install annular seal material, fill material, or other material through a tremie pipe.

turbulent flow. Water flow in which the flow lines are confused and heterogeneously mixed. It is typical of flow in surface-water bodies.

U

unbalanced mud system.* A mud system that contains two or more different hydraulic heads within the circulation system inside and outside a string of drill pipe or tubing. The pressure (hydraulic head) exerted by a fluid column is a function of the column height and the fluid weight. Thus, when different pressure heads occur in the circulation system, the fluid has unbalanced pressure heads and flows in response to the pressure gradient. For example, if the inside of a string of drill pipe contains 8.3 lb/gal water but is surrounded by 9.0 lb/gal drilling mud in the annulus outside the pipe, then the unbalanced system causes the water to flow out of the drill pipe at the land surface, as it is displaced by the denser drilling mud. An unbalanced mud system can result from thinning of mud from invasion of formation water (either due to zonal groundwater sampling operations or confined aquifer conditions), or by aeration of drilling mud due to invasion of pressurized gas.

unconfined aquifer. An aquifer where the water table is exposed to the atmosphere through openings in the overlying materials.

unconsolidated deposit.** Deposit of loosely bound sediment.

underream.* To enlarge the borehole diameter in the lower portion of the borehole, typically below an obstruction or casing string. Underreaming operations use special tools that can be rotated on an eccentric or otherwise enlarged to ream the lower portion of the borehole and still be tripped out when necessary. Underreaming tools typically are operated mechanically or hydraulically.

underreamer.* A retractable reamer that can be lowered through a relatively small-diameter borehole, and then opened to ream out only the lower portion of the borehole.

uniformity coefficient. A numerical expression of the variety in particle sizes in mixed natural soils, defined as the ratio of the sieve size in which 40% (by weight) of the material is retained to the sieve size in which 90% of the material is retained.

upgradient.** Of or pertaining to the place(s) from which groundwater originated or traveled through before reaching a given point in an aquifer.

V

vacuum. Pressure that is less than atmospheric pressure.

vadose zone. The zone containing water under pressure that is less than that of the atmosphere, including soil water, intermediate vadose water, and capillary water. This zone is limited above by the land surface and below by the surface of the zone of saturation (water table).

variable-speed motor.** Used to control flow in a system by varying the frequency of the motor. Recommended for circulating systems and any other system where the main head is from friction losses in the piping system.

venturi. A short tube that has a tapering constriction in the middle that causes an increase in the velocity of flow of a fluid and a corresponding decrease in fluid pressure. Used in measuring fluid flow or for creating a suction.

viscosity.* Resistance of a fluid to flow. This resistance acts against the motion of any solid object through the fluid and also against motion of the fluid itself past stationary obstacles. Viscosity also acts internally on the fluid between slower and faster moving adjacent layers. All fluids exhibit viscosity to some degree. It is optically recognized as thickness.

W

washover pipe.* An open-ended pipe used to remove sloughed material from around a stuck pipe. Drilling mud is circulated through the washover pipe as it is lowered over the drillpipe, which washes away the sloughed sediment.

water hammer.** Occurs in a closed piping system as a result of the pressure being rapidly increased when the liquid velocity suddenly is increased. This damaging effect usually is the result of sudden starting, stopping, change in pump speed, or the sudden opening or closing of a valve. Water hammer usually can be controlled by regulating the valve closure time, surge chambers, and relief valves, or via other means.

water table. The surface between the vadose zone and the saturated zone. That surface of unconfined groundwater at which the pressure is equal to that of the atmosphere.

water-bearing zone. A geologic material that transmits water to a well.

weathering. The in-situ physical disintegration and chemical decomposition of rock materials at or near the earth's surface.

well point. A short length of well screen attached to the lower end of the casing. The casing and well points are driven to the desired depth within a shallow aquifer. A forged steel point is attached to the lower end of the well point to facilitate penetration.

well screen. A filtering device used to keep sediment from entering a well.

well yield. The volume of water discharged from a well, measured in gallons per minute or cubic meters per day.

wireline-core drilling. A type of drilling in which continuous core samples are recovered by the use of a wire line that pulls the core tube out of the core barrel after each section of core has been cut. The advantage of wireline core recovery is that the drill pipe does not have to be tripped out of the hole to recover each sample.

Y

yield strength. The stress at which a material begins to plastically deform.

References

A.C. Schultes Inc. 2006. http://www.ACSchultes.com.

Agarwal, R. G. 1980. A new method to account for producing time effects when drawdown type curves are used to analyze pressure buildup and other test data. SPE Paper 9289 presented at the 55th SPE Annual Technical Conference and Exhibition, Dallas, TX, Sept. 21–24.

Allison, J. D., D. S. Brown, and K. J. Novo-Gradac. 1991. *MINTEQA2/ PRODEFA2, a geochemical assessment model for environmental systems: Version 3.0 user's manual.* Athens, GA: U.S. Environmental Protection Agency, Environmental Research Laboratory.

American Petroleum Institute. 1959. *Oil-well cementing practices in the United States.* Dallas, TX: American Petroleum Institute.

American Petroleum Institute, Southern District Study Committee on Drilling Fluids, ed. 1969. *Principles of Drilling Fluid Control.* Austin, TX: University of Texas at Austin, Petroleum Extension Service.

American Public Health Association and American Water Works Association. 2005. *Standard methods for the examination of water and wastewater.* 29th ed. Washington, DC: American Public Health Association.

American Water Works Association. 2006. *A100-06: Water wells.*

American Welding Society. 1981. *Structural Welding Code AWS D1.1.* Miami, FL: American Welding Society.

Angel, R. R. 1958. *Volume requirements for air and gas drilling.* Houston, TX: Gulf Publishing Company.

Archie, G. E. 1942. The electrical resistivity log as an aid in determining some reservoir characteristics. *Transcripts, American Institute of Mining and Metallurgic Engineers* 146:54–62.

Asquith, G. 1982. *Basic well log analysis for geologists.* Tulsa, OK: American Association of Petroleum Geologists.

Assaad, F., P. E. LaMoreaux, and T. H. Hughes, eds. 2004. *Field methods for geologists and hydrogeologists.* New York: Springer-Verlag.

Atkinson, L. C., T. M. Hanna, and J. W. Anthony. 1989. Investigation and implementation of mine dewatering systems. In *Proceedings of the first joint meeting between SME and AIMM, Reno NV.*

Ayers, R. S., and D. W. Wescot. 1976. *Water quality for agriculture.* FAO Irrigation and Drainage Paper 29. Rome, Italy: Food and Agriculture Organization of the United Nations.

Back, W., J. S. Rosenshein, and P. R. Seaber. 1988. *The geology of North America.* Vol. O-2 of *Hydrogeology.* Boulder, CO: Geologic Society of America.

Baker Hughes Inc. 2006. http://www.bakerhughes.com.

Baroid. 1980. *Baroid drilling fluid products for minerals exploration.* Houston, TX: ML Baroid/NL Industries.

Bartlett, R. 1992. *Solution mining: leaching and fluid recovery of materials.* Philadelphia, PA: Gordon and Breach Science Publishers.

Baski, H. 204. Catalog 6. Denver, CO: Baski, Inc.

Bates, R. L., and J. A. Jackson. 1984. *Dictionary of geological terms.* 3rd ed. New York: American Geological Institute, Anchor Books, a Division of Random House, Inc.

Bathhurst, R. G. C. 1975. *Carbonate sediments and their deposition.* Vol. 12 of *Developments in Sedimentology.* 2nd ed. New York: Elseiver Scientific Publishing Company.

Baver, L. D. 1956. *Soil physics.* 3rd ed. New York: John Wiley & Sons, Inc.

Bear, J. 1979. *Hydraulics of groundwater.* New York: McGraw-Hill Book Co.

Bear, J., C. Tsang, and G. de Marsily. 1993. *Flow and contaminant transport in fractured rock.* San Diego, CA: Academic Press Inc.

Bennett, T. W. 1970. On the design and construction of infiltration galleries. *Ground Water* 8(3):16–24.

Bernknopf, R. L., D. S. Brookshire, D. R. Soller, M. J. McKee, J. F. Sutter, J. C. Matti, and R. H. Campbell. 1993. *Societal value of geologic maps* (U.S. Geological Survey Circular 1111). Washington, DC: U.S. GPO.

Bethke, C. M. 1998. The geochemist's workbench—user's guide. Champaign-Urbana, IL: University of Illinois.

Bierschenk, W. H. 1964. Determining well efficiency by multiple step drawdown tests. *International Association of Scientific Hydrology* 64:493–507.

Bloom, N. S., and E. A. Crecelius. 1983. Determination of mercury in seawater at subnanogram per litre levels. *Marine Chemistry* 14:49–59.

Boyle, R. E. 2000. Practical, cost-effective solutions to water well problems. In *Water Well Rehabilitation Technology.* Concord, MA: The American Ground Water Trust.

BP Corporation North America Inc., and U.S. Environmental Protection Agency. 2002. *Monitoring well comparison study: An evaluation of direct-push versus conventional monitoring wells.*

Brace, W. F. 1980. Permeability of crystalline and argillaceous rocks. *International Journal of Rock Mechanics and Mining Sciences and Geomechanical Abstracts* 17:241–51.

Briggs, G. F., and A. G. Fiedler, eds. 1972. *Ground water and wells.* Saint Paul, MN: Johnson Division, Universal Oil Products Co.

Bureau of Reclamation. 1981. *Water measurement manual.* Denver, CO: U.S. Department of the Interior, U.S. Government Printing Office.

Butler, J. J., Jr. 1988. Pumping tests in nonuniform aquifers—the radially symmetric case. *Journal of Hydrology* 101:15–30.

Butler, J. J., Jr. 1997. *Theoretical analysis of impact of incomplete recovery on slug tests.* Kansas Geologic Survey, Open-File Report 97-59.

Butler, J. J., Jr., 1998. *The design, performance, and analysis of slug tests.* Boca Raton, FL: Lewis Publishers.

California Environmental Protection Agency. 1995. *Monitoring well design and construction for hydrogeologic characterization.* Sacramento, CA: The California Environmental Protection Agency.

Canadian Institute of Mining and Metallurgy, and L. F. Maier. 1965. Understanding surface casing waiting-on-cement time. Paper presented at the Canadian Institute of Mining and Metallurgy 16th Annual Technical Meeting, Calgary, Alberta, Canada.

Cedergren, H. R. 1977. *Seepage, drainage, and flow nets.* 2nd edition. New York: John Wiley and Sons, Inc.

Chapelle, F. H. 1993. *Ground-water microbiology and geochemistry.* New York: John Wiley and Sons.

Characklis W. G. 1980. *Biofilm development and destruction.* Houston, TX: Rice University.

Characklis, W. G., and K. C. Marshall, eds. 1990. *Biofilms.* New York: John Wiley and Sons.

Collins, W. D. 1923. Graphic representation of water analyses. *Industrial and Engineering Chemistry* 15:394.

Colt Industries. 1974. *Hydraulic handbook.* Kansas City, KS: Fairbanks Morse Pump Division.

Cooper, H. H., and C. E. Jacob. 1946. A generalized graphical method for evaluating formation constants and summarizing well-field history. *Eos, Transactions of the American Geophysical Union* 27:526–34.

Cooper, L. W., R. A. Hook, and B. R. Payne. 1977. *Air drilling techniques.* Dallas, TX: American Institute of Mining, Metallurgical, and Petroleum Engineers, Inc.

Cullimore, D. R. 1992. *Practical manual of ground-water microbiology.* Chelsea, MI: Lewis Publishers.

Cunningham, R. A., and J. G. Eenink. 1958. Laboratory study of effect of overburden, formation and mud column pressure on drilling rate. *Petroleum Transactions, AIME.*

Darcy, H. 1856. *Les fontaines publiques de la ville de Dijon.* Paris: V. Dalmont.

Davis, S. N., and R. J. M. DeWiest, 1966. *Hydrogeology.* New York: John Wiley and Sons, Inc.

Davis, S. N., and L. J. Turk. 1964. Optimum depth of wells in crystalline rocks. *Ground Water* 2(2):6–11.

Deere, D. U., and D. W. Deere. 1988. The rock quality designation (RQD) index in practice. In *Rock classification systems for engineering purposes,* pp. 91–101. Ed. L. Kirkaldie. ASTM STP 984. Philadelphia: American Society for Testing and Materials.

Doe, T. W., M. Zieger, C. Enachescu, and J. Böhner. 2006. In situ stress measurements in exploratory boreholes. *Felsbau* 24(4):39–47.

Doherty. 2005. *PEST Version 9 User's Guide.* Brisbane, Queensland, Australia: Watermark Numerical Computing.

Domenico, P. A., and F. A. Schwartz. 1990. *Physical and chemical hydrogeology.* 2nd ed. New York: John Wiley and Sons.

Driscoll, F. G. 1978. Blasting—It turns dry holes into wet ones. *Johnson Drillers Journal* Nov./Dec.

Driscoll, F. D., ed. 1986. *Ground water and wells.* St. Paul, MN: Johnson Screens.

Driscoll, F. G., D. T. Hanson, and L. J. Page. 1980. Well-efficiency project yields energy-saving data. Part 3. *Johnson Drillers Journal* Sept./Oct.

Dupuit, J. 1863. *Etudes theoriques et pratiques sur le movement des eaux dans les canaux decouverts et a travers les terrains permeables.* 2nd ed. Paris: Dunod.

Eaton, A. D., M. A. Franson, American Public Health Association, American Water Works Association, and Water Environment Federation. 2005. *Standard methods for the examination of water and wastewater.* 21st ed. Washington, DC: American Public Health Association.

Ellis, E. E. 1906. Occurrence of water in crystalline rocks. In *Underground-Water Papers*, USGS Water Supply Paper No. 160:19–28.

Fair, G. M., C. J. Geyer, and J. L. Okun. 1958. *Elements of water supply and waste-water disposal.* New York, NY: John Wiley & Sons, Inc.

Fair, G. M., C. J. Geyer, and D. A. Okun. 1971. *Elements of water supply and wastewater disposal.* 2nd ed. New York: John Wiley and Sons, Inc.

Fenchel, T., G. M. King, and T. H. Blackburn. 1988. *Bacterial biogeochemistry, the ecophysiology of mineral cycling.* London: Academic Press.

Ferris, J. G., D. B. Knowles, R. H. Brown, and R. W. Stallman. 1962. *Theory of aquifer tests.* U.S. Geological Survey Water-Supply Paper 1536-E. Washington, DC: U.S. GPO.

Fetter, C. W., Jr. 1980. *Applied hydrogeology.* Columbus, OH: Merrill Publishing Company.

Fetter, C. W. 2001. *Applied hydrogeology.* 4th ed. Upper Saddle River, NJ: Prentice-Hall.

Fink, J. B. 1978. On K-factors and gamma log calculations. *Geophysics* 43(7):1546–50.

Flemming, H. C., and J. W. Wingender. 2001. Structural ecological and functional aspects of EPS. In *Biofilm community interaction, chance or necessity.* Ed. P. Gilbert, D. Allison, M. Brading, J. Verran, and J. Walker, 175–89. Cardiff, UK: Bioline.

Fontana, M. G., and N. D. Greene. 1978. *Corrosion Engineering.* New York: McGraw-Hill Book Company.

Fournier, L. 2005. Horizontal wells in water supply. *Water Well Journal* (June).

Freeze, R. A., and J. A. Cherry. 1979. *Groundwater*, Englewood Cliffs, NJ: Prentice Hall.

Geoprobe. 2007. Sales materials. http://www.geoprobe.com.

Gibbs, C., ed. 1971. *Compressed air and gas data.* Woodcliff Lake, NJ: Ingersoll-Rand Company.

Gleeson, T., T. M. Hanna, and G. Wendling. 2005. Squeezing a few more drops from bedrock using dispersant to increase the yield of hydrofractured wells. *Water Well Journal* 59(8):16–17.

Goldstein, A. M., E. N. Alter, and J. K. Seaman. 1973. *Guar gum.* In *Industrial gums, polysaccharides and their derivatives.* 2nd ed. Ed. R. L. Whistler and J. N. BeMille. New York: Academic Press.

Grant, D. M. 1979. *Open channel flow measurement handbook.* Lincoln, NE: Instrumentation Specialties Company.

Gray, G. R. 1972. Drilling with mud: simple tests save time and money. *Water Well Journal* 26(3):33–35.

Griffith, P. 1984. Multiphase flow in pipes. *Journal of Petroleum Technology* (March), 361–67.

Halliburton Services. 1968. *Oil well cement manual.* Halliburton Services: Oklahoma City, OH.

Handbook of steel pipe. 1979. Washington, DC: Committee of Steel Pipe Producers, American Iron and Steel Institute.

Hanna, T. M. 2006. *Guide for using the hydrologic classification system for water well boreholes.* Westerville, OH: NGWA Press.

Hanna, T. M., P. G. Ivanci, and W. A. Creswell. 2003. Aquifer analysis and proper well development to maximize pumping capacity in alluvial wells. *Water Well Journal* 57(12):34–37.

Hantush, M. S. 1961. Drawdown around a partially penetrating well, *Journal of the Hydraulics Division, Proceedings of the American Society of Civil Engineering* 87(HY4): 83–98.

Hantush, M. S. 1964. Hydraulics of wells. In *Advances in Hydroscience,* ed. V. T. Chow. New York: Academic Press.

Harbaugh, A. W., E. R. Banta, M. C. Hill, and M. G. McDonald. 2000. *MODFLOW 2000, the U.S. Geological Survey modular ground-water model—User guide to modularization concepts and ground-water flow process.* U.S. Geological Survey Open-File Report 00-92.

Hazen, A. 1893. Some physical properties of sands and gravels. *Massachusetts State Board of Health, 24th Annual Report.*

Heap, R. D. 1979. *Heat pumps.* London, England: E. & F. N. Spon Ltd.

Heath, R. C. 1982. Classification of ground-water systems of the United States. *Ground Water* 20(4):393–401.

Heath, R. C., and F. W. Trainer. 1968. *Introduction to ground-water hydrology.* New York: John Wiley and Sons, Inc.

Hem, J. D. 1970. *Study and interpretation of the chemical characteristics of natural water.* 2nd ed. U.S. Geological Survey Water-Supply Paper 1473. Washington, DC: U.S. Department of the Interior.

Hem J. D. 1985. *Study and interpretation of the chemical characteristics of natural water.* USGS Water-Supply Paper 2254. Washington, DC: U.S. Government Printing Office.

Hem, J. D. 1992. *The study and interpretation of the chemical characteristics of natural waters.* 3rd ed. U.S. Geological Survey Water-Supply Paper 2254. Washington, DC: U.S. Government Printing Office.

Hestroni, G. 1982. *Handbook of multiphase systems.* Washington, DC: Hemisphere Publishing Corp.

Hill, R. A. 1940. Geochemical patterns in Coachella Valley, CA. *Eos, Transactions of the American Geophysical Union.*

Holt J. G., N. R. Krieg, P. H. Sneath, J. T. Staley, and S. T. Williams, eds. 1993. *Bergey's manual of determinative bacteriology.* 9th ed. Baltimore, MD: Williams & Wilkins.

Horne, R. N. 1995. *Modern well test analysis: a computer-aided approach.* 2nd ed. Palo Alto, CA: Petroway, Inc.

Howard, G. C., and C. R. Fast. 1970. *Hydraulic Fracturing.* Dallas, TX: American Institute of Mining, Metallurgical, and Petroleum Engineers, Inc., Millet and Printer.

Hubbert, M. K. 1940. The theory of groundwater motion. *Journal of Geology* 48:785–944.

Hunt, H. C. 1984. *The horizontal radial collector as a recharge well.* Poster presented at the 29th Annual Midwest Ground Water Conference, Lawrence, KS.

Hunt, H. C. 1985. *Design and construction of radial collector wells.* Presented in Water Wells Design and Construction course, University of Wisconsin, Madison.

Hunt, H. C. 2002. United States experience in installing horizontal collector wells. In *Riverbank filtration: improving source water quality,* ed. C. Ray, G. Melin, and R. Linsky. Dordrecht, The Netherlands: Kluwer Academic Publishers.

Hutchinson, S. O., and G. W. Anderson. 1974. What to consider when selecting drilling fluids. *World Oil* (Oct.) 83–86.

HydroSOLVE, Inc. 2006. AQTESOLV™ (software).

Imco Services (Division of Halliburton Company). 1975. *Applied mud technology.* 5th ed. Houston, TX: Imco Services Division of Halliburton Co.

Ingersoll-Rand. 1971. *Compressed air and gas data.* 2nd ed. Ed. C. W. Gibbs. Woodcliff Lake, NJ: Ingersoll-Rand Company.

Instrumentation Specialties Co. 1979. *Open channel flow measurement handbook.* Lincoln, NE: Instrumentation Specialties Co.

Jacob, C. E. 1946. Radial flow in a leaky artesian aquifer. *Transactions, American Geophysical Union* 27(2):198–205.

Jacob, C. E. and Lohman, S. W. 1952. Nonsteady flow to a well of a constant drawdown in an extensive aquifer. *Transactions, American Geophysical Union* 33(4):559–69.

Jorgensen, D. G. 1989. *Using geophysical logs to estimate porosity, water resistivity, and intrinsic permeability.* U.S. Geological Survey Water-Supply Paper 2321.

Karstgens, V., H. C. Flemming, J. Wingender, W. Borchard. 2000. Influence of calcium ion concentration on the mechanical properties of a model biofilm of *Pseudomonas aeruginosa. Water Science Technology* 43(1):49–57.

Kasenow, M. 2002. *Determination of hydraulic conductivity from grain size analysis.* Highlands Ranch, CO: Water Resources Publications.

Kazmann, R. G. 1948. The induced infiltration of river water to wells. *American Geophysical Union* 29(1).

Kazmann, R. G., and W. R. Whitehead. 1980. The spacing of heat pump supply and discharge wells. *Ground Water Heat Pump Journal.* Summer: 28–31.

Kelly, J. E., K. E. Anderson, and W. L. Burnham. 1980. *Practical problems of confined-aquifer test analyses.* New York: American Society of Civil Engineers.

Kemmer, F. N., ed. 1977. *Water: The universal solvent.* Oak Brook, IL: Nalco Chemical Company.

Kemmer, F. N., ed. 1979. *The NALCO Water Handbook.* New York: McGraw-Hill Book Co.

Keys, W. S. 1989. *Borehole geophysics applied to ground-water investigations.* Dublin, OH: National Ground Water Association.

Keys, W. S., and L. M. MacCary. 1971. Applications of borehole geophysics to water-resources investigations. In *Techniques of water-resources investigations of the United States Geological Survey,* ch. E1. Reston, VA: USGS.

Kim, Namhyo. 2005. *Analysis of mechanical stress on downhole screen by gravel packing.* Houston, TX: Weatherford Inc.

Kinniburgh, D. G., P. L. Smedley, J. Davies, C. J. Milne, I. Gaus, J. M. Trafford, S. Burden, S. M. Ihtishamul Huq, N. Ahmad, and K. Ahmed. 2003. The scale and causes of the groundwater arsenic problem in Bangladesh. In *Arsenic in Groundwater Geochemistry and Occurrence*, ed. A. H. Welch and K. G. Stollenwerk, 211–258. Dordrecht: Kluwer Academic Publishers.

Klahre, J., and H.C. Flemming. 2000. Monitoring of biofilm in paper mill water system. *Water Research* 34:3657–65.

Korom, S. F., K. F. Bekker, O. J. Helweg. 2003. Influence of Pump Intake Location on Well Efficiency. *ASCE: Journal of Hydrologic Engineering* July-August.

Kozeny, J. L. 1933. Theorie and Berechnung der Brunnen. 2nd ed. Wasserkraft u. Wasser Wirtschaft 29.

Kresic. 1997. *Quantitative solutions in hydrogeology and groundwater modeling.* Boca Raton, FL: Lewis Publishers.

Krumbein, W. C., and F. J. Pettijohn. 1938. *Manual of sedimentary petrography.* New York: Appleton-Century-Crofts, Inc.

Kruseman, G. P., and N. A. DeRidder. 1992. *Analysis and evaluation of pumping test data.* 2nd ed. Publication 47. Wageningen, The Netherlands: International Institute for Land Reclamation and Improvement.

Kuetzing, M. 1981. Air mist drilling. *Drilling – DCW* (June).

Langelier, W. F. 1936. The analytical control of anticorrosion water treatment. *AWWA Journal* 28:1500–21.

Langmuir, D. 1997. *Aqueous environmental geochemistry.* Upper Saddle River, NJ: Prentice Hall Inc.

Lapham, W. W., F. D. Wilde, and M. T. Koterba. 1997. *Guidelines and standard procedures for studies of ground-water quality: Selection and installation of wells, and supporting documents.* USGS Water-Resources Investigation Report 96-4233. Washington, DC.

Lappin-Scott, H. M., C. J. Bass, K. McAlpine, and P. E. Sanders. 1994. Survival mechanisms of hydrogen sulfide-producing bacteria isolated from extreme environments and their role in corrosion. *International Biodeterioration and Biodegredation* 34(3–4):305–19.

Leap, D. I., and P. G. Kaplan. 1988. Single-well tracing method estimating regional advective velocity in a confined aquifer: theory and preliminary laboratory verification. *Water Resources Research* 24(7):993–98.

Lehr, J., S. Hurlburt, B. Gallagher, and J. Voytek. 1988. *Design and construction of water wells.* New York: Van Nostrand Reinhold.

Lohman, S. W. 1979. *Ground-water hydraulics.* U.S. Geological Survey Professional Paper 708. Washington, DC.

Long, J. C. S. 1996. *Rock fractures and fluid flow.* Washington, DC: National Academy of Sciences, National Academy Press.

Magcobar. 1977. *Drilling fluid engineering manual.* Houston, TX: Dresser Industries, Inc., Magcobar Division

Magcobar. 1979. *Air drilling.* Aurora, CO: Dresser Industries, Inc., Water/Mineral Operations.

Mairs, D. F. 1967. Surface chloride distribution in Maine Lakes. *Water Resources Research* 1090–92.

Manahan, S. E. 1994. *Environmental chemistry.* 2nd ed. Boca Raton, FL: Lewis Publishers.

Mansuy, N. 1999. *Water well rehabilitation, a practical guide to understanding well problems.* Boca Raton, FL: Lewis Publishers.

Marsh, P. D., and D. J. Bradshaw. 1996. Organisms and multispecie biofilms. In *Microbial Biofilms.* Washington, DC: ASM Press.

McWhorter, D. B., and D. K. Sunada. 1977. *Ground-water hydrology and hydraulics.* Fort Collins, CO: Water Resources Publications.

Meinzer, O. E., ed. 1942. *Hydrology.* New York: McGraw-Hill Book Company.

Middlebrooks, T. A., and W. H. Jervis. 1946. Relief wells for dams and levees. *Proceedings, American Society of Civil Engineers* (June): 781–98.

Miller, J. 1999. *Groundwater atlas of the United States,* Hydrologic atlas Ch. 30-A–30-H.

Molin, S. 2000. Direct in situ observations of the metabolic activity of bacteria growing in biofilms. In *Biofilms 2000 ASM Conference Proceedings.* Washington, DC: ASM Press.

Morrison, R. D. 1983. *Ground water monitoring technology—Procedures, equipment and applications.* Prairie du Sac, WI: Timco Manufacturing, Inc.

Namhyo, K. 2005. *Analysis of mechanical stress on downhole screen by gravel packing.* New Brighton, MN: Weatherford.

National Academy of Science and National Academy of Engineering. 1972. *Water Quality Criteria Report of Committee on Water Quality Criteria.* Washington, DC: U.S. Environmental Protection Agency.

National Ground Water Association. 1998. *Manual of water well construction practices.* 2nd ed. Westerville, OH: NGWA.

National Research Council. 1994. *Alternatives for ground water cleanup.* Washington, DC: National Academy Press.

National Research Council. 1996. *Rock fractures and fluid flow.* Washington, DC: National Academy Press.

National Water Well Association and Plastics Pipe Institute (NWWA). 1981. *Manual on the selection and installation of thermoplastic water well casing.* Worthington, OH: NWWA.

Neu, T. 1996. Significance of bacterial surface active compounds in interaction of bacteria with interfaces. *Microbiological Review* 60:151–166.

Nordstrom, D. A., and F. D. Wilde, eds. 2005. Reduction-oxidation potential (electrode method). 2d ed. *National field manual for the collection of water-quality data,* bk. 9, ch. A6, sec. 6.5. http://water.usgs.gov/owg/FieldManual/Chapter6/Ch6_contents.html (accessed November 3, 2007).

Paillet, F. L. 2000. A field technique for estimating aquifer parameters using flow log data. *Ground Water* 38(4):510–21.

Paillet, F. L. 2001. Hydraulic head applications of flow logs in the study of heterogeneous aquifers. *Ground Water* 39(5):667–75.

Papadopoulos, I. S., and H. H. Cooper, Jr. 1967. Drawdown in a well of large diameter. *Water Resources Research* 3:241–44.

Parizek, R. R., and L. G. Drew. 1966. *Random drilling for water in carbonate rocks.* Park, PA: Pennsylvania State University, Institute for Research on Land and Water Resources.

Parkhurst, D. L. 1988. *User's Guide to PHREEQC—A computer program for speciation, reaction-path, advective-transport, and inverse geochemical calculations.* USGS Water Resources Investigations Report 95-4227.

Parshall, R. L. 1950. *Measuring Water in Irrigation Channels with Parshall Flumes and Small Weirs.* U.S. Soil Conservation Services, circular 843. Washington, DC: U.S. Department of Agriculture.

Perloff, W. H., and W. Baron. 1976. *Soil mechanics: Principals and applications.* New York: The Ronald Press Company.

Peters, W. C. 1978. *Exploration and mining geology.* Toronto: John Wiley & Sons.

Pettijohn, F. J., P. E. Potter, and R. Siever. 1972. *Sand and Sandstone.* New York: Springer-Verlag.

Piper, A. M. 1944. A graphic procedure in the geochemical interpretation of water analyses. *Eos, Transactions of the American Geophysical Union* 25:914–23.

Poland, J. F., B. E. Lofgren, R. L. Ireland, and R. G. Pugh. 1973. *Land Subsidence in the San Joaquin Valley, California as of 1972.* U.S. Geological Survey Professional Paper 437-H.

Powers, J. P. 1981. *Construction dewatering: A guide to theory and practice.* New York: John Wiley and Sons, Inc.

Powers, J. P., A. B. Corwin, P. C. Schmall, W. E. Kaeck, and C. J. Herridge, eds. 2007. *Construction dewatering and groundwater control: New methods and applications.* 3rd ed. Hoboken, NJ: John Wiley & Sons, Inc.

Puls, R. W., and M. J. Barcelona. 1996. *Ground-water issue paper: Low-flow (minimal drawdown) ground-water sampling procedures.* U.S. Environmental Protection Agency, EPA/540/S-95/504.

Purdue University, Division of Construction Engineering and Management. 2000. *Emerging construction technologies: In situ remediation using horizontal wells.* http://www.ecn.purdue.edu/ECT/Other/horizontalwell.htm (accessed September 17, 2007).

Pyne, R. David G. 2005. *Aquifer storage recovery: A guide to groundwater recharge through wells.* Gainesville, FL: ASR Press.

Radtke, D. B., J. K. Kurklin, and F. D. Wilde. 2005. Temperature. 2nd ed. *National field manual for the collection of water-quality data,* bk. 9, ch. A6, sec. 6.1. http://water.usgs.gov/owg/FieldManual/Chapter6/Ch6_contents.html (accessed November 3, 2007).

Ramey H. J., Jr., A. Kumar, and M. S. Gulati. 1973. *Gas well test analysis under water-drive conditions.* Arlington, VA: American Gas Association.

Raven, K. G. 1986. *Hydraulic characterization of a small ground-water flow system in fractured monzonitic gneiss.* IWD Scientific Series No. 149, Paper No. 30. Ottawa, Canada: National Hydrology Research Institute.

Reed, J. E. 1980. Type curves for selected problems of flow to wells in confined aquifers. In *Techniques of water resources investigations of the U.S. Geological Survey,* bk. 3, Applications of Hydraulics, ch. B3.

Reynolds, W. D., and D. E. Elrick. 1985. In situ measurement of field-saturated hydraulic conductivity, sorptivity and the a-parameter using the Guelph permeameter. *Soil Science* 140:292.

Rhodes, J. D. 1972. Quality of water for irrigation. *Soil Science* 113:277–84.

Ritter, F. R., R. C. Kochel, and J. R. Miller. 1995. *Process geomorphology.* 3rd ed. Dubuque, IA: Wm. C. Brown Publishers.

Rutledge, P. C. 1947. Discussion of paper, "Relief wells for dams and levees," by Middlebrooks and Jervis. *Proceedings, American Society of Civil Engineers* (Jan.): 65–71.

Schafer, D. C. 1971. Standard nomenclature needed for gravel pack. *Johnson Drillers Journal* July/Aug.

Schafer, D. C. 1978. Casing storage can affect pumping test data. *Johnson Drillers Journal* Jan./Feb.

Schafer, D. C. 1982. Efficient well design improves yield even in prolific aquifers. *Johnson Drillers Journal* (Q2).

Schafer, D. C. 1998. Determining Vertical Anisotropy Ratio Using a Graphical, Iteratvie Procedure Based on the Hantush Equation, *Ground Water* 36(2):293–304.

Schafer, D. C. 2007. Personal communication with editor.

Schnieders, J. H. 1998. Well chlorination. *Water Well Journal* 52(2):25–26.

Schnieders, J. H. 2001. Coliforms and disinfection of water wells. *Water Well Journal* 55(15):2–15

Schnieders, J. H. 2002. *McElhiney Lecture.* National Ground Water Association National Convention, Nashville, TN.

Schnieders, J. H. 2003. *Chemical cleaning, disinfection, and decontamination of water wells.* St. Paul, MN: Johnson Screens.

Schnieders, J. H. 2001. When the well runs dry: Keeping fouling in check. *Water Conditioning and Purification* 43(12):32–34.

Skogerboe G. V., R. S. Bennett, and W. R. Walker. 1973. *Selection and installation of cutthroat flumes for measuring irrigation and drainage water.* Technical Bulletin 120. Fort Collins, CO: Colorado State University.

Smedley, P. L. 2003. Arsenic in Groundwater—South and East Asia. In *Arsenic in Groundwater Geochemistry and Occurrence,* ed. A. H. Welch, and K. G. Stollenwerk. 179–210. Dordrecht: Kluwer Academic Publishers.

Smith, D. K. 1976. *Cementing.* Dallas, TX: American Institute of Mining, Metallurgical, and Petroleum Engineers, Inc.

Smith, S. A. 1989. *Manual of hydraulic fracturing for well stimulation and geologic studies.* Dublin, OH: National Water Well Association.

Smith, S. A. 1990. Well maintenance and rehabilitation in North America: An overview. In *Water well monitoring maintenance and rehabilitation,* ed. P. Howsam. London: E & F. N. Spon. 8–16.

Smith, S. A. 1995. *Monitoring and remediation wells, problem preventing, and remediation.* Boca Raton, FL: Lewis Publishers.

Snow, D. T. 1968. Rock fracture spacings, openings, and porosities. *ASCE Journal of Soil Mechanics & Foundations Division.*

Spiliotopulos, A., and C. B. Andrews. 2006. Analysis of Aquifer Test Data— MODFLOW and PEST. In *Conference Proceedings of MODFLOW and More 2006: Managing Ground-Water Systems.* Golden, CO: Colorado School of Mines.

Standard Methods for the Examination of Water and Wastewater. 2005. Washington, DC: American Public Health Association and American Water Works Association.

Stephens, D. B. 1996. *Vadose zone hydrology.* Boca Raton, FL: Lewis Publishers.

Stevens, J. C. 1975. *Stevens water resources data book.* Beaverton, OR: Leupold & Stevens, Inc.

Stiff, H. A. 1951. Interpretation of chemical water analyses by means of patterns. *Journal of Petroleum Technology* 3(10): §§ 1, 2, 3.

Streeter, V. L., and E. B. Wylie. 1975. *Fluid mechanics.* 6th ed. New York: McGraw-Hill Book Company.

Suman, G. O., Jr., R. C. Ellis, and R. E. Snyder. 1983. *Sand control handbook.* 2nd ed. Houston, TX: Gulf Publishing Company.

Sutherland, I. W. 2001. Biofilm exopolysaccharides: A strong and sticky framework. *Microbiology* 147(1):3–9.

Tardy, Y. 1971. Characterization of the principal weathering types by the geochemistry of waters from some European and African crystalline massifs. *Chemical Geology* 7:253–71.

Taitel, Y., and A. E. Dukler. 1980. Modeling flow pattern transitions for steady upward gas-liquid flow in vertical tubes. *AIChE Journal* 26:345–54.

Theis, C. V. 1935. The relation between the lowering of the piezometric surface and the rate and duration of discharge of a well using groundwater storage. *Eos, Transactions of the American Geophysical Union* 16:519–24.

Thiem, G. 1906. *Hydrologische methoden.* Leipzig: Gebhardt.

Thorpe, R., and G. Brown. 1985. *The field description of igneous rocks.* Milton Keynes, England: Open University Press.

Timoshenko, Stephen P. 1976. *Strength of materials.* 3rd ed. Huntington, NY: Krieger Publishing Co.

Trainer, F. W. 1987. *Hydrogeology of the plutonic and metamorphic rocks.* In *The geology of North America,* ed. W. Back, J. S. Rosenhein, and P. R. Seaber. Vol. O-2, *Hydrogeology,* 367–80. Boulder, CO: The Geological Society of America.

Tsang, C.-F., and J. A. Apps, eds. 2005. *Underground injection science and technology.* Boston: Elsevier.

Tschirley, N. K. 1978. *Manual of drilling fluids technology.* Houston, TX: Baroid Petroleum Services Company.

Turnbull, W. J., and C. I. Mansur, 1953. Relief well systems for dams and levees. *Proceedings, American Society of Civil Engineers,* vol. 79, Separate no. 192 (May 21).

United States Department of Agriculture. 1954. Diagnosis and improvement of saline and alkali soils. *Agriculture Handbook* 60, ed. L. A. Richards. Washington, DC: U.S. GPO.

United States Environmental Protection Agency. 1977. National secondary drinking water regulations. *Federal Register* 42:17144 (Mar. 31). Washington, DC: U.S. Government Printing Office.

United States Environmental Protection Agency. 1994. *How to evaluate alternative cleanup technologies for underground storage tank sites: A guide for corrective action plan reviewers.* http://www.epa.gov/oust/pubs/tums.htm (accessed December 11, 2007).

United States Environmental Protection Agency. 2002. *Monitoring well comparison study: An evaluation of direct-push versus conventional monitoring wells.* http://www.epa.gov/RCRIS-Region-5/wptdiv/r5lust/Monitoring_Well_Comparison.htm (accessed September 17, 2007).

Van der Kooij, D., W. A. Hijnen, and J. C. Kruithof. 1989. The effects of ozonation, biological filtration, and distribution on the concentration of easily assimilable organic carbon (AOC) in drinking water. *Ozone Science Engineer* 11:297–311.

Vukovic, M., and A. Soro. 1992. *Determination of hydraulic conductivity of porous media from grain-size distribution.* Highlands Ranch, CO: Water Resources Publications, LLC.

Walton, W. C. 1962. *Selected analytical methods for well and aquifer evaluation.* Bulletin No. 49. Urbana, IL: Illinois State Water Survey.

Walton, W. C. 1963. *Estimating the infiltration rate of a stream bed by aquifer testing analysis.* National Association of Scientific Hydrology, No. 63.

Walton, W. C. 1970. *Groundwater resource evaluation.* New York: McGraw-Hill Book Company.

Waltz, J., and T. L. Decker. 1981. Hydro-fracturing offers many benefits. *Johnson Drillers Journal* 53: 4–9.

Water and Power Resources Service. 1981. *Ground water manual.* Washington, DC: U.S. Department of the Interior, U.S. GPO.

Weight, D. W., and J. L. Sonderegger. 2001. *Manual of applied field hydrogeology.* New York: McGraw-Hill.

Welenco. 1996. *Water and environmental geophysical well logs, technical information and data.* 8th ed. Vol. 1. Bakersfield, CA: Welenco.

Wendling, G., R. P. Chapuis, and D. E. Gill. 1997. Quantifying the effects of well development in unconsolidated material. *Ground Water* 35(3):387–93.

Werner, H. D., T. F. Scherer, and T. O. Kajer. 1980. *Effects of irrigation well efficiency on energy requirements.* EM-78-G-01-5131. Staples, MN: U.S. Department of Energy.

Wenzel, L. K. 1942. *Methods for determining permeability of water-bearing materials, with special reference to discharging well methods,* U.S. Geological Survey, Water-Supply Paper 887.

Whistler, R. L., and K. Schweiger. 1957. Oxidation of amylopectin with hypochlorite at different hydrogen ions concentration. *Journal of the American Chemical Society* 79(24):6460–64.

Williamson, W. H., and D. R Woolley. 1980. *Hydraulic fracturing to improve the yield of bores in fractured rock.* Australian Water Resources Council, Technical Paper No. 55. Canberra, Australia: Australian Government Publishing Service.

World Health Organization. 2006. *Guidelines for Drinking Water Quality.* 3rd ed. Vol. 1, *Recommendations.* Geneva: World Health Organization.

Zall, L., and O. Russell. 1979. Ground water exploration programs in Africa. In *Satellite Hydrology. Proceedings of the Fifth Annual William T. Pecora Memorial Symposium on Remote Sensing, Sioux Falls, SD, June 10–15, 1979,* ed. M. Deutsch, D. R. Wiesnet, and A. Rango. 1981. Minneapolis, MN: American Water Resources Association.

Index